DATE DUE			

PHYSICAL ORGANIC CHEMISTRY

McGRAW-HILL SERIES IN ADVANCED CHEMISTRY

Amdur and Hammes Chemical Kinetics: Principles and Selected Topics
Bair Introduction to Chemical Instrumentation
Ballhausen Introduction to Ligand Field Theory
Benson The Foundations of Chemical Kinetics
Biemann Mass Spectrometry (Organic Chemical Applications)
Davidson Statistical Mechanics
Davydov (*Trans.* Kasha and Oppenheimer) Theory of Molecular Excitons
Dean Flame Photometry
Dewar The Molecular Orbital Theory of Organic Chemistry
Eliel Stereochemistry of Carbon Compounds
Fitts Nonequilibrium Thermodynamics
Fristrom and Westenberg Flame Structure
Hammett Physical Organic Chemistry: Reaction Rates, Equilibria, and Mechanisms
Helfferich Ion Exchange
Hill Statistical Mechanics
Hine Physical Organic Chemistry
Jencks Catalysis in Chemistry and Enzymology
Jensen and Rickborn Electrophilic Substitution of Organomercurials
Kan Organic Photochemistry
Kirkwood and Oppenheim Chemical Thermodynamics
Kosower Molecular Biochemistry
Laidler Theories of Chemical Reaction Rates
Laitinen Chemical Analysis
McDowell Mass Spectrometry
Mandelkern Crystallization of Polymers
March Advanced Organic Chemistry: Reactions, Mechanisms, and Structure
Memory Quantum Theory of Magnetic Resonance Parameters
Pitzer and Brewer (*Revision of* Lewis and Randall) Thermodynamics
Pople and Beveridge Approximate Molecular Orbital Theory
Pople, Schneider, and Bernstein High-resolution Nuclear Magnetic Resonance
Pryor Free Radicals
Raaen, Ropp, and Raaen Carbon-14
Roberts Nuclear Magnetic Resonance
Rossotti and Rossotti The Determination of Stability Constants
Shriver The Manipulation of Air-sensitive Compounds
Siggia Survey of Analytical Chemistry
Streitwieser Solvolytic Displacement Reactions
Sundheim Fused Salts
Wiberg Laboratory Technique in Organic Chemistry

PHYSICAL ORGANIC CHEMISTRY
REACTION RATES, EQUILIBRIA, AND MECHANISMS, Second Edition

LOUIS P. HAMMETT
Mitchill Professor Emeritus of Chemistry, Columbia University

McGRAW-HILL BOOK COMPANY
New York St. Louis San Francisco Düsseldorf
London Mexico Panama
Sydney Toronto

PHYSICAL ORGANIC CHEMISTRY

REACTION RATES, EQUILIBRIA, AND MECHANISMS

Library of Congress Catalog Card Number 73-91680

25905

2 3 4 5 6 7 8 9 0 MAMM 7 9 8 7 6 5 4 3 2 1

This book was set in Times New Roman by Spottiswoode, Ballantyne and Co. Ltd., and printed on permanent paper, and bound by The Maple Press Company.
The designer was J. Paul Kirouac;
the drawings were done by B. Handelman Associates, Inc.
The editors were James L. Smith and Maureen McMahon.
Matt Martino supervised the production.

PREFACE TO THE SECOND EDITION

When I was writing the first edition of this book some 30 years ago, the field of physical organic chemistry was not much more than 10 years old as an active subject of investigation. Rapid as the growth has been since that time, the subject is still far short of the dismal state to which Katchalsky refers.[1] "Whether we like it or not the ultimate goal of every science is to become trivial, to become a well-controlled apparatus for the solution of schoolbook exercises or for practical application in the construction of engines." That goal is still distant when we can be as completely surprised as we were a few years ago by the discovery that reactions involving bases can go 10^{13} times faster in dimethlsulfoxide than they do in methanol. And the time is still distant when we can make a schoolbook exercise out of the prediction of what substance will be a catalyst for what reaction.

Yet much that was tentative 30 years ago has become assured, closer approximations have replaced relationships that were then crude, and both the subject and its practitioners have matured considerably. The time seems ripe for a thorough-going reassessment of the subject matter of the earlier book.

Like the first edition, this book is concerned with reaction rates, equilibria, and mechanisms. More precisely it is concerned with these subjects in the limited area of reactions of the heterolytic type in solution. The subject of radical reactions occupied 27 pages of the 325 of the first edition; in 1957 it alone was the subject of a 600-page book.[2] I can add so little to Walling's treatise that I prefer not to discuss the subject at all. The first edition devoted 5 pages to molecular-orbital theory; this revision omits the subject for the same reason as in the case of radical reactions.

Even with these omissions the size of the book would be beyond all reasonable bounds if it attempted, as the first edition did, to be encyclopedic rather than illustrative; if for instance it tried to discuss all reactions for which information on the mechanism involved is available, instead of selecting examples which illustrate the ways in which mechanisms can be investigated.

It is my hope, however, that the treatment of the principles which can be applied to the study of reactions of the heterolytic type in solution is thorough enough, penetrating enough, and mature enough to make the book useful to the student and to the working research scientist.

[1] *Int. Sci. Technol.,* October, 1963, p. 43.

[2] C. Walling, "Free Radicals in Solution," John Wiley & Sons, Inc., New York, 1957.

This revision has grown from lectures and seminars I presented while a guest at the Union Carbide Research Institute, at the University of South Carolina, at the Brookhaven National Laboratory, at the Pennsylvania State University, and at Purdue University. Without the inspiration I derived from the staff and the students of these institutions it would never have been started. I am further deeply indebted to E. M. Arnett, M. M. Davis, H. L. Goering, R. W. Taft, and H. Zollinger, each of whom has read and commented helpfully on portions of the manuscript. The kindness of the Department of Chemistry of Princeton University in making it possible for me to use their excellent library has been very helpful and is much appreciated.

LOUIS P. HAMMETT

PREFACE TO THE FIRST EDITION

It is one of the commonest occurrences in the development of science that the necessary subdivision of the subject leads to a temporary neglect of phenomena lying on the borders between the specialized fields. Sooner or later the deficiency becomes too patent to be overlooked, and a new specialty makes its appearance. Something of this sort has been happening in the last two decades on the borderline between physical chemistry and organic chemistry. For a time it was almost a point of honor with both physical and organic chemists to profess ignorance of the other's field, and it remains a useful defense mechanism, if any is needed, to excuse the fact that specialization entails limitation as well as intensification of knowledge. Meanwhile there has grown up a body of fact, generalization, and theory that may properly be called *physical organic chemistry.* The name implies the investigation of the phenomena of organic chemistry by quantitative and mathematical methods.

One of the chief directions that the development of the subject has taken has been the study by quantitative methods of the mechanism of reactions and of the related problem of the effect of structure and environment on reactivity. In no other direction have its results been of such immediate practical importance for the basic problem of chemistry, the control of chemical processes. This part of physical organic chemistry forms the subject of the present book.

A physicist colleague once mockingly referred to this kind of investigation as the study of soapmaking, whereas any respectable chemist must today busy himself with the chemistry of the nucleus. The remark underestimates both the theoretical and the practical significance of soapmaking. Soap is by no means a negligible factor in human civilization; I am not sure that we know more about the fundamentals of soapmaking, which is to say ester hydrolysis, than we do about the nucleus; I think the theoretical problems involved are quite as interesting; and I am convinced that an understanding of the mechanism by which complex naturally occurring substances, the enzymes, accelerate hydrolysis would lead to a great advance toward the interpretation of the phenomena of life.

Part of my excuse for this book is therefore that the material is important and interesting. In further justification I urge that the subject has reached a point of development where a unified and consistent treatment is possible in terms of a few simple generalizations and theories. My final apology is that no complete and adequate treatment is available except in widely scattered periodical articles. It is quite as difficult to advise a course of reading for a student of physical chemistry who wishes to assess the significance of an investigation of isotopic exchange phenomena in organic compounds as it is to aid a student of organic chemistry who wishes to understand the acid catalysis of the Beckmann rearrangement or of the cyclodehydration reaction. My hope is that this book may be of value to both groups, and I have therefore tried to make the discussion intelligible to a student with a sound but elementary knowledge of both physical and organic chemistry. I can only apologize if it contains matter that seems trivial or obvious to the advanced practitioner in either field.

The theories and principles presented in the text are to a very minor extent my own. For the mistakes I have no doubt made in crediting them to their true originators, I can only plead the great difficulty of determining the priority of ideas, and acknowledge my debt in general terms. I am indebted to the editor of the Journal of the American Chemical Society, to the publishers of Chemical Reviews, and to the Faraday Society for permission to reproduce a number of figures; to my colleagues at Columbia University for inspiration and advice, and especially to Prof. George E. Kimball, who has read and criticized part of the manuscript; to the research students who have taught me more than I have taught them; and most of all to three great teachers, E. P. Kohler, H. Staudinger, and J. M. Nelson, who planted the seed from which this book has grown.

LOUIS P. HAMMETT

CONTENTS

PHYSICAL ORGANIC CHEMISTRY

1
Introduction

A major part of the job of the chemist, as I see it, is the prediction and control of the course of chemical reactions. For this, as for any other human attempt to master nature, two kinds of approach are possible. One is the construction of broad, far-reaching principles from which the detailed properties of matter may be deduced. The other involves the bit-by-bit development of empirical generalizations, aided by theories of approximate or limited validity whenever they seem either to rationalize a useful empirical conclusion or to suggest interesting lines of experimental investigation. By the nature of our material we chemists are forced to depend largely on the second pathway. As I have remarked in another connection,[1] "Chemists had arrived empirically at effective working principles long before the theoretical key to all the problems of chemistry was embodied in the Schrödinger equation of wave mechanics. Even today, the amount of information which the chemist can derive directly from that equation is only a small part of what he knows."

[1] *Int. Sci. Tech.*, January, 1946, p. 62.

Some chemists seem to be a bit shamefaced about this and to envy those scientists the nature of whose preoccupations entitles them to agree with Dirac[1] that "It is more important to have beauty in one's equations than to have them fit experiment." I tend rather to a sense of pride in a discipline which has accomplished so much by the resourceful use of every possible intellectual tool, including those that are clumsy and rough as well as those that are elegant and polished. To quote myself again:[2] "I hope that nothing I have said would lead you to believe that I reject theory or that I in any way derogate it. But I do think that the respect we give theory should not obscure, as it sometimes seems to do, the equal debt which science owes to empirical generalization. Consider, for instance, the enormous theoretical posterity which has sprung from the empirical discovery by a Swiss schoolmaster of an unexpected and rather odd looking quantitative relation between the frequencies of the lines in the hydrogen spectrum.

"And I think also that we sometimes overlook the great difference between exact theory and approximate theory. Again let me emphasize my respect even for approximate theory. When, for instance, molecular-orbital theory leads my colleague Breslow to predict the stability and the aromatic properties of so exotic a structure as the cyclopropenyl cation, it is obvious that, approximate though it be, molecular-orbital theory is a powerful tool for the discovery of unexpected phenomena. But if molecular-orbital theory predicts the impossibility of a particular new phenomenon or relationship, the conclusion should be taken only as somewhat, not as completely, discouraging. If one starts looking for an effect that can be predicted from this kind of theory, the odds are in one's favor that the time and money put into the investigation will be repaid; if one starts looking for an effect predicted by this kind of theory to be impossible, the odds are against a favorable outcome. Fortunately, however, the community of scientists, like that of horseplayers, contains some people who prefer to bet against the odds as well as a great many who always bet on the favorite. In science we should, I think, do all we can to encourage the man who is willing to gamble against reasonably long odds of this sort.

"This does not mean that we should encourage the fool or the ignoramus who wants to play against suicidal odds, the man who wants to spend his time and usually someone else's money looking for an effect incompatible with, let us say, one of the conclusions reached by Willard Gibbs. Gibbs started from thoroughly proven generalizations, the first and second laws of thermodynamics, and reasoned from them by exact mathematical procedures, and his conclusions are the best example I know of exact theory, theory against which it is futile to struggle.

[1] P. A. M. Dirac, *Sci. Am.*, **208**: 45 (1963).

[2] Willard Gibbs Medal Address, Chicago Section, American Chemical Society, May 19, 1961.

"But the powerful relationships discovered by Gibbs are abstract, and to translate them into concrete relationships involving such grubby matters as the concentrations of solutes requires either exact empirical equations of state or theories which are inevitably approximate. Caution is therefore still necessary, especially when the approximate theory gets entangled with the prestige of a distinguished scientist. Thus there was a considerable period in Nernst's old age when it was a rare and hardy soul who dared publish any conclusions which were inconsistent with the particular approximate equations of state with which Nernst in his youth had accomplished so much that was valuable. Those who tried were met by a Jovian blast that, until the days of G. N. Lewis, usually annihilated the offender.

"The moral of all this is: Have great respect for exact theory, but be very sure it is exact theory which dissuades you from something you would like to try and not merely some great man's pet brand of pain killer."

2

The Thermodynamics of Reactions in Solution

2.1 CHEMICAL POTENTIAL

With respect to its behavior in chemical reactions the key property of a substance i is its chemical potential μ_i, which may be defined as

$$\mu_i = \left(\frac{\partial G}{\partial n_i}\right)_{T,P,n_j,x} \tag{1}$$

where G is the value of the Gibbs energy, defined as $E - TS + PV$, in a particular phase, i.e., in a homogeneous portion of matter which contains substance i, and n_i is the number of moles of i present in the phase. The subscript n_j indicates that the quantities of all components of the system but i are constant; the subscript x indicates other restrictions which are required if electrical, magnetic, surface, or gravitational effects are present.

Gibbs, who invented the function μ_i, called it [1][1] the potential of substance i, but everyone seems to think he called it the chemical potential.

[1] Numbered references are listed at the end of each chapter.

The longer term probably avoids some danger of ambiguity. The chemical potential is the quantity which the pioneering Lewis and Randall "Thermodynamics" of 1923 called the molal free energy F_i when the substance i constitutes a pure phase but called the partial molal free energy $\bar{\text{F}}_i$ when i is present in solution. Chemists, who have let themselves get hot and bothered over the definition of the term free energy and the proper symbol for the quantity, have been lamentably careless about the really important distinction between three quantities; indeed they often use the term free energy for all of them. They are the extensive property G or F; the intensive property μ, F, or $\bar{\text{F}}$, which for a substance in solution is concentration-dependent; and the quantity μ° or $\bar{\text{F}}^\circ$, defined as

$$\mu^\circ = \lim_{c \to 0} (\mu - \mathbf{R}T \ln c) \tag{2}$$

which is independent of concentration. Much of the confusion derives no doubt from the fact that partial molal free energy is an unwieldy term and that small and large capitals are not easily distinguishable even in print, much less in manuscript, in typescript, or on the blackboard.

Gibbs defined the potential as

$$\mu_i = \left(\frac{\partial E}{\partial m_i}\right)_{S,V,m_j,x} \tag{3}$$

where E is energy, S is entropy, and m is mass in unspecified units. The two definitions are of thermodynamic necessity equivalent, but for the chemist Eq. (1) is a more usable operational definition. By virtue of this definition the potential of a particular substance in a particular phase is the rate of increase of the Gibbs energy G of the phase with increasing quantity of the substance, the temperature, the pressure, and certain other variables being constant during the addition and no other substance being added to or removed from the phase. This means that the difference in the values of the potential of a substance in two different states at the same temperature and pressure is the negative of the net reversible useful work per mole[1] involved in the transfer of the substance from the first state to the second.

Like the Gibbs energy, and indeed like energy itself, the chemical potential of a substance can be given a numerical value only by reference to some standard or base line. The difference in potential which accompanies the transfer of a substance from one system or state to another can, however, be assigned an unambiguous numerical value, as can the difference in potential which accompanies a chemical reaction. If, as is often convenient, the reference state is taken to be always at the same temperature and pressure as the state under consideration, it is important to remember that the temperature

[1] For the concept of reversible work see, for instance, [2], pp. 76–78, 140.

and pressure coefficients of μ depend on the reference state as well as on the state under consideration.

The importance of the chemical potential resides in the fact that if the values of this quantity, relative to some fixed base line, are known as functions of the composition of the reacting system, the temperature, and the pressure for all the substances involved in a chemical reaction, one can immediately compute for any set of conditions the extent to which reaction will have occurred when equilibrium in the reaction has been attained. One can also compute the thermal effects which accompany the reaction, the maximum quantity of useful work which can be obtained by letting the reaction proceed toward equilibrium, and the minimum work which must be expended on the system if it is to be forced away from equilibrium.

2.2 THE GIBBS ENERGY CHANGE IN A REACTION

The key relationship is

$$\left(\frac{\partial G}{\partial \xi}\right)_{T,P} = \Delta\mu \tag{4}$$

ξ, called the degree of advancement of the reaction, is a quantity such that $d\xi$ equals the change, as the reaction proceeds, in the number of moles of each substance involved in the reaction divided by the stoichiometric number ν for the reaction of that substance. ν_i is the number which precedes the chemical symbol of substance i when the chemical equation for the reaction is written in the form illustrated for the formation of ammonia from nitrogen and hydrogen as

$$2NH_3 - N_2 - 3H_2 = 0 \tag{I}$$

For this reaction the value of ν_i is +2 for NH_3, −1 for N_2, and −3 for H_2, and

$$d\xi = \tfrac{1}{2} dn_{NH_3} = -dn_{N_2} = -\tfrac{1}{3} dn_{H_2} \tag{5}$$

With respect to a chemical reaction the operator Δ applied to any variable x signifies that

$$\Delta x = \sum_i \nu_i x_i \tag{6}$$

Consequently for reaction (I)

$$\Delta\mu = 2\mu_{NH_3} - \mu_{N_2} - 3\mu_{H_2} \tag{7}$$

In terms of this symbolism

$$\Delta 1 = \sum_i \nu_i \tag{8}$$

The symbols ξ and ν are those introduced by de Donder in 1920, used in the treatise of Prigogine and Defay [3], and now recommended by the

IUPAC Council. Kirkwood and Oppenheim [4] substitute the symbol λ for ξ and call the quantity of the progress variable.

The validity of Eq. (4) follows directly from the principle that the Gibbs energy of a system is a property of the system, a principle which is a necessary consequence of the definition of the Gibbs energy and of the Carnot theorem.[1] By virtue of this principle

$$dG = \left(\frac{\partial G}{\partial T}\right)_{P,n} dT + \left(\frac{\partial G}{\partial P}\right)_{T,n} dP + \sum_j \mu_j \, dn_j \tag{9}$$

for any infinitesimal change, the summation being taken over all components of the system. If the system is maintained at constant temperature and pressure and the only change that occurs is a particular chemical reaction, this reduces to

$$dG = \sum_i \mu_i \, dn_i \tag{10}$$

the summation now being taken over those substances only which are involved in the reaction. From the definition of ξ

$$dn_i = \nu_i \, d\xi \tag{11}$$

from which

$$\frac{\partial G}{\partial \xi} = \sum_i \nu_i \mu_i = \Delta\mu_i \tag{12}$$

2.3 THE CRITERION OF EQUILIBRIUM IN A CHEMICAL REACTION

The necessary and sufficient condition for equilibrium in a chemical reaction is that

$$\Delta\mu = 0 \tag{13}$$

This follows from the basic consideration that when a system maintained at a fixed temperature and pressure is at equilibrium, neither an increase nor a decrease in ξ can be accompanied by a decrease in the Gibbs energy of the system. This can be the case only if

$$\left(\frac{\partial G}{\partial \xi}\right)_{T,P} = 0 \tag{14}$$

Equation (13) follows by virtue of Eq. (4). If a system has attained equilibrium under the constraints of fixed temperature and pressure, the extent of

[1] The proof of this conclusion can be deciphered with more or less difficulty from the discussion in any text on chemical thermodynamics. This is also true of the demonstration that $dG < 0$ for any spontaneous change in a system which is maintained at constant temperature and pressure.

reaction will not shift if other constraints, such as fixed volume or fixed entropy, are substituted.

The condition for equilibrium is often written as

$$\Delta F = 0 \tag{15}$$

ΔF being the change in F that accompanies the formation of ν_i moles of reaction product i in a system which either is composed solely of pure phases or is so large that this amount of reaction leads to no significant change in the composition of any phase. With this understanding of the meaning of the symbol ΔF, Eq. (15) is equivalent to Eq. (13).

For heterogeneous systems in which the phases are all of invariant composition, the second derivative $\partial^2 G/\partial \xi^2$ is zero because changes in ξ leave all the μ_i values unchanged. But if the composition of at least one phase changes as the reaction proceeds, one or more μ_i values will be a function of ξ. Since a change in ξ cannot decrease G when the system is already at equilibrium, the value of the second derivative must in this case be positive for the equilibrium composition.

In order to exploit the elegant and general relationship represented by Eq. (13) it is necessary to determine or to predict the way in which the potentials of the reactants depend on the composition of the system.

2.4 THE DILUTE-SOLUTION APPROXIMATION

It is often convenient to classify the constituents of a solution as, on the one hand, solutes which form a relatively small proportion of the mixture and, on the other hand, the solvent or mixture of solvents which constitute a large proportion. The value of the classification lies in the fact that, as a matter of experience which may be reinforced by statistical-mechanical considerations, the relationship

$$\mu_i = \mu_i^\circ + \mathbf{R}T \ln c_i \tag{16}$$

is a useful first approximation in the case of a solute, while the approximation

$$\mu_i = \mu_i^\circ \tag{17}$$

has about the same measure of validity for the solvent or a solvent constituent. Here c_i is the concentration of solute i in moles per liter, and μ_i° defined as

$$\mu_i^\circ = \lim_{c\to 0} (\mu_i - \mathbf{R}T \ln c_i) \tag{18}$$

for a solute and as

$$\mu_i^\circ = \lim_{c\to 0} \mu_i \tag{19}$$

for the solvent or a solvent constituent, the limit in both cases being for zero concentration of all solutes, is independent of solute concentration.

The approximation represented by Eqs. (16) and (17) may be expected to be good to about 1 percent in the value of c for solute concentrations up to 0.1 mole/liter except for ionized electrolytes and for high polymers.

Many chemists prefer other measures of concentration than c. For gases partial pressure in atmospheres is usual, but the operational definition of partial pressure P_i is ordinarily

$$P_i = c_i \mathbf{R}T \tag{20}$$

with $\mathbf{R} = 0.08205$, that is, in liter-atm/mole-deg. For liquid solutions molality m in moles solute per 1,000 g solvent and mole fraction x are common. To about the same degree of approximation as that which applies to Eq. (16), m and x in dilute solutions are related to c by the relationships

$$m = \frac{c}{\rho} \tag{21}$$

and

$$x = \frac{M_1 c}{1{,}000\rho} \tag{22}$$

where ρ is density in grams per cubic centimeter and M_1 is the molecular weight of the solvent. Consequently from Eq. (16)

$$\mu = (\mu^\circ + \mathbf{R}T \ln \rho^\circ) + \mathbf{R}T \ln m \tag{23}$$

and

$$\mu = \left(\mu^\circ + \mathbf{R}T \ln \frac{1{,}000\rho^\circ}{M_1}\right) + \mathbf{R}T \ln x \tag{24}$$

where ρ° is the density of the solvent. For dilute solutions therefore the form of the dependence on m and on x is the same as it is on c, but the quantities in parentheses replace the μ° of Eq. (16). The numerical value of μ° depends in any case upon the units in which concentration is expressed.

The argument for the mole-fraction representation is that for binary mixtures of very closely similar substances μ is linear in $\ln x$ with slope $\mathbf{R}T$ for both components all the way from $x = 0$ to $x = 1$. The argument for m is that, unlike x, it makes no assumptions about the molecular weight of the solvent in the solution, assumptions which cannot be verified, and that, unlike c, its value does not change with temperature. In favor of c it can be argued that the deviations from Eq. (16) are determined by the average distance between solute molecules and are therefore a function of volume of solution rather than of quantity of solvent.

2.5 THE STANDARD POTENTIAL

The quantity defined as μ° by Eq. (18) lacks any generally accepted name and symbol. In Lewis and Randall [2] it is called the standard free energy and is given the symbol $\bar{F}_i^\circ$. In the literature, unfortunately, the name is often shortened to free energy and the symbol $\bar{F}_i^\circ$ is often replaced by F. Lewis and Randall characterize it as the partial molal free energy of i in a hypothetical ideal solution in which $\bar{F}_i = \bar{F}_i^\circ$, in which therefore c_i is approximately but not exactly unity, but in which the partial molal enthalpy and heat capacity of the solute have the values of the infinitely dilute solution.

Kirkwood and Oppenheim [4] call the quantity the "reference value of the chemical potential" but usually employ the symbol μ_i° instead of words. Prigogine and Defay [3] call it the *potential chimique propre*, and use the symbol ζ_i. The *potential chimique propre* is contrasted with the *potential chimique de mélange*, which is the concentration-dependent quantity $\mu_i - \mu_i^\circ$. Gurney [5] calls μ° the "unitary part of the free energy" in constrast to $\mu_i - \mu_i^\circ$, which he calls the "cratic part of the free energy."

The name standard potential and the symbol μ° seem reasonable and will be used in what follows.

2.6 THE EQUILIBRIUM LAW IN THE DILUTE-SOLUTION APPROXIMATION

For a reaction in homogeneous solution the equilibrium constant K is defined as

$$K = \prod_j c_j^{\nu_j} \tag{25}$$

where the c_j's are the concentration at equilibrium of all solutes whose formulas appear in the stoichiometric equation. But even if the solvent is stoichiometrically involved, there is no factor representing the solvent in the definition. The equilibrium law in the dilute-solution approximation is

$$K = e^{-\Delta\mu^\circ/\mathbf{R}T} \tag{26a}$$

that is,

$$\Delta\mu^\circ = -\mathbf{R}T \ln K \tag{26b}$$

The precision of the approximation is greater the more dilute the solution. Since μ° values do not depend on solute concentration, K is independent of solute concentration. It does depend on temperature and on the nature of the solvent.

The summation represented by $\Delta\mu^\circ$ includes the μ° value of the solvent even though no factor concerned with the solvent appears in the definition of K. Thus the equilibrium law for the reaction whose stoichiometry is

$$\mathrm{A} + \mathrm{S} \rightleftharpoons \mathrm{B} \tag{II}$$

where A and B are solutes and S is the solvent, is

$$\frac{c_\mathrm{B}}{c_\mathrm{A}} = \exp \frac{\mu_\mathrm{A}^\circ + \mu_\mathrm{S}^\circ - \mu_\mathrm{B}^\circ}{\mathbf{R}T} \tag{27}$$

Equation (26) follows directly from the general equilibrium relationship and the dilute-solution approximation. At equilibrium by Eq. (13)

$$0 = \Delta\mu = \sum_i \nu_i \mu_i = \sum_j \nu_j \mu_j + \nu_S \mu_S \tag{28}$$

Here ν_S and μ_S refer to the solvent, ν_S being zero if the solvent is not stoichiometrically involved. The summation over the j's involves solutes only. By substitution from Eqs. (16) and (17)

$$\sum_j \nu_j \mu_j^\circ + \sum \nu_j \mathbf{R}T \ln c_j + \nu_S \mu_S^\circ = 0 \tag{29}$$

and

$$\sum_i \nu_i \mu_i^\circ = -\sum_j \mathbf{R}T \ln c_j^{\nu_j} \tag{30}$$

which is equivalent to Eq. (26).

2.7 THE ACTIVITY COEFFICIENT

G. N. Lewis's activity coefficient γ is an extremely useful measure of the deviation of real solutions from the dilute-solution approximation. For a solute j the definition is

$$\gamma_j = \frac{1}{c_j} \exp \frac{\mu_j - \mu_j^\circ}{\mathbf{R}T} \tag{31a}$$

that is,

$$\mathbf{R}T \ln \gamma_j = (\mu_j - \mathbf{R}T \ln c_j) - \mu_j^\circ \tag{31b}$$

For the solvent or a solvent constituent S the convention used in what follows is

$$\gamma_S = \exp \frac{\mu_S - \mu_S^\circ}{\mathbf{R}T} \tag{32}$$

By the nature of these definitions the activity coefficient approaches unity as the solute concentration approaches zero.

2.8 THE EXACT EQUILIBRIUM LAW

In terms of activity coefficients one can write the exact relationship

$$K = \frac{K^\circ}{\prod_i \gamma_i^{\nu_i}} \tag{33}$$

K is, as before, the function of solute concentrations at equilibrium defined by Eq. (25). K°, defined as

$$K^\circ = \exp\left(-\frac{\Delta\mu^\circ}{\mathbf{R}T}\right) \tag{34}$$

is the limit approached by K as the concentration of all solutes approaches zero. The activity-coefficient product is to be taken over all stoichiometric reactants including the solvent if this is involved. For reaction (II) Eq. (33) takes the form

$$K = K^{\circ} \frac{\gamma_A \gamma_S}{\gamma_B} \tag{35}$$

Equation (33) follows from Eqs. (13), (31), and (32) by elimination of μ_j and μ_S.

2.9 THE SIGN OF THE DERIVATIVE $(\partial\mu/\partial c)_{T,P}$

It is necessarily true that for a solute in a stable homogeneous solution

$$\frac{\partial \mu_i}{\partial c_i} \geqslant 0 \tag{36}$$

and, as a corollary, that

$$\frac{\partial \ln \gamma_i}{\partial \ln c_i} \geqslant -1 \tag{37}$$

This means that although γ_i can either decrease or increase with increasing c_i, the fractional rate of decrease in γ_i cannot be less than the fractional rate of increase in c_i.

The validity of these relationships can be demonstrated by the following argument. Given two portions, a and b, of solution which are at the same temperature and pressure and which are identical in composition except that the concentration of solute i is greater in a than in b. If the potential of i were less in a than in b, the transfer of i from b to a could occur spontaneously because the transfer would decrease the value of G in the system. This would be true even if the initial concentration difference were infinitesimal, and the process would continue so long as the potential of i in solution a is less than it is in solution b. Consequently a minute fluctuation in the concentration of i in an initially homogeneous solution would lead to the formation of two phases of different composition. This phenomenon appears in supersaturated, i.e., unstable solutions. The validity of the inequality (36) for stable solutions is therefore demonstrated. A more general and more elegant discussion of the sign of the derivative $\partial\mu/\partial c$, including other conditions than those of constant temperature and pressure, may be found in Kirkwood and Oppenheim [4, pp. 59–67].

From Eq. (36)

$$\frac{\partial \mu_i}{\partial \ln c_i} \geqslant 0 \tag{38}$$

and, since from Eq. (31)

$$\frac{\partial \mu_i}{\partial \ln c_i} = \mathbf{R}T + \mathbf{R}T\frac{\partial \ln \gamma_i}{\partial \ln c_i} \tag{39}$$

it must be true that

$$1 + \frac{\partial \ln \gamma_i}{\partial \ln c_i} \geqslant 0 \tag{40}$$

from which inequality (37) follows immediately.

2.10 ACTIVITY AND STANDARD ACTIVITY

It is convenient, especially in connection with the effect of medium on reactivity, to define the activity a_{ij} of component i in medium j by the relation

$$a_{ij} = \exp\frac{\mu_{ij} - \mu_i^{\circ\circ}}{\mathbf{R}T} \tag{41a}$$

i.e., by

$$\mathbf{R}T \ln a_{ij} = \mu_{ij} - \mu_i^{\circ\circ} \tag{41b}$$

Here μ_{ij} is the potential of substance i in medium j and $\mu_i^{\circ\circ}$ is the standard potential of i in a reference solvent at the same temperature and pressure. In the Lewis and Randall terminology this amounts to taking as the standard state a hypothetical ideal solution in the reference solvent.

It is further convenient to define a quantity a_{ij}° which will be called the standard activity of component i in solvent j by the relation

$$a_{ij}^{\circ} = \exp\frac{\mu_{ij}^{\circ} - \mu_i^{\circ\circ}}{\mathbf{R}T} \tag{42a}$$

i.e., by

$$\mathbf{R}T \ln a_{ij}^{\circ} = \mu_{ij}^{\circ} - \mu_i^{\circ\circ} \tag{42b}$$

The quantity $\mathbf{R}T \ln a_{ij}^{\circ}$ represents the Gibbs energy change per mole involved in the transfer of i from a very dilute solution in the reference solvent to a solution of the same concentration in solvent j.

It follows from these definitions and that of activity coefficient that

$$a_{ij} = a_{ij}^{\circ} \gamma_{ij} c_{ij} \tag{43}$$

for a solute and

$$a_{ij} = a_{ij}^{\circ} \gamma_{ij} \tag{44}$$

for a solvent component.

The quantity defined as standard activity by Eq. (42) has variously been called the degenerate activity coefficient [6], distribution coefficient [7], and solvent activity coefficient [8]. The symbol $^{\circ}\gamma_i^{S}$ is used by Parker and others.

2.11 THE SYSTEMATICS OF EQUILIBRIUM IN A VARYING MEDIUM

If $K^{\circ\circ}$ represents the limiting value for zero solute concentration of the equilibrium constant of a reaction in a reference solvent and K° the corresponding value in solvent j, then

$$K_j^{\circ} = \frac{K^{\circ\circ}}{\prod_i (a_i^{\circ})^{\nu_i}} \tag{45}$$

If further K_j represents the equilibrium constant at finite solute concentration in solvent j,

$$K_j = \frac{K^{\circ\circ}}{\prod_i a_i^{\nu_i}} = \frac{K^{\circ\circ}}{\left(\prod_i \gamma_i^{\nu_i}\right)\left(\prod_i a^{\circ\nu_i}\right)} \tag{46}$$

These relationships follow directly from the fundamental equilibrium relationship, Eq. (13), and the definitions of a, a°, and γ.

2.12 NUMBER AND CHOICE OF COMPONENTS

Gibbs wrote [1]: "If the conditions mentioned are satisfied, the choice of the substances which we are to regard as the components of the homogeneous mass considered, may be determined entirely by convenience, and independently of any theory in regard to the internal constitution of the mass." The conditions involve the number p of the components, which must be such that the values of the differentials $dn_1, dn_2, \ldots, dn_p$ "shall be independent, and shall express every possible variation in the composition of the homogeneous mass considered. . . ." In accordance with this principle it is possible to define a potential μ_i for any substance known or imagined to be present in a phase under consideration, but some of these μ_i values may turn out to be identical, and some may be interrelated in various ways.

With respect to the number of components the time scale of the observation is important. At room temperature and in the absence of a catalyst a mixture of hydrogen, oxygen, and water is a three-component system, because there is no interconversion within a humanly possible time of observation. At high temperatures or in the presence of a catalyst it is a two-component system, because the interconversion is so fast that over any humanly possible time of observation the proportion of water is determined by the ultimate composition of the system. Under intermediate conditions the behavior of the system will approach that of a three-component system for rapid observations and that of a two-component system for observations made on a slow time scale.

2.13 PRIMITIVE AND SOPHISTICATED VALUES OF CHEMICAL POTENTIAL

With the rapidly increasing sophistication of experimental techniques chemists are continually becoming more conscious of the existence of hitherto unknown mobile equilibria. These may be isomerizations like the chair-boat interconversion of cyclohexane; they may involve compound formation between a solute and the solvent; they may involve compound formation between two solutes.

If a substance A is rapidly and reversibly converted to a substance B by a process

$$A + xS \rightleftharpoons B \qquad \text{(III)}$$

in which S is the solvent or a component of a mixed solvent and x may be positive, zero, or negative, one investigator using primitive techniques might be ignorant of the existence of B and would recognize as the concentration of A a quantity which I shall call the primitive concentration of A and represent it by c_A, whereas in fact

$$c_A = [A] + [B] \qquad (47)$$

The quantity which this investigator would determine as the rate of increase of Gibbs energy per unit addition of A, a quantity which I shall call the primitive value of the potential of A and represent by $\mu_A{}^{(p)}$, would in fact be the rate of increase per unit addition of a mixture of A and B in the proportion $[B]/[A] = K_{AB}$, where K_{AB} is the equilibrium constant of reaction (III). This will be the case, even if the presence of B is known, whenever the time scale of the measurement of the change in Gibbs energy is slow compared with that of the A-B interconversion and even if the measurement involves the study of the extent of a reaction in which A is involved if the rate of that reaction is slow compared with the A-B interconversion.

Another investigator using more sophisticated techniques with a fast time scale might be able to determine the rate of increase of Gibbs energy per unit addition of A without the conversion to B. I shall use the symbol $\mu_A{}^{(s)}$ for the potential thus determined, the superscript s standing for sophisticated, as p does for primitive.

It turns out, however, that

$$\mu_A{}^{(p)} = \mu_A{}^{(s)} = \mu_B{}^{(s)} - x\mu^{(s)} \qquad (48)$$

i.e., the primitive and the sophisticated values of the potential of A are identical. The primitive value of the standard potential is, however, less than the sophisticated value with

$$\mu_A^{\circ(p)} = \mu_A^{\circ(s)} - \mathbf{R}T \ln (1 + K_{AB}^{\circ}) \qquad (49)$$

The difference is large if K°_{AB} is much larger than unity and negligible only if it is much less than unity.

These relationships can be generalized to a system involving a number of multiple equilibria symbolized by

$$A + x_i S \rightleftharpoons B_i \tag{IV}$$

with

$$c_A = [A] + \sum_i [B_i] \tag{50}$$

Equation (48) still applies, but Eq. (49) becomes

$$\mu_A^{\circ(p)} = \mu_A^{\circ(s)} - \mathbf{R}T \ln \left(1 + \sum_i K_i^{\circ}\right) \tag{51}$$

where at equilibrium

$$K_i^{\circ} = \lim_{c \to 0} \frac{[B_i]}{[A]} \tag{52}$$

The proof of these relationships follows. Since

$$\frac{[B_i]}{[A]} = K_i \tag{53}$$

Eq. (50) leads to

$$c_A = [A]\left(1 + \sum_i K_i\right) \tag{54}$$

and

$$[B_i] = \frac{c_A K_i}{1 + \sum K_i} \tag{55}$$

The addition of dn moles of A to the system under primitive conditions leads to the formation of $dn/(1 + \sum K_i)$ moles of A, to the formation of $(dn K_i)/(1 + \sum K_i)$ moles of each of the B_i substances, and to the disappearance of $dn(\sum x_i K_i)/(1 + \sum K_i)$ moles of S. The Gibbs energy change accompanying the addition is therefore

$$dG = \frac{dn}{1 + \sum K_i} [\mu_A^{(s)} + \sum (\mu_{B_i}^{(s)} K_i - x_i \mu_S K_i)] \tag{56}$$

But since $\mu_B^{(s)} - x_i \mu_S = \mu_A^{(s)}$, the bracket reduces to $\mu_A^{(s)}(1 + \sum K_i)$. The quantity $\partial G/\partial n$ is, by definition, $\mu_A^{(p)}$; consequently, $\mu_A^{(p)} = \mu_A^{(s)}$.

From the relationship

$$\mu_A^{(s)} = \mu_A^{\circ(s)} + \mathbf{R}T \ln [A] + \mathbf{R}T \ln \gamma_A \tag{57}$$

and Eqs. (48) and (55)

$$\mu_A{}^{(p)} = \mu_A^{\circ(s)} + \mathbf{R}T\ln c_A + \mathbf{R}T\ln \gamma_A - \mathbf{R}T\ln(1 + \sum K_i) \tag{58}$$

Consequently the quantity

$$\mu_A^{\circ(p)} = \lim_{c\to 0} (\mu_A{}^{(p)} - \mathbf{R}T\ln c_A) \tag{59}$$

is given by Eq. (51).

While relationships (49) and (51) are useful for bookkeeping purposes, they represent nothing really unfamiliar to chemists concerned with equilibria. For if the Gibbs energy change per mole involved in the addition to a system of an equilibrium mixture of A and B is $\mu_A{}^{(p)}$, the condition for equilibrium of A and B with a third substance M is

$$\mu_M - \mu_A{}^{(p)} = 0 \tag{60}$$

From this

$$\Delta\mu_M^{\circ(p)} = -\mathbf{R}T \ln K_M^{\circ(p)} \tag{61}$$

where at equilibrium

$$K_M{}^{(p)} = \frac{[M]}{[A] + [B]} \tag{62}$$

Consequently

$$\Delta\mu_M^{\circ(p)} - \Delta\mu_M^{\circ(s)} = -\mathbf{R}T\ln \frac{K_M^{\circ(p)}}{K_M^{\circ(s)}} \tag{63}$$

where at equilibrium

$$K_M{}^{(s)} = \frac{[M]}{[A]} \tag{64}$$

and

$$\Delta\mu_M^{\circ(s)} = -\mathbf{R}T\ln K_M^{\circ(s)} \tag{65}$$

Since

$$\Delta\mu_M^{\circ(p)} - \Delta\mu_M^{\circ(s)} = -\mu_A^{\circ(p)} + \mu_A^{\circ(s)} = \mathbf{R}T\ln(1 + K_{AB}^{\circ}) \tag{66}$$

Eq. (64) leads to

$$K_M^{\circ(p)} = \frac{K_M^{\circ(s)}}{1 + K_{AB}^{\circ}} \tag{67}$$

But this relationship can be obtained merely by substituting $K_M{}^{(s)} = [M]/[A]$ and $K_{AB} = [B]/[A]$ into Eq. (62).

If B is an association product or a dissociation product of A, that is, if the reaction is

$$nA + xS \rightleftharpoons B \qquad \text{(V)}$$

the same considerations lead to

$$\mu_A^{\circ(p)} = \mu_A^{\circ(s)} - \mathbf{R}T \ln (1 + nK_{AB}[A]^{n-1}) + \mathbf{R}T \ln \gamma_A \qquad (68)$$

For $n > 1$, that is, for an association of the solute, this reduces to

$$\mu_A^{\circ(p)} = \mu_A^{\circ(s)} \qquad (69)$$

which corresponds to the fact that in this case the degree of association approaches zero as the concentration c_A approaches zero. For $n < 1$, that is, for a dissociation of the solute, Eq. (68) reduces to

$$\mu_A^{\circ(p)} = \infty \qquad (70)$$

which corresponds to the fact that dissociation becomes complete as c_A approaches zero.

In any case the primitive value of the activity coefficient of A is given by

$$\gamma_A^{(p)} = \frac{\gamma_A^{(s)}}{1 + nK[A]^{n-1}} \qquad (71)$$

The variation of the experimentally observed value of $\gamma_A^{(p)}$ is in principle capable of detecting an association or a dissociation through the application of Eq. (71). But if K is small, or if the range of concentrations available for investigation is narrow, it is impossible to distinguish the effect of a reaction of this sort from a physical effect operating through the variation of the $\gamma^{(s)}$ values with the composition of the system.

If two different solutes react with each other, the relationships become more complicated but can be derived if necessary.

2.14 THE FUNCTION q°

It is convenient, and even illuminating, to define a quantity q_i° by the relation

$$q_i^\circ = e^{-\mu_i^\circ/\mathbf{R}T} \qquad (72)$$

Like the standard potential, q° is independent of solute concentration but varies from solvent to solvent and is a function of temperature and pressure. By virtue of Eq. (34) the limiting value of the equilibrium constant of a chemical reaction is related to the q° values of the substances involved by the equation

$$K^\circ = \prod_i (q_i^\circ)^{\nu_i} \qquad (73)$$

The product is to be taken over all reactants, including the solvent if it is involved. As with μ°, the function q° can be given a numerical value only by reference to an arbitrarily chosen reference state. But such products as appear in Eq. (73) have an unambiguous numerical value. The ratio of the q° values of substance i in two different solvents at the same temperature and pressure also has an unambiguous numerical value.

The primitive value of the function for a solute A which is in mobile equilibrium with the group of isomers or solvents which appears in Eq. (IV) is related to the sophisticated values for the individual substances by the equation

$$q_{\mathrm{A}}^{\circ(p)} = q_{\mathrm{A}}^{\circ(s)} + \sum_i \frac{q_{\mathrm{B}_i}^{\circ(s)}}{(q_{\mathrm{S}}^\circ)^{x_i}} \tag{74}$$

For a group of isomers in mobile equilibrium the primitive value of q° is simply the sum of the sophisticated values for the isomers; for a similar group differing in degree of solvation the q° value of the solvent appears with an appropriate exponent in the denominator of each term in the sum.

Equation (74) follows from the substitution

$$K_i = \frac{q_{\mathrm{B}_i}^{\circ(s)}}{q_{\mathrm{A}}^{\circ(s)}(q_{\mathrm{S}}^\circ)^{x_i}} \tag{75}$$

in Eq. (51), by which

$$\mu_{\mathrm{A}}^{\circ(p)} = \mu_{\mathrm{A}}^{\circ(s)} - \mathbf{R}T\ln\left[1 + \sum \frac{q_{\mathrm{B}_i}^{\circ(s)}}{q_{\mathrm{A}}^{\circ(s)}(q_{\mathrm{S}}^\circ)^{x_i}}\right] \tag{76}$$

or

$$q_{\mathrm{A}}^{\circ(p)} = q_{\mathrm{A}}^{\circ(s)}\left[1 + \sum \frac{q_{\mathrm{B}_i}^{\circ(s)}}{q_{\mathrm{A}}^{\circ(s)}(q_{\mathrm{S}}^\circ)^{x_i}}\right] \tag{77}$$

2.15 THE GIBBS-DUHEM EQUATION

The number of independent values of chemical potential for any phase is 1 less than the number of components, because the μ_i values satisfy the Gibbs-Duhem equation

$$\sum_i n_i \, d\mu_i = 0 \tag{78}$$

This is the quantitative expression of the familiar fact that the value of an intensive property depends upon the relative amounts of the components of a homogeneous phase but is independent of the total amount of the phase when the relative amounts are constant. The relationship can be developed on the following basis.

It is experimentally true that the Gibbs energy of a phase is directly proportional to the mass of the phase. For instance, the reversible work of a chemical reaction carried out in a galvanic cell is directly proportional to the quantity of material reacted provided that the changes in composition of the phases involved are either zero, as they are in a saturated Weston cell, or negligible. In principle, therefore, any homogeneous portion of matter can be built up by adding together at constant temperature and pressure successive increments of infinitesimal size, each of which has the same composition as the final mass and for each of which

$$dG = \sum_i \mu_i \, dn_i \tag{79}$$

Adding the amounts of the increments,

$$G = \sum_i \mu_i n_i \tag{80}$$

Differentiation of this expression at constant temperature and pressure leads to

$$dG = \sum_i \mu_i \, dn_i + \sum_i n_i \, d\mu_i \tag{81}$$

But at constant temperature and pressure

$$dG = \sum_i \mu_i \, dn_i \tag{82}$$

for a system at equilibrium. Equation (78) follows immediately.

2.16 MOLECULAR WEIGHTS IN SOLUTION

The molecular weight M of a gaseous substance is defined by virtue of Avogadro's law as

$$M = \lim_{P \to 0} \frac{w\mathbf{R}T}{PV} \tag{83}$$

where w is mass. For a solute the relation

$$\lim_{c \to 0} \frac{\partial \mu_A}{\partial \ln c_A} = \mathbf{R}T \tag{84}$$

can define the molecular weight of A since

$$\mu_A = M_A \frac{\partial G}{\partial w_A} \tag{85}$$

and $\partial G / \partial w_A$ is operationally defined. By virtue of Eq. (58) this is a unique definition even if the solute particles include a variety of solvates of different molecular weights, since from that equation

$$\lim_{c \to 0} \frac{\partial \mu_A{}^{(p)}}{\partial \ln c_A} = \mathbf{R}T \tag{86}$$

But since the potential of A in the solution must equal its potential in the gas phase in equilibrium with the solution, the molecular weight defined in this way for the solute must be the same as the molecular weight in the gas phase. This is so even if the solute is present chiefly as a stable compound of the species present in the gas with the solvent, although in that case the deviation from the limiting relationship grows more rapidly with increasing solute concentration.

The usual methods of determining the molecular weight of a solute depend upon a corollary of the Gibbs-Duhem equation, namely,

$$\lim_{x\to 0} \frac{d(\mu_1/M_1)}{d\chi} = -\frac{\mathbf{R}T}{1{,}000\rho^\circ} M_2 \tag{87}$$

where subscript 1 refers to solvent and subscript 2 to solute, χ is solute concentration in grams per liter, M is molecular weight, and ρ° is density of solvent in grams per milliliter. The value of the derivative on the left can be determined experimentally from the vapor pressure P of the solvent, because $d\mu_1 = \mathbf{R}T d\ln P$, or from the freezing point, boiling point, or osmotic pressure of the solution. The quantity μ_1/M_1 is independent of the molecular weight of the solvent, which need not therefore be known and lacks indeed any operational definition.

Equation (87) can be derived by putting Eq. (78) in the form

$$\frac{d\mu_1}{dc_2} = -\frac{n_2}{n_1}\frac{d\mu_2}{dc_2} = -\frac{n_2}{n_1 c_2}\frac{d\mu_2}{d\ln c_2} \tag{88}$$

and substituting the relationships

$$\lim_{c\to 0} \frac{n_2}{n_1} = \frac{M_1 c_2}{1{,}000\rho^\circ} \tag{89}$$

and

$$\lim_{c\to 0} \frac{d\mu_2}{d\ln c_2} = \mathbf{R}T \tag{90}$$

This leads to

$$\lim_{c\to 0} \frac{d\mu_1}{dc_2} = -\frac{M_1 \mathbf{R}T}{1{,}000\rho^\circ} \tag{91}$$

from which Eq. (87) follows by the substitution $d\chi = M_2 dc_2$.

2.17 THE GIBBS-DUHEM EQUATION FOR MULTICOMPONENT SYSTEMS

For two-component systems Eq. (78) requires that an increase in the potential of one component lead to a decrease in the potential of the other component. Since the potential of a solute necessarily increases with its concentration (Sec. 2.9), an increase in solute concentration necessarily entails a decrease in the potential and hence in the partial vapor pressure of the solvent. But with more than two components the equation has no such simple consequence, a fact which is sometimes overlooked. For three components the equation takes the form

$$n_1\,d\mu_1 + n_2\,d\mu_2 + n_3\,d\mu_3 = 0 \tag{92}$$

from which

$$n_1\frac{d\mu_1}{dc_3} + n_2\frac{d\mu_2}{dc_3} + n_3\frac{d\mu_3}{dc_3} = 0 \tag{93}$$

Since $d\mu_3/dc_3$ is necessarily positive, one of the other two terms, but not necessarily both, must be negative. It is therefore possible for the partial vapor pressure of one component of a mixed solvent to increase with increase in solute concentration.

If component 3 is a solute at low concentration, then to the dilute-solution approximation $n_3\,d\mu_3 = V\mathbf{R}Tdc_3$, and Eq. (92) reduces to

$$\frac{n_1}{V}\frac{d\mu_1}{dc_3} + \frac{n_2}{V}\frac{d\mu_2}{dc_3} + \mathbf{R}T = 0 \tag{94}$$

Consequently if the effect of the solute on the potential of component 1 is measured, the effect on the potential of component 2 can be estimated.[1]

If components 2 and 3 are both solutes in dilute solution, Eq. (93) reduces to

$$\frac{n_1}{V}d\mu_1 + \mathbf{R}T\,d(c_2 + c_3) = 0 \tag{95}$$

in the dilute-solution approximation.

2.18 THE CASE OF THE IONIC SOLUTE

As with so many other properties of strong electrolytes in water or in a water-like solvent, it is possible and useful to represent the chemical potential as the sum of the values of the ions which constitute the electrolyte. Certainly the tabulation of individual ionic values from which the values for the electrolytes composed of all possible combinations of those ions can be obtained represents a large economy.

To establish such a table one need only assign a value to one arbitrarily chosen ion and assume that the potential of any electrolyte $M_m X_x$ is given by the sum $m\mu_M + x\mu_X$. If then the assigned value for hydrogen ion is $\mu_{H^+}{}^{(a)}$, the value for chloride ion is $\mu_{HCl} - \mu_{H^+}{}^{(a)}$, the value for sodium ion is $\mu_{NaCl} - \mu_{HCl} + \mu_{H^+}{}^{(a)}$, and the value for bromide ion can be either $\mu_{HBr} - \mu_{H^+}{}^{(a)}$ or $\mu_{NaBr} - \mu_{NaCl} + \mu_{HCl} - \mu_{H^+}{}^{(a)}$. As a matter of experience the properties of a solution obtained by adding to water x moles/liter each of HCl and NaBr are

[1] For a qualitative application of this conclusion see [9].

identical with those of one obtained by adding x moles/liter each of HBr and NaCl. Consequently

$$\mu_{\mathrm{HCl}} + \mu_{\mathrm{NaBr}} = \mu_{\mathrm{HBr}} + \mu_{\mathrm{NaCl}} \tag{96}$$

the two values of $\mu_{\mathrm{Br}}{}^{(a)}$ are identical, and the assumption is justified. This remains true no matter what value one assigns to the potential of hydrogen ion, although for esthetic reasons one would avoid an assignment which would lead to negative values for any ion.

One cannot, however, attribute any physical meaning to the definition of the potential of hydrogen ion in an aqueous solution of hydrogen chloride and sodium chloride as

$$\left(\frac{\partial G}{\partial n_{\mathrm{H}^+}}\right)_{n_{\mathrm{Cl}^-}, n_{\mathrm{Na}^+}, Q}$$

for the differential dQ of the electric charge is, by Faraday's law,

$$dQ = \mathbf{F}(dn_{\mathrm{Cl}^-} - dn_{\mathrm{Na}^+} - dn_{\mathrm{H}^+}) \tag{97}$$

It is therefore not possible to add hydrogen ion to the solution while maintaining constant both the charge and the amounts of chloride ion and sodium ion.

The quantities

$$\left(\frac{\partial G}{\partial n_{\mathrm{H}^+}}\right)_{n_{\mathrm{Na}^+}, Q} \qquad \left(\frac{\partial G}{\partial n_{\mathrm{H}^+}}\right)_{n_{\mathrm{Cl}^-}, Q} \qquad \text{and} \qquad \left(\frac{\partial G}{\partial n_{\mathrm{H}^+}}\right)_{n_{\mathrm{Na}^+}, n_{\mathrm{Cl}^-}}$$

do have physical reality; but the first is identical with μ_{HCl} since the only way one can add hydrogen ion while keeping the quantity of sodium ion and the charge constant is to add an equivalent of chloride ion. By virtue of similar considerations the second equals $\mu_{\mathrm{HCl}} - \mu_{\mathrm{NaCl}}$. Neither of these quantities is therefore uniquely characteristic of the addition of hydrogen ion. The third quantity depends on the electric potential of the body of matter involved, a quantity which is not uniquely determined by the composition of the material even at a fixed value of charge. This is not therefore a useful quantity in a chemical sense.

The dependence on electric potential follows from the identity

$$\begin{aligned} dG &= \left(\frac{\partial G}{\partial n_{\mathrm{H}^+}}\right)_{n_{\mathrm{Na}^+}, Q} dn_{\mathrm{H}^+} + \left(\frac{\partial G}{\partial n_{\mathrm{Na}^+}}\right)_{n_{\mathrm{H}^+}, Q} dn_{\mathrm{Na}^+} + V\,dQ \\ &= \left(\frac{\partial G}{\partial n_{\mathrm{H}^+}}\right)_{n_{\mathrm{Na}^+}, n_{\mathrm{Cl}^-}} dn_{\mathrm{H}^+} + \left(\frac{\partial G}{\partial n_{\mathrm{Na}^+}}\right)_{n_{\mathrm{H}^+}, n_{\mathrm{Cl}^-}} dn_{\mathrm{Na}^+} + \left(\frac{\partial G}{\partial n_{\mathrm{Cl}^+}}\right)_{n_{\mathrm{H}^+}, n_{\mathrm{Na}^+}} dn_{\mathrm{Cl}^-} \end{aligned} \tag{98}$$

V being the electric potential. Since this is true for all possible variations, it is true for $dn_{Na^+} = dn_{Cl^-} = 0$, which requires that $dQ = -\mathbf{F}dn_{H^+}$, and since further

$$\left(\frac{\partial G}{\partial n_{H^+}}\right)_{n_{Na^+},Q} = \left(\frac{\partial G}{\partial n_{HCl}}\right)_{n_{NaCl},Q} \quad (99)$$

it follows that

$$\left(\frac{\partial G}{\partial n_{H^+}}\right)_{n_{Na^+},\, n_{Cl^-}} = \left(\frac{\partial G}{\partial n_{HCl}}\right)_{n_{NaCl},Q} - \mathbf{F}V \quad (100)$$

The dependence on concentration of the chemical potential of a binary strong electrolyte is considerably closer, especially in very dilute solution, to $\mu = \mu^\circ + 2\mathbf{R}T\ln c$ than to $\mu = \mu^\circ + \mathbf{R}T\ln c$. It is therefore reasonable to define a mean ionic-activity coefficient $\gamma_\pm$ by the relation

$$\mu = \mu^\circ + 2\mathbf{R}T\ln c + 2\mathbf{R}T\ln \gamma_\pm \quad (101)$$

and to represent $\gamma_\pm$ for electrolyte MX as

$$\gamma_\pm = \gamma_{M^+}\gamma_{X^-} \quad (102)$$

One can then assign a functional dependence of γ on concentration for an arbitrarily chosen ion, and obtain a functional dependence on concentration for all the ions which constitute the electrolytes for which the dependence of $\gamma_\pm$ on concentration is known. The Debye-Hückel theory limits to some extent the function to be chosen (Sec. 7.2).

In the same way one can usefully but arbitrarily assign activity values and standard-activity values to individual ions. For a strong electrolyte MX, for instance,

$$a^\circ_{MX} = a^\circ_{M^+}a^\circ_{X^-} \quad (103)$$

2.19 THE TEMPERATURE COEFFICIENT OF THE CHEMICAL POTENTIAL

As a necessary consequence of the second law of thermodynamics[1] the temperature coefficient of the chemical potential of component i is given by

$$\left(\frac{\partial \mu_i}{\partial T}\right)_{P,n} = -\bar{S}_i \quad (104)$$

where $\bar{S}_i$ is the molal entropy, given by

$$\bar{S}_i = \left(\frac{\partial S}{\partial n_i}\right)_{T,P,n_j,x} \quad (105)$$

[1] See, for instance, [4], pp. 53 and 91, or [2], p. 203.

S being the entropy of the system. This is equivalent to the relationship

$$\left[\frac{\partial(\mu_i/T)}{\partial T}\right]_{P,n} = -\frac{\bar{H}_i}{T^2} \tag{106}$$

Here $\bar{H}_i$, the molal enthalpy of component i, is given by

$$\bar{H}_i = \left(\frac{\partial H}{\partial n_i}\right)_{T,P,n_j,x} \tag{107}$$

H, the enthalpy of the system, is defined as $E + PV$, and by thermodynamic necessity

$$H = G + TS \tag{108}$$

In Eqs. (104) and (105) the subscript n means that the amounts of all components are constant; in Eqs. (105) and (107) the subscript n_j means that the amounts of all components except i are constant.

2.20 MOLAL ENTHALPY AND MOLAL ENTROPY AS FUNCTIONS OF CONCENTRATION

The dependence of the molal enthalpy of solute i on concentration is given by

$$\bar{H}_i = \bar{H}_i^\circ - \mathbf{R}T^2\left(\frac{\partial \ln \gamma_i}{\partial T}\right)_{P,n} - \mathbf{R}T^2\left[\frac{\partial \ln(\rho/\rho^\circ)}{\partial T}\right]_{P,n} \tag{109}$$

in which the standard enthalpy $\bar{H}^\circ$ is clearly

$$\bar{H}_i^\circ = \lim_{c\to 0} H_i \tag{110}$$

ρ is the density of the solution and ρ° that of the solvent. For the solvent or for a component j of a mixed solvent the standard enthalpy is the molal enthalpy in the solute-free solvent and is given by

$$\bar{H}_j = \bar{H}_j^\circ - \mathbf{R}T^2\left(\frac{\partial \ln \gamma_j}{\partial T}\right)_{P,n} \tag{111}$$

It should be noted that although the limit in Eq. (110) is for zero concentration in moles per liter, the derivatives in Eqs. (109) and (111) are at constant composition by weight, not at constant concentration.

The quantity $\bar{H} - \bar{H}^\circ$ is the heat effect per mole associated with the transfer of solute or solvent from the solution in question to the solute-free solvent. Its magnitude is smaller than that of the corresponding value of the quantity $\mu - \mu^\circ$, and to the dilute-solution approximation one may usefully set

$$\bar{H} = \bar{H}^\circ \tag{112}$$

Although for a solute i molal enthalpy is given by

$$\bar{H}_i = -T^2 \frac{\partial(\mu/T)}{\partial T} \tag{113}$$

standard enthalpy follows the more complicated relationship

$$\bar{H}_i^\circ = -T^2 \frac{\partial(\mu^\circ/T)}{\partial T} - \mathbf{R}T^2 \frac{\partial \ln \rho^\circ}{\partial T} \tag{114}$$

This is the rather irritating result of the choice of concentration in moles per liter as a measure of composition. For a solvent with a coefficient of expansion of 10^{-3} at 300°K the term involving ρ° increases the value of the standard enthalpy by 180 cal/mole; for water the increase is only 37. For the solvent or for component j of a mixed solvent, however,

$$\bar{H}_j^\circ = -T^2 \frac{\partial(\mu^\circ/T)}{\partial T} \tag{115}$$

For molal entropy

$$\bar{S}_i = \bar{S}_i^\circ - \mathbf{R} \ln c_i - \left[\frac{\partial(\mathbf{R}T \ln \gamma_i)}{\partial T}\right]_{P,n} - \mathbf{R}\left[\frac{\partial \ln(\rho/\rho^\circ)}{\partial T}\right]_{P,n} \tag{116}$$

for a solute i, and

$$\bar{S}_j = \bar{S}_j^\circ - \left[\frac{\partial(\mathbf{R}T \ln \gamma_j)}{\partial T}\right]_{P,n} \tag{117}$$

for the solvent or a solvent component j. Standard entropy $\bar{S}^\circ$ is

$$\bar{S}_i^\circ = \lim_{c \to 0} (\bar{S}_i + \mathbf{R} \ln c_i) \tag{118}$$

for the solute and

$$\bar{S}_j^\circ = \lim_{c \to 0} \bar{S}_j \tag{119}$$

for the solvent or a solvent component. To the dilute-solution approximation

$$\bar{S}_i^\circ = \bar{S}_i + \mathbf{R} \ln c_i \tag{120}$$

for a solute i, and

$$\bar{S}_j^\circ = \bar{S}_j \tag{121}$$

for the solvent or a solvent component j.

The relationships of this section can be derived from the defining equation, Eq. (31) or (32), for the activity coefficient. Division by T, differentiation, and substitution in Eq. (106) leads to

$$-\frac{\bar{H}_i}{T^2} = \left[\frac{\partial(\mu^\circ/T)}{\partial T}\right]_{P,n} + \mathbf{R}\left(\frac{\partial \ln \gamma_i}{\partial T}\right)_{P,n} + \mathbf{R}\left(\frac{\partial \ln c_i}{\partial T}\right)_{P,n} \tag{122}$$

Since

$$c_i = \frac{n_i}{V} = \frac{1{,}000\rho n_i}{\sum_i n_i M_i} \tag{123}$$

$$\left(\frac{\partial \ln c_i}{\partial T}\right)_{P,n} = \left(\frac{\partial \ln \rho}{\partial T}\right)_{P,n} \tag{124}$$

Substituting in Eq. (122) and taking limits

$$-\frac{\bar{H}^\circ}{T^2} = \left[\frac{\partial(\mu^\circ/T)}{\partial T}\right]_{P,n} + \mathbf{R}\left(\frac{\partial \ln \rho^\circ}{\partial T}\right)_{P,n} \tag{125}$$

and substitution of Eqs. (125) and (124) in Eq. (122) leads to Eq. (109). For the solvent or a solvent component Eq. (111) is obtained by the same development with the term involving c_i omitted in Eq. (122).

Direct differentiation of Eq. (31) and substitution in Eq. (104) leads to

$$\bar{S}_i = -\left(\frac{\partial \mu^\circ}{\partial T}\right)_{P,n} - \mathbf{R}\ln c_i - \mathbf{R}\left(\frac{\partial \ln \rho}{\partial T}\right)_{P,n} - \left[\frac{\partial(\mathbf{R}T\ln \gamma_i)}{\partial T}\right]_{P,n} \tag{126}$$

for a solute and to the corresponding equation with the term involving ρ omitted for the solvent. Taking limits leads to

$$\bar{S}_i^\circ = -\left(\frac{\partial \mu^\circ}{\partial T}\right)_{P,n} - \mathbf{R}T\left(\frac{\partial \ln \rho^\circ}{\partial T}\right)_{P,n} \tag{127}$$

and substitution in Eq. (126) then gives Eq. (116).

2.21 THE TEMPERATURE DEPENDENCE OF THE EQUILIBRIUM CONSTANT

For the equilibrium constant K at finite solute concentration [Eq. (25)]

$$\left(\frac{\partial \ln K}{\partial T}\right)_P = \frac{\Delta \bar{H}}{\mathbf{R}T^2} + (\sum \nu)\left(\frac{\partial \ln \rho}{\partial T}\right)_P \tag{128}$$

For the limiting value K° for zero solute concentration

$$\left(\frac{\partial \ln K^\circ}{\partial T}\right)_P = \frac{\Delta \bar{H}^\circ}{\mathbf{R}T^2} + (\sum \nu)\left(\frac{\partial \ln \rho^\circ}{\partial T}\right)_P \tag{129}$$

The quantity $\Delta\bar{H}$, defined as

$$\Delta \bar{H} = \sum_i \nu_i \bar{H}_i \tag{130}$$

is the calorimetrically measurable heat of reaction. The summation in Eq. (130) is over all stoichiometric reactants, but the summation $\sum \nu$ in Eqs. (128) and (129) is over solute reactants only.

The derivation of these relationships follows. From Eq. (114)

$$\frac{\partial(\Delta\mu^\circ/T)}{\partial T} = -\frac{\Delta\bar{H}^\circ}{T^2} - \mathbf{R}(\sum\nu)\frac{\partial\ln\rho^\circ}{\partial T} \tag{131}$$

and substitution of $-\mathbf{R}T\ln K^\circ$ for $\Delta\mu^\circ$ leads immediately to Eq. (129). By Eq. (109)

$$\Delta\frac{\partial\ln\gamma}{\partial T} = -\frac{\Delta\bar{H} - \Delta\bar{H}^\circ}{\mathbf{R}T^2} - (\sum\nu)\frac{\partial\ln(\rho/\rho^\circ)}{\partial T} \tag{132}$$

and by Eq. (33)

$$\frac{\partial\ln K}{\partial T} = \frac{\partial\ln K^\circ}{\partial T} - \Delta\frac{\partial\ln\gamma}{\partial T} \tag{133}$$

Substitution in Eq. (133) from Eqs. (129) and (132) leads immediately to Eq. (128).

2.22 THE EXPERIMENTAL ESTIMATION OF ENTHALPY OF REACTION AND OF STANDARD ENTROPY OF REACTION

Enthalpy of reaction $\Delta\bar{H}$ can be determined directly by calorimetry. It can also be calculated, usually with considerably less precision, from the temperature coefficient of equilibrium constant. For this purpose Eq. (128) is conveniently put in the form

$$\Delta\bar{H} = -\mathbf{R}\frac{\partial\ln K}{\partial(1/T)} + \mathbf{R}(\sum\nu)\frac{\partial\ln\rho}{\partial(1/T)} \tag{134}$$

Standard entropy of reaction $\Delta\bar{S}^\circ$ can be estimated from measurements of the equilibrium constant and of enthalpy of reaction, obtained by either method, by virtue of the relationship

$$\Delta\bar{S}^\circ = \frac{\Delta\bar{H}^\circ}{T} + \mathbf{R}\ln K^\circ \tag{135}$$

and also from measurements of the equilibrium constant alone by virtue of the relationship

$$\Delta\bar{S}^\circ = \left[\frac{\partial(\mathbf{R}T\ln K^\circ)}{\partial T}\right]_P - \mathbf{R}T(\sum\nu)\left(\frac{\partial\ln\rho^\circ}{\partial T}\right)_{P,n} \tag{136}$$

Equations (135) and (136) derive from fundamental entropy relationships. By virtue of Eq. (108)

$$\bar{H} = \mu + T\bar{S} \tag{137}$$

and

$$\Delta\bar{H}^\circ = \Delta\mu^\circ + T\Delta\bar{S}^\circ \tag{138}$$

from which Eq. (135) follows by substitution of $-\mathbf{R}T\ln K^\circ$ for $\Delta\mu^\circ$. By virtue of Eq. (104)

$$\Delta\bar{S}^\circ = -\left(\frac{\partial\Delta\mu^\circ}{\partial T}\right)_P \tag{139}$$

and Eq. (136) follows by substitution from Eqs. (114) and (115).

2.23 THE PRECISION PROBLEM IN THE ESTIMATION OF $\Delta\bar{H}^\circ$ AND $\Delta\bar{S}^\circ$

The estimation of enthalpy of reaction and entropy of reaction from the temperature coefficient of the equilibrium constant presents serious problems of precision, as does any procedure involving empirical differentiation. The plot of $\ln K$ against $1/T$ is in principle curved, although in most cases (acidity constants being a notable exception) the curvature is not experimentally detectable over the accessible temperature range. If the curvature is negligible and K is measured at two temperatures,

$$\Delta\bar{H} = -\mathbf{R}\frac{\ln K_2 - \ln K_1}{1/T_2 - 1/T_1} \tag{140}$$

and the uncertainty $D\Delta\bar{H}$ due to an uncertainty $D\ln K$ in the equilibrium constant is

$$D\,\Delta\bar{H} = 2^{1/2}\frac{\mathbf{R}T_1\,T_2}{T_2 - T_1}\frac{DK}{K} \tag{141}$$

If, for instance, DK/K is 0.05, the temperature is in the 300° region, and $T_2 - T_1$ is 50, $D\Delta\bar{H}$ is 300.

The validity of the estimate of $D\Delta\bar{H}$ is inherently less if the plot of $\ln K$ against $1/T$ is appreciably curved. In such cases measurement at more than two temperatures is especially helpful. There are additional precision problems which arise from uncertainty in the extrapolation needed to obtain $\Delta\bar{H}^\circ$. The term involving the temperature coefficient of the density is commonly neglected, although it may be significant when the effect of a change of solvent on the equilibrium is under consideration.

For measurements at two temperatures $\Delta\bar{S}^\circ$ is given approximately by

$$\Delta\bar{S}^\circ = \mathbf{R}\ln K^\circ + \mathbf{R}T\frac{\ln K_2 - \ln K_1}{T_2 - T_1} \tag{142}$$

T being the average temperature and K° the equilibrium constant at that temperature. The uncertainty of the first term on the right of this equation is inherently less than that of the second term. Consequently to an adequate precision

$$D\,\Delta\bar{S}^\circ = \frac{2^{1/2}\,\mathbf{R}T}{T_2 - T_1}\frac{DK^\circ}{K^\circ} \tag{143}$$

The uncertainty in $\Delta\bar{S}^\circ$ due to a 5 percent uncertainty in K° with temperatures in the 300° region and $T_2 - T_1 = 50$ is therefore 1 cal/mole-deg.

It is significant that the error in $\Delta\bar{H}^\circ$ which arises from a given error in dK°/K° is T times the error in $\Delta\bar{S}^\circ$. If therefore changes in solvent or in reactant structure have a negligible effect on K° and its temperature coefficient, random errors in K° will lead to a linear relation with slope T between $\Delta\bar{H}^\circ$ and $\Delta\bar{S}^\circ$.

2.24 PRIMITIVE VALUES OF STANDARD ENTHALPY, ENTROPY, AND HEAT CAPACITY

When a solute A is in mobile equilibrium with one or more isomers, or solvates, or both in reactions of the type of (IV), the primitive value of the standard enthalpy, defined as the limiting value of the ratio $\partial H/\partial n_A$ for the addition or the formation of A under conditions such that all the isomers and solvates are formed in effectively equilibrium proportions at all times, is given by

$$\bar{H}_A^{\circ(p)} = \bar{H}_A^{\circ(s)} + \frac{\sum_i K_i^\circ \Delta\bar{H}_i^\circ}{1 + \sum_i K_i^\circ} \tag{144}$$

$\bar{H}_A^{\circ(s)}$ is the corresponding ratio under conditions such that no A is converted to isomers or solvates during the addition or formation, and $\Delta\bar{H}_i^\circ$ is the standard enthalpy change for the conversion of A to the ith isomer or solvate.

The primitive value of the standard entropy is given by

$$\bar{S}_A^{\circ(p)} = \bar{S}_A^{\circ(s)} + \frac{1}{T}\frac{\sum_i K_i^\circ \Delta\bar{H}_i^\circ}{1 + \sum_i K_i^\circ} + \mathbf{R}\ln\left(1 + \sum_i K_i^\circ\right) \tag{145}$$

Since the K°'s are functions of temperature, $\bar{H}^{\circ(p)}$ and $\bar{S}^{\circ(p)}$ can obviously have a complicated dependence on temperature even if $\bar{H}^{\circ(s)}$ and the $\Delta\bar{H}^\circ$'s have simple ones.

If there is only one isomer or solvate B, Eqs. (144) and (145) reduce to

$$\bar{H}_A^{\circ(p)} = \bar{H}_A^{\circ(s)} + \frac{K_{AB}^\circ}{1 + K_{AB}^\circ}\Delta\bar{H}_{AB}^\circ \tag{146}$$

and

$$\bar{S}_A^{\circ(p)} = \bar{S}_A^{\circ(s)} + \frac{K_{AB}^\circ}{1 + K_{AB}^\circ}\frac{\Delta\bar{H}_{AB}^\circ}{T} + \mathbf{R}\ln(1 + K_{AB}^\circ) \tag{147}$$

The primitive value of the molal heat capacity is

$$\bar{C}_A^{\circ(p)} = \bar{C}_A^{\circ(s)} + \frac{K_{AB}^\circ}{1 + K_{AB}^\circ}\Delta\bar{C}_{AB}^\circ + \frac{K_{AB}^\circ}{\mathbf{R}(1 + K_{AB}^\circ)^2}\left(\frac{\Delta\bar{H}_{AB}^\circ}{T}\right)^2 \tag{148}$$

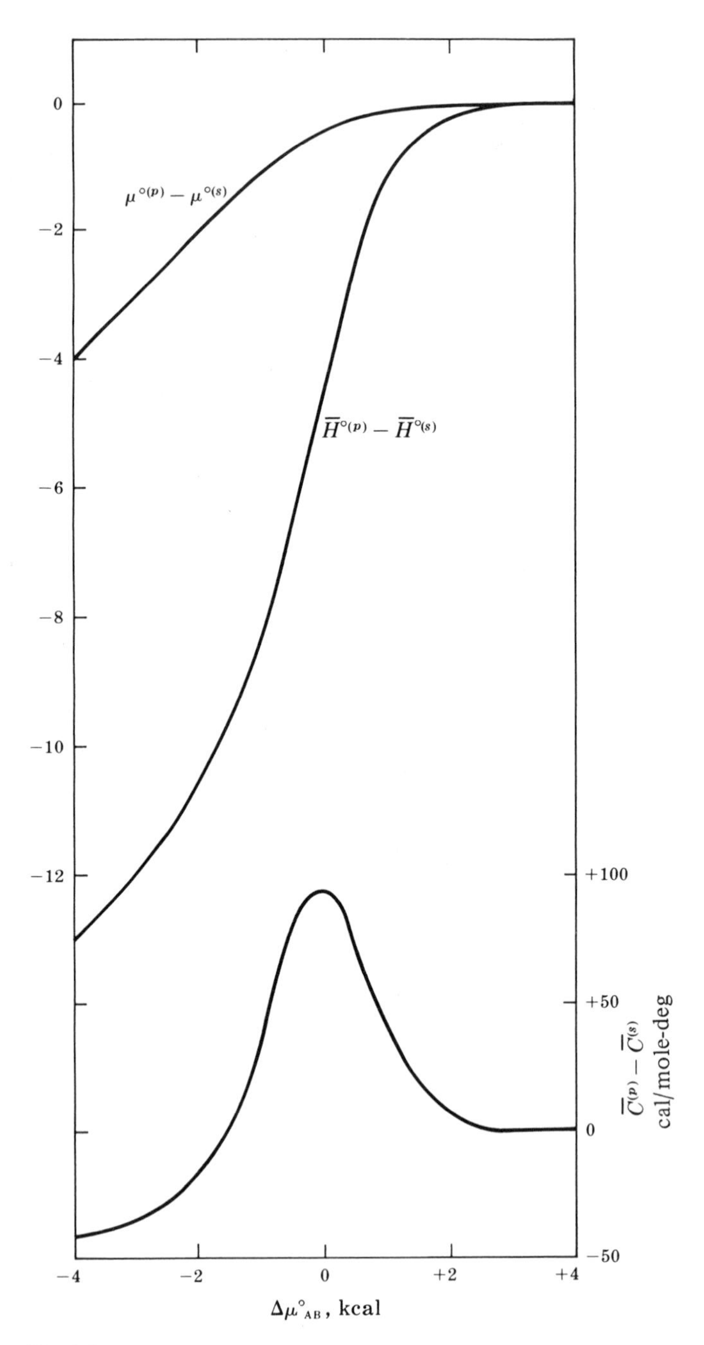
0
−2
−4
−6
−8
−10
−12
$\mu^{\circ(p)} - \mu^{\circ(s)}$
$\overline{H}^{\circ(p)} - \overline{H}^{\circ(s)}$
+100
+50
0
−50
$\overline{C}^{(p)} - \overline{C}^{(s)}$
cal/mole-deg
−4
−2
0
+2
+4
$\Delta\mu^{\circ}_{AB}$, kcal

Fig. 2.1.

When B is a hydrogen-bonded or other complex of A with solvent, $\Delta\bar{H}^\circ_{AB}$ is negative and of the order of several kilocalories. At the same time $\Delta\bar{S}^\circ_{AB}$ is also negative, and K°_{AB} is often not far from unity. Under these conditions the effect of a change in structure of reactant or in reaction medium on the difference $\bar{H}^{\circ(p)}_A - \bar{H}^{\circ(s)}_A$ is considerably greater than the effect on the difference $\mu^{\circ(p)}_A - \mu^{\circ(s)}_A$, and the difference $\bar{C}^{\circ(p)}_A - \bar{C}^{\circ(s)}_A$ goes through a rapid rise and fall. This behavior is illustrated in Fig. 2.1, in which the abscissa $\Delta\mu^\circ_{AB}$ measures the effect of the change in structure or in medium on K°_{AB}. The relationships of Eqs. (146), (147), and (148) are plotted for $\Delta\bar{H}^\circ_{AB} = -9{,}000 + \Delta\mu^\circ_{AB}$, $\Delta\bar{S}^\circ_{AB} = -30$, $\Delta\bar{C}^\circ_{AB} = -40$, and $T = 300°K$.

In cases of this sort $\bar{C}^{\circ(p)}_A - \bar{C}^{\circ(s)}_A$ goes through nearly as dramatic a variation with temperature as with changing structure or medium. This is illustrated in Fig. 2.2, which is plotted on the same basis as Fig. 2.1 except that the unvarying structure and medium are such that $K^\circ_{AB} = 1$ at 300°.

For gases and for many crystalline solids molal heat capacity can be adequately represented over a wide range of temperature by a power series of a few terms in T [2, p. 165]. But a power series is a poor tool for operations with a function which shows the behavior illustrated by the heat-capacity plots in Figs. 2.1 and 2.2. It should be noted that a heat-capacity behavior similar to that shown in Fig. 2.2 may appear even with a crystalline solid when an order-disorder transition is involved.[1]

Equation (144) can be derived by division of Eq. (51) by T, followed by differentiation with respect to T, using Eqs. (114) and (129) but omitting the usually negligible term involving the density.

[1] See, for instance, [10].

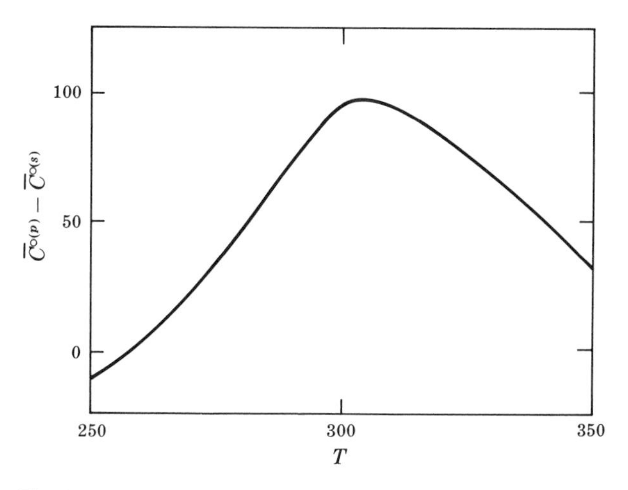

Fig. 2.2.

2.25 PRESSURE EFFECTS

The basic thermodynamic relationship is

$$\left(\frac{\partial \mu_i}{\partial P}\right)_{T,n} = \bar{V}_i \tag{149}$$

where $\bar{V}_i$, the molal volume of i, is defined as

$$\bar{V}_i = \left(\frac{\partial V}{\partial n_i}\right)_{T,P,n_j,x} \tag{150}$$

It is the rate of increase of the volume of the phase per added mole of i, the temperature, the pressure, and the quantities of all components but i being constant [2, p. 203]. In solutions which deviate largely from ideality V_i may differ considerably from the molal volume of i in the pure liquid state [2, p. 209]. By methods analogous to those used in connection with the effect of temperature the following relations are obtained:

$$\left(\frac{\partial \mu^\circ}{\partial P}\right)_{T,c} = \bar{V}_i - \mathbf{R}T\left(\frac{\partial \ln \gamma}{\partial P}\right)_{T,n} - \mathbf{R}T\left(\frac{\partial \ln \rho}{\partial P}\right)_{T,n} \tag{151}$$

$$\left(\frac{\partial \mu^\circ}{\partial P}\right)_{T,c} = \bar{V}_i^\circ - \mathbf{R}T\left(\frac{\partial \ln \rho^\circ}{\partial P}\right)_{T,n} \tag{152}$$

$$\left(\frac{\partial \ln K^\circ}{\partial P}\right)_{T} = -\frac{\Delta \bar{V}^\circ}{\mathbf{R}T} + (\textstyle\sum \nu)\left(\frac{\partial \ln \rho^\circ}{\partial P}\right)_{T} \tag{153}$$

$$\left(\frac{\partial \ln K}{\partial P}\right)_{T} = -\frac{\Delta \bar{V}}{\mathbf{R}T} + (\textstyle\sum \nu)\left(\frac{\partial \ln \rho}{\partial P}\right)_{T} \tag{154}$$

Since $\mathbf{R} = 82.05$ liter-atm/deg-mole, a ΔV value of 50 cm^3 at 300° leads to a fractional change in K of only 0.002 per atmosphere.

REFERENCES

1. Gibbs, J. W.: "The Collected Works of Willard Gibbs," vol. I, p. 63, Longmans, Green & Co., New York, 1928.
2. Lewis, G. N., and M. Randall: "Thermodynamics," 2nd ed., rev. by K. S. Pitzer and L. Brewer, McGraw-Hill Book Company, New York, 1961.
3. Prigogine, I., and R. Defay: "Thermodynamique chimique," Editions Desoer, Liège, 1950.
4. Kirkwood, J. G., and I. Oppenheim: "Chemical Thermodynamics," McGraw-Hill Book Company, New York, 1961.
5. Gurney, R. W.: "Ionic Processes in Solution," McGraw-Hill Book Company, New York, 1953.
6. Grunwald, E., and B. J. Berkowitz: *J. Am. Chem. Soc.*, **73**:4939 (1951).
7. Kolthoff, I. M., and S. Bruckenstein: "Treatise on Analytical Chemistry," vol. I, pt. I, I. M. Kolthoff and P. J. Elving (eds.), chap. 13, Interscience Publishers, Inc., New York, 1959.

8. Alexander, R., and A. J. Parker: *J. Am. Chem. Soc.*, **89**:5549 (1967).
9. Lucas, G. R., and L. P. Hammett: *J. Am. Chem. Soc.*, **64**:1928 (1942).
10. Davidson, N.: "Statistical Mechanics," pp. 377–378, McGraw-Hill Book Company, New York, 1962.

3

The Contribution from Statistical Mechanics

3.1 THE NECESSITY OF STATISTICAL MECHANICS

By themselves the principles of thermodynamics are coldly logical deductions from two empirical laws. They do not depend on models, on pictures in terms of molecular properties; rather they establish a framework within which any satisfactory model must fit. Merely by the addition of other empirically derived relationships, the perfect-gas law and Raoult's law for dilute solutions, they lead to many extremely useful applications in chemistry. These applications were indeed a main preoccupation of the science of physical chemistry in the two or three decades which began about 1880. Their effectiveness can be further improved by the superimposition of other purely empirical relationships. Thus Lewis and Brønsted were making important progress in the description and prediction of the properties of electrolyte solutions in this way in the first two decades of this century, but this progress was greatly accelerated by the development of a successful model by Debye and Hückel in 1923. The fact that this model is sometimes misapplied (Sec. 7.6) does not impugn the principle that science progresses much more rapidly when it has an adequate model than it does when it must depend solely on empirical generalization.

All successful models for chemical reactions involve the discipline of statistical mechanics, and in particular of quantum statistical mechanics. Without the quantum principle statistical mechanics had many accomplishments, but it faced hopeless contradictions; for instance, it predicted that all dissociation reactions would go to completion at all finite temperatures.

3.2 THE STATISTICAL MECHANICS OF THE PERFECT GAS

For the model of the perfect gas, i.e., for a system of widely separated small particles, between which the forces of interaction are minute, quantum statistical mechanics predicts for the key quantity μ° that

$$\mu^\circ = E_0 - \mathbf{R}T \ln \frac{Q}{N_0 V} \tag{1}$$

further that

$$\bar{H}^\circ = E_0 + \mathbf{R}T^2 \frac{\partial \ln (Q/V)}{\partial T} \tag{2}$$

and that

$$\bar{S}^\circ = \mathbf{R} \ln \frac{Q}{N_0 V} + \mathbf{R}T \frac{\partial \ln (Q/V)}{\partial T} \tag{3}$$

The quantity E_0 is the energy per mole which the substance would have if without change of physical state all the molecules were reduced to the lowest quantized energy level. The partition function Q, defined as

$$Q = \sum_i^\infty g_i \exp \frac{-(\epsilon_i - \epsilon_0)}{\mathbf{k}T} \tag{4}$$

is a sum of what are conveniently called Boltzmann terms. In these the ϵ_i's are the quantized energies that the molecule can possess and ϵ_0 is the lowest such level. The multiplicity g_i is the number of possible and equally probable states, differing for instance in orientation in space, which the molecule can have when the energy has the value ϵ_i; $\mathbf{k} = \mathbf{R}/N_0$ is the Boltzmann constant, and the summation is taken over all the permitted energy levels of the molecule. Equations (1), (2), and (3) apply both when the substance is a component of a mixture of gases and when it is present as a pure substance.

The proof that the relationship

$$\mu = E_0 - \mathbf{R}T \ln \frac{Q}{N} \tag{5}$$

N being the number of molecules, is a necessary consequence of the application of quantum-mechanical theory to the model may be found in texts on statistical mechanics.[1] These also show that for systems of chemical interest

$$Q = \left(\frac{2\pi m\mathbf{k}T}{\mathbf{h}^2}\right)^{3/2} V Q_{\text{int}} \tag{6}$$

m being the mass of the molecule and Q_{int}, the internal partition function, being independent of the volume V of the system. Substitution of the relation

$$N = N_0 V c \tag{7}$$

in Eq. (5) leads to

$$\mu - \mathbf{R}T \ln c = E_0 - \mathbf{R}T \ln \frac{Q}{N_0 V} \tag{8}$$

which is the equivalent of Eq. (1). By virtue of Eq. (6) the right side of Eq. (8) is independent of concentration, and

$$\mu^\circ = E_0 - \mathbf{R}T \ln \left(\frac{2\pi m\mathbf{k}T}{\mathbf{h}^2}\right)^{3/2} \frac{Q_{\text{int}}}{N_0} \tag{9}$$

3.3 THE NATURE OF THE PARTITION FUNCTION

The partition function of a substance is a convergent infinite series, the index i being zero for the lowest energy level which a molecule of the substance can possess, 1 for the next highest level, and so on. The value of the function depends (except for symmetry effects, which are sometimes important) upon the motion of the molecule through space and of its component parts with respect to each other, i.e., upon kinetic energies. E_0, on the other hand, is primarily a property of potential energies, although not exclusively so because of the zero-point kinetic energies (Sec. 3.8).

To a useful approximation the internal partition function can be represented as a product of factors, one for each of the normal modes in terms of which classical mechanics analyzes the motions involved. In these terms

$$Q = Q_{\text{tr}} Q_{\text{rot}} \prod_j Q_j \tag{10}$$

where each factor is still the sum of Boltzmann terms, i.e., of terms of the same form as those in the summation of Eq. (4). For Q_{tr} the g's and ϵ's are those pertaining to the translational motion only, i.e., to the motion of the molecule as a whole through space. Except for very low temperatures

$$Q_{\text{tr}} = \left(\frac{2\pi m\mathbf{k}T}{\mathbf{h}^2}\right)^{3/2} V \tag{11}$$

as indicated in Eq. (6). For Q_{rot} the g's and ϵ's pertain only to the rotation of the molecule as a whole. The value increases with increasing moment of

[1] For instance, [1], chaps. 1–7.

inertia of the molecule and varies inversely with the symmetry number σ, which is defined "as the number of different values of the rotational coordinates which all correspond to one orientation of the molecule, remembering that the identical atoms are indistinguishable" [2]. Each of the factors in the product of Eq. (10) depends on one of the internal modes of motion of the molecule, motions which may be vibrations, internal rotations, or the oscillatory rotations called librations. The product is taken over all the normal modes of these internal motions.

3.4 THE THERMODYNAMIC FUNCTIONS OF A SIMPLE HARMONIC VIBRATOR

Some of the Q_j factors of Eq. (10) may closely approximate those of a simple harmonic vibrator, i.e., a motion for which the restoring force is proportional to the displacement, but even those which do not will show a qualitatively similar behavior. Figure 3.1 shows how the contributions of the simple harmonic vibrator to important thermodynamic functions vary with the

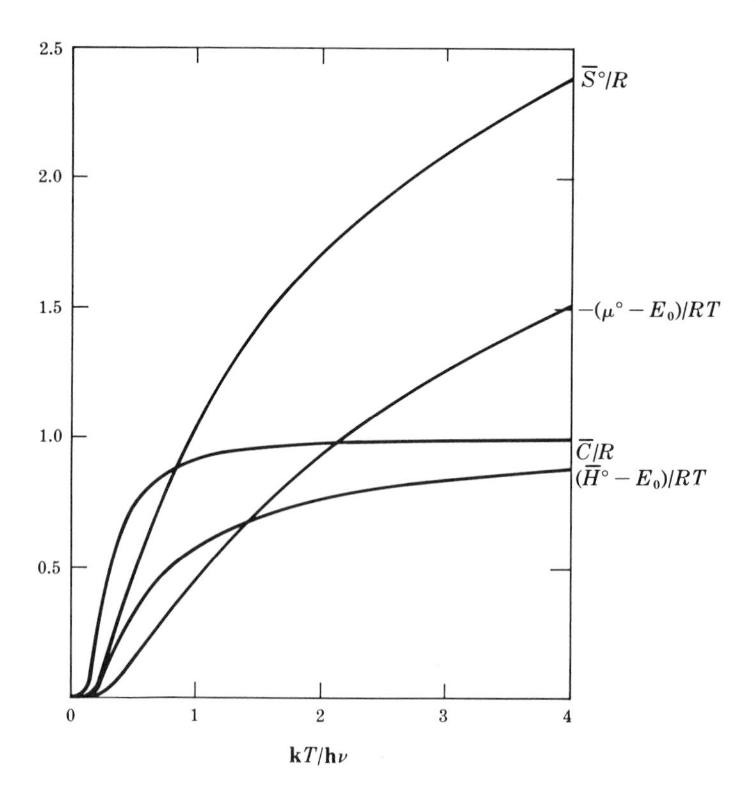

Fig. 3.1

temperature. The quantity $(\mu^\circ - E_0)/T$, which is commonly called the free-energy function, is equal to $-\mathbf{R} \ln Q$; the quantity $(\bar{H}^\circ - E_0)/T$, which is commonly called the heat-content function, is equal to $\mathbf{R}T\partial \ln Q/\partial T$.

All these functions start at zero at low temperatures. As the temperature increases, the first quantity to have a significant magnitude is the standard heat capacity, the next is the standard entropy, then the heat-content function, and finally the free-energy function. But the magnitudes of the free-energy function and the standard entropy increase indefinitely while heat capacity and heat-content function flatten off at the limiting value **R**. In the limit the mode of motion is said to be fully excited. Such a limit is characteristic not only for vibrations but for all varieties of motion. In the perfect gas the limit for translation is $^5/_2$**R**, and that for rotation is either **R** or $^3/_2$**R**, depending on the shape of the molecule.

The course of these curves is uniquely determined by the quantity $\mathbf{h}\nu/\mathbf{k}T$, in which ν, the classical vibration frequency, is given by

$$\nu = \frac{1}{2\pi}\sqrt{\frac{k}{m_r}} \tag{12}$$

where k is the proportionality constant of the restoring force and m_r is the reduced mass. At any temperature therefore the magnitudes of all of these thermodynamic functions will be greater, the stiffer the force and the lighter the mass.

Spectroscopists commonly set the boundary between the mid infrared and the far infrared at 200 cm^{-1}. At 300° the corresponding value of the abscissa in Fig. 3.1 is close to unity. At this frequency therefore the contribution of the vibration to the free-energy function is a bit less than 1 cal/deg-mole, and the contribution to the heat-content function is a bit over this value. At wave numbers greater than 1,000 the contribution to the heat-content function is less than 0.1 cal/deg-mole, and that to the free-energy function is appreciably less than this. At wave numbers less than 20 the contribution to the heat-content function is within 0.1 cal/deg-mole of the limiting value **R**, while the contribution to the free-energy function has become greater than 2.35**R**.

3.5 SOME TYPICAL NUMBERS

The partition function of a chemical substance is a large number in any temperature range of interest for chemical reactions. The value of the quantity $Q/N_0 V$ for gaseous isobutane at 300°K is 10^{11}. Partition functions increase with increasing temperature and with increasing molecular weight. The value for isobutane is 10 times larger at 400° than at 300°. At 300° it is 310 times larger for isobutane than it is for ethane. Partition functions are larger for flexible molecules than for rigid ones, and the value decreases with increasing symmetry. The value for 1-hexene is 1,150 times larger than for its more rigid

Table 3.1 Properties of gaseous isobutane at 300°K[a]

	Trans	*Rot*	*Vib*	*Total*
$\frac{\mu^\circ - E_0}{T}$	−26.79	−19.46	−3.55	−49.80
$\frac{\bar{H}^\circ - E_0}{T}$	4.97	2.98	6.44	14.39
$\bar{S}^\circ$	31.76	22.44	9.99	64.19
$\bar{C}^\circ$	4.97	2.98	15.30	23.25

[a] Based on calculations of Pitzer [3]. The values listed are in calories per degree-mole. μ° is defined as lim ($\mu - \mathbf{R}T\ln c$), that is, the standard state is 1 mole/liter not 1 atm.

isomer cyclohexane; it is about 6 times larger for the unsymmetrical monodeuterobenzene than it is for the symmetrical benzene.

A very large fraction of the total magnitude of the partition function of a gaseous substance derives from the translational and rotational contributions. Table 3.1 shows how the various modes of motion contribute to the thermodynamic properties of isobutane. It will be noted that (1) the magnitude of the free-energy function is much greater than that of the heat-content function; (2) the internal modes of motion make only a small contribution to the free-energy function, but both proportionately and in terms of absolute value they make a considerable contribution to the heat-content function; (3) the translational contribution to the heat-content function and to the heat capacity is $\frac{5}{2}\mathbf{R}$, and the rotational contribution is $\frac{3}{2}\mathbf{R}$.

3.6 THE ESTIMATION OF PARTITION FUNCTIONS

The partition function of a substance can be calculated if its molecular weight, its moments of inertia, and the frequencies of its internal motions are known. The molecular weight is known if the substance is a well-characterized chemical individual; and for the most part interatomic distances and bond angles are well enough known to make the calculation of the moments of inertia possible. In principle, frequencies of the internal motion can be determined from an analysis of the infrared and Raman spectra. It is in this way that Pitzer obtained the partition-function values on which Table 3.1 is based.

But isobutane is a favorable case because of the considerable symmetry of the molecule, and partition-function values for organic compounds of any complexity cannot usually be obtained in this way. Pitzer [4] has, however, developed semiempirical methods by which partition functions for a wide variety of hydrocarbons and for a few other organic compounds have been obtained [5].

3.7 THE STATISTICAL MECHANICS OF CHEMICAL EQUILIBRIUM IN THE GAS PHASE

For a chemical equilibrium Eqs. (1), (2), and (3) lead to

$$\Delta\mu^\circ = \Delta E_0 - \Delta\left(\mathbf{R}T\ln\frac{Q}{N_0 V}\right) \tag{13}$$

$$K^\circ = e^{-\Delta E_0/\mathbf{R}T}\prod_i\left(\frac{Q_i}{N_0 V}\right)^{\nu_i} \tag{14}$$

$$\Delta\bar{H}^\circ = \Delta E_0 + \Delta\left[\mathbf{R}T^2\frac{\partial\ln(Q/V)}{\partial T}\right] \tag{15}$$

$$\Delta\bar{S}^\circ = \Delta\left(\mathbf{R}\ln\frac{Q}{N_0 V}\right) + \Delta\left[\mathbf{R}T\frac{\partial\ln(Q/V)}{\partial T}\right] \tag{16}$$

Because partition functions are such large numbers, so much larger than their variation from substance to substance, the quantity $\prod (Q_i/N_0 V)^{\nu_i}$ is a large number for any reaction in which there is an increase in the number of molecules, and specifically for all dissociations. By Eq. (14) such reactions must therefore go largely toward completion unless the effect of the partition-function product is compensated by a small value of the exponential factor, i.e., by a large positive value of E_0 or by a low temperature.

Because the magnitude of the contributions of translation and rotation to the difference $\bar{H}^\circ - E_0$ is so much smaller than the corresponding contribution to the difference $\mu^\circ - E_0$, the difference between $\Delta\bar{H}^\circ$ and ΔE° is necessarily considerably less than that between $\Delta\mu^\circ$ and ΔE_0 for reactions in which the number of molecules changes. But the $\Delta\bar{H}^\circ - \Delta E_0$ difference is by no means negligible in reactions of complex molecules, and if there is no change in the number of molecules, its magnitude may be comparable to that of the $\Delta\mu^\circ - \Delta E_0$ difference. Thus for the conversion of 1-hexene to cyclohexane at 300°, $\Delta\bar{H}^\circ - \Delta E_0$ is –2.16 kcal while $\Delta\mu^\circ - \Delta E_0$ is +4.14 [5]. At this temperature 2.16 kcal represents a factor of 76 in the equilibrium constant, an effect which cannot reasonably be overlooked. For reactions of this sort the contribution to $\bar{H}^\circ - E_0$ from translation and rotation is the same for reactants and products. The 2.16 kcal derives therefore from the disappearance of or the decided stiffening of vibrations or librations whose wave number lies in the 20 to 1,000 range (Sec. 3.4). For the higher frequencies in this range the contribution to $\bar{H}^\circ - E_0$ is greater than that to $\mu^\circ - E_0$; for the lower frequencies the reverse is true.

3.8 ENTHALPY CHANGE AND POTENTIAL-ENERGY CHANGE

It is a not uncommon misconception that the enthalpy change in a chemical reaction is a close approximation to the potential-energy change, i.e., the change in potential energy which would accompany the reaction if the atoms of all the substances involved in the reaction were frozen in the positions of lowest potential energy. It is with potential-energy changes that one is concerned in theoretical calculations of such matters as the effect of structure on reactivity, and one would like to identify the calculated quantity with an experimental one. But as the last section shows, the identification of $\Delta\bar{H}°$ with ΔE_0 is not a reliable one, and the situation is further complicated by the fact that the E_0 of Eqs. (1) and (2) differs from the potential energy E_p by virtue of the relation

$$E_0 = E_p + \frac{1}{2}\sum_i \mathbf{h}\nu_i \tag{17}$$

in which the summation is taken over all the normal modes of vibration of the molecule. The quantity $\frac{1}{2}\mathbf{h}\nu$, required by quantum theory,[1] is called the zero-point energy of the vibration. It is the higher-frequency vibrations, those which contribute least to $\Delta\bar{H} - \Delta E_0$, which contribute most to $E_0 - E_p$.

A related misconception confuses the entropy change in a reaction with the quantity $\Delta[\mathbf{R}\ln(Q/N_0 V)]$, from which it differs by the same amount $\Delta[\mathbf{R}T\partial\ln(Q/V)/\partial T]$ that $\Delta\bar{H}°/T$ differs from $\Delta E_0/T$. The temptation to identify the two quantities is strong because the entropy change can always be determined experimentally whereas there does not appear to be even any hope of a reliable estimation of the quantity $Q/N_0 V$ for a reaction in solution.

3.9 THE STATISTICAL MECHANICS OF A SOLUTE IN DILUTE SOLUTION

The model of a system of widely separated particles between which the forces of interaction are minute is applicable to a solute in dilute solution as well as to a dilute gas. There are, however, two important differences: (1) in the solute case the particle includes not only the molecule of the dissolved solute but also the neighboring solvent molecules whose behavior is appreciably affected by the presence of the solute molecule; (2) the solute molecule does not move freely throughout the volume of the phase as the molecule of the gas does.

As a result of the first of these differences Eq. (4) is replaced by

$$Q = \sum_i \frac{(N_0 V)^{\nu_i - 1} Q_i}{Q_S^{\nu_i}} \tag{18}$$

where Q_i is a summation over Boltzmann terms for the quantized states of a solute-solvent aggregate containing ν_i molecules of solvent and Q_S is the

[1] See, for instance, [1], p. 31.

corresponding summation over the states of the solvent. This change is necessary because the chemical potential of the solute measures the Gibbs energy change per mole associated with the addition of the solute to the solution and this involves the effect of the solute on the motions of the adjacent solvent molecules as well as the effect of the solvent on the motions of the solute molecule.

As a result of the second difference both Q_{tr} and Q_{rot} are considerably smaller for a solute than for the same substance in the gas state. This is an aspect of the general quantum-mechanical principle that a decrease in the freedom of motion of a particle widens the spacing of the energy levels and thereby decreases the partition function. The proportionality of the translational partition function of a gas to the volume is another example of the same principle, and so is the effect of the force constant of a vibrator on its partition function. One may picture the translational and rotational motion of the gas molecule converted in the solution to a vibrational motion in what Frank and Evans [6] call a free-volume box.

The applicability of the limiting law of chemical equilibrium to reactions in solution demonstrates, however, that to the dilute-solution approximation the ratio Q/V is still independent of concentration in the solution.

Furthermore the transfer of a substance from the gas phase to a solution has little effect on the contribution which the internal motions of the molecule, the $\prod Q_j$ of Eq. (10), make to the partition function. As pointed out by Frank and Evans [6], "This follows from the fact that the position of Raman lines and infrared bands are not greatly changed on passing from the vapor to the liquid state, which means that the vibrations are, to a good approximation, not changed in frequency or that the vibrational motions are not greatly perturbed."

3.10 THE BARCLAY-BUTLER RULE

According to the empirical and decidedly approximate rule of Barclay and Butler, the $\Delta\bar{S}°$ and $\Delta\bar{H}°$ values for the transfer of a molecule from the liquid to the gas phase are linearly related for systems in which strong interactions due to hydrogen bonding, charge-transfer complexing, dipole-dipole interaction, and the like are absent [7]. According to Frank [8], the best value of the slope at temperatures in the neighborhood of 300°K is 0.00124. There is some ambiguity in the intercept because of the standard state employed, but a reasonable figure leads to

$$\Delta\bar{S}° = 1.83 + 0.00124\Delta\bar{H}° \tag{19}$$

for a standard state in moles per liter both for gas and for liquid.

By virtue of Eqs. (2) and (3) this is equivalent to

$$\Delta \mathbf{R} \ln \frac{Q}{N_0 V} + \Delta \mathbf{R} T \frac{\partial \ln(Q/V)}{\partial T} = 1.83 + 0.00124 \left[\Delta E_0 + \Delta \mathbf{R} T^2 \frac{\partial \ln(Q/V)}{\partial T} \right] \quad (20)$$

As Fig. 3.1 shows, the quantities $\mathbf{R} \ln(Q/N_0 V) = (\mu^\circ - E)/T$ and

$$\mathbf{R} T \partial \ln \frac{(Q/V)}{\partial T} = \frac{(\bar{H}^\circ - E_0)}{T}$$

are not linearly related when both are variable. The linear relationship of Eq. (20) is therefore possible only if the vibrations in the free-volume box in the liquid state as well as the translation and rotation in the gas state are fully excited and the value of $\mathbf{R} T \partial \ln(Q/V)/\partial T$ in solution is consequently equal to an integral multiple of $\mathbf{R}/2$.

The linearity of Eq. (20) also requires that ΔE_0 and $\Delta \ln(Q/N_0 V)$ be linearly related. A parallelism, if not perhaps a linear relation, between these quantities would be expected, for a stronger interaction between solute and solvent molecules which would lower the E_0 value for the liquid would also increase the spacing of the energy levels of the vibration and decrease the value of Q.

3.11 SOME PECULIARITIES OF AQUEOUS SOLUTIONS

When there are strong specific interactions between the solute and the solvent or between solvent molecules, the Barclay-Butler rule fails seriously, and this is especially the case with aqueous solutions. For the inert gases and some lighter hydrocarbons in water solution there is still a linear relation between the $\Delta \bar{S}^\circ$ and the $\Delta \bar{H}^\circ$ values for transfer of the solute to the gas phase, but $\Delta \bar{H}^\circ$ is 2 to 4 kcal more positive than for the same solute in a solvent like benzene, and $\Delta \bar{S}^\circ$ is relatively even more positive, the relation to $\Delta \bar{H}^\circ$ being [6]

$$\Delta \bar{S}^\circ = 14 + 0.0019 \Delta \bar{H}^\circ \quad (21)$$

Frank and Evans argue from these facts and from the enormous molal heat capacity (up to 60 cal/deg-mole) of the inert gases in aqueous solution that the solution of a nonpolar molecule in water modifies the water structure in the direction of greater crystallinity, that the water, so to speak, builds a microscopic iceberg around the solute molecule. This "freezing" lowers the energy and by restricting the freedom of motion of the water molecules lowers Q.

By contrast the molal entropy of such charged entities as the alkali and the halide ions in aqueous solution is remarkably high, so much so that the process

$$2\text{Ar} \rightarrow \text{K}^+ + \text{Cl}^- \quad \text{(I)}$$

has a calculated $\Delta\bar{S}^\circ$ value of +8.5 cal/deg. At the same time the $\Delta\bar{H}^\circ$ of transfer from aqueous solution to the gas phase runs from 60 to 120 kcal for ions of this sort compared with about 3 for argon. The introduction of these electrically charged entities into water is accompanied therefore by an extremely large decrease in energy while at the same time the motion of the oscillators which determine the value of the partition function is freer than when the solute is electrically neutral. In terms of the Frank and Evans picture, the ions have a structure-breaking effect while the neutral molecules have a structure-building effect.

The situation is further complicated by the fact that the $\Delta\bar{S}^\circ$ value for the ionization of a carboxylic acid in water

$$RCOOH + H_2O \rightleftharpoons RCOO^- + OH_3^- \qquad (II)$$

is negative and has the considerable magnitude of 15 to 30 cal/deg.

3.12 STANDARD ENTROPY CHANGES FOR REACTIONS IN SOLUTION

Not only is the standard entropy of a solute lower than that of the same substance in the gas state, but the difference between the standard entropies of similar substances of different molecular weight is less. In the gas state the standard entropy of ethane is 10.35 cal/deg more positive than that of methane [5], in benzene solution [9] the difference is 7.55, and in aqueous solution [6] it is 6.7.

Consequently the standard-entropy increase in a dissociation reaction in solution is less positive than it is in the gas phase, and the difference tends to be greater the higher the molecular weight of the reactants. In the tabulation by Leffler and Grunwald [10] of $\Delta\bar{S}^\circ$ values for the dissociation of compounds of the charge-transfer and hydrogen-bonding type the numbers run from 1.8 cal/deg for the acenaphthene–picric acid compound in ethylene dichloride solution to 19.8 for the dimer of acetic acid in carbon tetrachloride, with many

Table 3.2 Dissociation of aldehyde and ketone hydrates in aqueous solution at 25°C[a]

Compound	$\Delta\bar{S}^\circ$, *cal/deg*	$\Delta\bar{H}^\circ$, *kcal*	$\Delta\mu^\circ$, *kcal*
Formaldehyde	30.8	14.6	5.4
Chloral	30.2	12.7	3.68
s-Dichloracetone	14.8	5.7	1.27
asym-Dichloracetone	16.4	5.5	0.62
Acetaldehyde	16.4	5.1	0.23
Diacetyl	12.7	4.5	0.72
Monochloracetone	7.7	2.0	−0.28

[a] Data of Bell and McDougall [11].

Table 3.3 Data on the iodine chloride reaction (IV)[a]

Medium	*$\Delta\bar{S}^\circ$, cal/deg*	*$\Delta\bar{H}^\circ$, kcal*	*$\Delta\mu^\circ$, kcal*
Gas	2.7	−6.56	−7.37
CCl_4	0.4	−7.94	−8.04

[a] Data of Blair and Yost [12].

values in the neighborhood of 10. $\Delta\bar{S}^\circ$ values for dissociation reactions in the gas phase of molecules of similar size and complexity are in the range of 30 to 45. There is no obvious pattern of dependence on molecular weight and size or on the nature of the compound in the data cited by Leffler and Grunwald.

In aqueous solution the data of Bell and McDougall [11] on the reaction

$$R_2C(OH)_2 \rightleftharpoons R_2C{=}O + H_2O \qquad \text{(III)}$$

at 25°C show about the same range of $\Delta\bar{S}^\circ$ values and a similar lack of pattern of dependence on the nature of the reactant. As Table 3.2 shows, there is, however, a decided parallelism of $\Delta\bar{S}^\circ$ with $\Delta\bar{H}^\circ$ and therefore of both with $\Delta\mu^\circ$. This can reasonably be interpreted as resulting from the same influences as those which lead to the Barclay-Butler rule.

For reactions in which there is no change in the number of molecules, the transfer from gas to a solution in which strong interactions are absent would not be expected to have a large effect on the thermodynamic properties. For the reaction

$$I_2 + Cl_2 \rightleftharpoons 2ICl \qquad \text{(IV)}$$

Blair and Yost report the values in Table 3.3 for gas and for solution in carbon tetrachloride. The differences between the values in the two media are indeed not large.

3.13 THE RELATION TO THE PROBLEM OF STRUCTURE AND REACTIVITY

The effect of a change in the structure of a reactant on the equilibrium constant of a reaction can always be reduced to the value of the equilibrium constant of a reaction in which there is no change in the number of molecules. Thus if K_V is the equilibrium constant of the reaction

$$H_3NB(CH_3)_3 \rightleftharpoons H_3N + B(CH_3)_3 \qquad \text{(V)}$$

and K_{VI} that of the reaction

$$(CH_3)_3NB(CH_3)_3 \rightleftharpoons (CH_3)_3N + B(CH_3)_3 \quad \text{(VI)}$$

then the equilibrium constant of the reaction

$$(CH_3)_3N + H_3NB(CH_3)_3 \rightleftharpoons (CH_3)_3NB(CH_3)_3 + H_3N \quad \text{(VII)}$$

is given by

$$K_{VII} = \frac{K_V}{K_{VI}} \quad (22)$$

and measures the effect of the change in structure from ammonia to trimethylamine on the dissociation of the trimethylboron complex.

From Brown's [13] measurements of K_V and K_{VI} in the gas phase at 0 and 100°C, K_{VII} is 9.75 at 373°K and 67 at 273°K. From these the $\Delta\bar{S}°$ value for reaction (VII) is –5.85 at a temperature in the neighborhood of 323°K. The translational and rotational contributions to the quantity $\Delta \mathbf{R}T\partial\ln(Q/V)/\partial T$ are both zero, the translational contribution to $\Delta \mathbf{R}\ln(Q/N_0 V)$ can be calculated from Eq. (11) as –2.34, and the rotational contribution to this quantity should also be considerable and in the same direction. The magnitude of the contribution from internal motions to the sum $\Delta \mathbf{R}\ln(Q/N_0 V) + \Delta \mathbf{R}T\partial\ln(Q/V)/\partial T$ must therefore be considerably less than 3.5 cal/deg, and that of the contribution to either term of the sum must be still less.

Reaction (VII) represents an extreme case. The magnitudes of the translational and rotational contributions to the standard-entropy change are large as such things go. The freedom of internal motion should be considerably less in $(CH_3)_3NB(CH_3)_3$ than in any of the other substances involved, and this would lead to a relatively large negative contribution from the internal motions. By contrast the translational contribution to the standard-entropy change for the reaction in the gas phase

$$(CH_3)_3N + NH_4^+ \rightleftharpoons (CH_3)_3NH^+ + NH_3 \quad \text{(VIII)}$$

is only –0.1 cal/deg, and the magnitude of the contributions from rotation and from internal motion should be considerably less than those for reaction (VII). Yet the standard-entropy change for reaction (VIII) in aqueous solution is –14.7 cal/deg [14]. The indication is clear that this large effect derives from the interaction of the solutes with the solvent and not directly from the properties of the formal reactants.

Love, Cohen, and Taft [15] report strong evidence of the relative unimportance of the terms involving $\ln(Q/NV)$ and $\partial\ln(Q/V)/\partial T$ in reactions in the gas phase and of their importance in reactions in polar solvents. For instance, the $\Delta\bar{S}°$ value for the reaction in the gas phase

$$CF_3CH_2NH_2B(CH_3)_3 + CH_3CH_2NH_2 \rightleftharpoons CF_3CH_2NH_2 + CH_3CH_2NH_2B(CH_3)_3 \quad \text{(IX)}$$

is –0.1 cal/deg although the $\Delta\mu^\circ$ at 324°K is –3860 cal. By contrast the $\Delta\bar{S}^\circ$ value is 5.3 and the $\Delta\mu^\circ$ value –6850 for the reaction

$$CF_3CH_2NH_3^+ + CH_3CH_2NH_2 \rightleftharpoons CF_3CH_2NH_2 + CH_3CH_2NH_3^+ \tag{X}$$

in aqueous solution at 298°.

3.14 THE PARTITION FUNCTION q°

The function q° was defined in thermodynamic terms as

$$q_A^\circ = \exp\frac{-\mu_A^\circ}{\mathbf{R}T} \tag{2.72}$$

By Eqs. (1) and (4) it is therefore

$$q_A^\circ = \frac{1}{N_0 V}\exp\frac{-E_0}{\mathbf{R}T}\sum_i g_i \exp\frac{-(\epsilon_i - \epsilon_0)}{\mathbf{k}T} \tag{23}$$

and, since $E_0/\mathbf{R} = \epsilon_0/\mathbf{k}$,

$$q_A^\circ = \frac{1}{N_0 V}\sum_i g_i \exp\frac{-\epsilon_i}{\mathbf{k}T} \tag{24}$$

q° is therefore $1/N_0 V$ times the sum of Boltzmann terms over all significantly occupied energy levels of substance A. It differs from the partition function as it was defined in Eq. (4) in that the energy is measured from the same base line for all substances involved in a reaction instead of being measured for each substance from the lowest level of that substance, and by the factor $1/N_0 V$.

If a substance A is in mobile equilibrium with an isomer B, the primitive value of q° is by Eq. (2.74)

$$q_A^{\circ(p)} = q_A^{\circ(s)} + q_B^{\circ(s)} \tag{25}$$

By Eq. (24)

$$q_A^{\circ(p)} = \frac{1}{N_0 V}\sum_i g_i \exp\frac{-\epsilon_i}{\mathbf{k}T} \tag{26}$$

where the i summation is taken over all significantly occupied energy levels of both A and B.

In classical chemistry one had either a molecule of A or a molecule of B and no nonsense about it. But in terms of Eq. (26) the quantity $q_A^{\circ(p)}$ which determines the thermodynamic properties of a system containing A and B in mobile equilibrium does not recognize any distinction between a pair of states which belong to substance A and a pair of states one of which belongs to A and one to B. There is, of course, a distinction, but it is one of timing, not of equilibrium. If there are two collections A and B of quantized states of the same number and kind of atoms for which transitions from one state to another within the same collection have a high frequency while transitions from a state in one collection to a state in another have a low frequency, there unmistakably are two chemical substances A and B. But as the frequency of transition between a state in one collection and a state in the other increases, the differentiation of A and B as chemical substances blurs and finally disappears.

If a solute A is in mobile equilibrium with one or more solvates by the reaction

$$A_0 + x_i S \rightleftharpoons A_i \tag{IX}$$

then

$$q^{\circ(p)} = \sum_i \frac{q_i^{\circ(s)}}{(q_S^\circ)^{x_i}} \tag{27}$$

where q_S° refers to the solvent. This is merely another way of expressing Eq. (2.74). It is equivalent to

$$q^{\circ(p)} = \sum_i \frac{(N_0 V)^{x_i - 1} g_i \exp(-\epsilon_i/\mathbf{k}T)}{\left[\sum_j g_j \exp(-\epsilon_j/\mathbf{k}T)\right]^{x_i}} \tag{28}$$

where the ϵ_i's are the energies of all significantly occupied states both of A and of its solvates and the ϵ_j's are the energies of a solvent molecule in the absence of the solute. Equation (27) is further equivalent to

$$q^{\circ(p)} = e^{-E_0/\mathbf{R}T} \sum_i \frac{(N_0 V)^{x_i - 1} Q_i}{Q_S{}^{x_i}} \tag{29}$$

and to

$$Q^{(p)} = \sum_i \frac{(N_0 V)^{x_i - 1} Q_i}{Q_S{}^{x_i}} \tag{30}$$

The argument presented here is the justification for the acceptance of Eq. (18) (Sec. 3.9) as generally applicable. A compound of solute with x_i moles of solvent is no more than an aggregate consisting of the solute molecule together with those solvent molecules whose motions are significantly modified by the presence of the solute molecule.

REFERENCES

1. Davidson, N.: "Statistical Mechanics," McGraw-Hill Book Company, New York, 1962.
2. Mayer, J. E., and M. G. Mayer: "Statistical Mechanics," p. 195, John Wiley & Sons, Inc., London, 1940.
3. Pitzer, K. S.: *J. Chem. Phys.*, **5**:474 (1937); *Chem. Rev.*, **27**:39 (1940).
4. Pitzer, K. S.: *J. Chem. Phys.*, **6**:68 (1938).

5. Rossini, F. D., et al.: "Selected Values of Physical and Thermodynamic Properties of Hydrocarbons and Related Compounds," Carnegie Press, Carnegie Institute of Technology, Pittsburgh, 1953, and supplements.
6. Frank, H. S., and M. W. Evans: *J. Chem. Phys.*, **13**:507 (1945).
7. Barclay, I. M., and J. A. V. Butler: *Trans. Faraday Soc.*, **34**:1445 (1938).
8. Frank, H. S.: *J. Chem. Phys.*, **13**:493 (1945).
9. Bell, R. P.: *Trans. Faraday Soc.*, **33**:496 (1937).
10. Leffler, J. E., and E. Grunwald: "Rates and Equilibria of Organic Reactions," p. 52, John Wiley & Sons, Inc., New York, 1963.
11. Bell, R. P., and A. O. McDougall: *Trans. Faraday Soc.*, **56**:1280 (1960).
12. Blair, C. M., and D. M. Yost: *J. Am. Chem. Soc.*, **55**:4489 (1933).
13. Brown, H. C.: *J. Am. Chem. Soc.*, **67**:378 (1945).
14. Everett, D. H., and W. F. K. Wynne-Jones: *Proc. Roy. Soc.* (*London*), **A177**:499 (1941).
15. Love, P., R. B. Cohen, and R. W. Taft: *J. Am. Chem. Soc.*, **90**:2455 (1968).

4

The Evaluation of Rate Data

4.1 THE IDEAL LAW OF MASS ACTION

The core principle of chemical reaction kinetics is the ideal law of mass action, namely, within the precision of the dilute-solution approximation, the rate of any chemical reaction is proportional to the product of the concentrations of the substances actually involved in the reaction and depends on no other concentration nor upon the presence or absence of any other reactions. The law is to be interpreted in the sense that a substance may react with itself, in which case the rate is proportional to the square, or even to the cube or a higher power, of the concentration of that substance. In particular the forward and the reverse phases of a reversible reaction are independent reactions, and the net rate of a reversible reaction is the difference between the rates of a forward and of a reverse process, each of which has the same dependence on concentrations of reactants that it would have in the absence of the opposing process.

Observed rates of reaction frequently deviate from what would be predicted on an unsophisticated basis from the application of the law to the stoichiometry of the reaction involved. As an extreme case [1] the rate of the reaction

$$30ROH + B_{10}H_{14} \rightarrow 10B(OR)_3 + 22H_2 \tag{I}$$

is proportional to the product $[ROH][B_{10}H_{14}]$. Sometimes the rate is independent of the concentration of a substance which is actually consumed in the reaction. Sometimes the rate is proportional to the concentration of a substance, a catalyst, whose formula does not even appear in the stoichiometric equation. Sometimes no simple proportionality to any concentration appears, but the rate depends on complicated two- and three-parameter equations. It is a necessary corollary of the law that in all such cases the overall reaction occurs by way of a sequence of reaction steps, each of which has a rate consistent with the law. Such a sequence is called a reaction mechanism. It does not appear ever to have been impossible to devise a mechanism to fit any observed dependence of rate on concentrations; indeed the number of mechanisms consistent with the behavior of a particular reaction is often embarrassing.

4.2 SYSTEMATICS AND NOMENCLATURE

Reaction rate v is best defined as

$$v = \pm \frac{1}{V}\frac{dn}{dt} \tag{1}$$

where V is volume and n is number of moles of reactant or of product. The plus sign applies for a product, the minus sign for a reactant. In solution, but not necessarily in gases, volume changes accompanying reaction are so small that this definition is practically identical with

$$v = \pm \frac{dc}{dt} \tag{2}$$

where $c = n/V$ is concentration. Concentration is usually expressed in moles per liter for reactions in solution; it is highly desirable that times always be measured in seconds (cf. [2]).

In what follows the term kinetically simple irreversible reaction will mean one in which the rate is proportional, within the precision of the dilute-solution approximation, to a product of powers of concentrations. The powers involved may be positive, negative, or zero, and even fractional. The sum of the powers involved is called the order of the reaction. Thus if A, B, and C are three different substances, all the reactions to which the following rate equations apply are third order:

$$\frac{d[\mathrm{A}]}{dt} = -k[\mathrm{A}]^3 \tag{3}$$

$$\frac{d[\mathrm{A}]}{dt} = -k[\mathrm{B}][\mathrm{A}]^2 \tag{4}$$

$$\frac{d[\mathrm{A}]}{dt} = -k[\mathrm{A}][\mathrm{B}][\mathrm{C}] \tag{5}$$

The first of these is also said to be third order in A, the second to be second order in A and first order in B, and the third to be first order in each of the three substances. The proportionality constant k which appears in equations of this sort is called the specific rate or the rate constant. The former term is preferable and records the fact that the value of k is the value the rate would have if each concentration which appears in the rate equation were unity. It is proper to use the term first-order specific rate for the quantity

$$-\frac{1}{[\mathrm{A}]}\frac{d[\mathrm{A}]}{dt}$$

even when the rate differs measurably from exact proportionality to the concentration of A or is measurably dependent on other concentrations than that of A. A corresponding meaning may be assigned to the term second-order specific rate.

If the rate equation for a reaction is

$$v = k[\mathrm{A}][\mathrm{B}] \tag{6}$$

but [B] is essentially independent of time, the reaction is said to have a first-order time dependence or to be pseudo first order. Such a situation may arise merely because the initial reaction mix contained so much more B than A that a negligible fraction of the B will be consumed during the time required for the reaction of all the A. It may also arise because B is a catalyst, i.e., a substance which is regenerated essentially as fast as it is consumed (Sec. 5.26).

The term kinetically simple reversible reaction will be used in what follows for a reaction whose net rate is the difference between two terms each of which corresponds to a kinetically simple irreversible form.

4.3 THE RELATION BETWEEN RATE AND EQUILIBRIUM

Whatever the form of the rate equation for a reversible reaction, it must be consistent with the requirement that the rate be zero when the concentrations correspond to the state of equilibrium. For a kinetically simple reaction this requires that to the precision of the dilute-solution approximation

$$\frac{k_1}{k_{-1}} = K^x \tag{7}$$

where k_1 is the specific rate of the reaction from left to right and k_{-1} is the specific rate of the opposing reaction. K is the thermodynamically defined equilibrium constant, and x may have any value. It is, however, always possible to write the equilibrium expression in such a form that $x = 1$. It is further necessary that when in a reaction whose stoichiometry is

$$a\text{A} + b\text{B} + \cdots \rightleftharpoons m\text{M} + n\text{N} + \cdots \tag{II}$$

the rate from left to right is given by

$$v_1 = k_1[\text{A}]^\alpha [\text{B}]^\beta \cdots \tag{8}$$

the net rate v be given by

$$v = k_1[\text{A}]^\alpha [\text{B}]^\beta \cdots - k_{-1}[\text{M}]^{mx} [\text{N}]^{nx} [\text{A}]^{\alpha - ax} [\text{B}]^{\beta - \beta x} \tag{9}$$

This conclusion can be verified merely by setting $v = 0$ in Eq. (9), substituting the ratio k_1/k_{-1} from Eq. (7), and comparing with the equilibrium relationship

$$\frac{[\text{M}]^m [\text{N}]^n \cdots}{[\text{A}]^a [\text{B}]^b \cdots} = K \tag{10}$$

For example the rate v_1 of the bromination of a ketone

$$\text{RCOCH}_3 + \text{Br}_2 \rightarrow \text{RCOCH}_2\text{Br} + \text{H}^+ + \text{Br}^- \tag{III}$$

in dilute strong-acid solution is experimentally

$$v_1 = k_1[\text{RCOCH}_3][\text{H}^+] \tag{11}$$

The rate v_{-1} of the reverse process must then satisfy the relationship

$$v_{-1} = k_{-1}[\text{RCOCH}_2\text{Br}]\frac{[\text{H}^+]^2 [\text{Br}^-]}{[\text{Br}_2]} \tag{12}$$

The requirement of consistency between rate and equilibrium expressions leads to an important conclusion about deviations from the ideal law of mass action. For solutions in a single solvent the equilibrium condition for the reaction

$$\text{A} + \text{B} \rightleftharpoons \text{M} + \text{N} \tag{IV}$$

is (Sec. 2.8)

$$\frac{[\text{M}][\text{N}]}{[\text{A}][\text{B}]} = K^\circ \frac{\gamma_\text{A} \gamma_\text{B}}{\gamma_\text{M} \gamma_\text{N}} \tag{13}$$

in which the γ's are functions of the concentrations of all solutes present in the solution. It is therefore impossible for both of the equations

$$v_1 = k_1[A][B] \tag{14}$$

$$v_{-1} = k_{-1}[M][N] \tag{15}$$

with k_1 and k_{-1} independent of composition to be exactly valid, and very unlikely that either one is. The Brønsted equation (Sec. 7.1), which in this case becomes

$$v_1 = k_1[A][B]\frac{\gamma_A \gamma_B}{\gamma_\ddagger} \tag{16}$$

$$v_{-1} = k_{-1}[M][N]\frac{\gamma_M \gamma_N}{\gamma_\ddagger} \tag{17}$$

satisfies the consistency requirement and has been thoroughly verified for reactions involving ions, in which $\gamma_\ddagger$ depends on the medium in the way predicted for an entity whose electric charge is the algebraic sum of the charges on A and B, which is also the sum of the charges on M and N.

4.4 THE EXPERIMENTAL APPROACH TO A KINETIC PROBLEM

The experimental investigation of the kinetics of a reaction or of a group of related reactions may be undertaken for a variety of reasons. From an immediate practical point of view one may wish to describe the time required for an adequate amount of reaction under various conditions as the basis for the design of an industrial process. From a longer-range point of view kinetic investigations constitute an indispensable tool for the translation of the qualitative and diffuse knowledge which makes up so much of chemistry into quantitative and systematic relationships. In this task of systematization an understanding of reaction mechanism is essential, and the interpretation of mechanism begins with a knowledge of the kinetics involved. Finally the untangling of a complex mechanism is an esthetically gratifying accomplishment, and one which has always fascinated chemists, even though it has sometimes been fashionable to deny this.

Whatever the motives, the first task of a kinetic investigation is that of defining the reaction, the second is that of determining the functional relation between the rate and the composition of the reacting system, and the third is that of determining with suitable precision the values of the parameters involved in the function. The first of these tasks requires the determination of the extent, if any, to which the reaction of interest is accompanied by competing reactions which lead to products whose amounts are not related stoichiometrically to the amount of the product of interest. It requires the determination of the extent to which the reaction is reversible. It requires the identification of those reaction intermediates, if any, which are present in recognizable quantity during the course of the reaction. This nonkinetic information is an absolute prerequisite to any useful kinetic investigation. It has been greatly facilitated in recent years by the advances in such analytical techniques as spectrophotometry and vapor-phase chromatography.

The second task includes the recognition of the effect of catalysts and of inhibitors as well as that of varying concentration of known reactants and the influence, if any, of container surface and of light intensity.

With respect to the third task much depends upon the nature of the reaction and upon the precision required for the problem in hand. For kinetically simple reactions, and for those which approach this condition closely, carried out in solutions dilute enough to make the deviations from ideality unimportant, a precision of a few percent in the specific rate is easily attained by determining the extent to which reaction has occurred at a succession of time intervals and estimating the slope of a suitable linear function of concentration. Spectrophotometric methods often make it possible to work in solutions so dilute that deviations from ideality are insignificant.

4.5 LINEAR FORMS FOR KINETICALLY SIMPLE IRREVERSIBLE REACTIONS

Reactions having a first-order time dependence are of common occurrence. For such reactions

$$\frac{dc}{dt} = -kc \tag{18}$$

c being the single time-dependent concentration upon which the rate depends. Separation of variables and integration leads to

$$\ln c_0 - \ln c = kt \tag{19}$$

Here $\ln c_0$ is an integration constant, c_0 being the concentration at some arbitrarily chosen time from which the value of t is reckoned. For a reaction of this type a plot of $\ln c$ against time is linear, and the slope[1] is the specific rate k.

Reactions are often second order in a single substance. This is, for instance, true of the dimerization of cyclopentadiene, both in the gas [4] and in

[1] Brønsted used the symbol k for the slope of a plot of log c against time, which is 0.4343 times the k of Eqs. (18) and (19). This convention was followed in the paper by Brønsted, Kilpatrick, and Kilpatrick [3] with respect to the first-order constants, designated k_1 and k_2. The second-order constants, designated k_3 and k_4, which also derive from a logarithmic function, are, however, as Dr. Mary Kilpatrick has kindly informed me, true specific rates. There has been some confusion on this matter, for which I am largely responsible.

the liquid [5] phase. The rate equation is

$$\frac{dc}{dt} = -kc^2 \tag{20}$$

The same equation applies in the more common case in which the reaction mixture for the second-order reaction, $A + B \rightarrow$ products, is so set up that the initial concentrations of A and B are equal. For then $[A] = [B] = c$ throughout the course of the reaction, and the equation

$$\frac{d[A]}{dt} = \frac{d[B]}{dt} = -k[A][B] \tag{21}$$

is equivalent to Eq. (20). Separation of variables and integration leads to

$$\frac{1}{c} - \frac{1}{c_0} = kt \tag{22}$$

For a reaction of this type a plot of $1/c$ against time is linear, and the slope is the specific rate k.

If the stoichiometry is not 1:1 in cases of this sort, suitable integral factors must be inserted. Thus the reaction of benzyl chloride (RCl) with mercuric ion occurs by the process [6]

$$2RCl + Hg^{++} + 2H_2O \rightarrow 2ROH + HgCl_2 + 2H^+ \tag{V}$$

and the observed rate equation is

$$\frac{d[RCl]}{dt} = 2\frac{d[Hg^{++}]}{dt} = -k[RCl][Hg^{++}] \tag{23}$$

If the initial concentration of benzyl chloride is twice that of mercuric ion, it will be true at all times that $[RCl] = 2[Hg^{++}]$, and the integrated form may be written either as

$$\frac{1}{[RCl]} - \frac{1}{[RCl]_0} = \frac{1}{2}kt \tag{24}$$

or as

$$\frac{1}{[Hg^{++}]} - \frac{1}{[Hg^{++}]_0} = kt \tag{25}$$

When the initial concentrations of the two reactants are not equal in a second-order reaction of 1:1 stoichiometry, the difference between the two concentrations will be independent of time. If this difference is represented by Δ and the concentration of one of the reactants by c, the rate equation becomes

$$\frac{dc}{dt} = -kc(c + \Delta) \tag{26}$$

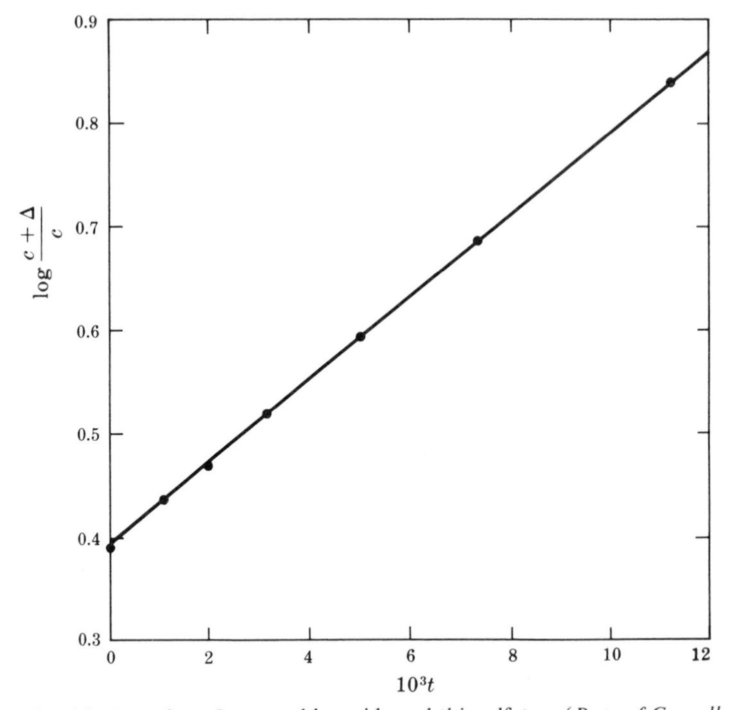

Fig. 4.1 Reaction of *n*-propyl bromide and thiosulfate. (*Data of Crowell and Hammett* [7].)

This integrates to

$$\ln\frac{c+\Delta}{c} - \ln\frac{c_0+\Delta}{c_0} = \Delta kt \tag{27}$$

For a reaction of this sort a plot of the quantity $\ln[(c+\Delta)/c]$ against time is linear, and the slope is the product of the specific rate by the difference Δ. Figure 4.1 is a plot of this sort for the reaction [7]

$$n\text{-}C_3H_7Br + S_2O_3^{--} \rightarrow n\text{-}C_3H_7S_2O_3^{-} + Br^{-} \tag{VI}$$

c being the concentration of propyl bromide and $c+\Delta$ that of thiosulfate. The linearity is good over a range of 75 percent reaction.

For the reaction of mercuric ion, concentration c, with benzyl chloride, concentration $2c+\Delta$, the integrated form is

$$\ln\frac{2c+\Delta}{2c} - \ln\frac{2c_0+\Delta}{2c_0} = \Delta kt \tag{28}$$

When Δ is small compared with c over most of the course of the reaction, the quantity $\ln[(c+\Delta)/c]$ is a small difference between the two large quantities

$\ln(c + \Delta)$ and $\ln c$. The easiest way to attain adequate precision in the calculation of k is to convert Eq. (27) to

$$\left(\frac{1}{c} - \frac{\Delta}{2c^2} + \frac{\Delta^2}{3c^3} \cdots\right) - \left(\frac{1}{c_0} - \frac{\Delta}{2c_0^{\,2}} + \frac{\Delta^2}{3c_0^{\,3}} \cdots\right) = kt \tag{29}$$

by expanding the logarithms. The slope of a plot against t of the first quantity in parentheses on the left of this equation is the specific rate. Enough terms in the expansion are employed to give the desired precision.

The rate of nitration of benzene in the solvent nitromethane by a large excess of nitric acid, about 5 M acid to 0.1 M benzene, is independent of the concentration of benzene and is the same for a number of substituted benzenes as it is for benzene itself [8]. The rate does depend on the concentration of nitric acid, but under the conditions used the acid concentration decreased by only 2 percent when the total amount of benzene present had reacted. The reaction is said to be zero order or, more properly, to have a zero-order time dependence. In terms of the law of mass action the situation is possible only because a relatively slow reaction involving nitric acid produces an intermediate which reacts relatively rapidly with benzene or with the substituted benzenes. For a reaction of this type a plot of benzene concentration against time is linear.

Third-order reactions and even those of higher order are not uncommon in solution. Usually, however, one of the reactants is a catalyst whose concentration is effectively independent of time. The time dependence in such a case is that of a second-order reaction. The integrated forms for a reaction showing a third-order time dependence are easily obtained if they are needed, which is not often the case.

If a reaction is of fractional order, i.e., if

$$\frac{dc}{dt} = -kc^{1/n} \tag{30}$$

with $n > 1$, the integrated form is

$$c^{(n+1)/n} - c_0^{(n+1)/n} = \frac{n+1}{n} kt \tag{31}$$

Reactions of fractional order in one reactant are not uncommon; for instance the reaction of vinyllithium with 1,1-diphenylethylene in tetrahydrofuran solution is first order in diphenylethylene and one-third order in vinyllithium [9]. Such a situation can be accounted for in terms of a mobile reversible dissociation of a polymerized vinyllithium to form a monomer which reacts relatively slowly with the diphenylethylene. The mathematics is unpleasant for the general case of a reaction of this sort, but if the diphenylethylene concentration is much larger than that of the vinyllithium, Eqs. (30) and (31) apply. Investigators tend, however, to study such reactions by estimating the slope of a plot of concentration against time at a variety of concentrations.

4.6 THE PROBLEM OF PRECISION

The matter of precision becomes critical when the effect of changes in temperature, or of changes in reaction medium, or of changes in structure of reactant is under consideration. Collins remarks [10, p. 63] that, because of lacking precision "many conclusions concerning the magnitude, direction and significance of small rate differences of isotopic reactions must be considered suspect." The same gloomy conclusion applies to many arguments about entropy and enthalpy of activation drawn from estimates of the effect of temperature on reaction rate.

The estimation of the rate of a reaction from measurements of quantity reacted at successive time intervals requires an empirical differentiation; i.e., it requires the estimation of the slope of a plot of concentration against time. Unfortunately empirical differentiation is inherently a precision-destroying operation, even when the data to which it is applied are subject only to random error, and it is even more so when there may be bias as well as random error. The task of estimating the slope is easier if one rectifies the plot by the devices reported in the previous section, but this facilitation may be accompanied by a decided decrease in potential precision. The very rectification introduces bias because it assumes that the reaction rate is exactly proportional to a product of powers of concentration. This assumption may be in error because of deviations from ideal solution behavior, because of nearly submerged equilibria involving the reactants (Sec. 4.20), because the reaction takes place by way of two or more steps of comparable rate (Sec. 4.14), or because of undetected side reactions.

Furthermore, the rectification involves a particular kind of weighting of the experimental data. In this connection it is important to consider the quantity actually observed, which is never the concentration of reactant itself. In fortunate cases it is proportional to this concentration. This is so when the quantity measured is the extinction coefficient for light of a wavelength which is absorbed by the reactant and not by the reaction product or when it is the volume of a reagent required to yield a titration end point with the reactant. In such cases

$$x = bc \tag{32}$$

where x is the measured quantity and b a proportionality constant. In terms of x the integrated form for a first-order reaction becomes

$$\ln x_0 - \ln x = kt \tag{33}$$

and the two forms for a second-order reaction become

$$\frac{1}{x} - \frac{1}{x_0} = \frac{k}{b}t \tag{34}$$

and

$$\ln\left(1+\frac{b\Delta}{x}\right)-\ln\left(1+\frac{b\Delta}{x_0}\right)=\Delta kt \tag{35}$$

For the first-order case, but for this only, the specific rate can be estimated without knowing or caring about the value of the proportionality constant b.

If in the first-order case one fits a best straight line graphically to a plot of $\ln x$ against t, one tries to minimize the sum for all experimental points of the quantity

$$|\vartheta \ln x| = |\ln x_{\mathrm{ob}} - \ln x_{\mathrm{cal}}| = \ln\left|\frac{x_{\mathrm{ob}}}{x_{\mathrm{cal}}}\right|$$

where x_{ob} is the observed value for a given value of t and x_{cal} the value given by the line for the same t. If one makes a linear least-squares fit, one minimizes the sum of the squares of the same quantity. This is equivalent to assuming that the probability of an experimental error in $\ln x$ is independent of the value of x, whereas it is more likely in most cases that the probable error in x itself is independent of the value of x. Since for small ϑ

$$\vartheta \ln x = \frac{\vartheta x}{x} \tag{36}$$

a given error in x leads to an error in $\ln x$ which is greater the smaller the value of x. Consequently both graphical and least-squares methods give as much weight to points afflicted with large error as to points with small error. One can compensate for this by a weighted least-squares analysis. Or one can write Eq. (33) in the form

$$x = x_0 e^{-kt} \tag{37}$$

and, at least with modern computers, obtain values of x_0 and k whose standard-error estimates are minimized [10, pp. 66–71].

The difficulties arising from incorrect weighting are even greater for second-order than for first-order reactions. The error in the plotted quantity $1/x$ in Eq. (34) arising from an error ϑx in the observed quantity is

$$\vartheta\frac{1}{x} = -\frac{1}{x^2}\vartheta x \tag{38}$$

and the corresponding error for reactions to which Eq. (35) applies is

$$\vartheta \ln\left(1-\frac{b\Delta}{x}\right) = -\frac{1}{x^2/b\Delta + x}\vartheta x \tag{39}$$

Analytical chemistry being what it is even after its recent great advances, the experimenter is often constrained to depend upon the measurement of a property which is linearly related to the concentration of the reactant but is not proportional to that concentration. Such a property might be the concentration of a reaction product or rather some quantity proportional to that concentration; it might be the extinction coefficient for light of a wavelength at which both reactant and product absorb; it might be electric conductance; it might be rotation of the plane of polarized light; it might be the level of the column of liquid in a dilatometer. If under these circumstances y is the value of the measured property, the linear relationship may be represented by

$$y = y_\infty + bc \tag{40}$$

where y_∞ is the value y takes when $c = 0$, that is, when the reaction has gone to completion. In terms of y the integrated form for a first-order reaction is

$$\ln|y_0 - y_\infty| - \ln|y - y_\infty| = kt \tag{41}$$

and the two forms for a second-order reaction are

$$\frac{1}{y - y_\infty} - \frac{1}{y_0 - y_\infty} = \frac{k}{b}t \tag{42}$$

and

$$\ln\left(1 + \frac{b\Delta}{y - y_\infty}\right) - \ln\left(1 + \frac{b\Delta}{y_0 - y_\infty}\right) = \Delta kt \tag{43}$$

y_0 being the value of y at time $t = 0$.

It is an unfortunate feature of this situation that the value of y_∞, which is known with no more reliability than any other value of y and frequently with less reliability, enters into the determination of the ordinate of each point of the plot. In estimating a value of k by unweighted least-squares or graphical methods one gives y_∞ therefore a weight n times greater than that of any other value of y, where n is the number of observations of y other than that of y_∞. Guggenheim [12] cited data from 24 observations at successive time intervals of an unspecified property in an unspecified reaction for which a small change in the value of y_∞ employed led to a large change in the estimated value of the first-order specific rate. Using the resources of a modern computer, Collins and Lietzke [10, p. 66] have applied an unweighted linear least-squares procedure to the Guggenheim data and obtained the following pairs of values of y_∞ and $k(\times 100)$: 6.488 and 1.5222; 6.492 and 1.5084; 6.497 and 1.4917. The standard-error estimates for k were respectively 0.0031, 0.0030, and 0.0032. It is therefore possible merely by varying the value of y_∞ by 0.15 percent, which is no more than the probable error of the experimental estimation of the quantity, to obtain estimates of the value of the specific rate which vary over a range of 2 percent, all of which have the same apparent reliability. Collins and Lietzke also used a linear least-squares procedure in which each point was given a weight equal to the magnitude of the observation and a nonlinear least-squares procedure in which the standard-error estimates of y_∞, k, and t in the equation

$$\frac{y}{y_\infty} = 1 - e^{-k(t-t_0)} \tag{44}$$

were minimized with results which did not differ significantly from those obtained by the unweighted least-squares procedure. With any of the pairs of y_∞ and k values none of the Guggenheim data varied by more than ± 0.1 percent from the calculated value; yet with this high consistency of the measurement the reliability of the specific rate was certainly no more than 2 percent.

Guggenheim [11] suggested a method of treating both k and y_∞ as adjustable parameters without elaborate computation, which has however the disadvantage of requiring a precise scheduling of the times at which y is measured. Nowadays it is probably economical to go to the computer.

An additional source of possible bias is the fact that the linear relationship between the observed quantity and the quantity of reactant is likely to be an approximation. Thus the level of the column in a dilatometer is proportional to the volume of the solution. For a reaction $A \rightarrow B + C$ in which A, B, and C are solutes in dilute solution the volume is given to the dilute-solution approximation by

$$V = V_0 + a[A] + b[B] + c[C] \tag{45}$$

in which a, b, c, and V_0 are independent of the concentrations. By material balance

$$[A]_0 - [A] = [B] - [B]_0 = [C] - [C]_0$$

where the subscript 0 refers to concentration at time zero. From this

$$V = \{b([B]_0 + [A]_0) + c([C]_0 + [A]_0) + V_0\} + (a - b - c)\,[A] \tag{46}$$

This is a linear relation between V and [A] and leads to a linear relation between dilatometer reading and [A] but one valid to the dilute-solution approximation only.

4.7 THE EFFECT OF SYSTEMATIC DEVIATIONS FROM THE LINEAR FORM

Figure 4.2 plots the quantity $\log(y_\infty - y)$ against time for the hydrolysis of ethyl toluenesulfonate in a water-dioxane mixture with an initial ester concentration of 0.1628 M [12]. The value of y is the number of cubic centimeters of alkali used in the titration of the acid produced by the hydrolysis, and y_∞ is calculated from the initial concentration of the ester. The plot looks linear, and the data can be fitted by the equation

$$\log(y_\infty - y) = 1.5021 - 2.526 \times 10^{-6}\, t \tag{47}$$

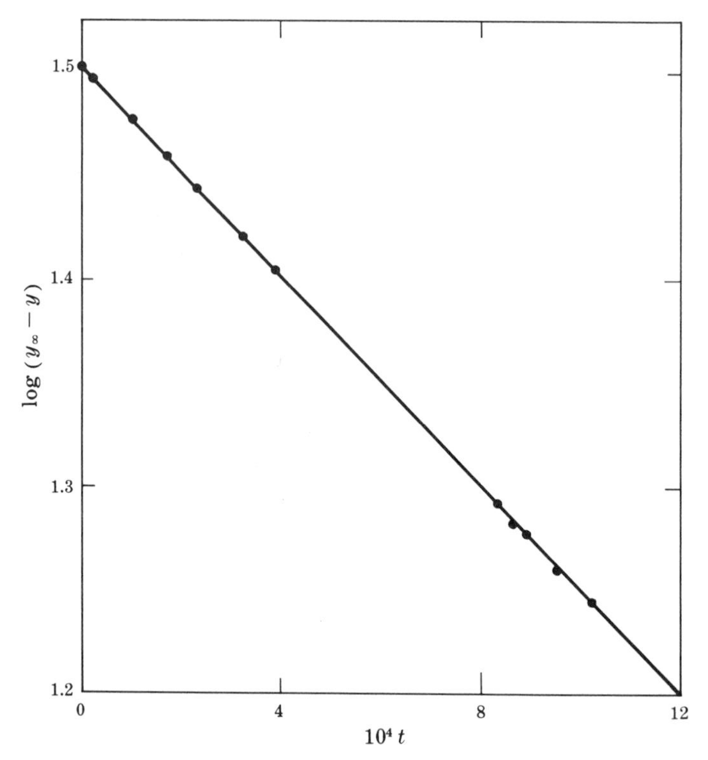

Fig. 4.2 First-order plot for hydrolysis of ethyl toluenesulfonate. (*Data of McCleary and Hammett* [12].)

with a rms deviation of 0.0009. But a larger-scale plot suggests a small curvature, and the equation

$$\log(y_\infty - y) = 1.5012 - 2.470 \times 10^{-6}\,t - 5 \times 10^{-13}\,t^2 \tag{48}$$

fits the data with a deviation of 0.0007. The suspicion that the curvature is real is supported by the fact that some two dozen other experiments involving different initial concentrations of ester in the presence and in the absence of various added electrolytes all suggest the same kind of curvature. It is further supported by the fact that the initial specific rate, the value of $d\ln c/dt$ at zero time, clearly decreases with increasing ester concentration, the decrease amounting to 8.5 percent between 0.1 and 0.2 *M*. The significant feature of this situation is that one can alter one's estimate of the initial specific rate, which is 2.303 times the coefficient of t in Eq. (47) or (48), by 2 percent, depending on whether one does or does not recognize the possibility of curvature in the plot.

4.8 THE RECOGNITION OF REACTION ORDER

For a second-order reaction involving a single reactant a plot of $1/c$ against t is linear. If the data for the toluenesulfonate hydrolysis are plotted in this way, as they are in Fig. 4.3 the first seven points lie so close to a straight line that it is not obvious whether the deviations are random or represent a real curvature. A more detailed study shows, however, a systematic curvature and a rms deviation 3 times greater than that for the first-order plot. Nevertheless if the experimenter had remained satisfied with the data he got during some 11 hr of observation, within which the reaction had gone 20 percent toward completion, he would not have had a high degree of certainty that the reaction is not second order. But he did return a second day to obtain the subsequent points, which clearly demonstrate the failure of the second-order relationship. The same assurance can be derived with even more certainty from the fact that in a series of experiments with differing values of c_0 the initial slope of the plot of $1/c$ against t varies inversely with c_0 instead of being constant, as it would be for a second-order reaction. This follows from the fact that if

$$\frac{dc}{dt} = -kc \tag{49}$$

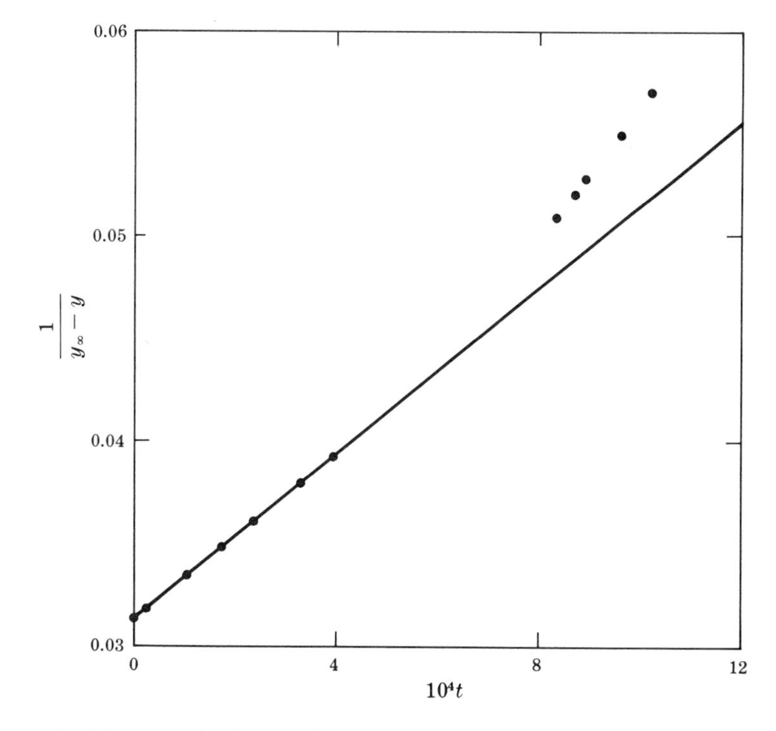

Fig. 4.3 Second-order plot for hydrolysis of ethyl toluenesulfonate.

then

$$\frac{d(1/c)}{dt} = -\frac{1}{c^2}\frac{dc}{dt} = \frac{k}{c} \tag{50}$$

4.9 THE STIRRED-FLOW REACTOR

Something like an order-of-magnitude gain in precision can be attained by the use of the stirred-flow reactor because the rate itself rather than the quantity reacted is determined. Although the principle of the stirred-flow reactor has been familiar in industry for many years, the device was first applied to the measurement of reaction rates by Denbigh [13]. In this procedure the reactor consists of a vessel of fixed volume provided with two or more inlets and one outlet, all of small diameter, and with an efficient stirring mechanism. A reagent solution enters the reactor through each inlet at a carefully controlled flow rate which is either constant or oscillates rapidly around a constant rate [14]. Since the volume changes which accompany reaction in solution are small, liquid leaves through the outlet at a rate essentially equal to the sum of the inlet rates. For such a system from simple material-balance considerations

$$\frac{dc}{dt} = \frac{u}{V}(c_0 - c) + v \tag{51}$$

where v is the rate of formation, under the conditions which exist in the reactor, of the substance whose concentration in the reactor is c; u is the outlet flow rate, V the volume of the reactor, and c_0 the concentration which would exist if the inputs were mixed in the ratio of their flow rates but no reaction occurred. c_0 is zero for a reaction product or an intermediate unless this is deliberately introduced in the input. v is positive if the substance is a reaction product, negative if it is a reactant, and may be positive, negative, or zero if it is an intermediate. If dc/dt is positive at any time, the right side of Eq. (51) will decrease with increasing time and dc/dt will become less positive. Similarly if dc/dt is negative, it will become less negative as time goes on, and if it is zero, it will stay zero. In the self-maintaining steady state which the system inevitably approaches

$$v = \frac{u}{V}(c - c_0) \tag{52}$$

If therefore one flows solution through the reactor until the steady state is attained within any desired precision and can measure u, V, c_0, and c, the rate v of reaction can be obtained by substitution in Eq. (52). c may be measured either in the reactor by physical methods [15] or in the output by rapid quenching or by continuous titration methods [16]. The attainment of the steady state can be verified by determining that c has become independent of time. By varying flow rate and input concentrations it is possible to vary the concentrations of the various substances present in the reactor at steady state and thus to determine the functional dependence of the rate on the composition of the solution in which the reaction is taking place.

An apparent disadvantage of the stirred-flow reactor is the waste of solution which must flow through the reactor in order to establish the steady state. This waste need never be more than 7 times the reactor volume [17], and the material consumed in obtaining one value of rate is comparable to that consumed in obtaining seven or fewer points on a plot of extent of reaction against time. The precision of the rate determined by the stirred-flow method, however, is decidedly superior to that obtained by empirical differentiation of the data on the time dependence of extent of reaction.

4.10 KINETICALLY SIMPLE REVERSIBLE REACTIONS

It is easier to determine the equilibrium constant of a measurably reversible reaction than to determine its rate. Consequently the equilibrium constant may be taken as known in approaching the investigation of the kinetics of such a reaction.

For the reaction $A \rightleftharpoons B$, first order in both directions,

$$\ln|[A]_e - [A]_0| - \ln|[A]_e - [A]| = (k_1 + k_{-1})\,t \tag{53}$$

the subscript 0 referring to concentration at time $t = 0$ and the subscript e to concentration at equilibrium. For a measured quantity y linearly related to [A]

$$\ln|y_e - y_0| - \ln|y_e - y| = (k_1 + k_{-1})\,t \tag{54}$$

The slope of a plot of $\ln|y_e - y|$ against time is therefore the sum $k_1 + k_{-1}$. Since the ratio of the two specific rates is the equilibrium constant, both specific rates can be obtained. Equations (53) and (54) are just as valid for the case where [A] increases with time, including that in which B alone is present initially, as they are for the case where the net reaction is from left to right.

For the reaction $A \rightleftharpoons B + C$ with the rate equation

$$\frac{d[A]}{dt} = -k_1[A] + k_{-1}[B]\,[C] \tag{55}$$

it is convenient to define

$$m = 2[A] + [B] + [C] \tag{56}$$

$$n = [(K + [C] - [B])^2 + 4K([A] + [B])]^{\frac{1}{2}} \tag{57}$$

In these terms the integrated form is

$$\ln\frac{2[A] - m - n}{2[A] - m + n} = k_{-1}\,nt + C \tag{58}$$

C being an integration constant. The quantities m and n are independent of time by virtue of the stoichiometry of the reaction and can be calculated from the composition of the reaction mix if K is known. If a plot of the left side of this equation against time is linear over a sufficient range, the applicability of Eq. (55) is verified and the specific rates can be computed from the slope of the plot and the values of K, m, and n. Equation (58) is valid both when the net reaction is from left to right and when it is from right to left.

For the reaction A + B = C + D, second order in both directions, the integrated form is

$$\frac{1}{a(p-q)} \ln \frac{x-p}{x-q} = k_{-1} t + C \tag{59}$$

in which p and q are the roots of the quadratic equation $ax^2 + bx + c$ with

$$x = [\mathrm{A}]_0 - [\mathrm{A}]$$

$$a = K - 1 \tag{60}$$

$$b = -\{K([\mathrm{A}]_0 + [\mathrm{B}]_0) + [\mathrm{C}]_0 + [\mathrm{D}]_0\} \tag{61}$$

$$c = K[\mathrm{A}]_0 [\mathrm{B}]_0 - [\mathrm{C}]_0 [\mathrm{D}]_0 \tag{62}$$

For $K = 1$, $a = 0$, and Eq. (29) reduces to

$$\frac{1}{b} \ln (bx + c) = k_{-1} t + C \tag{63}$$

For values of K near unity it would be advantageous to expand the left side of Eq. (59) in powers of a.

For the reaction 2A $\rightleftharpoons$ C + D Eq. (59) still applies, but

$$a = K - \tfrac{1}{4} \tag{64}$$

$$b = -\{K[\mathrm{A}]_0 + \tfrac{1}{2}([\mathrm{C}]_0 + [\mathrm{D}]_0)\} \tag{65}$$

$$c = K[\mathrm{A}]_0^2 - [\mathrm{C}]_0 [\mathrm{D}]_0 \tag{66}$$

All the integrated forms in this section can be obtained by substituting suitable material-balance relations in the rate equation and using tabulated integrals.

4.11 KINETICALLY COMPLEX REACTIONS

The appearance of kinetically complex behavior supplies clues to the mechanism of the reaction involved. Thus Bodenstein and Lind [18] showed that the reaction of hydrogen and bromine in the gas phase has a rate consistent with the two-parameter equation

$$\frac{d[\mathrm{HBr}]}{dt} = \frac{k_a[\mathrm{H_2}][\mathrm{Br_2}]^{1/2}}{1 + k_b[\mathrm{HBr}]/[\mathrm{Br_2}]} \tag{67}$$

and 13 years later Christiansen, Herzfeld, and Polanyi independently and almost simultaneously [19] proposed a mechanism which adequately accounts for the equation. The idea of free-radical chain mechanisms thus introduced lies at the basis of important areas of modern chemical science and technology.

For the interpretation of a complex kinetic rate law one imagines a reaction mechanism and can then set down the differential equations which correspond to the mechanism. From there on the going becomes tougher. This would not be so if in spite of its great advances analytical chemistry were more nearly perfect, if one could determine experimentally as functions of time the concentrations of reactant, of reaction product, and of those intermediates which appear in more than minute quantities.

An elegant example of what can be accomplished is the study by Juvet and Chiu [20] of the methanolysis of diethyl acetal. The concentrations of diethyl acetal, of dimethyl acetal, and of the intermediate methyl ethyl acetal can all be determined by gas chromatography. Figure 4.4 shows how the peak heights vary with time in a particular reaction mixture and at a particular temperature. From the slopes of any two of these plots at a particular time, the independently determined equilibrium constants, and the calibration of the chromatograph, all four specific rates for the two-step reversible reaction can be estimated.

Until recently this kind of a study was inconceivable, and even now it is not always possible. Much of what has been done in the investigation of

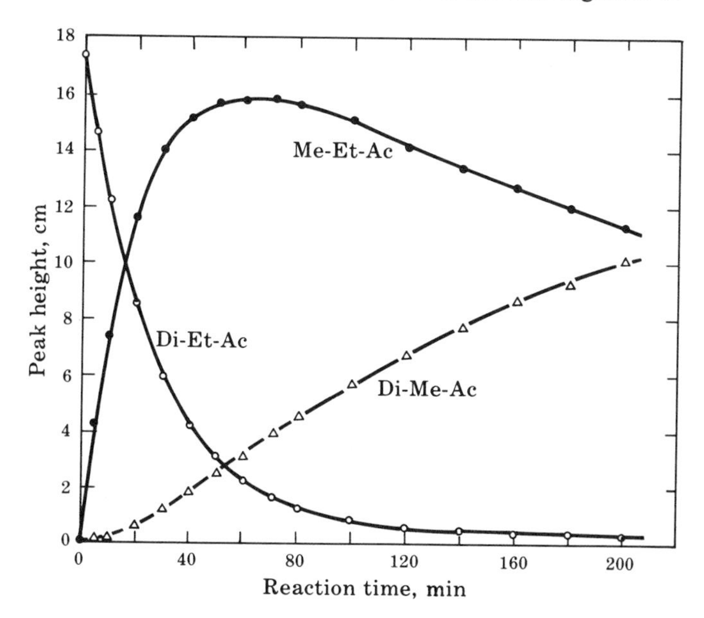

Fig. 4.4 Methanolysis of diethyl acetal. (*By permission of Juvet and Chiu* [20].)

kinetically complex reactions has depended on such kinds of data as the production of acid in a two-step hydrolysis

$$A \rightarrow B + H^+ \qquad B \rightarrow C + H^+ \tag{VII}$$

for which the rate equation is

$$\frac{d[H^+]}{dt} = k_1[A] + k_2[B] \tag{68}$$

with neither [A] nor [B] observable experimentally. One can add to Eq. (68) the relations

$$\frac{d[A]}{dt} = -k_1[A] \tag{69}$$

and

$$\frac{d[B]}{dt} = k_1[A] - k_2[B] \tag{70}$$

Given the initial concentrations, the system of equations then becomes determinate. It can be integrated in closed form if the reactions are first order but only rarely if any reaction step is of another order.

With currently available digital and analog computers comparison with experiment is possible without the integration.[1]

No matter what tools one uses in the analysis of the data on a kinetically complex reaction, it is well to keep in mind the remarkable adaptability of a multiple-parameter function to data afflicted with the scatter to which all experimental quantities are heir. One should not therefore be easily satisfied that a particular function and the mechanism which corresponds to it uniquely represent the data. Neither should one expect high precision in estimation of the values of the parameters even when only two are involved. Usually a considerable range of pairs of values of the parameters shows nearly equal goodness of fit to the data (cf. Sec. 4.6).

It requires a smaller number of parameters and a less complicated function to describe a reaction which is not measurably reversible than to describe one in which the rates in both directions are of comparable magnitude. Sometimes a reaction which would otherwise be significantly reversible can be made effectively irreversible by the addition of a reagent which reacts rapidly and irreversibly with a reaction product without otherwise interfering with the reaction under investigation. Thus Bartlett and Vincent [22] facilitated their investigation of the reaction

$$C_6H_5COCH_3 + I_2 \rightleftharpoons C_6H_5COCH_2I + I^- + H^+ \tag{VIII}$$

by adding a nitrate or an iodate, either of which reacts rapidly and irreversibly with iodide ion and thus suppresses the reaction from right to left.

[1] See, for instance, [21].

4.12 THE EXPERIMENTAL RECOGNITION OF A PURELY FIRST-ORDER REACTION SYSTEM

It is sometimes helpful to know whether all the reaction steps in a particular reaction system have a first-order time dependence. Any system of reactions —consecutive, competitive or both, reversible or irreversible—for which each step has a first-order time dependence will be representable by a system of differential equations which are all of the first degree. If a, b, c, etc., are concentrations, and a_0, b_0, c_0, etc., the corresponding concentrations at time zero, the equations will be of the form

$$\frac{da}{dt} = k_1 a + k_2 b + k_3 c + \cdots \tag{71}$$

from which

$$\frac{d(a/a_0)}{dt} = k_1 \frac{a}{a_0} + k_2 \frac{b_0}{a_0} \frac{b}{b_0} + k_3 \frac{c_0}{a_0} \frac{c}{c_0} \tag{72}$$

If therefore one runs a series of experiments, each with a different set of initial concentrations but all with the same values of the ratios b_0/a_0, c_0/a_0, etc., the ratios a/a_0, b/b_0, c/c_0, etc., must be the same function of time in all the experiments. A plot of a/a_0, for instance, against time will therefore include the points for all the runs. This would not be true if any of the differential equations contained nonlinear terms, i.e., if any of the steps had other than a first-order or zero-order time dependence.

4.13 THE INTEGRATED FORM FOR A FIRST-ORDER SYSTEM

For the purpose of comparing a supposed mechanism with experimental data the integration of the rate equations has become a matter of economics rather than of necessity through the availability of high-speed computers. Integration can also be avoided by using the stirred-flow-reactor technique. But there are areas in which an integrated form can be a source of considerable enlightenment. Integration is always possible when all the reaction steps in a system have a first-order dependence [23, 24]. The general method is adequately illustrated by the system

$$\mathrm{A} \underset{k_{-1}}{\overset{k_1}{\rightleftharpoons}} \mathrm{B} \qquad \mathrm{B} \xrightarrow{k_2} \mathrm{C} \tag{IX}$$

The rate equations are

$$\frac{d[\mathrm{A}]}{dt} = -k_1[\mathrm{A}] + k_{-1}[\mathrm{B}] \tag{73}$$

$$\frac{d[\mathrm{B}]}{dt} = k_1[\mathrm{A}] - k_{-1}[\mathrm{B}] - k_2[\mathrm{B}] \tag{74}$$

$$\frac{d[\mathrm{C}]}{dt} = k_2[\mathrm{B}] \tag{75}$$

Only two of these equations are independent because of the material-balance requirement

$$[\mathrm{A}] + [\mathrm{B}] + [\mathrm{C}] = 0 \tag{76}$$

Differentiating Eq. (74) with respect to t leads to

$$\frac{d^2[\mathrm{B}]}{dt^2} = k_1 \frac{d[\mathrm{A}]}{dt} - (k_{-1} + k_2)\frac{d[\mathrm{B}]}{dt} \tag{77}$$

Elimination of [A] and $d[\mathrm{A}]/dt$ between Eqs. (73), (74), and (77) leads to

$$\frac{d^2[\mathrm{B}]}{dt^2} + (k_1 + k_{-1} + k_2)\frac{d[\mathrm{B}]}{dt} + k_1 k_2[\mathrm{B}] = 0 \tag{78}$$

This is a homogeneous differential equation of the second order and first degree with a single dependent variable. By trial of

$$[\mathrm{B}] = e^{-\rho t} \tag{79}$$

it appears that Eq. (78) will be satisfied if

$$\rho = \tfrac{1}{2}\left[k_1 + k_{-1} + k_2 \pm \sqrt{(k_1 + k_{-1} + k_2)^2 - 4k_1 k_2}\right] \tag{80}$$

The general solution of the second-order equation is therefore

$$[\mathrm{B}] = \lambda_1 e^{-\rho_1 t} + \lambda_2 e^{-\rho_2 t} \tag{81}$$

in which ρ_1 is given by Eq. (80) with the plus sign and ρ_2 by the same equation with the minus sign. λ_1 and λ_2 are to be determined by the boundary conditions.

If, for example, A alone is present at time zero, Eq. (81) leads immediately to

$$0 = \lambda_1 + \lambda_2 \tag{82}$$

Differentiation of Eq. (81) leads to

$$\frac{d[\mathrm{B}]}{dt} = -\lambda_1 \rho_1 e^{-\rho_1 t} - \lambda_2 \rho_2 e^{-\rho_2 t} \tag{83}$$

With no B present at time zero Eq. (74) leads to

$$\left(\frac{d[\mathrm{B}]}{dt}\right)_{t=0} = -k_1[\mathrm{A}]_0 \tag{84}$$

from which by Eq. (83)

$$k_1[\mathrm{A}]_0 = -\lambda_1 \rho_1 + \lambda_2 \rho_2 \tag{85}$$

and from Eq. (82)

$$\lambda_2 = -\lambda_1 = \frac{k_1[\mathrm{A}]_0}{\rho_1 - \rho_2} \tag{86}$$

Consequently

$$\frac{[B]}{[A]_0} = \frac{k_1}{\rho_1 - \rho_2}(-e^{-\rho_1 t} + e^{-\rho_2 t}) \tag{87}$$

By differentiation of Eq. (87) the quantities $d[B]/dt$ and $d^2[B]/dt^2$ are obtained and substituted in Eq. (77). This leads to the value of $d[A]/dt$, from which by integration

$$\frac{[A]}{[A]_0} = \frac{\rho_1 - k_{-1} - k_2}{\rho_1 - \rho_2} e^{-\rho_1 t} - \frac{\rho_2 - k_{-1} - k_2}{\rho_1 - \rho_2} e^{-\rho_2 t} \tag{88}$$

From Eq. (76)

$$\frac{[C]}{[A]_0} = 1 + \frac{\rho_2}{\rho_1 - \rho_2} e^{-\rho_1 t} - \frac{\rho_1}{\rho_1 - \rho_2} e^{-\rho_2 t} \tag{89}$$

Even in this three-parameter case it would not be a simple matter to determine whether the equations fit the data on the dependence on time of the concentration of A, or of B, or of C, or of such a measured quantity as the quantity of acid produced by the hydrolysis of the ester of a dibasic acid. Nor would it be a simple matter to estimate the values of k_1, k_{-1}, and k_2 from such experimental evidence.

4.14 THE INTERPRETATION OF RATE LAWS INVOLVING TWO EXPONENTIAL TERMS

Sometimes negative evidence is valuable. If the logarithm of $[A]/[A]_0$ or of $1 - [C]/[A]_0$ plots linearly against time, the negative root in Eq. (80) must be much smaller than the positive one. If so, the slope of the plot is ρ_1, that is, $k_1 + k_{-1} + k_2$; further $k_1 k_2 \ll (k_1 + k_{-1} + k_2)^2$. This requires either that $k_{-1} \gg k_1 + k_2$ or that k_1 and k_2 have very different values.[1]

Equations (87) to (89) simplify considerably if step 1 is effectively irreversible, i.e., if k_{-1} may be neglected compared with $k_1 + k_2$, becoming

$$\frac{[A]}{[A]_0} = e^{-k_1 t} \tag{90}$$

$$\frac{[B]}{[A]_0} = \frac{k_1}{k_1 - k_2}(e^{-k_2 t} - e^{-k_1 t}) \tag{91}$$

$$1 - \frac{[C]}{[A]_0} = \frac{k_1}{k_1 - k_2} e^{-k_2 t} - \frac{k_2}{k_1 - k_2} e^{-k_1 t} \tag{92}$$

[1] For an example of the application of this argument see [25].

By differentiation of Eq. (92) the slope s of a plot of the quantity $\ln(1 - [C]/[A]_0)$ against time is given by

$$s = -k_1 k_2 \frac{e^{-k_1 t} - e^{-k_2 t}}{k_2 e^{-k_1 t} - k_1 e^{-k_2 t}} \tag{93}$$

With the definition $\Delta = k_2 - k_1$ this becomes

$$s = -\frac{k_1(k_1 + \Delta)}{k_1 + \Delta/(1 - e^{-\Delta t})} \tag{94}$$

The slope is zero at time zero and becomes negative with increasing time. The change is more rapid the greater the magnitude of Δ. The ultimate value is $-k_1$ if $k_2 > k_1$ and $-k_2$ if $k_2 < k_1$. If k_2 is much larger than k_1 Eq. (94) reduces, except for very short reaction time, to

$$s = -k_1(1 - e^{-k_2 t}) \tag{95}$$

Specifically if $k_2 = 100k_1$, only about 2 percent of the initial reactant will have disappeared during the time required for the slope to approach within 1 percent of the limiting value $-k_1$. During most of the period of observation, therefore, the apparent first-order specific rate will be essentially constant at k_1. Similarly if k_2 is much smaller than k_1, the apparent first-order specific rate will be effectively constant at k_2 except for a brief initial period. When the magnitude of Δ is small, Eq. (94) reduces to

$$s = -\frac{k_1 k_2}{k_1 + 1/t} \tag{96}$$

The acid production h in the acid-catalyzed hydrolysis of a bifunctional ester is given by

$$\frac{h}{[A]_0} = \frac{[B]}{[A]_0} + 2\frac{[C]}{[A]_0} \tag{97}$$

where A is diester, B is monoester, and C is acid. From Eqs. (91) and (92)

$$\frac{h}{[A]_0} = 2 - \frac{k_1 - 2k_2}{k_1 - k_2} e^{-k_1 t} - \frac{k_1}{k_1 - k_2} e^{-k_2 t} \tag{98}$$

Because there are two reaction sites for the conversion of A to B and only one for the conversion of B to C, the value of k_1 in such cases is often close to $2k_2$. If $k_1 = 2k_2$, Eq. (98) reduces to

$$2 - \frac{h}{[A]_0} = 2e^{-k_2 t} \tag{99}$$

More generally the slope varies from $-\frac{1}{2} k_1$ at small t to $-k_2$ at large t.

Rate laws involving a sum of exponential terms may derive from parallel as well as from consecutive reactions. The acid produced from a mixture of

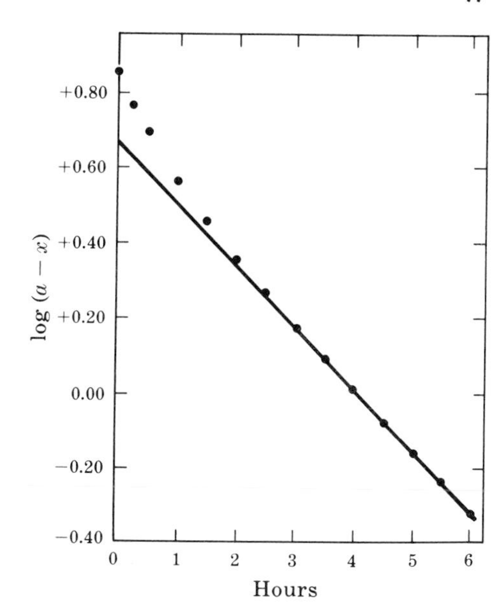

Fig. 4.5 Hydrolysis of diethyl-*t*-butyl carbinyl chloride. (*By permission of Brown and Fletcher* [26].)

two alkyl halides, A and B, solvolyzing by first-order processes is given by

$$1 - \frac{h}{[\mathrm{A}]_0 + [\mathrm{B}]_0} = \frac{[\mathrm{A}]_0}{[\mathrm{A}]_0 + [\mathrm{B}]_0} e^{-k_\mathrm{A} t} + \frac{[\mathrm{B}]_0}{[\mathrm{A}]_0 + [\mathrm{B}]_0} e^{-k_\mathrm{B} t} \tag{100}$$

The slope of a plot of the logarithm of the quantity on the left is independent of time if $k_A = k_B$. There may also be ranges of essentially constant slope if the two specific rates differ, especially if they differ by a considerable amount. Figure 4.5 shows this kind of plot for the data of Brown and Fletcher [26] on the solvolysis of what was supposed to be diethyl-*t*-butyl carbinyl chloride, but which was successfully interpreted as a mixture of two chlorides. From the slope and intercept of the linear portion of the plot the quantities k_B and $[B]_0/([A]_0 + [B]_0)$ were estimated. The kinetic measurements therefore indicated that a mixture rather than a single substance was reacting and determined the proportions of the constituents of the mixture.

4.15 THE BODENSTEIN, OR STEADY-STATE, APPROXIMATION

When the concentration of an intermediate B is at all times during the course of a reaction small compared with the sum of the concentrations of reactant and product, it is a valid and useful approximation to set the derivative $d[\mathrm{B}]/dt$ equal to zero in the rate equation. Thus in the mechanism

$$\mathrm{KH} \underset{k_{-1}[\mathrm{H}^+]}{\overset{k_1[\mathrm{H}^+]}{\rightleftharpoons}} \mathrm{EH} \tag{X}$$

$$\mathrm{EH} + \mathrm{I}_2 \xrightarrow{k_2} \mathrm{P} + \mathrm{H}^+ + \mathrm{I}^-$$

for the conversion of acetophenone (KH) to iodoacetophenone (P) by way of the enol (EH), whose concentration is too low for direct observation, the rate equation

$$\frac{d[\mathrm{EH}]}{dt} = k_1[\mathrm{H}^+][\mathrm{KH}] - (k_{-1}[\mathrm{H}^+] + k_2)[\mathrm{EH}] \tag{101}$$

can be satisfactorily approximated by

$$0 = k_1[\mathrm{H}^+][\mathrm{KH}] - (k_{-1}[\mathrm{H}^+] + k_2)[\mathrm{EH}] \tag{102}$$

This together with the relation

$$\frac{d[\mathrm{I}_2]}{dt} = -k_2[\mathrm{EH}][\mathrm{I}_2] \tag{103}$$

leads to

$$\frac{d[\mathrm{I}_2]}{dt} = -\frac{k_1 k_2[\mathrm{H}^+]}{k_{-1}[\mathrm{H}^+] + k_2}[\mathrm{KH}][\mathrm{I}_2] \tag{104}$$

Equation (104) can be compared with experiment either by using estimated slopes of plots of $[\mathrm{I}_2]$ against time or, since $[\mathrm{H}^+]$ is independent of time, by integrating to obtain a verifiable relation between $[\mathrm{I}_2]$ and t.

The approximation is justified, not because $d[\mathrm{EH}]/dt$ is zero but because it is the small difference between two relatively large quantities. This must be so because if it were not, the concentration of EH would rise to a measurable value. At time zero the rate of increase of the concentration of EH is equal to the rate of decrease of the concentration of KH. The EH concentration can level off at a low value only because the term $(k_{-1}[\mathrm{H}^+] + k_2)[\mathrm{EH}]$ has become nearly equal to the term $k_1[\mathrm{H}^+][\mathrm{KH}]$. If $k_{-1}[\mathrm{H}^+] + k_2$ is considerably larger than $k_1[\mathrm{H}^+]$, this will happen at a low value of [EH] and before more than a little of the KH has reacted. After traversing a maximum, the EH concentration decreases but remains a small difference between the larger numbers on the right of Eq. (101).

The introduction of this mathematical device by Bodenstein [27] in 1913 had a profound and favorable influence on the development of reaction kinetics and of reaction mechanisms. For no good reason the approximation is usually called the steady-state approximation; it is more reasonable to call it the Bodenstein approximation.

The limits of validity of the approximation can be appreciated by considering the reaction sequence (IX) with all steps having a first-order time dependence and with $k_{-1} + k_2 \gg k_1$. Equation (80) can be written

$$\rho = \frac{1}{2}(k_{-1} + k_2)\left[1 \pm \sqrt{\left(1 + \frac{k_1}{k_{-1} + k_2}\right)^2 - \frac{4k_1 k_2}{(k_{-1} + k_2)^2}}\right] + \frac{1}{2}k_1 \tag{105}$$

from which it is clear that as a first approximation

$$\rho_1 = k_{-1} + k_2 + \frac{k_1 k_{-1}}{(k_{-1} + k_2)} \tag{106}$$

and

$$\rho_2 = \frac{k_1 k_2}{k_{-1} + k_2} \tag{107}$$

By Eq. (87)

$$\frac{[B]}{[A]_0} = \frac{k_1}{k_{-1} + k_2}(-e^{-\rho_1 t} + e^{-\rho_2 t}) \tag{108}$$

and by Eq. (88)

$$\frac{[A]}{[A]_0} = \frac{k_1 k_{-1}}{(k_{-1} + k_2)^2} e^{-\rho_1 t} + e^{-\rho_2 t} \tag{109}$$

Because ρ_1 is much larger than ρ_2 ,the quantity $\exp(-\rho_1 t)$ will decrease with increasing time much faster than the quantity $\exp(-\rho_2 t)$. The time required, for instance, for the first term in Eq. (108) to decrease to 1 percent of the value of the second term is $4.6/(k_{-1} + k_2)$. During this period the fraction of the A initially present which has reacted will be $\exp[(4.6k_1 k_2)/(k_{-1} + k_2)^2]$, that is, not more than and perhaps considerably less than $4.6k_1/k_2$.

After the first terms in Eqs. (108) and (109) have become negligible, the ratio [B]/[A] will remain constant at the small value $k_1/(k_{-1} + k_2)$, and the concentration of A will be given by

$$\ln \frac{[A]}{[A]_0} = -\frac{k_1 k_2}{k_{-1} + k_2} t \tag{110}$$

In summary, when k_1 is considerably less than $k_{-1} + k_2$, the concentration of the intermediate will at all times be a small fraction of the concentration of the reactant. Except for an initial period during which a fraction of the order of $5k_1/k_2$ of the reactant has reacted, the kinetics will be close to first order with an empirical specific rate of $k_1 k_2/(k_{-1} + k_2)$.

If the interconversion of A and B or the conversion of B to C has other than a first-order time dependence, the mathematics becomes more complicated. It has been thoroughly explored,[1] and there is no reason to doubt that qualitatively the conclusions are similar to those which apply to the first-order case.

4.16 THE PRECISION PROBLEM IN THE MULTIPLE-PARAMETER CASE

In an investigation of the iodination of acetophenone Zucker and Hammett [29] used the device of Bartlett and Vincent [22] of adding nitrite or iodate to

[1] See for instance [28].

suppress the reverse reaction. This regenerates ½ mole of iodine for every mole of acetophenone which reacts, the reaction in the nitrite case being

$$I^- + NO_2^- + 2H^+ \rightarrow \tfrac{1}{2} I_2 + NO + H_2O \qquad \text{(XI)}$$

Because of this the relationship applicable to mechanism X is

$$\frac{d[I_2]}{dt} = -\frac{1}{2}\frac{k_1 k_2[H^+][KH][I_2]}{k_{-1}[H^+] + k_2[I_2]} \qquad (111)$$

instead of Eq. (104). Furthermore the relationship between the concentration of iodine and that of acetophenone is

$$[I_2] - \tfrac{1}{2}[KH] = \Delta \qquad (112)$$

with Δ independent of time.

At low acidities Eq. (111) reduces to

$$\frac{d[I_2]}{dt} = -\frac{1}{2}k_1[H^+][KH] \qquad (113)$$

from which with Eq. (112)

$$\frac{d\ln([I_2] - \Delta)}{dt} = -k_1[H^+] \qquad (114)$$

In aqueous solutions of sulfuric or of perchloric acid in the range from 0.5 to 15% Zucker and Hammett obtained data which fit this first-order equation with an estimated precision of 1 percent in the value of $k_1[H^+]$. The reactant concentrations were so low that in this range the hydrogen concentration is essentially independent of time.

At sulfuric acid concentrations in the region of 51% the experimental results agree well with the equation

$$\frac{d[I_2]}{dt} = \frac{k_1 k_2}{k_{-1}}[I_2]([I_2] - \Delta) \qquad (115)$$

to which Eq. (111) reduces when $k_{-1}[H^+] \gg k_2[I_2]$.

Operationally this is a second-order rate equation with the single parameter $k_1 k_2/k_{-1}$.

But at intermediate acid concentrations the data are inconsistent with either of these limiting forms of Eq. (111). This equation is a two-parameter form which frequently appears in kinetic investigations. A method often used in comparing it with experimental data involves the estimation of the initial slopes of plots of concentration against time. Because such plots are curved, this is inevitably a procedure of low precision. But within these precision limits it is easy to verify the validity of the relationship and to estimate the values of the two independent parameters. The equation can be written as

$$\frac{[I_2]-\Delta}{v}=\frac{1}{k_1[H^+]}+\frac{k_{-1}}{k_1 k_2}\times\frac{1}{[I_2]} \tag{116}$$

where $v=-d[I_2]/dt$. The slope of a plot of the quantity on the left, which can be calculated from the experimental data, against the reciprocal of the iodine concentration is then $k_{-1}/k_1 k_2$, and the intercept is $1/k_1[H^+]$. Alternatively one can write

$$\frac{([I_2]-\Delta)[I_2]}{v}=\frac{k_{-1}}{k_1 k_2}+\frac{1}{k_1[H^+]}[I_2] \tag{117}$$

and estimate $k_1[H^+]$ from the slope and $k_{-1}/k_1 k_2$ from the intercept. The choice between the two forms depends on whether the low or the high iodine concentrations are thought to be known with the greater precision.

Equation (111) can, however, be integrated and put into the form

$$\left(\frac{\varkappa}{\Delta}-1\right)\log\frac{\Delta-c_0}{\Delta-c}-\frac{\varkappa}{\Delta}\log\frac{c_0}{c}=k't \tag{118}$$

in which $c=[I_2]$, $\varkappa=k_{-1}[H^+]/k_2$, and $k'=0.4343k_1[H^+]$. By cut-and-try methods one can then select a value of $\varkappa$ such that the left side of this equation plots against time as a straight line through the origin and that the plots coincide for experiments with different values of c_0 and of Δ. Such a plot for six experiments in 39.5% sulfuric acid is shown in Fig. 4.6. In these experiments the initial acetophenone concentration varied from 5×10^{-4} to 81×10^{-4}, and the initial iodine concentration from 5×10^{-4} to 7×10^{-4}.

Clearly this large accumulation of data is consistent with Eq. (118). But the experimenter noted that a considerable range of pairs of values of $\varkappa$

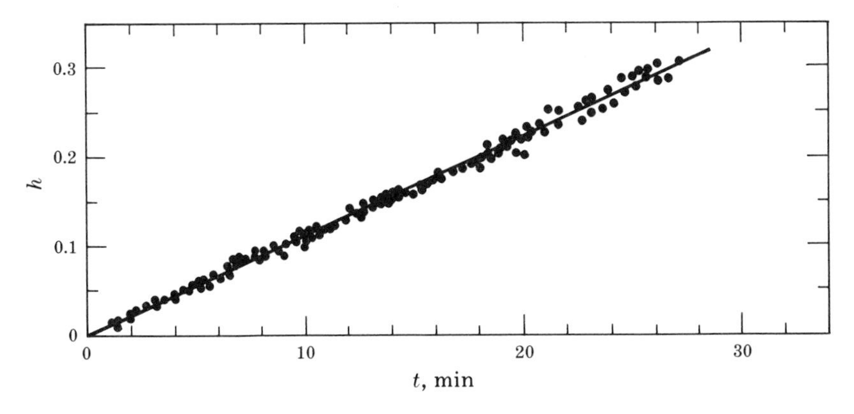

Fig. 4.6 Integrated form for iodination of acetophenone in 39.5% sulfuric acid. [*By permission of L. Zucker and L. P. Hammett, J. Am. Chem. Soc.,* **61**:2791 (1939).]

and k' gave nearly the same degree of linearity and estimated an uncertainty of 15 percent in the values both of k' and of $\varkappa$. This contrasts with an estimated uncertainty of 1 percent for the single parameter in the region in which Eq. (114) applies and illustrates well the difficulty of estimating with any precision the values of the parameters in a multiple-parameter relationship.

Nowadays one would do the job of fitting the equation to the data with a high-speed computer with much less effort than was required in 1939, but there is no reason to suppose that it would be done with much greater precision in the values of the parameters.

4.17 NOTE ON THE MICHAELIS-MENTEN EQUATION

In the mechanism

$$E + S \underset{k_{-1}}{\overset{k_1}{\rightleftharpoons}} ES \qquad \text{(XII)}$$

$$ES \xrightarrow{k_2} P + E$$

where E = enzyme

S = substrate

P = reaction product

ES = enzyme-substrate compound

the conditions for the use of the Bodenstein approximation are satisfied if, as is usually the case experimentally, the molar concentration of enzyme is much smaller than the sum of the concentrations of substrate and product [30], because then the concentration of the intermediate is always much smaller than the sum of the concentrations of reactant and product. By the approximation

$$0 = k_1[E][S] - (k_{-1} + k_2)[ES] \qquad (119)$$

If $[E]_0$ represents the total concentration of combined and uncombined enzyme,

$$[ES] + [E] = [E]_0 \qquad (120)$$

from which with Eq. (119)

$$[ES] = \frac{k_1[E]_0[S]}{k_{-1} + k_2 + k_1[S]} \qquad (121)$$

and

$$v = \frac{d[P]}{dt} = \frac{k_1 k_2[E]_0[S]}{k_{-1} + k_2 + k_1[S]} \qquad (122)$$

Michaelis and Menten [31] had derived the relationship

$$v = \frac{k_1 k_2 [\mathrm{E}]_0 [\mathrm{S}]}{k_{-1} + k_1 [\mathrm{S}]} \tag{123}$$

on the supposition that the formation of the enzyme-substrate compound is a mobile reversible process, i.e., that k_{-1} is much greater than k_2. This is now known to be not always the case as a result of experiments in which the concentration of the intermediate was determined spectrophotometrically [32].

Because the catalytic activity of enzymes often changes during the course of their action on a substrate, the tendency is strong to operate by estimating the initial slope of a plot of substrate concentration against time. One can then obtain values of the parameters $k_2[\mathrm{E}]_0$ and $(k_{-1} + k_2)/k_1$ from the reciprocal of the intercept and the ratio of the slope to the intercept in the relationship

$$\frac{1}{v} = \frac{1}{k_2[\mathrm{E}]_0} + \frac{k_{-1} + k_2}{k_1 k_2 [\mathrm{E}]_0} \frac{1}{[\mathrm{S}]} \tag{124}$$

as suggested by Lineweaver and Burk [33] or from the intercept and the slope in the relationship

$$v = k_2[\mathrm{E}]_0 - \frac{k_{-1} + k_2}{k_1} \frac{v}{[\mathrm{S}]_0} \tag{125}$$

which Eadie [34] believes gives a sounder weighting of the data.

4.18 SYSTEMS INVOLVING AN INITIAL MOBILE EQUILIBRIUM

Under conditions of high acidity the rate equation (104) for the iodination of acetophenone by way of the enol form, reaction (X), reduces to [cf. Eq. (115)]

$$\frac{d[\mathrm{I}_2]}{dt} = -\frac{k_1 k_2}{k_{-1}} [\mathrm{KH}][\mathrm{I}_2] \tag{126}$$

This may be written

$$\frac{d[\mathrm{I}_2]}{dt} = -K_1 k_2 [\mathrm{KH}][\mathrm{I}_2] \tag{127}$$

where $K_1 = k_1/k_{-1}$ is the equilibrium constant for the keto-enol interconversion. The only observable phenomenon at this acidity is the proportionality of the rate to the product of the concentrations of the keto form and of iodine. This is consistent with Eq. (127) and therefore with reaction by way of the enol form, but it is equally consistent with a second-order reaction of keto form with iodine without the intervention of the enol form. From the behavior at high acidity one would consequently have no basis whatsoever for preferring one mechanism over the other. However the smooth transition from what is unambiguously a two-step mechanism by way of the enol at lower acidities creates a strong supposition that the same mechanism applies at the high acidity.

By virtue of Eq. (102) with $k_{-1}[H^+] \gg k_2$ one has

$$\frac{[EH]}{[KH]} = \frac{k_1}{k_{-1}} = K_1 \tag{128}$$

Except for the very transitory initial period in which Eq. (102) is not yet applicable, the relation between the concentrations of enol and keto forms is the same as if these were in equilibrium in the absence of the reaction with iodine.

In the ketone halogenation the value of K is so small that the concentration of the enol form is much less than that of the keto form under all conditions and at all stages of reaction, and Eqs. (127) and (128) could be derived by way of the Bodenstein approximation. The equations are, however, applicable whenever $k_{-1} \gg k_2$, regardless of the value of k_1. For even if k_1 were equal to or larger than k_{-1}, the time required for the ratio [EH]/[KH] to come very close to K_1 would be so small that very little halogenation would have occurred. The conclusions about the indistinguishability of the mechanisms would therefore be just as valid if K_1 is large as they are when it is small.

That this is true when all the reaction steps are first order is easily seen from Eq. (80), from which, with $k_2 \ll k_{-1}$,

$$\rho_1 = k_1 + k_{-1} \tag{129}$$

$$\rho_2 = \frac{k_1 k_2}{k_1 + k_{-1}} = k_2 \frac{K_1}{1 + K_1} \tag{130}$$

Since ρ_2, which cannot be larger than k_2, is so much smaller than ρ_1, $\exp(-\rho_1 t)$ becomes negligible during a time interval in which $\exp(-\rho_2 t)$ has hardly changed from unity. Except for a brief initial period Eqs. (87) and (88) reduce to

$$\frac{[B]}{[A]_0} = \frac{k_1}{k_1 + k_{-1}} e^{-\rho_2 t} \tag{131}$$

and

$$\frac{[A]}{[A]_0} = \frac{k_{-1}}{k_1 + k_{-1}} e^{-\rho_2 t} \tag{132}$$

From these

$$\frac{[B]}{[A]} = \frac{k_1}{k_{-1}} = K_1 \tag{133}$$

independent of time, except for the transitory initial interval. The primitive concentration $c_A = [A] + [B]$ is given by

$$\frac{c_A}{[A]_0} = e^{-\rho_2 t} \tag{134}$$

This is the equation for an uncomplicated first-order reaction with the specific rate ρ_2. As far as the kinetics is concerned one need not know or care whether or not this specific rate is in fact the function given by Eq. (130) of the specific rates of the steps in a two-step reaction. Nor need one know or care that some of the A initially present is rapidly and reversibly converted to B. Certainly one gets no evidence with respect to the mechanism from the kinetics. If the mechanism were $B \rightleftharpoons A \rightharpoonup C$ instead of $A \rightleftharpoons B \rightarrow C$, the observed ρ_2 in Eq. (134) would be interpretable as $k_{-1}k_2/(k_1 + k_{-1})$ instead of by Eq. (130) but the observed reaction would still be an uncomplicated first-order process.

4.19 THE EFFECT OF AN ASSOCIATION EQUILIBRIUM

If substance A and substance B are rapidly and reversibly converted to a compound AB and a product P is formed at a relatively slow rate, the concentrations of A, B, and AB will be given by

$$\frac{[AB]}{[A][B]} = K \tag{135}$$

except for a brief initial period. Since the concentration of AB is proportional to the product of the concentrations of A and B, there is no observable kinetic difference between the mechanism in which P is formed by a first-order reaction of AB and one in which it is formed by a second-order reaction of A with B in which AB is not an intermediate. In the language of the former interpretation one writes a first-order rate equation

$$\frac{1}{[AB]}\frac{d[P]}{dt} = k_1 \tag{136}$$

in the language of the latter one writes a second-order equation

$$\frac{1}{[A][B]}\frac{d[P]}{dt} = k_2 \tag{137}$$

By virtue of Eq. (135)

$$k_2 = Kk_1 \tag{138}$$

In terms of the primitive concentrations

$$c_A = [A] + [AB] \tag{139}$$

and

$$c_B = [B] + [AB] \tag{140}$$

which are frequently the only known concentrations

$$\frac{[AB]}{(c_A - [AB])(c_B - [AB])} = K \tag{141}$$

Here, as is often the case with multistep reactions, the equations are easier to interpret if they are written in terms of reciprocal rates instead of in terms of rates. Equation (141) can be solved to give

$$\frac{1}{[\mathrm{AB}]}=\frac{1}{2}\left[\frac{1}{c_{\mathrm{A}}}+\frac{1}{c_{\mathrm{B}}}+\frac{1}{Kc_{\mathrm{A}}c_{\mathrm{B}}}+\sqrt{\left(\frac{1}{c_{\mathrm{A}}}+\frac{1}{c_{\mathrm{B}}}+\frac{1}{Kc_{\mathrm{A}}c_{\mathrm{B}}}\right)^2-\frac{4}{c_{\mathrm{A}}c_{\mathrm{B}}}}\right] \tag{142}$$

The other root of the quadratic has no physical significance because it leads to negative values either of [A] or of [B]. The primitive value $k^{(p)}$ of the specific rate is given by

$$k^{(p)}=\frac{v}{c_{\mathrm{A}}c_{\mathrm{B}}}=\frac{k_1[\mathrm{AB}]}{c_{\mathrm{A}}c_{\mathrm{B}}} \tag{143}$$

and from this with Eq. (142)

$$\frac{1}{k^{(p)}}=\frac{1}{2k_1}\left[c_{\mathrm{A}}+c_{\mathrm{B}}+\frac{1}{K}+\sqrt{\left(c_{\mathrm{A}}+c_{\mathrm{B}}+\frac{1}{K}\right)^2-4c_{\mathrm{A}}c_{\mathrm{B}}}\right] \tag{144}$$

This is an unpleasantly complicated equation, but it reduces to more manageable forms under suitable conditions.

If $c_{\mathrm{A}}+c_{\mathrm{B}} \ll 1/K$, it reduces in the limit to $k^{(p)}=Kk_1$. If, therefore, K is so small or the solution so dilute that association is negligible, the kinetics becomes that of an uncomplicated second-order reaction. This is hardly surprising. For somewhat larger K or smaller $c_{\mathrm{A}}+c_{\mathrm{B}}$ values Eq. (144) reduces to

$$\frac{1}{k^{(p)}}=\frac{1}{k_1}\left(\frac{1}{K}+c_{\mathrm{A}}+c_{\mathrm{B}}\right) \tag{145}$$

If c_{B} is considerably smaller than c_{A}, the equation reduces in the first order of small quantities to

$$\frac{1}{k^{(p)}}=\frac{1}{k_1}\left(\frac{1}{K}+c_{\mathrm{A}}\right) \tag{146}$$

Table 4.1 Reaction of aniline (A) with dinitrochlorobenzene (B)[a]

B	A	$10^5k^{(p)}$, *liters/mole-sec*
0.04993	0.2004	7.28
0.05210	0.5009	6.44
0.05230	0.6737	6.14
0.04950	1.0106	5.33

[a] Data of Ross and Kuntz [35]

Ross and Kuntz [35] obtained the results shown in Table 4.1 for the primitive specific rate of the reaction of aniline (A) with dinitrochlorobenzene (B) in ethanol to form dinitrodiphenylamine. The specific rate decreases with increasing concentration of the reactant aniline. In Fig. 4.7 $1/k^{(p)}$ is plotted against c_A. The plot is satisfactorily linear, and from the intercept and slope one gets by way of Eq. (146) $k_1 = 1.63 \times 10^{-4}$ and $K = 0.49$. The kinetics alone therefore provides evidence for the existence of the association equilibrium and an estimate of the association constant. There is independent spectroscopic evidence for the association although not such as to allow an estimate of the equilibrium constant. The spectrum of the association product suggests that this is a charge-transfer complex, and Ross and Kuntz consider that this kind of complex is an unlikely intermediate for the formation of dinitrodiphenylamine because it brings aniline and dinitrochlorobenzene together in an orientation poorly adapted for rearrangement to that substance. This is of course an argument from structure; the kinetics is impartial.

In terms of rate rather than of specific rate Eq. (146) becomes

$$v = \frac{k_1 c_A c_B}{1/K + c_A} \tag{147}$$

a relation of the same mathematical form as the Michaelis-Menten equation (Sec. 4.17). As with that equation, the rate at a given c_B concentration approaches an upper limit with increasing c_A. This saturation effect corresponds to an essentially complete conversion of the available B to the compound AB.

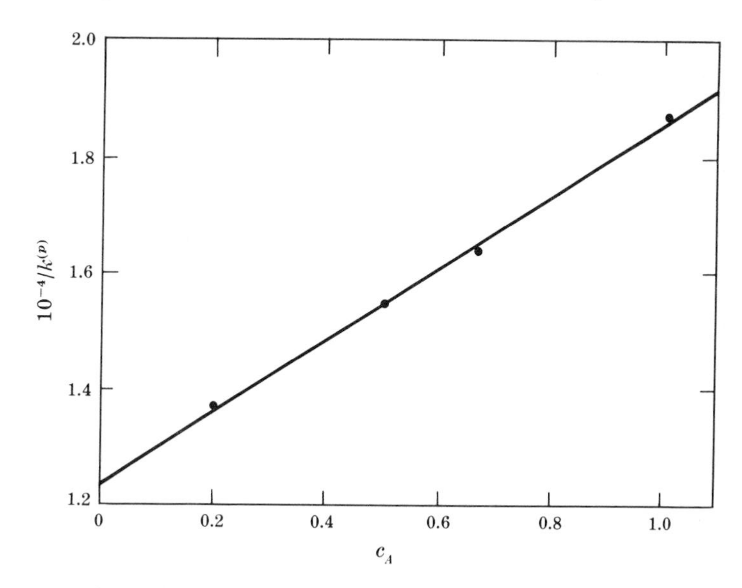

Fig. 4.7 The dinitrochlorobenzene–aniline reaction. (*Data of Ross and Kuntz* [35].)

If AB is an intermediate, further addition of A cannot increase the concentration of AB and hence cannot increase the rate; if AB is not an intermediate, addition of A at constant AB concentration decreases the concentration of B and leaves the product [A][B] unchanged.

In enzyme catalysis the compound ES can be proved to be an intermediate in those cases in which its concentration can be determined during the course of the reaction; it is reasonable but not necessary to suppose the enzyme-substrate compound is an intermediate even when this is not the case.

4.20 THE RECOGNIZABILITY OF REACTION COMPLEXITY

An important question in the interpretation of rate data is the extent to which direct evidence for the presence of a multistep reaction can be obtained from the observed kinetics. A quantitative answer can be obtained for a system of first-order reactions; the conclusions should be qualitatively applicable to systems which involve other reaction orders.

For the first-order conversion of substance A to substance C the logarithmic conversion $\log(1 - [C]/[A]_0)$ is linear in time; a plot of the same quantity against time for the system

$$A \underset{k_{-1}}{\overset{k_1}{\rightleftharpoons}} B \xrightarrow{k_2} C \qquad \text{(IX)}$$

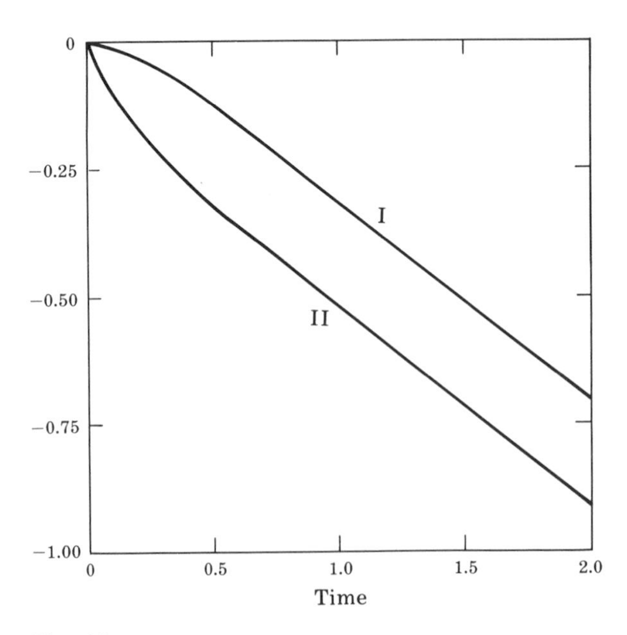

Fig. 4.8

with $k_1 = k_{-1} = k_2 = 2.303$ and with A alone present at time zero is shown by curve I in Fig. 4.8. The corresponding plot for the system

$$A \underset{k_{-1}}{\overset{k_1}{\rightleftharpoons}} B \quad A \xrightarrow{k_2} C \tag{XIII}$$

also with A alone present at time zero, is shown by curve II. Clearly there would be no difficulty in recognizing the complexity of this kind of reaction system when the three specific rates are equal, for the plots show decided curvature through the first 20 percent of reaction. Furthermore there would be no difficulty in distinguishing a system in which C is formed directly from A from one in which B is an intermediate, the curvature being opposite in sign in the two cases.

But a difference of only one order of magnitude in the specific rates of the steps erases almost completely the evidence of complexity and the distinguishability of the two mechanisms. If, for instance, $k_1 = k_{-1} = 10k_2$, there is a small hook at the beginning of the plot of logarithmic conversion against time. But after only 4 percent conversion the plot is linear to the equivalent of 1 percent in concentration, and the value of [A] extrapolated from the linear plot is only 2½ percent high if B is an intermediate or 2½ percent low if A goes directly to C. It would require experimental data of more than ordinary precision to recognize effects of this magnitude with any assurance.

4.21 THE STIRRED-FLOW REACTOR IN A MULTIPLE-STEP REACTION

In the case of a multiple-step reaction the stirred-flow-reactor technique can make the difference between a precision so low that important effects are overlooked and one that recognizes them. An example is the hydrolysis in alkaline solution of the bifunctional ester diethyl succinate [14]. If in this case a represents the steady-state concentration in the reactor of diethyl succinate, b the corresponding concentration of sodium hydroxide, $w = u/V$ the reduced flow rate, v_1 the rate of conversion of diethyl succinate to monoethyl succinate ion, and v_2 the rate of formation of succinate ion, then in the steady state

$$w(a_0 - a) - v_1 = 0 \tag{148}$$

and

$$w(b_0 - b) - v_1 - v_2 = 0 \tag{149}$$

If the ideal law of mass action in the form

$$v_1 = k_1 ab \tag{150}$$

$$v_2 = k_2 bc \tag{151}$$

were exactly applicable, values of the two specific rates could have been obtained from any pair of sets of values of the experimentally accessible quantities w, a_0, b, and b_0, using the relation

$$2a + 2c - b = 2a_0 - b_0 \tag{152}$$

c being the concentration of monoethyl succinate ion. It turned out, however, that values of k_1 obtained in this way varied over a range of 20 percent and values of k_2 varied by a factor of 2. Indeed one pair of sets of experimental quantities led to imaginary values of k_1 and k_2.

If a method had been available for the determination of the concentration of succinic acid in the presence of monoethyl succinate ion and succinate ion, values of v_1 and v_2 could have been obtained from Eqs. (148) and (149) for any reactor composition and their dependence on the composition determined.

But because salts of monoethyl succinate ion can be prepared, it is possible to investigate the dependence of v_2 on the composition of the medium, and it developed that the k_2 of Eq. (151) is a fairly sensitive function of cation composition, increasing from 0.0175 to 0.0237 as the sodium-ion concentration increases from 0.048 to 0.115. With v_2 known in this way, it was possible to obtain v_1 values of good precision. These showed that k_1 is decidedly dependent on the concentration of succinate ion and that it probably is also dependent on the concentration of other doubly charged anions. This was a completely unexpected effect, and one which had not been revealed by previous careful investigations of the hydrolysis of esters of dibasic acids; indeed it could hardly have been detected without the increased precision which the stirred-flow-reactor technique made possible.

4.22 THE TUBULAR-FLOW REACTOR

The twin problems of mixing of reactants and measurement of time interval present no serious difficulties in the study of a reaction with a half time of an hour or more, i.e., one in which the time required for the reaction of half of the reactant initially present is as much as an hour. They present difficulties (but not insuperable ones) in the way of the precise estimation of specific rate for reactions with half times in the interval from an hour to a second [36, 37]. For faster reactions the time problem can be alleviated by estimating the extent of reaction by way of an automatic device which records as a function of time the value of a physical property which adjusts rapidly to the composition of the solution. It is a considerable advantage if the value of the property is linearly related to the extent of reaction.

An effective way of exploiting the advantages of this kind of measurement and at the same time of alleviating the mixing problem is the tubular-flow reactor. The development of this device by Hartridge and Roughton [38] extended the limits of usefully measurable reaction rates to systems with half times of as little as 0.001 sec and opened up a region of reaction kinetics which had previously been completely inaccessible. Techniques of operation have been highly developed, much has been done in the way of automation, and the results have been important.[1]

In this technique two solutions of liquid flowing at constant velocity are rapidly and thoroughly mixed and allowed to pass through a tube of constant diameter. Under favorable conditions the composition of a thin cylindrical lamina of solution at a distance l from the point of mixing is then the same as if the mixed solution had reacted without flow for a time interval t given by

$$t = \frac{Al}{u} \tag{153}$$

where A is the area of cross section of the tube and u is the flow rate in volume per unit time. The measurement of a physical property which is dependent on extent of reaction as a function of the distance l supplies therefore the same information about the kinetics of the reaction as measurement of the property as a function of time would in a nonflowing system.

It is critically important in this kind of measurement that the composition of the solution be essentially constant throughout any perpendicular cross section of the tube, that mixing and diffusion parallel to the axis of the tube be negligible, and especially that observations should begin at a point at whch mixing of the input solution is essentially complete. In an incompletely mixed system reaction occurs in a hodgepodge of volume elements of varying composition, and the observed extent of reaction is meaningless.

4.23 THE METHOD OF COMPETING REACTIONS FOR THE STUDY OF RELATIVE REACTIVITY

The mixing problem may also present serious difficulties in the estimation of the relative rates of two reactions by the method of competing reactions. If two reactants A and B react simultaneously and in the same solution with a reagent X to form the respective products U and V, and if both reactions are kinetically simple, irreversible, and of the same order, the relevant rate equations are

$$-\frac{d[\mathrm{A}]}{dt} = k_{\mathrm{A}}[\mathrm{A}]^a [\mathrm{X}]^x \tag{154}$$

and

$$-\frac{d[\mathrm{B}]}{dt} = k_{\mathrm{B}}[\mathrm{B}]^a [\mathrm{X}]^x \tag{155}$$

[1] For a review see the sections by F. J. W. Roughton and by B. Chance in [39].

From these

$$\frac{d[\mathrm{A}]}{d[\mathrm{B}]} = \frac{k_\mathrm{A}}{k_\mathrm{B}}\left(\frac{[\mathrm{A}]}{[\mathrm{B}]}\right)^a \tag{156}$$

The integral depends upon the value of a. If it is 1,

$$\frac{\ln([\mathrm{A}]/[\mathrm{A}]_0)}{\ln([\mathrm{B}]/[\mathrm{B}]_0)} = \frac{k_\mathrm{A}}{k_\mathrm{B}} \tag{157}$$

If then the concentrations of A and of B can be measured after some convenient time, which may be determined by using an amount of X insufficient for complete reaction of either A or B, and waiting until the reaction has come to an end, the ratio of the two specific rates follows immediately.

If the measurable quantity is the relative amount of U and V, then since

$$[\mathrm{U}] = [\mathrm{A}]_0 - [\mathrm{A}] \tag{158}$$

$$[\mathrm{V}] = [\mathrm{B}]_0 - [\mathrm{B}] \tag{159}$$

Equation (157) can be written

$$\frac{\ln(1 - [\mathrm{U}]/[\mathrm{A}]_0)}{\ln(1 - [\mathrm{V}]/[\mathrm{B}]_0)} = \frac{k_\mathrm{A}}{k_\mathrm{B}} \tag{160}$$

One can therefore determine the ratio of the specific rates by measuring the amounts of U and V produced in a given time from known amounts of A and B, provided the value of the exponent a is known. Even if it is not known, the method may be used because no matter what the reaction order with respect to A and B is, the integrated equation reduces to

$$\frac{[\mathrm{U}]/[\mathrm{A}]_0}{[\mathrm{V}]/[\mathrm{B}]_0} = \frac{k_\mathrm{A}}{k_\mathrm{B}} \tag{161}$$

when the amount of X is so small that when reaction is complete both $[\mathrm{U}]/[\mathrm{A}]_0$ and $[\mathrm{V}]/[\mathrm{B}]_0$ are small compared with unity [40]. This method of determining relative reaction rates has gained greatly in convenience and utility from the availability of gas chromatography [41]. It has in any case the advantage that one compares time-independent amounts of reaction products instead of estimating rates of reaction.

The method is especially advantageous when the reactions are fast, but it has dangers. Unless the chemical reaction rate is slow enough to make essentially complete mixing possible within a time interval in which little reaction occurs, the relative rates obtained may be the relative rates of the diffusion of A and B from a volume element rich in A and B to one rich in X. And if the chemical reaction time is of the same order as the time of mixing, the observed ratio of rates will lie somewhere between the ratio of the rates of diffusion and the ratio of the chemical reactivities. If this is the case, the relative amounts of U and V produced are likely to depend on stirring rate and on the concentration of the reactants, which affects the chemical reaction time. Both these effects have been noted by Tolgyesi [42] in the competitive nitration of benzene and toluene by nitronium fluoborate in tetramethylenesulfone solution. In competitive experiments on the aluminum chloride–promoted chlorination and bromination of benzene and toluene Caille and Corrin [43] find that the ratio of the amounts of toluene and benzene produced is considerably smaller than the ratio of the specific rates of reaction of the two substances in noncompetitive experiments. In the competitive experiments the ratio depends on the initial concentrations of the hydrocarbons.

Collins [10, p. 74] has discussed in detail the application of the competitive method in the study of isotope effects.

The mixing problem is not a factor in the study of such questions as the relative reactivity in the ortho, meta, and para positions of a monosubstituted benzene [44]. If a substance A can form two different substances U and V by the same mechanism, the rate equations are

$$\frac{d[\mathrm{U}]}{dt} = k_{\mathrm{U}} f(\mathrm{A},\mathrm{X}, \ldots) \tag{162}$$

and

$$\frac{d[\mathrm{V}]}{dt} = k_{\mathrm{V}} f(\mathrm{A},\mathrm{X}, \ldots) \tag{163}$$

Even if the reactions are kinetically complex, and even if the function f depends on the effectiveness of mixing, it will still be true that

$$\frac{d[\mathrm{U}]}{d[\mathrm{V}]} = \frac{k_{\mathrm{U}}}{k_{\mathrm{V}}} \tag{164}$$

where the k's measure the chemical reactivities of the sites in the structure of A from which U and V respectively derive.

4.24 VERY FAST REACTIONS: THE DIFFUSION LIMIT

The rates of reactions with half-lives less than 0.001 sec cannot be measured satisfactorily by any process which requires the mixing of reagents. They can, however, be estimated by relaxation techniques whose development is largely due to Eigen.[1] In these a system in equilibrium is subjected to a rapid change in such an external parameter as temperature, pressure, or electric field strength. This brings the system to a different state of equilibrium, and the time required for its establishment, which may be observed in various ways, is a known function of the specific rates of the forward and reverse reactions.

A reaction between solutes requires the diffusing together of the reactants, except that a proton transfer may occur through a short chain of water or

[1] See the reviews by Eigen and Johnson [45], and by Eigen and de Maeyer [39].

waterlike molecules by the mechanism which is responsible for the high mobility of hydrogen and hydroxyl ions in aqueous solution [46]. Even then the reactants must diffuse to a separation measured by a few diameters of the solvent molecule. The theory of this kind of diffusion was developed in detail by Debye [47], and there is much evidence for its validity.[1] In terms of this theory diffusion sets an upper limit in the range of 10^{10} to 10^{11} liters/mole-sec to the specific rate of a reaction between two solutes in aqueous solution. The value would be lower for a more viscous medium.

Recent studies by Eigen[2] indicate a specific rate of the order of 10^9 to 10^{10} for the rupture of a hydrogen bond. The specific rate of the reverse reaction must be within an order of magnitude or two the same as that of the rupture.

The rates of extremely fast reactions can also be estimated by spectroscopic methods.[3]

4.25 THE EVIDENCE FOR THE IDEAL LAW OF MASS ACTION IN SOLUTION[4]

In so far as reactions in solution are concerned, the ideal law of mass action is one of those principles which, first derived from limited observations, become established through the accumulation of observations consistent with the principle and the absence of contradictory evidence. Such rationalization as may be supplied through transition-state theory furnishes no detailed molecular model; indeed the problem of a detailed molecular model for the liquid state is still far from solution [50].

Partly because of this situation chemists interested in reaction kinetics have tended to sort themselves out into a gas-kinetics school and a solution-kinetics school, schools between which there has been meager communication and often slightly veiled contempt. Another reason for this schism is the fact that (in a practical as opposed to a theoretical sense) it has been much more difficult to work with the kinetics of gaseous reactions than with that of reactions in solution. This is because in a great many cases the conditions needed to produce a measurable reaction rate lead to a complicated system of competitive and consecutive reactions. Bodenstein, who was the outstanding contributor to the elucidation of systems of this sort, has remarked [51] that what he called abnormal reaction courses have been again and again observed[5] "especially in gas reaction in which—in contrast to those in solution—they far outnumber the cases of decent ones." In fact it is as easy to find chemically

[1] See for instance the discussion by Grunwald [48].

[2] Reported in [49].

[3] See the review by H. Strehlow in [39].

[4] The remainder of this chapter is reproduced with the permission of the editor and with some revision from *J. Chem. Educ.*, **43**:464 (1966).

[5] My translation is a free one. The German word I have translated as "decent" is *braven*.

uncomplicated reactions of measurable rate—reactions which are insensitive to traces of impurities or to the area of the container, reactions which are clean and free from side reactions—in solution as it is hard to find them in the gas phase. Insofar as this may have led solution kineticists to take the easy way and shun the complicated reactions, the effect is unfortunate. On the other hand, it has had much to do with the establishment of the ideal law of mass action on a firm basis.

One may consider the schism between gas kineticist and solution kineticist a lamentable example of the fact, which we like to gloss over, that scientists are human beings. It is, however, the kind of thing that is inevitable so long as the temperaments of scientists range from the pure esthete who pursues elegance in theory with complete unconcern for the degree to which the theory has contact with reality to the complete pragmatist who does not care that a rule of thumb makes no sense so long as it works.

The law of mass action was proposed by Guldberg and Waage in 1867 on the basis of meager empirical observation. It was for a long time possible to be skeptical of the generality of the principle, and many scientists were indeed skeptical. Certainly it was and is the exception rather than the rule that one can write down the stoichiometric equation for a reaction and find that the rate of the reaction is proportional to the product of the concentrations of the substances whose formulas appear on the left side of the equation. In a remarkably prescient booklet "Études de dynamique chimique," which appeared in 1884, van't Hoff concluded that this sort of apparent failure of the law of mass action is only apparent and is to be attributed to the formation and further reaction of intermediates with the rate of each step in the overall process consistent with the law.

4.26 THE INDEPENDENT COEXISTENCE OF REACTIONS

During the 1890s much activity in the Ostwald school of physical chemistry was concerned with testing what was called the principle of the independent coexistence of reactions, namely, the rule that the rate of any reaction is independent of the presence or absence of other reactions. An important aspect of this principle concerned the approach to the state of equilibrium in a reversible reaction. In a pioneer investigation inspired by Ostwald, Kistiakowsky [52] studied the rate of formation and of hydrolysis of a number of esters in an ethanol-water medium, and demonstrated that the net rate can be represented as the difference between the rates of two completely independent and opposing processes, each of which conforms to the law of mass action.

At about the same time as the Kistiakowsky experiments Bodenstein [53] demonstrated that the rate of the reaction

$$H_2 + I_2 \rightleftharpoons 2HI \qquad \text{(XIV)}$$

in the gas phase conforms to the equation

$$\frac{d[\mathrm{HI}]}{dt} = 2k_1[\mathrm{H_2}][\mathrm{I_2}] - k_{-1}[\mathrm{HI}]^2 \tag{165}$$

Since that time countless tests have been made of the principle that the rate of a reversible reaction is given by the difference between two terms, one of which represents the rate of the process going from left to right, the other the independent rate of the process going from right to left.

4.27 CATALYZED REACTIONS AND ZERO-ORDER REACTIONS

By the turn of the century a number of chemists had become convinced of the universal validity of the law of mass action, although Ostwald himself appears always to have had reservations. Bredig and Stern [54], finding the rate of the benzoin condensation (a reaction in which 2 moles of benzaldehyde combine under the specific catalytic effect of ionized cyanides) to be proportional to the quantity $[C_6H_5CHO]^2[CN^-]$, could say with respect to the mechanism of the reaction, "One must reject all hypotheses which are not consistent with the kinetic laws of the reaction." They concluded that one molecule of benzaldehyde combines rapidly and reversibly with one cyanide ion to form an intermediate which then reacts (in what is now called a rate-determining step) with a second molecule of benzaldehyde to form the product benzoin, simultaneously releasing a cyanide ion. There was no hedging about this; no longer any mystical attribution of the catalytic effect of the cyanide to a subtle effluvium; cyanide ion can only be a catalyst because it is involved in a chemical reaction and is regenerated in a subsequent chemical reaction.

At about the same time two remarkable articles by Lapworth appeared [55]. The first, on the basis of qualitative observations on the rate of the cyanhydrin reaction

$$R_2CO + HCN \rightarrow R_2C(OH)CN \tag{XV}$$

which is accelerated by bases and retarded by acids, proposed that the reaction goes in two steps

$$R_2CO + CN^- \rightarrow R_2C(CN)O^- \tag{XVI}$$

$$R_2C(CN)O^- + HCN \rightarrow R_2C(OH)CN + CN^- \tag{XVII}$$

the first being what would now be called rate-determining.

In the second paper Lapworth showed quantitatively that the rate of bromination of acetone in acid solution is independent of the concentration of bromine but proportional to the first power of the concentration of acetone and to the first power of the concentration of catalyzing strong acid. He concluded: "It may be observed that the independence of the velocity of reaction on the concentration of bromine shows clearly, first, that the reaction proceeds in at least two stages, in one or more of which the bromine is not involved, and secondly, that in the stage or stages in which the bromine takes part, the velocity of reaction is so great that the time occupied is not measurable. The approximate proportionality of the velocity to the concentration of the acetone indicates that in the reaction representing the velocity of that stage, the velocity of which is measured, only one molecule of acetone takes part, whilst the observations as to the influence of acids of different concentration are best explained on the supposition that in this reaction one hydrogen ion is involved." He wrote further: "It is clear, also, that the independence of the speed of reaction on the concentration of bromine shows that the velocity with which the second form of the acetone is brominated must be incomparably greater than that of the reverse change of the labile to the normal form."

4.28 THE DARK AGES AND THE RENAISSANCE

These papers by Bredig and Stern and by Lapworth established on a firm basis the whole technique of kinetic investigation of reaction mechanisms. Yet oddly enough the subject did not catch on. Chemists continued to erect elaborate structures of theory about reaction mechanisms which could have been demolished, and later were demolished, by a few simple kinetic experiments, but which were accepted and taught for a generation or more. Influential organic chemists, perhaps in reaction to these speculations, claimed and probably believed, that they did not use ideas about mechanism in planning their investigations. Lapworth himself published only one more investigation in the field [56], again an important pioneering one. In this he showed that the retarding effect of water on the rate of the acid-catalyzed esterification of an acid in alcohol solution corresponds exactly to the retarding effect of ammonia upon the rate of an acid-catalyzed reaction in water.

Goldschmidt[1] in Norway continued the remarkable investigations he had started in 1899 on acid-base systems in the solvent aniline and contributed significantly to the understanding that water is a base in alcohol. There were quantitative studies by Martinsen [58], also in Norway, on the rates of nitration. There was a distinguished but isolated study by Meerwein and van Emster [59] on the camphene hydrochloride rearrangement. Excellent as these investigations were, they were out of the mainstream. The 1921 edition of Henrich's "Theorien der organischen Chemie," which was the bible of thoughtful organic chemists of its time, contains no mention whatsoever of kinetic investigations or of kinetic evidence for reaction mechanisms.

And then suddenly Bartlett and Ingold and Pedersen in the late twenties and early thirties were studying mechanisms and accepting without question or

[1] Reviewed by Goldschmidt in [57].

comment the absolute validity of the law of mass action. The sudden upsurge of this kind of work is as difficult to explain as its sudden eclipse. It is true that some remarkable things happened during these Dark Ages in the parallel but usually isolated culture of reaction kinetics in the gas phase, very largely through the brilliantly pioneering work of Bodenstein [51]. Mechanisms were found and confirmed in a variety of ways which explained the complicated kinetics of the reactions of hydrogen with chlorine and with bromine, and the introduction of the steady-state approximation (Sec. 4.15) represented a major advance in the quantitative treatment of reaction systems involving intermediates present only in minute proportions. This technique may have triggered the Renaissance in solution kinetics; at any rate it was rapidly put to work by the new enthusiasts for the study of reaction mechanisms in solution.

Perhaps the clinching evidence for the law of mass action was supplied by the investigations during the 1930s of the halogenation of ketones and related reactions. These showed with respect to the acid-catalyzed reaction that, except at very high acidity, the rate is zero order in halogen and the same for chlorine, bromine, and iodine; that the rate of racemization of an optically active ketone of the type

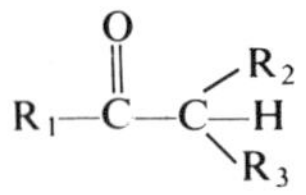

$$R_1{-}\overset{\displaystyle O}{\overset{\|}{C}}{-}C{\overset{\nearrow R_2}{\underset{\searrow R_3}{-H}}}$$

is the same as the rate of halogenation under comparable conditions [60, 61]. These results constitute convincing evidence for the mechanism proposed by Lapworth, his "labile form of the ketone" being the enol

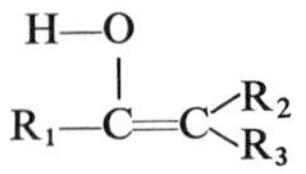

$$R_1{-}\overset{\displaystyle H{-}O}{\overset{|}{C}}{=}C{\overset{\nearrow R_2}{\underset{\searrow R_3}{}}}$$

which is present only in minute amounts, which reacts more rapidly with halogen than it returns to the keto form, and which is inactive when formed from an optically active ketone. The way in which the kinetics changes from zero order in halogen to first order as the acidity increases (Sec. 4.16) is particularly strong evidence both for the mechanism and for the complete applicability of the law of mass action. Similar investigations in the same period showed that in alkaline solutions the reaction is zero order in halogen with identical rates for bromination and iodination [62]; that for an optically active ketone the rates of bromination and of racemization are identical [63]; that the rates of racemization and of deuterium uptake by the ketone are nearly the same and are probably identical if properly corrected for minor complications [64]. Chlorination rate is lower than that of bromination or iodination, and the rate depends on chlorine concentration in the same way in which it depends on iodine concentration in the iodination at higher acidity [61]. All of this is consistent with the exact application of the law of mass action to a two-step mechanism in which the intermediate may be either the enol or the anion

$$\left[R_1-C\overset{O}{\vdots}\!\cdots C\begin{matrix} R_2 \\ R_3 \end{matrix} \right]^-$$

The principle of the universal applicability of the ideal law of mass action does not appear to have been seriously questioned for 30 years, and may be considered one of the most firmly established generalizations in chemistry.

REFERENCES

1. Beachell, H. C., and T. R. Meeker: *J. Am. Chem. Soc.*, **78**:1796 (1956).
2. Tables of Chemical Kinetics, *Natl. Bur. Std. Circ.* 510, p. xviii, 1951.
3. Brønsted, J. N., M. Kilpatrick, and M. Kilpatrick: *J. Am. Chem. Soc.*, **51**:428 (1929).
4. Kistiakowsky, G. B., and W. Mears: *J. Chem. Phys.*, **5**: 687 (1937).
5. Kaufmann, H., and A. Wassermann: *Chem. Soc. (London) Trans.*, **1939**:870.
6. Roberts, I., and L. P. Hammett: *J. Am. Chem. Soc.*, **59**:1063 (1937).
7. Crowell, T. I., and L. P. Hammett: *J. Am. Chem. Soc.*, **70**:3444 (1948).
8. Benford, G. A., and C. K. Ingold: *J. Chem. Soc.*, **1938**:929.
9. Waack, R., and P. E. Stevenson: *J. Am. Chem. Soc.*, **87**:1183 (1965).
10. Collins, C. J.: *Advan. Phys. Org. Chem.*, **2** (1964).
11. Guggenheim, E. A.: *Phil. Mag.*, (7) **2**:538 (1936).
12. McCleary, H. R., and L. P. Hammett: *J. Am. Chem. Soc.*, **63**:2254 (1941).
13. Denbigh, K. G.: *Trans. Faraday Soc.*, **40**:352 (1944).
14. Burnett, R. L., and L. P. Hammett: *J. Am. Chem. Soc.*, **80**:2415 (1958).
15. Rand, M. J., and L. P. Hammett: *J. Am. Chem. Soc.*, **72**:287 (1950).
16. Saldick, J., and L. P. Hammett: *J. Am. Chem. Soc.*, **72**:283 (1950); H. M. Humphreys and L. P. Hammett: *ibid.*, **78**:521 (1956).
17. Young, H. H., Jr., and L. P. Hammett: *J. Am. Chem. Soc.*, **72**:280 (1950).
18. Bodenstein, M., and S. C. Lind: *Z. Physik. Chem.*, **57**:168 (1906).
19. Christiansen, J. A.: *Kgl. Danske Videnskab. Selskab., Mat.-Fys. Medd.*, **1**:14 (1919); K. F. Herzfeld: *Z. Elektrochem.*, **25**:301 (1919); M. Polanyi: *ibid.*, **26**:50 (1920).
20. Juvet, R. S., Jr., and J. Chiu: *J. Am. Chem. Soc.*, **83**:1560 (1961).
21. Bartlett, P. D., S. D. Ross, and C. G. Swain: *J. Am. Chem. Soc.*, **69**:2971 (1947); T. J. Williams: *Ind. Eng. Chem.*, **80**:1631 (1958); *Chem. Eng. News*, Jan. 8, 1962, p. 88; K. B. Wiberg and W. H. Richardson: *J. Am. Chem. Soc.*, **84**:2800 (1962); L. J. Schaad: *ibid.*, **85**:3588 (1963); K. B. Wiberg: "Physical Organic Chemistry," app. 8, John Wiley & Sons, Inc., New York, 1964.
22. Bartlett, P. D., and J. R. Vincent: *J. Am. Chem. Soc.*, **55**:4992 (1933).
23. Rakowski, A.: *Z. Physik. Chem.*, **57**:321 (1907).
24. Matsen, F. A., and J. F. Franklin: *J. Am. Chem. Soc.*, **72**:3337 (1950).
25. Levy, J. B., R.W. Taft, Jr., D. Aaron, and L. P. Hammett: *J. Am. Chem. Soc.*, **75**:3955 (1953).
26. Brown, H. C., and R. S. Fletcher: *J. Am. Chem. Soc.*, **71**:1845 (1949).
27. Bodenstein, M.: *Z. Physik. Chem.*, **85**:329 (1913).
28. Hirschfelder, J. O.: *J. Chem. Phys.*, **26**:271 (1957); J. T-F. Wong: *J. Am. Chem. Soc.*, **87**:1788 (1965).

29. Zucker, L., and L. P. Hammett: *J. Am. Chem. Soc.*, **61**:2791 (1939).
30. Briggs, G. E., and J. B. S. Haldane: *Biochem. J.*, **19**:338 (1925).
31. Michaelis, L., and M. L. Menten: *Biochem. Z.*, **49**:333 (1913).
32. Chance, B.: *J. Franklin Inst.*, **228**:459 (1940).
33. Lineweaver, H., and D. Burk: *J. Am. Chem. Soc.*, **56**:658 (1934).
34. Eadie, G. S.: *J. Biol. Chem.*, **146**:85 (1942).
35. Ross, S. D., and I. Kuntz: *J. Am. Chem. Soc.*, **76**:3000 (1954).
36. Leimu, R., R. Korte, E. Laaksonen, and U. Lehmuskoski: *Suomen Kemistilehti*, **19B**:93 (1946).
37. Humphreys, H. M., and L. P. Hammett: *J. Am. Chem. Soc.*, **78**:521 (1956).
38. Hartridge, H., and F. J. H. Roughton: *Proc. Roy. Soc.* (*London*), **A104**:376 (1923).
39. Friess, S. L., E. S. Lewis, and A. Weissberger (eds.): "Technique of Organic Chemistry," vol. VIII, pt. I, "Investigation of Rates and Mechanisms of Reactions," 2nd ed., Interscience Publishers, Inc., New York, 1961.
40. Ingold, C. K.: "Structure and Mechanism in Organic Chemistry," p. 245, Cornell University Press, Ithaca, N.Y., 1953.
41. Walling, C., and W. Helmreich: *J. Am. Chem. Soc.*, **81**:1144 (1959).
42. Tolgyesi, W. S.: *Can. J. Chem.*, **43**:343 (1965).
43. Caille, S. Y., and R. J. P. Corrin: *Chem. Commun.*, **1967**:1251.
44. Scheffer, F. E. C., and W. F. Brandsma: *Rec. Trav. Chim.*, **45**:522 (1926); A. E. Bradfield and B. Jones: *J. Chem. Soc.*, **1928**:1006.
45. Eigen, M., and J. S. Johnson: *Ann. Rev. Phys. Chem.*, **11**:309 (1960).
46. Eigen, M., and L. de Maeyer: *Proc. Roy. Soc.* (*London*), **A247**:505 (1958).
47. Debye, P.: *Trans. Electrochem. Soc.*, **82**:265 (1942).
48. Grunwald, E.: *Progr. Phys. Org. Chem.*, **3**:318 (1965).
49. *Chem. Eng. News*, Dec. 2, 1963, p. 38.
50. Eyring, H., J. H. Hildebrand, and S. A. Rice: *Int. Sci. Tech.*, March, 1963, p. 56.
51. Bodenstein, M.: *Z. Elektrochem.*, **38**:911 (1932).
52. Kistiakowsky, W.: *Z. Physik. Chem.*, **27**:250 (1898). The work had been published 8 years earlier in Russian journals.
53. Bodenstein, M.: *Z. Physik. Chem.*, **13**:56 (1894); **22**:1 (1897).
54. Bredig, G., and H. Stern: *Z. Elektrochem.*, **10**:582 (1904).
55. Lapworth, A.: *J. Chem. Soc.*, **83**:995 (1903); **85**:30 (1904).
56. Fitzgerald, E., and A. Lapworth: *J. Chem. Soc.*, **93**:2163 (1908); A. Lapworth: *ibid.*, 2187.
57. Goldschmidt, H.: *Z. Elektrochem.*, **36**:662 (1930).
58. Martinsen, H.: *Z. Physik. Chem.*, **50**:385 (1905); **59**:605 (1907); **62**:713 (1908).
59. Meerwein, H., and K. van Emster: *Ber.*, **55**:2500 (1922).
60. Ingold, C. K., and C. L. Wilson: *J. Chem. Soc.*, **1934**:773.
61. Bartlett, P. D., and C. H. Stauffer: *J. Am. Chem. Soc.*, **57**:2580 (1935).
62. Bartlett, P. D.: *J. Am. Chem. Soc.*, **56**:967 (1934).
63. Hsü, S. K., and C. L. Wilson: *J. Chem. Soc.*, **1936**:623.
64. Hsü, S. K., C. K. Ingold, and C. L. Wilson: *J. Chem. Soc.*, **1938**:78.

5
Transition-state Theory

5.1 GENERAL THEORY OF THE TRANSITION STATE

Any general theory of reaction rate in solution is essentially forced to treat the specific rate k as the product of two quantities[1]

$$k = k^{\ddagger} K^{\ddagger} \tag{1}$$

$K^{\ddagger}$ has many of the properties of an equilibrium constant for the formation from the reactants of what has variously been called the critical complex or the transition state. $k^{\ddagger}$ is some sort of a generalized rate which is nearly independent of temperature and does not depend on the medium in which the reaction occurs or on the structure of the reactants. The reasons for accepting this conclusion are the following:

1. A plot of the logarithm of the specific rate against reciprocal temperature is usually a straight line within the precision of the data just as a plot of the logarithm of an equilibrium constant is. Observable deviations

[1] The symbol $\ddagger$ is called a double dagger or diesis.

from linearity in the rate case occur under the same conditions as observable deviations in the equilibrium case [1–3]. The linear relation in the rate case is called the Arrhenius equation.

2. Changes in the kind and concentration of ions present in a solution have the same effect upon the rate of a reaction between ions in that solution as they do upon an equilibrium which involves the bringing together of ions having the same charges as those reactants. This is the salt-effect equation discovered by Brønsted in 1922 [4] (Sec. 4.3). It is reasonable to suppose, as Brønsted did, that this is merely an easily observable case (observable because activity coefficients of ions are predictable in dilute solution) of the general relationship

$$k = k^\circ \frac{\prod_i (\gamma_i)^{\nu_i}}{\gamma_\ddagger} \tag{2}$$

In this equation $\gamma_\ddagger$ is the activity coefficient of the transition state, the product is taken over the activity coefficients of the reactants, and k° is the limit approached by k as the concentrations of all solutes involved in the reaction approach zero.

3. Within wide limits the effect of changes in structure of a reactant upon specific rates can be quantitatively correlated with the effect of the same or similar changes upon equilibrium constants. These correlations, which are called linear free-energy relationships, are linear relations which apply indiscriminately to the logarithm of the specific rate and to the logarithm of the equilibrium constant (Sec. 11.2).

5.2 CONSIDERATIONS RELATED TO POTENTIAL ENERGIES

The idea of a transition state which is in equilibrium with the reactants gains greatly in precision and in usefulness from considerations which were developed by Polanyi[1] beginning in 1931. The idea of a simultaneous addition and dissociation in connection with the Walden inversion had been proposed by Werner in 1911 [6] and restated by Lewis [7] in 1923. But Polanyi compared the value of 11 kcal for the recently determined energy of activation of the process

$$H + H_2(\text{ortho}) \rightarrow H_2(\text{para}) + H \tag{I}$$

with the 100 kcal energy of dissociation of H_2 into atoms. Applying theoretical considerations which had originated with London [8], he produced the now familiar diagram (Fig. 5.1) for the process which is called the displacement reaction and is represented by the symbolism

$$A + BC \rightarrow AB + C \tag{II}$$

[1] Reviewed by Evans and Polanyi [5].

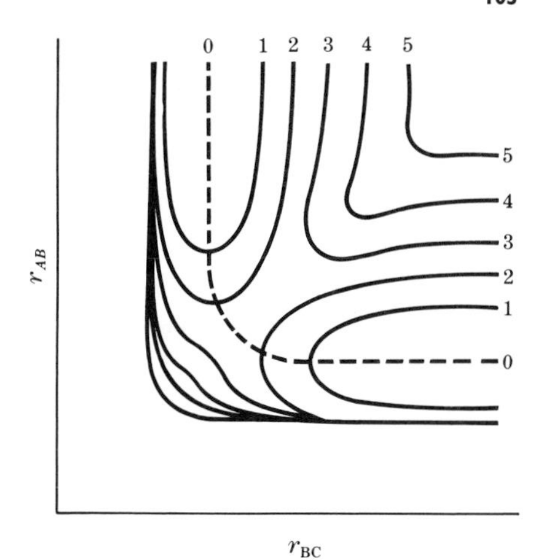

Fig. 5.1 Energy contours for a system of A, B, and C atoms.

A typical example in organic chemistry would be

$$HO^- + CH_3Br \rightarrow HOCH_3 + Br^- \qquad \text{(III)}$$

In this diagram the abscissa r_{BC} is the distance between the centers of the atoms in the B and C structures which are directly involved in the reaction, the carbon and the bromine in reaction (III). The ordinate r_{AB} is the corresponding distance in the A and B structures, e.g., the oxygen and the carbon in reaction (III). The curved solid lines are contour lines of constant potential energy. Such a diagram is an abstraction from a more complete diagram which would require a space of several dimensions. Even in the simple case of reaction (I) one more coordinate specifying the angle H—H—H would be necessary for completeness. A more complicated system would require many more coordinates, including, for a reaction in solution, those specifying the positions of the atoms in all the solvent molecules whose energy is appreciably affected by the presence of the reacting molecules. But for any given pair of values of the coordinates r_{BC} and r_{AB} there will be one set of values for all the other coordinates which will correspond to the lowest possible energy value consistent with those values of r_{BC} and r_{AB}. It is understood in diagrams of this sort that the values of the missing coordinates are those which correspond in this way to the lowest energy. Thus it seems reasonable to expect that for reaction (I) this situation of lowest energy will correspond to the three hydrogen atoms lying in a straight line. It is likewise reasonable to expect the O—C—Br angle in reaction (III) to be 180° or nearly so.

5.3 THE REACTION COORDINATE

Figure 5.1 indicates that when an A atom approaches a B—C structure, the energy will be lower if the B—C bond stretches somewhat and stretches more the closer the approach of the A atom. It is possible to draw a line, the dotted

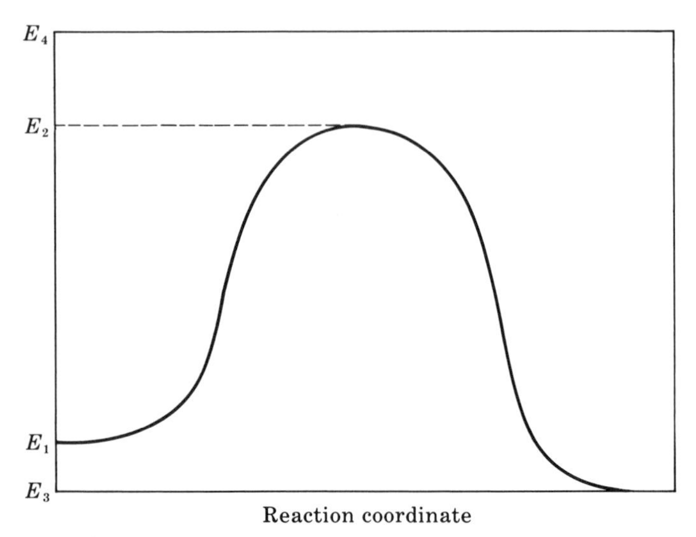

Fig. 5.2 Energy against reaction coordinate.

line in the figure, whose abscissa for any value of the ordinate represents the value of the former for which the energy has the lowest possible value. That one out of the many possible reaction paths which requires at all times the least possible increase in potential energy is represented by the movement of a point along this line from the upper left of the diagram to the lower right. Distances along this line are referred to as values of the reaction coordinate. As the reaction coordinate increases, the distance r_{AB} decreases and the distance r_{BC} increases, both monotonically. At first the potential energy increases, but it reaches a maximum in a saddle, or col, in the lower left of the diagram and thenceforward decreases continuously. The altitude of the col above the level of the valley in the upper left of the diagram represents the minimum amount by which the potential energy of the reactants must be increased if reaction is to occur. This increase, called the potential energy of activation, is much less than the energy required to break the B—C bond.

Figure 5.2 represents the relationships in a different form. Here E_1 indicates the potential energy of a B—C structure in the absence of A, E_2 that of the transition state, E_3 that of an A—B structure in the absence of C, and E_4 that of a system in which A, B, and C are all widely separated, one in which both the A—B and the B—C bonds are completely broken. The quantity $E_2 - E_1$ is the potential energy of activation, $E_3 - E_1$ is the overall difference in potential energy between reactants and products, $E_4 - E_1$ is the energy required to dissociate a B—C bond, and $E_4 - E_3$ that required to dissociate an A—B bond.

The theory which underlies the construction of diagrams like those of Figs. 5.1 and 5.2 can hardly be considered to be more than qualitative and suggestive. Even so, it has had a profound influence on the development both of theoretical and of practical organic chemistry. Certainly it has been all-important for the understanding of the stereochemistry of chemical reactions and consequently for the remarkable development of the techniques of stereospecific synthesis. Thirty years ago everything connected with the Walden inversion constituted a black art whose practitioners seemed to revel in the mystification of the uninitiated.

The qualitative picture has also had great influence on thinking about the effect on reactivity of changes in structure of reactant or in the medium in which reaction occurs. The picture according to which the rupture of an old bond is accompanied by the formation of a new bond and in which the energy released in the formation contributes to the energy needed for the rupture has important corollaries for these problems. As was repeatedly emphasized by Polanyi, the potential energy of activation should be the greater in a series of reactions involving the same A and B but different C's the greater the work required to dissociate the B—C bond and should be the less in a series involving the same B and C but different A's the more the work required to dissociate the A—B bond. That is, the potential energy of activation is the less the weaker the bond being broken and the stronger the bond being formed.

Rather intuitive rules of this sort had long had much influence on the thinking of organic chemists. Through Polanyi's arguments they attained a kind of respectability which they had previously lacked, and the prospect of transforming them into quantitative relationships became much brighter. There remained, however, the difficulty that a theorem about potential energies still lacks a great deal from being a useful theorem about chemical equilibrium and chemical reaction rates.

5.4 DETAILED TRANSITION-STATE THEORY

The gap was filled by a proposal by Eyring [9] that the $k^{\ddagger}$ of Eq. (1) be set at $\mathbf{k}T/\mathbf{h}$ and that the $K^{\ddagger}$ be interpreted in terms of the partition function of a system which is changing rather than in terms of the partition function of a stable molecule. According to this proposal, the limiting specific rate k° of a kinetically simple reaction is given by

$$k^{\circ} = \frac{\mathbf{k}T}{\mathbf{h}} e^{-\Delta E_0^{\ddagger}/\mathbf{R}T} \frac{Q^{\ddagger}/N_0 V}{\prod_j (Q_j^{\circ}/N_0 V)^{\nu_j}} \tag{3}$$

$\Delta E_0^{\ddagger}$ is the energy per mole required to form the transition state from the reactants, all the molecules both of reactants and of the transition state being in the lowest permitted energy level. The product $\prod_j$ is taken over all the substances involved in the formation of the transition state, including (when appropriate) the solvent. $Q^{\ddagger}$ is the partition function of the transition-state structure divided by the partition function for motion along the reaction coordinate; it is therefore a sum of Boltzmann terms. The operational definition of k° is

$$k^\circ = \lim_{c \to 0} \frac{v}{\prod_i c_i^{\nu_i}} \tag{4}$$

the product $\prod_i$ being taken over the concentrations of solutes only.

Equation (3) may usefully be written

$$k^\circ = \frac{\mathbf{k}T}{\mathbf{h}} \frac{q^{\ddagger}}{\prod_j (q_j^\circ)^{\nu_j}} \tag{5}$$

with $q^{\ddagger}$ defined as (cf. Sec. 3.14)

$$q^{\ddagger} = e^{-E_0^{\ddagger}/\mathbf{R}T} \frac{Q^{\ddagger}}{N_0 V} \tag{6}$$

Because $Q^{\ddagger}$ is a sum of Boltzmann terms, it is reasonable and useful to define a complement of functions which are interdependent in the same way as the analogous thermodynamic functions, namely, an equilibrium constant

$$K^{\ddagger} = \frac{q^{\ddagger}}{\prod_j (q_j^\circ)^{\nu_j}} \tag{7}$$

the standard potential of activation

$$\Delta\mu^{\ddagger} = -\mathbf{R}T \ln K^{\ddagger} \tag{8}$$

a standard entropy of activation

$$\Delta\bar{S}^{\ddagger} = -\left(\frac{\partial \Delta\mu^{\ddagger}}{\partial T}\right)_P \tag{9}$$

and a standard enthalpy of activation

$$\Delta\bar{H}^{\ddagger} = \Delta\mu^{\ddagger} + T\Delta\bar{S}^{\ddagger} \tag{10}$$

In terms of partition functions Eqs. (8) to (10) are equivalent to

$$\mu^{\ddagger} = E_0^{\ddagger} - \mathbf{R}T \ln \frac{Q^{\ddagger}}{N_0 V} \tag{11}$$

$$\bar{S}^{\ddagger} = \mathbf{R} \ln \frac{Q^{\ddagger}}{N_0 V} + \mathbf{R}T \left[\frac{\partial \ln (Q^{\ddagger}/V)}{\partial T}\right]_P \tag{12}$$

and

$$\bar{H}^{\ddagger} = E_0^{\ddagger} + \mathbf{R}T^2 \left[\frac{\partial \ln (Q^{\ddagger}/V)}{\partial T}\right]_P \tag{13}$$

Operationally, entropy and enthalpy of activation are obtained from the temperature coefficient of the specific rate, using the relationships

$$\Delta\bar{S}^{\ddagger} = \left[\frac{\partial(\mathbf{R}T\ln k^{\circ})}{\partial T}\right]_P - \mathbf{R}\ln\frac{\mathbf{ek}T}{\mathbf{h}} - \mathbf{R}(\textstyle\sum\nu)\left(\frac{\partial\ln\rho^{\circ}}{\partial T}\right)_P \tag{14}$$

and

$$\Delta\bar{H}^{\ddagger} = -\mathbf{R}\left[\frac{\partial\ln k^{\circ}}{\partial(1/T)}\right]_P - \mathbf{R}T + \mathbf{R}(\textstyle\sum\nu)\left[\frac{\partial\ln\rho^{\circ}}{\partial(1/T)}\right]_P \tag{15}$$

$\Sigma\nu$ is 0 for a first-order and -1 for a second-order reaction. The terms involving the solvent density ρ° may usually be neglected.

Some useful numerical quantities are

$$\frac{\mathbf{k}}{\mathbf{h}} = 2.0836 \times 10^{10} \qquad \log\frac{\mathbf{k}}{\mathbf{h}} = 10.31882$$

$$\frac{\mathbf{ek}}{\mathbf{h}} = 5.6638 \times 10^{10} \qquad \log\frac{\mathbf{ek}}{\mathbf{h}} = 10.75311$$

$$298.2\frac{\mathbf{k}}{\mathbf{h}} = 6.213 \times 10^{12} \qquad \log 298{\cdot}2\frac{\mathbf{k}}{\mathbf{h}} = 12.7933$$

$$298.2\frac{\mathbf{ek}}{\mathbf{h}} = 1.689 \times 10^{13} \qquad \log 298.2\frac{\mathbf{ek}}{\mathbf{h}} = 13.2276$$

In the Arrhenius equation

$$k = Ae^{-E/\mathbf{R}T} \tag{16}$$

which originated from observations made in the 1880s, the activation energy E and the preexponential factor A are supposed independent of temperature. It follows that

$$E = \Delta\bar{H}^{\ddagger} + \mathbf{R}T - \mathbf{R}(\textstyle\sum\nu)\left[\frac{\partial\ln\rho^{\circ}}{\partial(1/T)}\right]_P \tag{17}$$

and

$$R\ln A = \Delta\bar{S}^{\ddagger} - \mathbf{R}\ln\frac{\mathbf{ek}T}{\mathbf{h}} - \mathbf{R}T(\textstyle\sum\nu)\left(\frac{\partial\ln\rho^{\circ}}{\partial T}\right)_P \tag{18}$$

5.5 THE THEORETICAL BACKGROUND OF THE DETAILED TRANSITION-STATE EQUATION

The following argument is essentially that of Eyring [9]. To treat the transition state as a chemical compound in equilibrium with the reactants, attractive as it may seem, is impossible. The maximum in the plot of potential energy against reaction coordinate is a mathematical point, and the number of systems which have the exact arrangement of the maximum is therefore zero. If one specifies the number of systems in the transition state as the number for which the reaction coordinate lies within a narrow range δ which includes the maximum, the number will depend upon the length of the range and for a small enough range will be proportional to it. Consequently

$$N_t = N_0 V c_t \delta \tag{19}$$

where N_t is the number of systems whose reaction coordinate lies within the range δ, V is the volume in which the reaction is occurring, and the proportionality constant c_t has the dimensions of concentration/length. If dx/dt is the rate at which the reaction coordinate x increases with time, then every system which lies within the range at any given time will have passed out of the transition-state system during the subsequent time interval $\delta/(dx/dt)$, because this is the time required for a system located at the beginning of the range to traverse it completely. Since the number of systems which react in this time interval is $N_0 V c_t$, the number of systems which react in unit time is $N_0 V c_t\, dx/dt$. The rate of reaction in moles/liter-sec is therefore given by

$$v = c_t \frac{dx}{dt} \tag{20}$$

In order to apply statistical-mechanical theory one next considers the situation in which the reaction whose rate from left to right is under consideration is in the state of chemical equilibrium. Then by conventional statistical-mechanical arguments

$$\frac{c_t \delta}{\prod c_r} = \frac{1}{2} e^{-\Delta E_0^{\ddagger}/\mathbf{R}T} \frac{Q_t^\circ / N_0 V}{\prod (Q_r^\circ / N_0 V)} \tag{21}$$

Q_t° is the partition function for a system at the maximum, and the subscript r refers to the reactants. The factor ½ enters because at equilibrium one half of the systems at the maximum will be in the course of reaction from left to right and one half from right to left. It seems reasonable to suppose, especially in view of the principle of the independent coexistence of reactions (Sec. 4.26), that the number reacting from left to right would remain unchanged if the reaction from right to left were suppressed, for instance by the addition of a reagent which combines rapidly and irreversibly with one of the substances on the right of the reaction equation. Consequently Eq. (21) may be presumed to be valid both in the absence and in the presence of the reverse reaction. With this conclusion, probably the most critical in the whole argument, the transition is made from equilibrium theory to rate theory.

Like any other partition function, Q_t° may be taken to be the product of factors, one for each of the independent modes of motion into which the movements of the atoms making up the system can be analyzed. One of these modes involves motion along the reaction coordinate. A reasonable value for the factor which corresponds to this mode is the theoretical partition function for a one-dimensional perfect gas confined in a box of length δ. On this basis

$$Q_t^\circ = \frac{\delta}{\mathbf{h}}(2\pi m_r \mathbf{k}T)^{1/2} Q^{+} \tag{22}$$

in which Q^{+} is the product of the partition-function factors for all the modes of motion of the transition-state system with the exception of the one which involves the reaction coordinate. m_r is a reduced mass for motion along this coordinate. By the same kind of reasoning the quantity dx/dt may be set equal to the average velocity of molecules of mass m_r in the one-dimensional gas, by which

$$\frac{dx}{dt} = \left(\frac{2\mathbf{k}T}{\pi m_r}\right)^{1/2} \tag{23}$$

From Eqs. (20) to (23)

$$k^\circ = \frac{\mathbf{k}T}{\mathbf{h}} e^{-\Delta E_0^{\ddagger}/\mathbf{R}T} \frac{Q^{+}/N_0 V}{\prod (Q_r^\circ/N_0 V)} \tag{24}$$

It is customary to insert on the right side of this equation a factor $\varkappa$, called a transmission coefficient, which corrects for the number of systems that pass through the transmission state but are reflected back instead of going on to complete reaction. Theorists seem to expect $\varkappa$ to lie between ½ and 1 for most reactions.

5.6 THE VALIDITY OF DETAILED TRANSITION-STATE THEORY

Equation (24) is theoretically plausible, and it yields the right order of magnitude for the entropy of activation for certain reactions of very simple molecules in the gas phase for which an a priori calculation is possible [10]. It is consistent with what I have called general transition-state theory, but so would any equation be which represents the specific rate as the product of a universal frequency by a factor which responds in the same way as an equilibrium constant does to changes in temperature, in structure of reactant, and in reaction medium. Consistency with the general theory does require that the transmission coefficient $\varkappa$, if it is different from unity, be independent of medium and of structure of reactant. It is for this reason that I have omitted it. The exponential factor and the partition-function ratio in Eq. (24) are so strongly dependent on temperature that the appearance of temperature in the frequency factor $\mathbf{k}T/\mathbf{h}$ is unimportant.

Regardless of the exact validity of Eq. (24), the wide applicability of general transition-state theory requires that (1) the quantity dx/dt in Eq. (20) be independent of structure of reactant and of reaction medium and insensitive to temperature; (2) the quantity Q_t° in Eq. (21) be proportional to δ; and

(3) Q_t° have the same value when the reverse reaction is suppressed that it has when the system is in overall equilibrium. Condition 3 amounts to the requirement that, per unit time, the number of systems which in the equilibrium situation traverse the transition state from the right side of the reaction equation be small compared with the number which reach the transition state from the left and return to the left. For only if this is so will the suppression of the right-to-left reaction reduce the population of the transition state by the required factor of 2. But at equilibrium the number which traverse the transition state from right to left is the same as the number which traverse it left to right. Consequently condition 3 requires that the number of systems which traverse any transition state be small compared with the number which attain the transition state but fall back. Unless this requirement is satisfied, neither general nor detailed transition-state theory will be applicable.

For a reaction in solution the condition for the application of transition-state theory requires that all the interactions of the transition-state system with the medium be established fast enough to be the same in the absence as they are in the presence of the reverse reaction. These interactions include not only short-range ones, such as the orientation of solvent molecules, but also the long-range ones between a charged transition state and the ions in the solution. The rates of very fast reactions may therefore be less than would be predicted from transition-state theory. The validity of the Brønsted salt-effect equation shows, however, that significant failure of the transition-state theory in this way has not set in with reactions whose half times are of the order of minutes or hours. It is possible, but by no means certain, that it has not set in for any reaction of measurable rate.

5.7 GENERALIZATION TO OTHER TYPES OF REACTION

The development of the transition-state equations in the previous sections was based on the potential-energy diagram of a displacement reaction, but there is no difficulty in generalizing the result to other types of reaction. An uncatalyzed cis-trans isomerization can reasonably be pictured as a rotation of one unsaturated carbon with its attached groups about the bond which joins it to the other unsaturated carbon. The angle of rotation θ is a suitable reaction coordinate, and the plot of potential energy against θ will be of the same kind as Fig. 5.2. Again the diagram is an abstraction because other bond angles and distances will change simultaneously with the change in θ. But again there will be one value of each of these variables which for any value of θ corresponds to the lowest possible potential energy. It is the succession of these lowest possible energies which appears in the plot.

The abstraction required for visualization is somewhat more difficult when three bond distances or angles are directly involved in the reaction mechanism. Thus a reasonable picture [10] of the reaction of hydrogen with iodine in the gas phase involves the approach of the two molecules side by side. In the transition state the H—H bond length has been estimated to be 30 percent greater than in the normal H_2 molecule and the I—I length 10 percent greater than in the normal molecule. The two H—I distances are still 8 percent greater than they will be when HI is fully formed and the two HI molecules have separated from each other. It is still possible to prepare a diagram which qualitatively resembles Fig. 5.1. In one way of doing this the ordinate is the H—I distance and the abscissa the H—H distance. The energy contours then represent the potential energy of systems in which the I—I distance is always that corresponding to the lowest energy compatible with each pair of values of the H—I and H—H distances. Distances along a line drawn on the bottom of the valley of the diagram will then be a satisfactory reaction coordinate.

Much the same approach is applicable to concerted displacement reactions, such as the one which has been proposed (Sec. 10.13) for the enolization of carbonyl compounds

$$B + HCH_2COR + HA \rightarrow BH^+ + CH_2{=}C(OH)R + A^- \tag{IV}$$

Here a base B abstracts a proton from the α carbon at the same time that an acid HA adds a proton to the carbonyl oxygen. The transition state may be pictured as

B···H···CH₂╲
        C⋯O···H···A
R╱

(A)

where the four bonds being made or broken are represented by dotted lines. In terms of the Polanyi theorem (Sec. 5.3) the potential energy of activation will be greater the stronger the C—H and H—A bonds and the weaker the H—B and O—H bonds.

5.8 THE EXTENSION TO NONIDEAL SOLUTIONS

Although the transition-state equations are derived from the statistical mechanics of infinitely dilute systems, it is natural to extend them to moderately concentrated ones. Indeed the extension is essentially forced by the validity of the Brønsted salt-effect relationship (Secs. 4.3 and 5.1). The obvious form of the extension is the treatment of the $\Delta\mu^{\ddagger}$ of Eq. (8) as a thermodynamic quantity and the representation of $K^{\ddagger}$ as

$$K^{\ddagger} = (K^{\ddagger})^{\circ} \frac{\prod_i (\gamma_i)^{\nu_i}}{\gamma_{\ddagger}} \tag{25}$$

Here the γ_i's are the usual thermodynamic activity coefficients of the reactants and $\gamma_{\ddagger}$ is an analogous quantity for systems in the transition state. $(K^{\ddagger})^{\circ}$ is the limit approached by $K^{\ddagger}$ as all solute concentrations approach zero.

5.9 COMPOSITION OF THE TRANSITION STATE

For a kinetically simple reaction whose rate is given by

$$v = k[\mathrm{A}]^a[\mathrm{B}]^b \cdots \tag{26}$$

there is at least one transition state, a rate-determining one, whose composition is $a\mathrm{A} + b\mathrm{B} + \cdots + x\mathrm{S}$, where S is the solvent. The value of x, which may be positive, negative, or zero, is not fixed by the kinetics of the reaction. The coefficients a, b, etc., may also be negative as well as positive, or even fractional (Sec. 4.2).

With respect to the solute reactants this conclusion represents no more than the application of the material-balance rule to the transition-state picture. With respect to the solvent it reflects the fact that the degree to which any solute combines with the solvent is an unknown quantity (Sec. 2.16). More explicitly it corresponds to the fact that one determines the order of a reaction with respect to any reactant only by observing the variation of the rate of reaction with varying concentration of that reactant under dilute-solution conditions. But one cannot vary the concentration of the solvent significantly without transgressing the limits of the dilute-solution relationships.

A kinetically complex reaction can always be resolved into kinetically simple reactions or into kinetically simple reactions modified by the effect of mobile equilibria.

5.10 RATE-DETERMINING TRANSITION STATE OR RATE-DETERMINING TRANSITION STATES

The demonstration that a reaction is kinetically simple does not prove the presence of a unique rate-determining transition state. In the sequence

$$\begin{aligned} &\mathrm{A} \underset{k_{-1}}{\overset{k_1}{\rightleftharpoons}} \mathrm{B} \\ &\mathrm{B} \xrightarrow{k_2} \mathrm{C} \end{aligned} \tag{V}$$

for which a schematic diagram of standard potentials is shown in Fig. 5.3, it is only necessary for the standard potential of the intermediate B to be a couple of kilocalories or more higher than that of A for the Bodenstein steady-state approximation to apply (Sec. 4.15). If it does, the rate of reaction is given by

$$v = \frac{k_1 k_2}{k_{-1} + k_2}[\mathrm{A}] \tag{27}$$

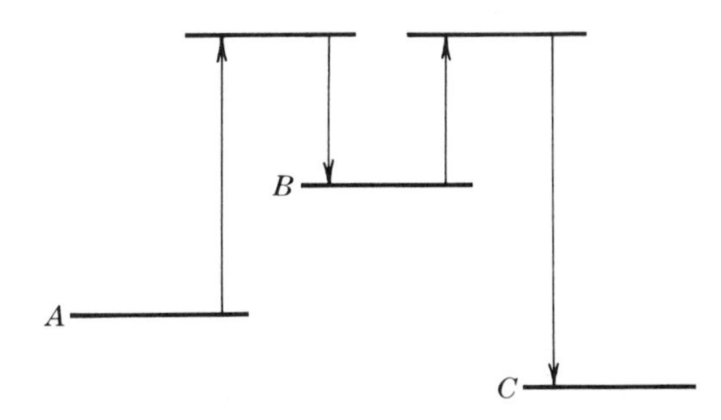

Fig. 5.3 Standard potentials for the sequence $A \rightleftharpoons B \rightarrow C$.

i.e., it is proportional to the concentration of A, just as it is if A goes to C through a single rate-determining transition state.

By the substitution of q^{+}/q° ratios for each k Eq. (27) becomes

$$k^{(p)} = \frac{\mathbf{k}T}{\mathbf{h}} \frac{1}{q_A^{\circ}[(1/q_1{}^{+}) + (1/q_2{}^{+})]} \tag{28}$$

Here

$$q_A^{\circ} = e^{-\mu_A^{\circ}/\mathbf{R}T} = e^{-E_0/\mathbf{R}T} \frac{Q_A}{N_0 V} \tag{29}$$

and q_1^{+} and q_2^{+} are the analogous quantities for the first and the second transition state. Equation (28) brings out the fact that if the standard potentials of the two transition states are equal, neither has any claim to precedence as the rate-determining one. If the standard states are decidedly unequal, the reaction rate is determined by the transition state which has the higher standard potential and the lower q^{+} value, no matter whether it is the first or the second transition state.

Equation (28) also brings out the important fact that when two transition states are separated by an intermediate whose standard potential is a little higher than the sum of the standard potentials of the reactants, the kinetics of the reaction does not depend on the standard potential of the intermediate. Conversely the study of the kinetics can reveal nothing about standard potential, entropy, or enthalpy of the intermediate.

There is an amusing apparent paradox here. If q_1^{+} and q_2^{+} are equal, Eq. (28) becomes

$$k^{(p)} = \frac{\mathbf{k}T}{\mathbf{h}} \frac{q^{+}}{2q_A^{\circ}} \tag{30}$$

This means of course that in this situation one half of the A molecules which are converted to the intermediate in any given period return to the reactant state and only half go on to form the reaction product. But if one pictures the standard potential of the intermediate as gradually increasing, the factor of

2 in the denominator must disappear not later than when the level of the intermediate reaches that of the transition state because then there no longer is an intermediate and

$$k^{(p)} = \frac{\mathbf{k}T}{\mathbf{h}} \frac{q^{\ddagger}}{q_{\mathrm{A}}^{\circ}} \tag{31}$$

It seems hardly likely that this disappearance is exactly coincident with the arrival of the standard potentials at the same level.

5.11 PARALLEL TRANSITION STATES

One may also picture parallel transition states. The partition function of a transition state is in any case a sum of Boltzmann terms whose energy lies within a range of a few kilocalories above that of the lowest pass over the barrier between reactants and products. The systems which correspond to these terms may differ in geometry and in multiplicity as well as in energy, but they all are structures in which the bond-making and bond-breaking processes required for the conversion of reactants to products are under way. Some of them may involve a strong interaction with the solvent; some may not.

If some of these systems differ considerably from the others in geometry or in solvent content, one might (if one knew about it) refer to the two groups as isomeric transition states or as transition states which differ in solvent content. This is semantics; what is important is that the $q^{\ddagger}$ value of the transition state of a particular reaction may be subject to the same complications (Sec. 2.24) with respect to the effect of a change in temperature, with respect to the effect of a change in structure of reactant, and with respect to the effect of a change in pressure that the q° value of a stable solute is.

Furthermore, two or more groups of transition-state systems which differ in composition otherwise than in solvent content may contribute significantly to the frequency of passage over the barrier which separates given reactants from given products (Sec. 5.26).

5.12 OBLIGATORY OR NONOBLIGATORY INTERMEDIATES

The experiments of Juvet and Chiu (Sec. 4.11) demonstrate that methyl ethyl acetal is an obligatory intermediate in the acid catalyzed conversion of diethyl acetal to dimethyl acetal. That is to say, the kinetics demonstrates that no measurable fraction of the process evades the intermediate and goes directly from the diethyl to the dimethyl compound. By microscopic reversibility (Sec. 5.29) the mixed compound must also intervene in the reverse process. In terms of the schematic diagram of Fig. 5.4 this means that a system which has attained the T_1 level of standard potential, which is 21 kcal above the level of dimethyl acetal, must return to the latter level in the form of methyl ethyl

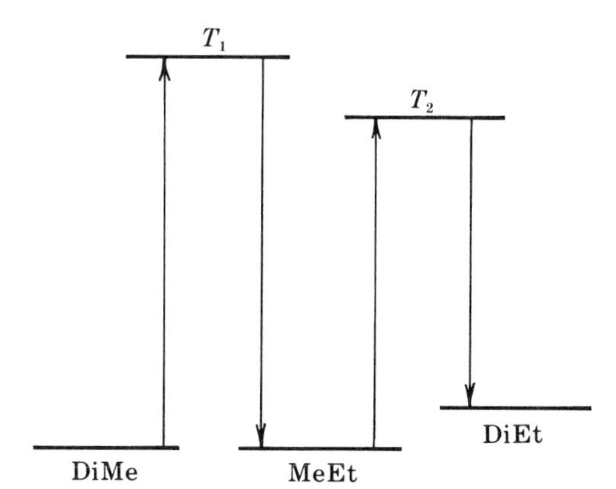

Fig. 5.4 Standard potentials for the conversion of dimethyl acetal to diethyl acetal.

acetal before it can attain the T_2 structure whose level is 1.2 kcal lower that that of T_1.

It is probable (Sec. 10.10) that both these transition states are multiple ones with an intermediate of the structure B for T_1 and C for T_2 and that the transition-state structures which immediately precede and succeed the methyl ethyl compounds are D and E respectively.

CH_3, H, O—CH_3 on C^+ (B)

CH_3, H, O—C_2H_5 on C^+ (C)

CH_3, H on C; O—CH_3; ···O(H)—C_2H_5 (D)

CH_3, H on C; ···O(H)—CH_3; O—C_2H_5 (E)

It might seem surprising that the preferred path from one transition state to the other which is a little downhill from it should be by the way of the initial loss and the subsequent regain of a large amount of energy. It must, however, be recognized that the two transition states differ in the position of a proton, in a lengthening and shortening of C—O bonds, and by a redistribution of solvent molecules. It is therefore probable that any progression from T_1 to T_2 which does not go by way of the intermediate must surmount a barrier which is appreciably higher than T_1 or T_2. Since the population of the transition state T_1 is much smaller than that of the intermediate methyl ethyl acetal, passage over even a low barrier between T_1 and T_2 would be less frequent than passage from the heavily populated intermediate over the high barrier T_2.

In situations of this sort in which a considerable number of spatial coordinates are required to describe the system it is perilous to trust energy contours drawn in a two-dimensional diagram or to put faith in mechanical analogies.

Leffler and Temple [11] have presented convincing evidence for an obligatory intermediate in a reaction which may reasonably be pictured as

$$\phi\text{—N=N=N} + \text{P}\phi_3 \rightleftarrows [\phi\text{—N=N=N}\cdots\text{P}\phi_3] \rightleftarrows \phi\text{—N=N=N—P}\phi_3$$

$$\rightleftarrows \left[\begin{array}{c}\phi\text{—N}\cdots\text{P}\phi_3 \\ \vdots \quad \vdots \\ \text{N=N}\end{array}\right] \rightleftarrows \begin{array}{c}\phi\text{—N—P}\phi_3 \\ \\ \text{N}\equiv\text{N}\end{array} \qquad \text{(VI)}$$

The two transition states, represented by the structures in brackets, have about the same standard potentials. But the direct conversion of the one to the other evidently involves enough in the way of bond distortion and the making and breaking of bonds to account for what is, so to speak, a considerable activation energy for the process.

5.13 THE PROGRESSION FROM REACTANT TO TRANSITION STATE

In terms of classical kinetics the rate of formation of a product C from a substance B which is in mobile equilibrium with a substance A is given by (Sec. 4.18)

$$v = k_2[\mathrm{B}] = K_1 k_2[\mathrm{A}] \qquad (32)$$

where k_2 is the specific rate for the conversion of B to C and K_1 is the equilibrium constant for the A-B interconversion. In terms of transition-state theory this becomes

$$v = \frac{\mathbf{k}T}{\mathbf{h}} \frac{q_{\mathrm{B}}^{\circ} q^{\ddagger}}{q_{\mathrm{A}}^{\circ} q_{\mathrm{B}}^{\circ}} [\mathrm{A}] \qquad (33)$$

and therefore

$$v = \frac{\mathbf{k}T}{\mathbf{h}} \frac{q^{\ddagger}}{q_{\mathrm{A}}^{\circ}} [\mathrm{A}] \qquad (34)$$

which is the relation which would apply if C were formed directly from A.

Without transition-state theory it was evident that the mechanisms are kinetically indistinguishable, but the theory makes it clear that the effect of temperature, of pressure, of medium, or of structure, including isotopic substitution, on reaction rate is determined by the difference between the effect on the standard potential of the transition state and the sum of the effect on the reactants. None of these effects depends on the mechanism by which the transition state is attained, and none of them supplies any information on that mechanism.

Transition-state theory also makes it clear that the primitive value of the specific rate of a reaction in which the reactant is a mobile equilibrium mixture is determined by the primitive value of the q° function of the reactant (Sec. 3.14). From Eq. (34) and the relations

$$\frac{[\mathrm{B}]}{[\mathrm{A}]} = \frac{q^\circ_\mathrm{B}}{q^\circ_\mathrm{A}} \tag{35}$$

and

$$c^{(p)} = [\mathrm{A}] + [\mathrm{B}] \tag{36}$$

it follows that

$$k^{(p)} = \frac{v}{c^{(p)}} = \frac{\mathbf{k}T}{\mathbf{h}} \frac{q^\ddagger}{q^\circ_\mathrm{A} + q^\circ_\mathrm{B}} \tag{37}$$

5.14 THE QUESTION OF MECHANISM: MEANINGLESS OR NOT

Bridgman [12] pointed out some 40 years ago that when one cannot find any operational method of distinguishing between conceptual alternatives it is well to consider whether these really are alternatives. Perhaps one is trying to answer a meaningless question. A consideration of the reaction of such a substance as 1-chloropropane with a strong base to form an olefin may be illuminating.

The chloro compound is a mixture at room temperature of three substances F, G, and H

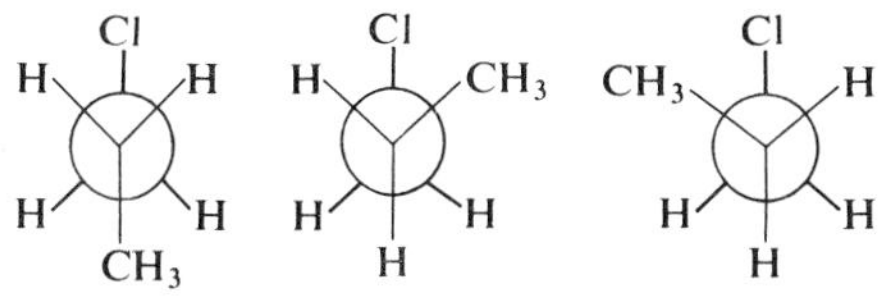

(F) (G) (H)

in mobile equilibrium and in not very different proportions. Chemists call these conformers, but there is a barrier of 3 or 4 kcal between them, and the relation of the three differs only in degree and not in kind from that between stable isomers. Indeed if the ethane carbon atoms form part of a ring, the same atomic arrangements constitute isomers which are not easily interconvertible. With the ring compounds olefin formation is found to be difficult unless the chlorine atom and a hydrogen atom are permitted by the ring structure to occupy positions similar to those of the chlorine atom and the downward-pointing hydrogen atom in structures G or H. It is therefore reasonable to suppose that the most favorable orientation of the transition state in the acyclic as well as in the cyclic case is that shown in structure I or in its mirror image.

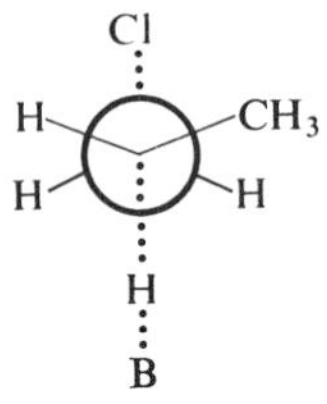

Cl
H CH$_3$
H H
H
B

(I)

This is presumably because in this orientation and in this alone incipient formation of the π bond of the olefin significantly lowers the energy of the transition state.

There is therefore strong evidence that structurally the transition state for the olefin formation resembles conformers G and H more closely than it does conformer F. On the other hand, there is no obvious reason why a molecule of conformer F should not go to the transition state by a process in which rotation about the ethane bond occurs simultaneously with the increase in energy and with the other changes necessary to attain the transition state. If then one asks the question: "Must conformer F be converted to conformer G or H before it can be converted to the transition state?" the answer would seem to be no.

But because of the structural similarity, the conversion of G to I must surely be a more frequent occurrence than the conversion of F to I. The answer to the question: "Which conformer of the reactant immediately precedes the transition state in time?" would seem to be, more frequently G or H than I.

It must be recognized, however, that many systems come very close to the transition state and then fall back. Presumably they fall back more often to the structurally similar G or H than to the dissimilar F. If then one asks: "What are the relative net rates of production of transition-state systems from the three conformers?" the best answer would seem to be that the three are equal or nearly so.

Even in conceptual terms the answer to the question of the mechanism of the reaction seems therefore to be ambiguous because the question is. In any case the question is irrelevant to any presently observable phenomena, even if not inherently meaningless.

The question about the structure of the transition state is by contrast a decidedly meaningful one, and the difference between the question about mechanism and the question about structure is not merely semantic. The argument for structure I is the kind of argument from structural parallelisms on which so much of the success of organic chemistry is based, and the conclusion about the structure bears on important problems involved in the stereochemical control of chemical processes.

5.15 THE PROGRESSION FROM TRANSITION STATE TO REACTION PRODUCT

If the conversion of chloro compound to olefin were significantly reversible, the situation on the chloro compound side of the transition state would be nearly the same as it is when the reaction is essentially irreversible. There would still be busy traffic back and forth between chloro compound and structures just short of the transition state, with only a few systems coming through from the olefin side. If, however, the process became essentially irreversible in the direction of the chloro compound, the number of systems approaching the transition state from the chloro compound side would become negligible but the probable downhill path of a system, which now must have come from the olefin side, would be unchanged. A transition-state structure like I would lead chiefly to conformer G of the chloro compound.

So long as the rate of interconversion of the F, G, and H conformers is large compared with the rate of formation of the chloro compound, the only tangible product would be an equilibrium mixture of the conformers. The product would be what is often called thermodynamically controlled. But if instead of mobile conformers the products are ring compounds, which are not readily interconvertible, the chief product from a transition state analogous to I will have a structure analogous to G.

5.16 THE CURTIN PRINCIPLE[1]

The close interrelationship between transition-state structure and product structure becomes particularly important when a nonstoichiometric mixture of reaction products which are not readily interconvertible is formed from a single reactant. 1,2-Diphenyl-1-chlorethane reacts with strong bases to form a mixture of *cis*- and *trans*-stilbene. These are not easily interconvertible, and the proportions vary continuously with changing reaction conditions. By the argument of the previous section the transition state which leads to

[1] Curtin [13]. Because Curtin is very generous in attributing credit, this is sometimes referred to as the Curtin-Hammett principle.

cis-stilbene must have a structure like J while that which leads to *trans*-stilbene must have a structure like K.

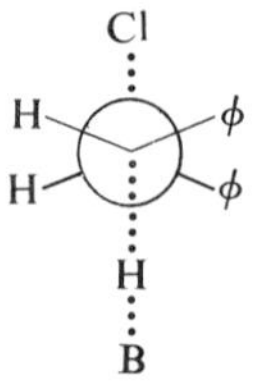

(J) 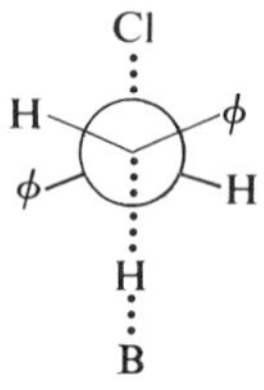 (K)

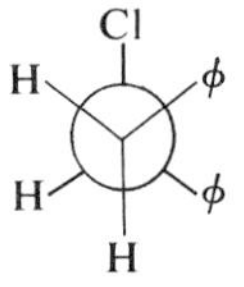

(L) 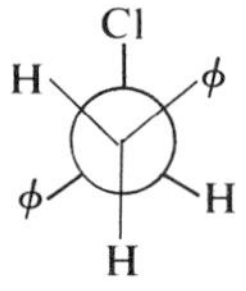 (M)

Of the three conformers of the reactant, one, L, called a gauche conformer, looks a good bit like transition state J, while another, M, called the anti conformer, looks like transition state K. It would be easy to conclude that the observed predominance of *trans*-stilbene in the reaction product measures a corresponding predominance of the anti conformer in the reactant. The Curtin principle denies this conclusion and states that the ratio of the rates of formation of *cis*- and *trans*-stilbene is determined solely by the difference in the standard potentials of transition states J and K. Consequently

$$\frac{d[\mathrm{S}_t]/dt}{d[\mathrm{S}_c]/dt} = \frac{q_t^{\ddagger}}{q_c^{\ddagger}} \tag{38}$$

where S is stilbene and subscripts c and t refer to cis and trans.

Because the three conformers of the reactant are in highly mobile equilibrium, the rate $d\mathrm{S}_t/dt$ is given (Sec. 5.13) by

$$\frac{d\mathrm{S}_t}{dt} = \frac{\mathbf{k}T}{\mathbf{h}} \frac{q_t^{\ddagger}}{\sum q^{\circ}} \tag{39}$$

where the summation is over the three conformers. Similarly

$$\frac{d\mathrm{S}_c}{dt} = \frac{\mathbf{k}T}{\mathbf{h}} \frac{q_c^{\ddagger}}{\sum q^{\circ}} \tag{40}$$

Equation (38) follows immediately.

The product distribution in cases like this is said to be kinetically controlled.

5.17 THE STILBENE-BROMINE REACTION IN METHANOL

The parallel transition states which lead to a kinetically controlled product distribution may follow instead of constituting the rate-controlling transition state. The study of cases of this kind in which the parallel states differ in composition otherwise than in solvent content has been extremely profitable in terms of information and understanding. The classical example is the investigation by Bartlett and Tarbell [14] of the reaction of stilbene with bromine in methanol solution.

The reaction produces two products, a dibromide N, and a methoxybromide O,

$$C_6H_5-\underset{\substack{|\\H}}{\overset{\substack{Br\\|}}{C}}-\underset{\substack{|\\H}}{\overset{\substack{Br\\|}}{C}}-C_6H_5 \qquad C_6H_5-\underset{\substack{|\\H}}{\overset{\substack{Br\\|}}{C}}-\underset{\substack{|\\H}}{\overset{\substack{OCH_3\\|}}{C}}-C_6H_5$$

(N) (O)

in a ratio which depends on the bromide-ion concentration of the solution. When allowance is made for the mobile reversible reaction

$$Br_2 + CH_3OH \rightleftharpoons CH_3OBr + Br^- + H^+ \tag{VII}$$

whose equilibrium constant is known independently of the reaction with stilbene, the rate of consumption of bromine is proportional to the product of the concentrations of stilbene and of bromine. There must therefore be a rate-determining transition state containing stilbene and bromine, and possibly also solvent, followed by an intermediate X whose rate of conversion to methoxybromide is given by

$$\frac{dc_O}{dt} = \frac{\mathbf{k}T}{\mathbf{h}} \frac{q_O^{\ddagger}}{q_X^{\circ}} [X] \tag{41}$$

and whose rate of conversion to dibromide by

$$\frac{dc_N}{dt} = \frac{\mathbf{k}T}{\mathbf{h}} \frac{q_N^{\ddagger}}{q_X^{\circ} q_b^{\circ}} [X][Br^-] \tag{42}$$

Consequently

$$\frac{dc_N/dt}{dc_O/dt} = \frac{q_N^{\ddagger}}{q_O^{\ddagger}\, q_b^{\circ}} [Br^-] \tag{43}$$

In these equations subscript X refers to the intermediate, N to the dibromide, O to the methoxybromide, and b to bromide ion. Equation (43) is quantitatively in agreement with the experimental results in the product distribution.

The statement that there must be an intermediate, which may be defined as a substance whose standard potential is less than the values for the transition states which precede and follow it, requires careful examination. The rate-determining transition state might rearrange and lose energy to form the dibromide without any intermediate, or it might expel the elements of hydrogen bromide and settle down as the methoxybromide, again without an intermediate. In terms of the argument of Sec. 5.16 the relative amounts of the products would be determined by the structure or structures which make up this transition state. They would not be affected by the bromide-ion concentration of the solution. The fact that variation in bromide-ion concentration alters the product distribution without altering the total rate of reaction is therefore the critical evidence for the presence of an intermediate.

A satisfactory picture assigns the composition and structure P to the intermediate.

```
          Br+
         /  \
C6H5—C—C—C6H5
        |    |
        H    H
```

(P)

Roberts and Kimball [15] pointed out that the structure *Q*

```
         Br
         |    +
C6H5—C—C—C6H5
         |    |
         H    H
```

(Q)

is unsatisfactory both because it puts a carbon atom which carries only a sextet of electrons close to the unshared pairs on the bromine atom and because it fails to account for the stereospecificity of the addition of bromine to an olefin as structure P does.

The composition of the intermediate is not, however, uniquely determined by the kinetics even aside from its solvent content. It could still contain the two bromine atoms of the rate-determining transition state instead of one. Even though the mechanisms which correspond to this composition of the intermediate are kinetically possible, they seem decidedly less attractive than the one which involves structure P.

It must be recognized that the rate of the reaction of the intermediate with bromide ion may possibly be determined by the diffusion together of intermediate and bromide. This process, like the purely chemical one, would have a rate proportional to the product of the concentrations of intermediate and of bromide ion. The kinetics yields no information on the thermodynamic properties of the intermediate except that its standard potential is lower than the standard potentials for its conversion to dibromide or to methoxybromide.

5.18 THE MECHANISM QUESTION FOR A REACTION INVOLVING IONS

Chemists have attempted to answer the mechanism question for a reaction involving ions after, as well as before, Weill and Morris [16] pointed out the impossibility of doing so, in connection with an investigation of the chloramine reaction.

Ammonium ion and hypochlorite ion are in mobile equilibrium with ammonia and hypochlorous acid. The equilibrium constant K° with

$$K^\circ = \frac{[NH_3][HOCl]}{[NH_4{}^+][OCl^-]} \tag{44}$$

is 0.017 at 25°C, so that an equimolar mixture of ammonium and hypochlorite ions would be some 13 percent converted to ammonia and hypochlorous acid. A solution containing these substances reacts relatively slowly to form chloramine, NH_2Cl, at a rate given by

$$v = k[NH_4{}^+][OCl^-] \tag{45}$$

But by virtue of Eq. (44) the rate is also given by

$$v = \frac{k}{K}[NH_3][HOCl] \tag{46}$$

The transition state has the composition NH_4OCl plus or minus a molecule or so of solvent. An economical and reasonable structure is R, but S or even T is equally consistent with the kinetics, and so also are cyclic structures containing a larger number of water molecules.

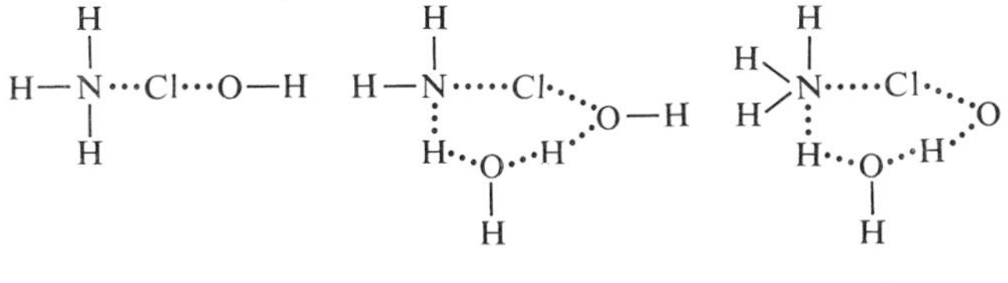

```
     H                     H                       H
     |                     |                    H\ |
H—N···Cl···O—H      H—N·····Cl··.               >N·····Cl··.
     |                     :        ·O—H        H/  :        ·O
     H                     H··O··H·                H··O··H·
                              |                       |
                              H                       H

    (R)                       (S)                     (T)
```

Whatever the structure, k, which is the specific rate of a process involving the bringing together of ions of opposite charge, must and does decrease with increasing total ion concentration (Sec. 7.2). The effect of varying ion concentration on K is closely the same as the effect on k. Consequently the quantity k/K, which is the specific rate of the formation of a neutral complex from neutral reactants, must and does show little dependence on ion concentration.

Because K is so large, the primitive value of the specific rate

$$k^{(p)} = \frac{v}{c_N c_c} \tag{47}$$

where

$$c_N = [NH_4^+] + [NH_3] \tag{48}$$

and

$$c_c = [HOCl] + [OCl^-] \tag{49}$$

is a somewhat complicated but not an unintelligible function of c_N, c_c, and, if other acids or bases are added, of the hydrogen-ion concentration of the solution.

5.19 STRUCTURAL EFFECTS IN A SYSTEM INVOLVING A MOBILE EQUILIBRIUM

When an aldehyde or ketone reacts with such nitrogen bases as hydroxylamine or semicarbazide, two products are formed.[1] One of these, the oxime, semicarbazone, or the like, is the isolable end product. The other, not usually isolable but recognizable spectroscopically, may reasonably be supposed to be the carbinolamine U.

$$\begin{matrix} R_1 \diagdown & & \diagup O-H \\ & C & \\ R_2 \diagup & & \diagdown N-R_3 \\ & & | \\ & & H \end{matrix}$$

(U)

In aqueous solution at pH values near neutrality the formation of the carbinolamine is mobile and reversible and the formation of the oxime or the like relatively slow. The equilibrium constant for carbinolamine formation is such that with concentrations of carbonyl compound and base of the order of 10^{-3} the concentration of carbinolamine is small compared with the concentrations of these reactants. Under these conditions the rate of reaction is essentially proportional to the product of the primitive concentrations of carbonyl compound and base (Sec. 4.19). That it is so proportional for oxime formation from a wide variety of carbonyl compounds was shown by Fitzpatrick and Gettler [18] in a careful investigation in which reactant concentrations were varied sixteenfold and data were obtained up to 70 or 80 percent reaction.

At pH values in the neighborhood of 4, on the other hand, the reaction is unmistakably complex, with the carbinolamine an unambiguous intermediate. With decreasing acidity the rate of conversion of the carbinolamine to

[1] The discovery by Jencks [17] that this is the case is a notable example of the kind of contribution which ingenuity and modern instrumentation can make to the understanding of familiar reactions.

oxime or the like slows down, and the situation changes continuously to one with a single rate-determining step. There is therefore a high probability that the transition state in the pH region near 7 has a structure closely related to the carbinolamine, i.e., that it is something like V.

$$\begin{array}{c} \mathrm{H} \\ | \\ \mathrm{R_1}\searrow\; \cdot\cdot\mathrm{O}\cdots\mathrm{H}\cdots\mathrm{A} \\ \mathrm{C} \\ \mathrm{R_2}\nearrow\; \searrow\mathrm{N}-\mathrm{R_3} \\ | \\ \mathrm{H} \end{array}$$

(V)

The carbinolamine is still being formed at these pH values, but its formation is now mobile and reversible and has no effect on the rate of formation of oxime or semicarbazone for which the specific rate is given by

$$k = \frac{v}{[\mathrm{A}][\mathrm{B}][\mathrm{HA}]} = \frac{\mathbf{k}T}{\mathbf{h}} \frac{q^{\ddagger}}{q_{\mathrm{A}}^{\circ} q_{\mathrm{B}}^{\circ} q_{\mathrm{HA}}^{\circ}} \tag{50}$$

where A = carbonyl compound
B = nitrogen base
HA = acid catalyst

In a study of the reaction of a series of substituted benzaldehydes with semicarbazone Anderson and Jencks [19] obtained values both of the quantity k[HA] and of the equilibrium constant K for the formation of the carbinolamine. As Table 5.1 shows, k is nearly independent of the substitution while K varies widely. This means that the substitution has nearly the same effect on the standard potential of the transition state that it has on that of benzalde-

Table 5.1 Reaction of substituted benzaldehydes with semicarbazide in 25% ethanol at approximately neutral pH and at 25°C[a]

Substituent	k[HA], *min*	K
p-CH_3O	0.44	0.34
p-CH_3	0.56	0.62
None	1.08	1.32
p-Cl	0.87	4.14
m-NO_2	0.57	18.3
p-NO_2	0.96	40.1

[a] Data of Anderson and Jencks [19].

hyde but that the effect on the standard potential of the carbinolamine is very different. In terms of the picture that the carbinolamine is an intermediate in the formation of the semicarbazone at this acidity, one can state that the near constancy of k is the resultant of opposite variations in K and in the specific rate of the conversion of carbinolamine to semicarbazone. In terms of the concept that the question of mechanism is irrelevant in this context, the statement means no more than that opposite variations in the quantities $\mu_X^\circ - \mu_A^\circ$ and $\mu^\ddagger - \mu_X^\circ$, μ_X being the standard potential of the carbinolamine, lead to no change in the quantity $\mu^\ddagger - \mu_A^\circ$.

5.20 THE PROBLEM OF STOICHIOMETRIC INVOLVEMENT OF THE SOLVENT

When an alkyl or aralkyl halide dissolved in water or an alcohol reacts with the solvent to form an alcohol or an ether, it is in principle possible for the carbon-oxygen bond of the product to be in the process of formation in the rate-determining transition state, which may be pictured as

```
      R3 R4
R1     \ /
  >O···C···X
H      |
       R2
```

(W)

where the R's are alkyl, aryl, or hydrogen and X is halide ion. In the Ingold terminology the mechanism is S_N2.

There are, however, unambiguous cases in which the process has two steps, the rate-determining process being the separation into a carbonium ion $R_2R_3R_4C^+$ and a halide ion. This is called an S_N1 mechanism. A major difference between the two mechanisms is the presence in the rate-determining transition state of the S_N2 process of a solvent molecule which is in the process of becoming attached to the reacting system by a valence bond. This may be called a stoichiometric involvement of the solvent to distinguish it from the variety of other ways in which a solvent molecule may be attached to the reactant or to the transition state.

Problems connected with the operational recognition of the stoichiometric involvement of the solvent have occupied much attention in the investigations of physical organic chemists. They are not easy to solve.

5.21 ENTROPY OF ACTIVATION

Because of the preponderant influence of the translational and rotational contributions to the standard entropy, the standard-entropy change in a reaction in the gas phase rather closely reflects the $\sum \nu$ value of the reaction. Even in the extreme case of the isomerization of 1-hexene to cyclohexane (Sec. 3.5) the decrease in standard entropy is only 6.3 cal/deg, and in most cases where $\sum \nu$ is zero the magnitude of the change is considerably less than this. For the dimerization of propene to cyclohexane ($\sum \nu = -1$) the value of $\Delta \bar{S}^\circ$ is -50 (for a standard state of 1 mole/liter), and for the trimerization of acetylene to benzene it is -74.

In agreement with this classification and in accordance with transition-state theory, the coming together of two molecules to form the transition state of a second-order reaction in the gas state is accompanied by a $\Delta \bar{S}^{\ddagger}$ value which ranges from -12 for the reaction $H_2 + I_2 \rightarrow 2HI$ to -40 for the dimerization of cyclopentadiene. There is a general tendency for the magnitude of the change to increase with increase in molecular complexity. For the third-order reaction $2NO + O_2 \rightarrow 2NO_2$, $\Delta \bar{S}^{\ddagger} = -47$ at 350°K.

In solution, however, the motions that correspond to the translation and rotation in the gas state make smaller contributions to the entropy than the translational and rotational motions do in the gas state (Sec. 3.12). Consequently the magnitude of the entropy changes that accompany reactions for which $\sum \nu$ is not zero is smaller in solution than in the gas state. Furthermore the magnitude of the standard-entropy changes in reactions for which $\sum \nu = 0$ becomes larger in the solution than in the gas. For instance from the data of Table 3.2 $\Delta \bar{S}^\circ$ is -24 for the reaction

$$CH_2(OH)_2 + ClCH_2COCH_3 \rightleftharpoons CH_2O + ClCH_2C(OH)_2CH_3 \qquad \text{(VIII)}$$

This is of course because nonstoichiometric involvement of solvent is so important in solution.

The prospect of detecting stoichiometric involvement of the solvent in the formation of a transition state in solution by way of the entropy of activation is not therefore good. The problem is discussed in a thoughtful and comprehensive review by Schaleger and Long [20].

5.22 STRUCTURAL ISOTOPE EFFECTS

One of the normal modes of vibration of a molecule containing hydrogen closely approximates a motion of the hydrogen atom toward and away from the atom to which it is attached. In organic compounds the frequency of this stretching vibration is usually quoted as in the range 2,800 to 3,300 cm^{-1} [21].

In quantum mechanics the energy levels of a harmonic oscillator are given by

$$\epsilon = (n + \tfrac{1}{2})\mathbf{h}\nu \qquad (51)$$

where ν is the frequency emitted or absorbed in the transition between adjacent levels and n is 0, 1, 2, etc. For the frequency of the hydrogen bond-stretching motion the spacing of the levels is large enough to make the population of any but the lowest level minute at temperatures of interest for the reactions of organic compounds in solution. In the lowest level there remains a half-quantum, ½ **h**ν, of vibrational energy. The actual energy of the molecule is therefore higher than the potential energy, the energy it would possess if all motions could be halted, the difference being at least the sum of the half-quanta for the normal modes of vibration of the molecule. Since to a good approximation the frequency is inversely proportional to the square root of the mass of the vibrating light atom, it should be 0.71 times as large when that atom is deuterium as when it is protium and 0.58 times as large when it is tritium. The effect of the substitution of D for H on the energy of a molecule is therefore a decrease in the range of 1200 to 1500 cal.

In reactions in which a hydrogen atom, a hydrogen ion, or a hydride ion is transferred from one linkage to another the stretching vibration of the hydrogen being transferred may be expected to disappear largely or completely in the transition state. If the disappearance is complete, the energy of the transition state will be the same when the atom transferred is D or T as when it is H, but the energy increase in the formation of the transition state from the reactant will be 1200 to 1500 cal greater with D than with H and still greater with T. If no other factors are involved, the rate will be 8 to 12 times slower when a D atom is transferred than when the atom transferred is H.

Observed values of the ratio k_H/k_D for reactions in which a proton appears to be in the process of transfer in the rate-determining transition state range from 3.3 to 24. A variety of excuses can be offered for the width of this range. To begin with there are serious problems of precision in the determination of the ratio [22].

There may be successive transition states of comparable standard potentials. Then by Eq. (28)

$$\frac{k_H}{k_D} = \frac{q_D^\circ}{q_H^\circ} \frac{1/q_{aD}^\ddagger + 1/q_{bD}^\ddagger}{1/q_{aH}^\ddagger + 1/q_{bH}^\ddagger} \tag{52}$$

when there are two such transition states a and b. If hydrogen is being transferred in state b and not in state a, then approximately $q_{bD}^\ddagger = q_{bH}^\ddagger$ and $q_{aD}^\ddagger/q_{aH}^\ddagger = q_D^\circ/q_H^\circ$ and Eq. (52) reduces, regardless of the sequence of the two transition states, to

$$\frac{k_H}{k_D} = \frac{q_b^\ddagger + q_{aD}^\ddagger}{q_b^\ddagger + q_{aH}^\ddagger} \tag{53}$$

The isotope effect runs therefore from unity when $q_b^\ddagger \gg q_a^\ddagger$:, that is when transition state a is rate-determining, to the normal value $q_{aD}^\ddagger/q_{aH}^\ddagger = q_D^\circ/q_H^\circ$ when transition state b is rate-determining.

The presence of an initial mobile equilibrium is not an effective excuse. If the equilibrium involves substances A and B,

$$\frac{k_H}{k_D} = \frac{q_H^\ddagger}{q_D^\ddagger} \frac{q_{AD}^\circ + q_{BD}^\circ}{q_{AH}^\circ + q_{BH}^\circ} \tag{54}$$

where $q_H^{\ddagger}$ and $q_D^{\ddagger}$ apply to the transition states for the relatively slow conversion to another substance. The isotope effect lies therefore in the range between $q_{AD}^{\circ}/q_{AH}^{\circ}$ and $q_{BD}^{\circ}/q_{AH}^{\circ}$. The mechanism, if there is a mechanism, of the approach to the transition state has no influence on the value of k_H/k_D.

Many of the available data involve reactants with multiple substitution of D for H. In the reaction of CH_3NO_2 with a base to form $CH_2NO_2^-$ only one proton is transferred, but the frequencies of the vibrations of the remaining protons may change as the transition state is formed from the reactants. The resulting changes in zero-point energy are superimposed on the change due to the proton being transferred. This is a secondary isotope effect.

The modes of motion of the reactant molecule include two which approximate a bending of the bond which attaches the hydrogen atom. In the transition state these motions become essentially vibrations of the hydrogen atom at right angles to the line joining the groups A and B to which it is attached in the reactant and in the product. The conventional representation is X.

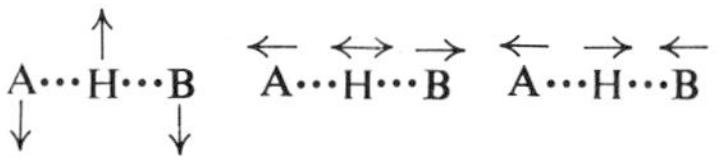

```
    ↑          ←  ↔  →      ←  →  ←
A···H···B    A···H···B    A···H···B
↓       ↓
   (X)          (Y)          (Z)
```

There is some likelihood that the frequency of this motion may be greater in the transition state than in the reactant [21, p. 191]. If it is, the net isotope effect will be smaller than that due to the stretching vibration alone.

The transition state also contains a mode of motion Y as well as the mode Z, which is the zero-frequency motion along the reaction coordinate. The analog of mode Y in the reactant is one of the translational degrees of freedom for which the zero-point energy is zero; consequently the mode increases the zero-point energy of the transition state relative to the reactants and decreases the k_H/k_D ratio. The frequency of the vibration will be small and the effect on the isotope-effect ratio small if the force constants operating between H and A and between H and B are nearly equal. But if the rupture of the A—H and the formation of the H—B bond are little advanced in the transition state, or if the rupture and formation are nearly complete, the effect might be considerable [23, 24]. There is evidence that this effect is smallest and the net isotope effect largest when groups A and B are equal in basicity [25–27].

The remarkably large k_H/k_D value of 19.5 at 25°C is reported by Bell and Goodall [28] for the reaction of 2-nitropropane with 2,6-dimethylpyridine in water solution, and Lewis and Funderburk [27] report the value of 24.1 for the same reaction in a *t*-butyl alcohol–water medium and one of 24.3 for the reaction with 2,4,6-trimethylpyridine. For less sterically hindered pyridine bases, even those with a single 2-methyl substituent, the ratio is not over 14.6, and it is only 9.8 for pyridine itself. Both Bell and Lewis ascribe the very large values to a quantum-mechanical tunnel effect.[1]

There is no doubt that secondary isotope effects exist. Thus k_H/k_D for the solvolysis of $CH_3CD_2CCl(CD_3)_2$ in an ethanol-water solvent at 25°C is 2.35 [29], and secondary effects as large as 3.3 have been observed. Their study should have value in the interpretation on a fine scale of the changes that take place in the structure of a molecule when it is converted to a transition state. There has been much discussion of the reasons for the secondary effect and much experimental investigation.[2]

With all these complications a large kinetic isotope effect, one of the order of 5 or more in k_H/k_D, seems to be reliably diagnostic for the transfer of a hydrogen in the rate-determining step of the reaction. A striking example of its use is the finding by Westheimer and Nicolaides [31] that the oxidation of $(CH_3)_2CHOH$ by chromic acid is 6 times as fast as that of $(CH_3)_2CDOH$. This indicates clearly that hydrogen attached to the carbonium carbon is being transferred in the rate-determining step.

5.23 SOLVENT ISOTOPE EFFECTS

The standard potential μ_H° of a solute in H_2O solution differs from that μ_D° of the same solute in D_2O solution by

$$\mu_H^\circ - \mu_D^\circ = -RT \ln \frac{q_H^{\circ(p)}}{q_D^{\circ(p)}} \tag{55}$$

where the $q^{\circ(p)}$ values are primitive ones. If there is significant interaction between solute and solvent, then by Eq. (3.27)

$$\frac{q_H^{\circ(p)}}{q_D^{\circ(p)}} = \frac{\sum_i q_H^{\circ(s)}/(q_{H_2O}^\circ)^{x_i}}{\sum_i q_D^{\circ(s)}/(q_{D_2O}^\circ)^{x_i}} \tag{56}$$

where $q_{H_2O}^\circ$ and $q_{D_2O}^\circ$ are the partition functions of uncombined H_2O and D_2O, respectively, and x_i is the number of solvent molecules influenced by the presence of the solute. A not inconsiderable isotope effect is therefore easily possible.

The ratio $q_H^{\circ(p)}/q_D^{\circ(p)}$ can be determined experimentally in some cases since it is the inverse of the ratio of the partial pressures of the solute from the two solvents. For CH_3F, CH_3Cl, CH_3Br, and CH_3I at 40°C the values are 0.95, 1.03, 1.065, and 1.08 respectively [32]. For $(CH_3)_2SO_4$ at 25° it is 1.25 [32]. For *t*-butyl chloride at 15° it is 1 within an experimental uncertainty of 0.05 [33]. It is rather surprising that these isotope effects are so near unity. The

[1] For a discussion of this effect see [21], pp. 205–214.

[2] For recent reviews see [30].

changes in partial molal volume, in standard entropy, and in standard heat capacity on solution of these alkyl halides from the gas phase indicate that there is strong interaction between solute and solvent [34]. As Thornton points out [35], it seems necessary to suppose that some force constants are increased while others are decreased by the solute-solvent interaction.

The cancellation is less complete in the hydrolysis of these substances. The ratio k_{H_2O}/k_{D_2O} of the specific rates in H_2O and D_2O has the values 1.36, 1.28, and 1.33 for CH_3Cl, CH_3Br, and CH_3I at 40°, of 1.13 for $(CH_3)_2SO_4$ at 25°, and of 1.35 for *t*-butyl chloride at 15°. It follows that the ratio of the $q^{\ddagger}$ values of the transition states in the two solvents has the values 1.40, 1.36, 1.44, 1.41, and 1.35 for these reactants.

In acid-base reactions of measurable rate and in acid- or base-catalyzed reactions solvent isotope effects are more striking. Bunton and Shiner [36] list k_{H_2O}/k_{D_2O} values ranging from 0.5 to nearly 6 and present an interpretation in terms of the vibration changes of all the isotopically substituted hydrogens of the reactant, the transition state, and the solvent molecules hydrogen-bonded to either. The interpretation is also discussed by Swain and Thornton [37], by Kreevoy, Steinwand, and Kayser [38], and by Kresge and Onwood [39], among others.

The hope, which at one time seemed bright, for a simple correlation of the solvent isotope effect with the mechanism of a reaction involving proton transfer or with the stoichiometric involvement of the solvent in the transition state has proved vain.

5.24 THE EFFECT OF PRESSURE ON REACTION RATE

By transition-state theory the dependence of a specific rate on pressure is given by

$$\left(\frac{\partial \ln k^{\circ}}{\partial P}\right)_T = -\frac{1}{\mathrm{R}T}(\bar{V}^{\ddagger} - \prod V^{\circ}) - (n-1)\left(\frac{\partial \ln \rho^{\circ}}{\partial P}\right)_T \tag{57}$$

where the V°'s are the limiting partial molal volumes of the reactants and $V^{\ddagger}$ is that of the transition state. ρ° is the density of the solvent, which enters because k is expressed in terms of moles per liter, and n is the order of the reaction. Since the V's often depend markedly on pressure, it is dangerous to substitute the ratio of finite differences for the derivative [40].

If there is significant interaction between solute and solvent, the V's are primitive values, because Eq. (57) depends on the primitive values of the standard potentials, i.e.,

$$\frac{\partial \ln k^{\circ}}{\partial P} = -\frac{1}{\mathrm{R}T}\frac{\partial(\mu^{\ddagger(p)}/\sum \mu^{\circ(p)})}{\partial P} \tag{58}$$

By differentiation of Eq. (2.51) and substitution from Eq. (2.152), omitting the terms involving the density

$$\bar{V}^{\circ(p)} = \bar{V}_0^{\circ(s)} + \frac{\mathbf{R}T \sum K_i^\circ(\partial \ln K_i^\circ/\partial P)}{1 + \sum_i K_i^\circ} \tag{59}$$

and since

$$-\mathbf{R}T \ln K_i = \mu_i^\circ - x_i \mu_S^\circ - \mu_0 \tag{60}$$

we have

$$\bar{V}^{\circ(p)} = \bar{V}_0^{\circ(s)} + \sum_i \frac{K_i^\circ}{1 + K_i^\circ}(\bar{V}_i - \bar{V}_0^\circ - x_i \bar{V}_S) \tag{61}$$

Since the K's are functions of pressure, $V^{\circ(p)}$ can be a complicated function of the pressure, the nature of the solute or transition state, and the number and kind of solvates or isomers involved.

There appear nevertheless to be regularities. The $\Delta \bar{V}^\circ$ value for a reaction in which ions are formed from neutral molecules in a polar solvent is invariably negative, being for instance about -15 cm^3/mole for the ionization of monobasic acids in water. The $\Delta \bar{V}^\ddagger$ values for such reactions as solvolysis, the quaternization of a tertiary amine, and nucleophilic aromatic substitution are also negative with magnitudes up to 70.[1] These are reactions in which a highly polar transition state is formed from less polar reactants, and the negative $\Delta \bar{V}^\ddagger$ may reasonably be attributed to the intense interaction of an ion or of a molecule which contains a strong dipole with the polar molecule of the solvent.

For such reactions as $CH_3Br + OH^- \rightarrow CH_3OH + Br^-$, in which transition state and reactant have the same charge, the $\Delta \bar{V}^\ddagger$ values in the neighborhood of -8 may measure the solute volume change [40]. And the positive values of 9 to 10 in the hydrolysis of substituted benzenediazonium ions may represent a dispersal of the charge from the nitrogen to the ring carbons as the reaction approaches the transition state and a consequent decrease in the interaction with the solvent.

Whalley [40] finds that acid-catalyzed reactions in water are divisible into two groups, one with $\Delta \bar{V}^\ddagger$ values running from -2 to $+6$ cm^3/mole, the other with values mostly between -6 and -10 but with a few considerably more negative. He suggests, in somewhat different terms, that there is stoichiometric involvement of the solvent in the second group and not in the first.

All in all the study of these pressure effects has considerable promise for the understanding of the composition and structure of transition states.

[1] See the survey by le Noble [41].

5.25 SYSTEMS WITH MOBILE EQUILIBRIA PRESENT BOTH IN REACTANT AND IN PRODUCT

There is an impressive body of evidence[1] that cyclohexanol consists of a mixture in mobile equilibrium of two conformational isomers, an axial (A) of structure AA, and an equatorial (E) of structure BB.

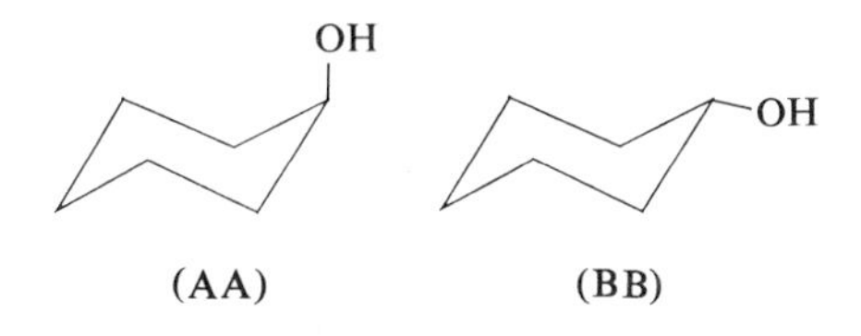

(AA) (BB)

The standard potential of the barrier between them is estimated to be of the order of 10 kcal above that of the conformers. The specific rate of the interconversion of the conformers should therefore be of the order of 10^5 sec^{-1}, i.e., very large compared with the specific rates of such reactions as the esterification of the alcohol with acetic anhydride in pyridine, which are of the order of 10^{-4} liter/mole-sec. A barrier of about the same height as in the alcohols exists between the conformers of the acetates, and, since the acetylation does not involve the ring atoms, there is reason to suppose that the quantized systems which constitute the transition state in the acetylation can be classified into two groups T_A and T_E which have respectively the axial and the equatorial conformation. The specific rate of formation of the acetate is proportional to the sum $c_A^\ddagger + c_E^\ddagger$ of the concentrations of the systems in the two transition states. Since T_A is in effective equilibrium with A and A is in equilibrium with E,

$$\frac{c_A^\ddagger}{[A]} = \frac{q_A^\ddagger}{q_A^\circ} \tag{62}$$

and

$$\frac{[A]}{c_A} = \frac{q_A^\circ}{q_A^\circ + q_E^\circ} \tag{63}$$

where $c_A = [A] + [E]$. Consequently

$$\frac{c_A^\ddagger}{c_A} = \frac{q_A^\ddagger}{q_A^\circ + q_E^\circ} \tag{64}$$

Similarly

$$\frac{c_E^\ddagger}{c_A} = \frac{q_E^\ddagger}{q_A^\circ + q_E^\circ} \tag{65}$$

[1] See for instance [42].

It follows that

$$k^{(p)} = \frac{\mathbf{k}T}{\mathbf{h}} \frac{q_A^{\ddagger} + q_E^{\ddagger}}{q_A^{\circ} + q_E^{\circ}} \tag{66}$$

This is identical with, although it does not look like, the relationship which derives from the principle of the independent coexistence of reactions (Sec. 4.26). For if

$$v = k_A[A] + k_E[E] \tag{67}$$

then

$$k^{(p)} = \frac{v}{c_A} = \frac{k_A}{1+K} + \frac{k_E K}{1+K} \tag{68}$$

where K is the equilibrium constant for the conversion of axial to equatorial. From this

$$\frac{\mathbf{h}}{\mathbf{k}T} k^{(p)} = \frac{q_A^{\ddagger}}{q_A^{\circ}} \frac{1}{1 + q_E^{\circ}/q_A^{\circ}} + \frac{q_E^{\ddagger}}{q_E^{\circ}} \frac{q_E^{\circ}/q_A^{\circ}}{1 + q_E^{\circ}/q_A^{\circ}} \tag{69}$$

which is identical to Eq. (66).

Equation (66) may be written in the form

$$k^{(p)} = \frac{\mathbf{k}T}{\mathbf{h}} \frac{q_A^{\ddagger}/q_A^{\circ} + K(q_E^{\ddagger}/q_E^{\circ})}{1+K} \tag{70}$$

in which it was derived by Winstein and Holness [43] and by Eliel and Lukach [44].

4-*t*-Butylcyclohexanol exists in either of two configurational isomers, cis and trans, which are not readily interconvertible. Because of the bulk of the *t*-butyl group it is probable that it can be present only in the equatorial conformation; consequently the hydroxyl group will be equatorial in the trans *t*-butyl derivative (CC) and axial in the cis isomer (DD).

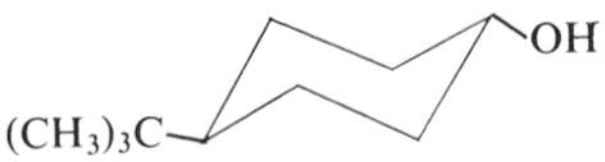

$(CH_3)_3C$— —OH

(CC)

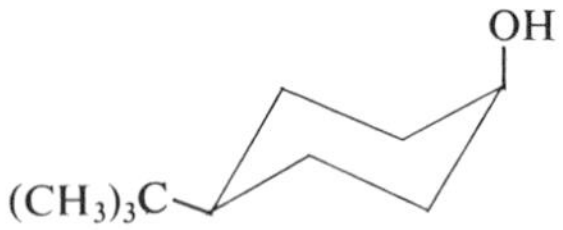

OH

$(CH_3)_3C$—

(DD)

Since the *t*-butyl group and the hydroxyl group are well separated, it is not unreasonable to suppose that the effect of the *t*-butyl group on the standard potential of the axial conformer of the transition state in the acetylation will be nearly the same as its effect on that of the axial conformer of cyclohexanol. If so, the ratio $q_A^{\ddagger}/q_A^{\circ}$ will be closely the same for the cis *t*-butyl derivative as it is for unsubstituted cyclohexanol. By the same token one may expect the ratio $q_E^{\ddagger}/q_E^{\circ}$ to be the same in the trans *t*-butyl derivative as it is in the unsubstituted cyclohexanol. On this basis the kinetic method of conformational analysis [43] proposes that k_c, the specific rate of the acetylation of *cis-t*-butylcyclohexanol, be substituted for the quantity

$$\frac{\mathbf{k}T}{\mathbf{h}} \frac{q_{\mathrm{A}}^{\ddagger}}{q_{\mathrm{A}}^{\circ}}$$

in Eq. (70) and that k_t, the specific rate of the acetylation of *trans-t*-butylcyclohexanol, be substituted for the quantity

$$\frac{\mathbf{k}T}{\mathbf{h}} \frac{q_{\mathrm{E}}^{\ddagger}}{q_{\mathrm{E}}^{\circ}}$$

This leads to the relation

$$k^{(p)} = \frac{k_c + Kk_t}{1 + K} \tag{71}$$

Under conditions for which the observed value of $k^{(p)}$ for the acetylation of cyclohexanol is 8.60×10^{-5}, k_c and k_t for the acetylation of the two *t*-butylcyclohexanols are 2.92×10^{-5} and 10.8×10^{-5}, respectively. From these values K is 2.58, which is not too far from the values ranging from 2.8 to 3.3 obtained by other methods of conformational analysis [45]. A comparable agreement is obtained in many but not in all cases in which the kinetic method of estimating K values for cyclohexane derivatives has been compared with other methods of estimating the quantity [46].

If, however, bonds to a ring carbon atom are being broken in a reaction, it is conceivable that the distinction between axial and equatorial conformations should disappear in the transition state. In that case Eq. (70) is replaced by

$$k^{(p)} = \frac{kT}{\mathbf{h}} \frac{q^{\ddagger}}{q_{\mathrm{A}}^{\circ} + q_{\mathrm{E}}^{\circ}} \tag{72}$$

and Eq. (71) by

$$\frac{1}{k^{(p)}} = \frac{1}{k_c} + \frac{1}{k_t} \tag{73}$$

In this situation $k^{(p)}$ will be equal to or less than the smaller of the two quantities k_c and k_t, whereas when Eq. (71) applies, it will always lie between them. There does not appear to be any clear-cut case in which the experimental value of $k^{(p)}$ does lie outside the range limited by k_c and k_t [47].

It has been supposed that when Eq. (71) applies, the primitive value $\Delta\bar{H}^{\ddagger(p)}$ of the enthalpy of activation must lie between $\Delta\bar{H}_c^{\ddagger}$ and $\Delta\bar{H}_t^{\ddagger}$ [48].

But differentiation of Eq. (71) and application of the relationship

$$\frac{dK}{dT} = \frac{K\Delta\bar{H}^\circ}{RT^2}$$

leads to

$$\Delta\bar{H}^{\ddagger(p)} = \frac{k_c\Delta\bar{H}_c^\ddagger + Kk_t\Delta\bar{H}_t^\ddagger}{k_c + Kk_t} + \frac{K(k_t - k_c)}{(1+K)(k_c + Kk_t)}\Delta\bar{H}^\circ \tag{74}$$

where $\Delta\bar{H}^\circ$ is the standard-enthalpy change for the conversion of axial reactant to equatorial. The first term on the right of this equation is a weighted mean of the values of $\Delta\bar{H}_c^\ddagger$ and $\Delta\bar{H}_t^\ddagger$, but because of the second term the value of $\Delta\bar{H}^{\ddagger(p)}$ may be outside the range of mean values.

5.26 CATALYSIS

When the rate of conversion of a substance A to a product P is accelerated by the presence of a substance C without any change in the stoichiometry of the A-P conversion, C is called a catalyst for the conversion. A is often called the substrate. There are many cases in which clear kinetic evidence exists that the catalyzed reaction is a multistep process in which A and C react to form an intermediate and the catalyst is released in the subsequent conversion of the intermediate to P. As early as 1902 Federlin [49] showed that the kinetics of the reaction of $K_2S_2O_8$ with H_3PO_3 catalyzed by HI can be completely accounted for as the resultant of two independent reactions of comparable rate, one the reduction of persulfate by iodide, the other the oxidation of phosphite by iodine.

Crowell and Peck [50] found complex kinetics in the catalysis by butylamine of the condensation of piperonal with nitromethane. These are of a kind which clearly demonstrates that the Schiff base EE is an intermediate in the reaction.

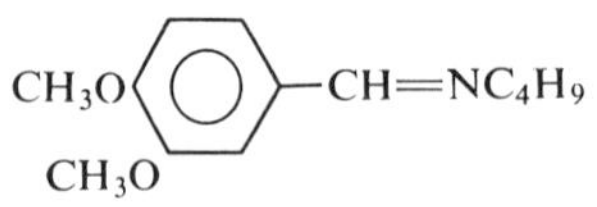

CH_3O $CH{=}NC_4H_9$
CH_3O

(EE)

In the catalysis by imidazole of the hydrolysis of *p*-nitrophenyl acetate the intermediacy of acetylimidazole FF

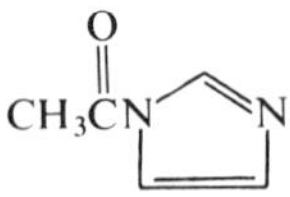

O
CH_3CN N

(FF)

has been demonstrated by quantitative studies of the kinetics of the formation and decomposition of this substance [51]. The reaction of acetyl phenyl phosphate or of acetyl ethyl phosphate with thiols, whose rate is negligible in the absence of a catalyst, is catalyzed by imidazole in a reaction whose rate is independent of the concentration of the thiol [52]. There must therefore be an intermediate, presumably acetylimidazole, which is formed by the reaction of the phosphate derivative with imidazole and which reacts rapidly with the thiol. Many other examples of catalytic effects of this sort, which is often called nucleophilic catalysis, are listed in the reviews by Bender [53] and by Jencks [54].

The kinetics of systems of this sort present no problems other than those involved in the study of any kinetically complex reaction. The existence of the catalysis, on the other hand, presents fascinating and important problems with respect to the relation of structure and reactivity. Why should the reaction of *p*-nitrophenyl acetate with imidazole be faster than its hydrolysis when the product of the reaction with imidazole is less stable with respect to hydrolysis than *p*-nitrophenyl acetate is? Given the existence of the catalysis of the hydrolysis of the nitrophenyl acetate, why does imidazole not catalyze the hydrolysis of ethyl acetate?

The standard potentials involved are illustrated schematically in Fig. 5.5. In terms of the Polanyi theorem (Sec. 5.3), to which chemists are now thoroughly conditioned, this is all wrong. Since the energy of I is higher than

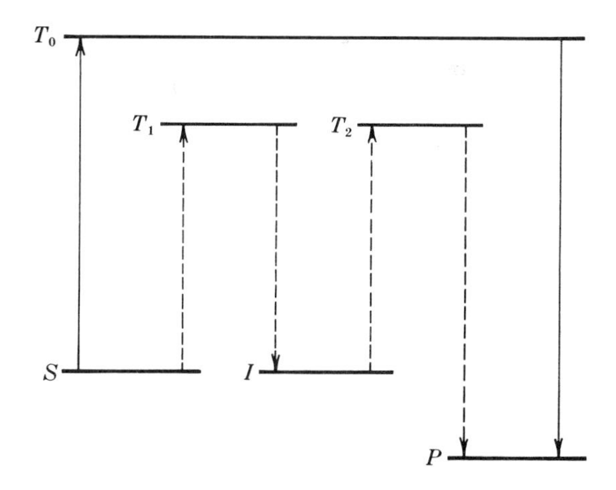

Fig. 5.5 Standard potentials for catalyzed and uncatalyzed reactions. S = substrate, P = product, I = intermediate, T_0 = transition state of uncatalyzed reaction, T_1 = transition state for conversion of S to I, T_2 = transition state for conversion of I to P; solid arrows represent the course of the uncatalyzed reaction and dashed arrows that of the catalyzed reaction.

that of P, the energy of T_1 should be higher not lower than that of T_0, and since the energy decrease from I to P is greater than that from S to I, the energy of T_2 should be lower than that of T_1 instead of being about equal to it. The catalysis involves therefore a double failure of the widely applicable Polanyi rule.

If a reactant A and a substance C are in mobile equilibrium with a compound AC which has the same composition as the rate-determining transition state for the conversion of A to P, the rate of the catalyzed formation of P can be expressed either as

$$v = \frac{\mathbf{k}T}{\mathbf{h}} \frac{q^{\ddagger}_{AC}}{q^{\circ}_{AC}} [AC] \tag{75}$$

or as

$$v = \frac{\mathbf{k}T}{\mathbf{h}} \frac{q^{\ddagger}_{AC}}{q^{\circ}_{A} q^{\circ}_{C}} [A][C] \tag{76}$$

where $q^{\ddagger}_{AC}$ refers to the transition state of the catalyzed reaction. The question whether the transition state is attained by means of the initial formation of AC or directly from A and C without the intervention of the compound is irrelevant and perhaps meaningless (Sec. 5.14). It must therefore be recognized that the catalysis is possible without the formation of a compound of A with C, unless one chooses to call the transition state such a compound. Indeed a compound AC which is not a transition state may have a structure which represents a retrogression from, rather than a progression toward, the transition state.

When, as often happens, there is a significant uncatalyzed reaction as well as the catalyzed one, there must be significantly occupied states along the barrier between A and P which do not contain the elements of C as well as those that do. The rate of formation of P is therefore

$$v = \frac{\mathbf{k}T}{\mathbf{h}} \left(\frac{q^{\ddagger}_{A}}{q_{A}} [A] + \frac{q^{\ddagger}_{AC}}{q^{\circ}_{A} q^{\circ}_{C}} [A][C] \right) \tag{77}$$

where $q^{\ddagger}_{AC}$ is the sum of Boltzmann terms for the states which do contain C and $q^{\ddagger}_{A}$ is the corresponding sum over those that do not. This can also be written

$$v = \frac{\mathbf{k}T}{\mathbf{h}} \frac{q^{\ddagger}_{A}}{q^{\circ}_{A}} [A] \left(1 + \frac{q^{\ddagger}_{AC}}{q^{\ddagger}_{A} q^{\circ}_{C}} [C] \right) \tag{78}$$

The quantity $q^{\ddagger}_{AC}/q^{\ddagger}_{A}\, q^{\circ}_{C}$ may reasonably be called the equilibrium constant $K^{\ddagger}_{AC}$ for the conversion of a transition state which does not contain C to one which does.[1]

[1] The argument which follows is essentially that of Kurz [55].

If there is insignificant formation of compound AC, the primitive concentration c_A equals [A] and

$$k^{(p)} = \frac{\mathbf{k}T}{\mathbf{h}} \frac{q_A^{\ddagger}}{q_A^{\circ}} (1 + K_{AC}^{\ddagger}[C]) \tag{79}$$

If one defines the acceleration produced by the catalyst as

$$\alpha = \frac{k^{(p)} - k_u}{k_u} \tag{80}$$

where k_u is the specific rate of the uncatalyzed reaction, then

$$\alpha = K_{AC}^{\ddagger}[C] \tag{81}$$

A clear-cut example of this kind of catalysis is found in the effect of salts on the rate of many solvolytic reactions in poorly ionizing solvents such as acetic acid, acetone, tetrahydrofuran, and the like [56]. For a wide range of solvolyzing substances and solvents and for a variety of salts the effect of the addition of a salt S conforms closely to the equation

$$k = k^{\circ}(1 + b[S]) \tag{82}$$

although there is a measurable term in $[S]^2$ in some cases, especially when the effect is very large, and lithium perchlorate sometimes has a very different effect (Sec. 6.15). Values of b as large as 20,000 have been observed (for the effect of lithium perchlorate on the solvolysis of spirodienyl *p*-nitrobenzoate in acetone), but 10 to 40 is typical of the effect in acetic acid.

In terms of Eq. (79) the value of b is the equilibrium constant for the conversion of the salt-free transition state to one containing one molecule of salt. The fact that the plot of k against [S] is linear or has a positive curvature demonstrates that the extent to which the reactant combines with the salt is too small to affect the kinetics. A reasonable interpretation of this salt effect involves the formation of something of the nature of a multipolar complex (Sec. 8.30) between the transition state and the salt, which is present predominantly as an ion pair.

When there is any considerable formation of the compound AC, the quantities [A] and [C] in Eq. (78) are determined by the relations

$$\frac{[AC]}{[A][C]} = K_{AC}^{\circ} = \frac{q_{AC}^{\circ}}{q_A^{\circ} q_C^{\circ}} \tag{83}$$

$$c_A = [A] + [AC] \tag{84}$$

and

$$c_C = [C] + [AC] \tag{85}$$

where c_A and c_C are primitive concentrations. An explicit solution is possible but complicated. Two limiting cases are of interest and lead to simpler forms.

If c_C is large compared with c_A or is well buffered, then to a good approximation $[C] = c_C$ and

$$[A] = \frac{c_A}{1 + K_{AC}^{\circ} c_C} \tag{86}$$

From this, by Eq. (78),

$$k^{(p)} = k^{\circ} \frac{1 + K_{AC}^{\ddagger} c_C}{1 + K_{AC}^{\circ} c_C} \tag{87}$$

Since from this

$$\frac{dk^{(p)}}{dc_C} = \frac{K_{AC}^{\ddagger} - K_{AC}^{\circ}}{(1 + K_{AC}^{\circ} c_C)^2} \tag{88}$$

there will be positive acceleration only if $K_{AC}^{\ddagger} > K_{AC}^{\circ}$, that is, only if the complex formed by the transition state is more stable than that formed by the reactant. In any case a plot of $k^{(p)}$ against c_C will show considerable curvature with a sign opposite to that of the slope. The condition required for the application of Eq. (87) can be easily and usefully attained in most if not in all cases of catalysis by acids or by bases.

If c_C is small compared with c_A and is not buffered, then, because to a good approximation $[A] = c_A$,

$$[C] = \frac{c_C}{1 + K_{AC}^{\circ} c_A} \tag{89}$$

and

$$k^{(p)} = k^{\circ} \left(1 + \frac{K_{AC}^{\ddagger} c_C}{1 + K_{AC}^{\circ} c_A}\right) \tag{90}$$

There will be positive acceleration whenever $K_{AC}^{\ddagger} > 0$, that is, whenever the transition state forms a complex of significant stability with C. $k^{(p)}$ will be linear in c_C with a slope which decreases with increasing c_A to a limiting value of k°. If the uncatalyzed rate is negligible compared with the catalyzed rate, Eq. (90) reduces to

$$k^{(p)} = \frac{k_{AC} K_{AC}^{\circ} c_C}{1 + K_{AC}^{\circ} c_A} \tag{91}$$

by virtue of the relationships

$$\frac{k^{\circ} K_{AC}^{\ddagger}}{K_{AC}^{\circ}} = \frac{\mathbf{k}T}{\mathbf{h}} \frac{q_A^{\ddagger}(q_{AC}^{\ddagger}/q_A^{\ddagger} q_C^{\circ})}{q_A^{\circ}(q_{AC}^{\circ}/q_A^{\circ} q_C^{\circ})} = \frac{\mathbf{k}T}{\mathbf{h}} \frac{q_{AC}^{\ddagger}}{q_{AC}^{\circ}} = k_{AC} \tag{92}$$

where k_{AC} is the specific rate of the conversion of AC to the reaction product. With increasing c_A at constant c_C the rate $v = k^{(p)} c_A$ approaches the constant value $k_{AC} c_C$.

5.27 THE PROGRESSION FROM TRANSITION STATE TO PRODUCT IN A CATALYZED REACTION

It is possible that an intermediate which still contains C intervenes between the rate-determining transition state of a catalyzed reaction and the ultimate product. It is, however, no more necessary in principle that such an intervention occur than it is that a compound of catalyst C with reactant A be an intermediate in the formation of the transition state.

The hypothesis that the progression from transition state to product goes chiefly by the process which least disturbs the geometry of the transition state suggests (Sec. 5.15), that the first product is often one in which P and C are in contact, although not combined, and are confined in a cage of solvent molecules [57]. Diffusion apart of C and P then requires passage over a further energy barrier. This diffusion barrier alone may in principle be high enough to permit the formation of more than one reaction product from a single rate-determining transition state. There is evidence (Sec. 6.9) that this sometimes happens. The proportion in which any such product is formed would then depend inversely on the standard potential of the barrier which opposes its formation relative to that of the diffusion barrier.

5.28 NOTES ON ENZYME AND ON HETEROGENEOUS CATALYSIS

Equation (91) is identical with the form which the Michaelis-Menten equation (Sec. 4.17) takes when enzyme and substrate are in mobile equilibrium with the enzyme-substrate compound. The general form of that equation is equivalent to

$$\frac{\mathbf{k}T}{\mathbf{h}}\frac{c_{\mathrm{E}}\,c_{\mathrm{S}}}{v} = q^{\circ}_{\mathrm{E}} q^{\circ}_{\mathrm{S}}\left(\frac{1}{q_1^{\ddagger}} + \frac{1}{q_2^{\ddagger}}\right) + \frac{q^{\circ}_{\mathrm{ES}}}{q_2^{\ddagger}}\,c_{\mathrm{S}} \tag{93}$$

The rate at low substrate concentrations is therefore independent of the standard potential of the enzyme-substrate compound; the rate at high substrate concentrations is independent of the standard potentials of the enzyme and of the substrate.

The relationships developed from homogeneous catalysis are applicable to heterogeneous catalysis with one modification. The quantity [C] in those relationships is to be replaced by the quantity σm_{C} in which m_{C} is the mass of the catalyst and σ is $1/N_0$ times the number of catalytically active sites per unit mass of catalyst. This is true both when the sites are distributed throughout the volume of the catalyst, as they are in ion-exchange resin catalysts [58], and also when they are restricted to the surface of the catalyst particles. In the latter case σ is the product of the density of sites per unit area of the particles by the ratio of surface to mass of the catalyst. Since the energy of an unoccupied site may vary widely from site to site within a single catalyst, and since the same is true of sites occupied by reactant molecules, whether they are in the transition-state condition or not, the summations which determine the values of the q functions must be taken over all the pertinent varieties of sites.

5.29 MICROSCOPIC REVERSIBILITY, OR DETAILED BALANCING

The principle of microscopic reversibility, or detailed balancing, is easily derived from transition-state theory and is not easily derived in any other way. The principle states that in a system of reactions such as

$$\begin{array}{ccc} \mathrm{A} & \underset{k_{-3}}{\overset{k_3}{\rightleftharpoons}} & \mathrm{P} \\ {\scriptstyle k_{-1}}\nwarrow\searrow{\scriptstyle k_1} & & {\scriptstyle k_2}\nearrow\swarrow{\scriptstyle k_{-2}} \\ & \mathrm{X} & \end{array} \qquad \text{(IX)}$$

in which the k's are independent of the concentrations of A, X, and P but may be functions of other concentrations, only five independent parameters are involved because the six k's are subject to the relationship

$$\frac{k_3}{k_{-3}} = \frac{k_1 k_2}{k_{-1} k_{-2}} \qquad (94)$$

The equilibrium constant K_i can be substituted for any or all of the k_i/k_{-i} ratios.

Equation (94) can be shown to be required by transition-state theory merely by substituting $q_i^{\ddagger}/q_i^{\circ}$ for each k_i. This leads to

$$\frac{q_3^{\ddagger}/q_{\mathrm{A}}^{\circ}}{q_3^{\ddagger}/q_{\mathrm{P}}^{\circ}} = \frac{(q_1^{\ddagger}/q_{\mathrm{A}}^{\circ})(q_2^{\ddagger}/q_{\mathrm{X}}^{\circ})}{(q_1^{\ddagger}/q_{\mathrm{X}}^{\circ})(q_2^{\ddagger}/q_{\mathrm{P}}^{\circ})} \qquad (95)$$

This is an identity, each side of the equation reducing to $q_{\mathrm{P}}^{\circ}/q_{\mathrm{A}}^{\circ}$, a quantity which is the thermodynamic equilibrium constant for the conversion of A to P.

If the principle of microscopic reversibility is accepted, the possibility of what Skrabel [59] calls a *Zirkulargleichgewicht* is eliminated. In its extreme case a *Zirkulargleichgewicht* would set $k_{-3} = k_1 = k_2 = 0$ and would have A going to P only by the direct reaction and P returning to A only by the indirect reaction through X. Indeed there would be some circulation in this sense if Eq. (94) were not exactly satisfied, clockwise if the left side of that equation is greater than the right side, counterclockwise if the left side is less than the right.

The principle can be extended to cycles containing a greater number of substances. Its use can avoid perilous traps in the consideration of reactions which can go both by a catalyzed and by an uncatalyzed path.

Bruice and Bruno [60], for instance, proposed the following mechanism for the catalysis by imidazole (ImH) of the hydrolysis of δ-thiovalerolactone (L):

$$\begin{aligned}
&\mathrm{ImH} + \mathrm{L} \underset{k_{-1}}{\overset{k_1}{\rightleftharpoons}} \mathrm{IH} \\
&\mathrm{ImH} \overset{K_2}{\rightleftharpoons} \mathrm{Im}^- + \mathrm{H}^+ \\
&\mathrm{Im}^- + \mathrm{L} \underset{k_{-3}}{\overset{k_3}{\rightleftharpoons}} \mathrm{I}^- \\
&\mathrm{I}^- + \mathrm{H}^+ \overset{K_4}{\rightleftharpoons} \mathrm{IH} \\
&\mathrm{IH} \xrightarrow{k_5} \mathrm{P}
\end{aligned} \tag{X}$$

P represents thiovaleric acid plus imidazole, and I^- and IH are intermediates to which the Bodenstein steady-state approximation may be applied. To fit the observed dependence of rate on acidity it was necessary to suppose that $K_2 k_3$ is considerably less than k_1 but that k_{-3}/K_4 is comparable to k_{-1}. As Westheimer and Bender [61] point out, this assumption is inconsistent with microscopic reversibility. It amounts indeed to the acceptance of a circulation in which IH is formed without the intermediacy of Im^- but returns to ImH + L at comparable rates by both paths.

Reaction system (X) involves two paths by which I^- can be formed from ImH + L, and the application of the microscopic reversibility principle to these paths leads to

$$K_2 \frac{k_3}{k_{-3}} = \frac{1}{K_4} \frac{k_1}{k_{-1}} \tag{96}$$

This is equivalent to

$$\frac{K_2 k_3}{k_1} = \frac{k_{-3}/K_4}{k_{-1}} \tag{97}$$

which is inconsistent with the Bruice and Bruno assumption.

The principle of microscopic reversibility has a large and frequently confusing literature,[1] which seems to have started with a proposal by Tolman [62].

Davidson [63] merely states and illustrates the theorem "relying on the preceding discussion of time reversal in classical mechanics to make it plausible." Onsager in his classical paper [64] on irreversible thermodynamics considers the rate equations of a system like (IX), namely,

$$\frac{d[\mathrm{P}]}{dt} = k_3[\mathrm{A}] + k_2[\mathrm{X}] - (k_{-2} + k_{-3})[\mathrm{P}] \tag{98}$$

$$\frac{d[\mathrm{A}]}{dt} = -(k_1 + k_3)[\mathrm{A}] + k_{-3}[\mathrm{P}] + k_{-1}[\mathrm{X}] \tag{99}$$

When the whole system is at equilibrium, both $d[\mathrm{P}]/dt$ and $d[\mathrm{A}]/dt$ are zero

[1] This is reviewed by Skrabel [59].

and by eliminating $[X]_e$, the concentration of X in the equilibrium system, one gets

$$\frac{[P]_e}{[A]_e} = \frac{k_1 k_2 + k_{-1} k_3 + k_2 k_3}{k_{-1} k_{-2} + k_{-1} k_{-3} + k_2 k_{-3}} \tag{100}$$

"Here however," says Onsager, "chemists are accustomed to impose a very interesting additional restriction, namely, when the equilibrium is reached each individual reaction must balance itself. They require that the transition $A_e \rightarrow P_e$ must take place just as frequently as the reverse transition $P_e \rightarrow A_e$, etc." The restriction is equivalent to the equation

$$k_{-3}[P]_e = k_3[A]_e \tag{101}$$

by which Eq. (100) becomes

$$1 = \frac{k_{-1} + k_2 + k_1 k_2/k_3}{k_{-1} + k_2 + k_{-1} k_{-2}/k_{-3}} \tag{102}$$

or

$$\frac{k_{-1} k_{-2}}{k_{-3}} = \frac{k_1 k_2}{k_3} \tag{103}$$

which is equivalent to Eq. (94).

REFERENCES

1. LaMer, V. K., and M. L. Miller: *J. Am. Chem. Soc.*, **57:**2674 (1935).
2. Hulett, J. R.: *Quart. Rev. (London)*, **18:**227 (1964).
3. Leffek, K. T., R. E. Robertson, and S. Sugamori: *J. Am. Chem. Soc.*, **87:**2097 (1965).
4. Brønsted, J. N.: *Z. Physik. Chem.*, **102:**169 (1922).
5. Evans, M. G., and M. Polanyi: *Trans. Faraday Soc.*, **34:**11 (1938).
6. Werner, A.: *Ber.*, **44:**873 (1911).
7. Lewis, G. N.: "Valence and the Structure of Atoms and Molecules," Chemical Catalog Co., New York, 1923.
8. London, F.: *Z. Elektrochem.*, **35:**552 (1929).
9. Eyring, H.: *J. Chem. Phys.*, **3:**107 (1935).
10. Wheeler, A., B. Topley, and H. Eyring: *J. Chem. Phys.*, **4:**178 (1936).
11. Leffler, J. E., and R. D. Temple: *J. Am. Chem. Soc.*, **89:**5235 (1967).
12. Bridgman, P. W.: "The Logic of Modern Physics," The Macmillan Company, New York, 1927.
13. Curtin, D. Y.: *Rec. Chem. Progr., Kresge-Hooker Sci. Library*, **15:**111 (1954).
14. Bartlett, P. D., and S. D. Tarbell: *J. Am. Chem. Soc.*, **58:**466 (1936). See also R. P. Bell and M. Pring: *J. Chem. Soc.*, **1966B:**1119.
15. Roberts, I., and G. E. Kimball: *J. Am. Chem. Soc.*, **59:**947 (1937).
16. Weill, I., and J. C. Morris: *J. Am. Chem. Soc.*, **71:**1664 (1949).
17. Jencks, W. P.: *J. Am. Chem. Soc.*, **81:**475 (1959).
18. Fitzpatrick, F. W., and J. D. Gettler: *J. Am. Chem. Soc.*, **78:**530 (1956).
19. Anderson, B. M., and W. P. Jencks: *J. Am. Chem. Soc.*, **82:**1773 (1960).
20. Schaleger, L. L., and F. A. Long: *Advan. Phys. Org. Chem.*, **1:**1 (1963).
21. Bell, R. P.: "The Proton in Chemistry," Cornell University Press, Ithaca, N.Y., 1959.

22. Collins, C. J.: *Advan. Phys. Org. Chem.*, **2:**60 (1964).
23. Westheimer, F. H.: *Chem. Rev.*, **61:**265 (1961).
24. Melander, L.: "Isotope Effects on Reaction Rates," The Ronald Press Company, New York, 1962; R. P. Bell: *Discussions Faraday Soc.*, **39:**16 (1965).
25. Gruen, L. C., and F. A. Long: *J. Am. Chem. Soc.*, **89:**1287 (1967).
26. Longridge, J. L., and F. A. Long: *J. Am. Chem. Soc.*, **89:**1292 (1967).
27. Lewis, E. S., and L. H. Funderburk: *J. Am. Chem. Soc.*, **89:**2322 (1967).
28. Bell, R. P., and D. M. Goodall: *Proc. Roy. Soc.* (*London*), **A294:**273 (1966).
29. Shiner, V. J.: *J. Am. Chem. Soc.*, **75:**2925 (1953).
30. Halevi, E. A.: *Progr. Phys. Org. Chem.*, **1:**109 (1963); E. R. Thornton: *Ann. Rev. Phys. Chem.*, **17:**349 (1966).
31. Westheimer, F. H., and N. Nicolaides: *J. Am. Chem. Soc.*, **71:**25 (1949).
32. Swain, C. G., and E. R. Thornton: *J. Am. Chem. Soc.*, **84:**822 (1962).
33. Clarke, G. A., T. R. Williams, and R. W. Taft: *J. Am. Chem. Soc.*, **84:**2292 (1962).
34. Laughton, P. M., and R. E. Robertson: *Can. J. Chem.*, **43:**154 (1965).
35. Thornton, E. R.: *Ann. Rev. Phys. Chem.*, **17:**367 (1966).
36. Bunton, C. A., and V. J. Shiner: *J. Am. Chem. Soc.*, **83:**3207, 3214 (1961).
37. Swain, C. G., and E. R. Thornton: *J. Am. Chem. Soc.*, **83:**3884 (1961).
38. Kreevoy, M. M., P. J. Steinwand, and W. V. Kayser: *J. Am. Chem. Soc.*, **86:**5013 (1964).
39. Kresge, A. J., and D. P. Onwood: *J. Am. Chem. Soc.*, **86:**5014 (1964).
40. Whalley, E.: *Advan. Phys. Org. Chem.*, **2:**93 (1964).
41. le Noble, W. J.: *Progr. Phys. Org. Chem.*, **5:**207 (1967).
42. Eliel, E. L.: "Stereochemistry of Carbon Compounds," chap. 8, McGraw-Hill Book Company, New York, 1962.
43. Winstein, S., and N. J. Holness: *J. Am. Chem. Soc.*, **77:**5562 (1955).
44. Eliel, E. L., and C. A. Lukach: *J. Am. Chem. Soc.*, **79:**5986 (1957).
45. Eliel, E. L., and S. Schroeter: *J. Am. Chem. Soc.*, **87:**5031 (1965).
46. Eliel, E. L., and F. J. Biros: *J. Am. Chem. Soc.*, **88:**3334 (1966).
47. Mateos, J. L., C. Perez, and H. Kwart: *Chem. Commun.*, **1967:**125.
48. Kwart, H., and T. Takeshita: *J. Am. Chem. Soc.*, **86:**1161 (1964).
49. Federlin, W.: *Z. Physik. Chem.*, **41:**565 (1902).
50. Crowell, T. I., and D. W. Peck: *J. Am. Chem. Soc.*, **75:**1075 (1953).
51. Brouwer, D. M., M. J. v. d. Vlugt, and E. Havinga, *Koninkl. Ned. Akad. Wetenschap.-Proc.*, **B60:**275 (1957).
52. Jencks, W. P., and J. Carriuolo: *J. Biol. Chem.*, **234:**1272 (1959).
53. Bender, M. L.: *Chem. Rev.*, **60:**53 (1960).
54. Jencks, W. P.: *Progr. Phys. Org. Chem.*, **2:**99 (1964).
55. Kurz, J. L.: *J. Am. Chem. Soc.*, **85:**987 (1963).
56. Fainberg, A. H., and S. Winstein: *J. Am. Chem. Soc.*, **78:**2763; 2780 (1956); S. Winstein, S. Smith, and D. Darwish: *ibid.*, **81:**5511 (1959); S. Winstein, E. C. Friedrich, and S. Smith: *ibid.*, **86:**305 (1964).
57. Franck, J., and E. Rabinowitch: *Trans. Faraday Soc.*, **30:**120 (1934).
58. Haskell, V. C., and L. P. Hammett: *J. Am. Chem. Soc.*, **71:**1284 (1949); S. A. Bernhard and L. P. Hammett: *ibid.*, **75:**1798 (1953).
59. Skrabel, A.: *Monatsh.*, **81:**239 (1950).
60. Bruice, T. C., and J. J. Bruno: *J. Am. Chem. Soc.*, **84:**2128 (1962).
61. Westheimer, F. H., and M. L. Bender: *J. Am. Chem. Soc.*, **84:**4908 (1962).
62. Tolman, R. C.: "Statistical Mechanics with Applications to Physics and Chemistry," Chemical Catalog Co., New York, 1927.
63. Davidson, N.: "Statistical Mechanics," p. 231, McGraw-Hill Book Company, New York, 1962.
64. Onsager, L.: *Phys. Rev.*, **37:**405 (1931).

6 Some Displacement Reactions

6.1 THE SECOND-ORDER NUCLEOPHILIC DISPLACEMENT ON CARBON

A nucleophilic displacement on carbon is a reaction in which a new bond to carbon is formed and an old one broken and in which both the atom which forms the new bond and the one previously bonded carry an unshared electron pair. When the displacing and the displaced atoms are not in the same molecule as the carbon atom on which the displacement occurs, the molecules or ions which contain them are called nucleophiles. Examples of nucleophilic displacements which may be but are not necessarily second order kinetically are

$$I^- + R_3CCl \rightarrow R_3CI + Cl^- \quad \text{(I)}$$

$$HO^- + R_3CCl \rightarrow HOCR_3 + Cl^- \quad \text{(II)}$$

$$R_3N + R_3CCl \rightarrow R_3NCR_3 + Cl^- \quad \text{(III)}$$

$$HO^- + R_3NCR_3^+ \rightarrow HOCR_3 + NR_3 \quad \text{(IV)}$$

$$R_3N + R_3CSR_2^+ \rightarrow R_3NCR_3 + SR_2 \quad \text{(V)}$$

In these formulas R may represent hydrogen, alkyl, aralykl, or aryl.

If the three R's attached to the carbon on which the displacement occurs are different, the substance involved may be obtained in optically active form.

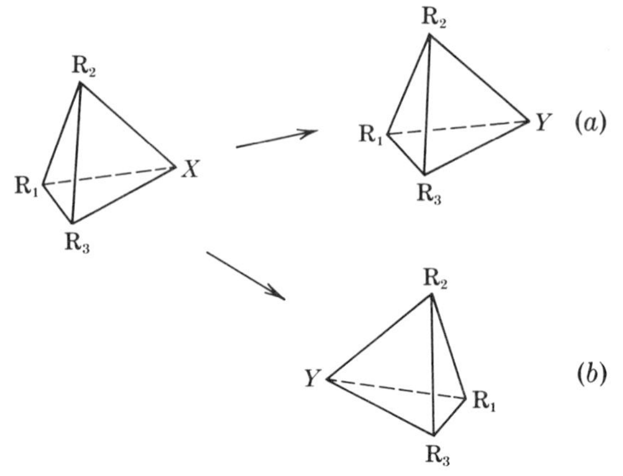

Fig. 6.1 Retention (*a*) and inversion (*b*) of configuration in displacement reactions.

Without exception in the many cases investigated an operationally second-order displacement of this kind has been found to involve an inversion of configuration in the sense of Fig. 6.1*b*, where R_1, R_2, and R_3 are the groups attached to the carbon on which the displacement occurs, Y is the displacing nucleophile, and X the displaced nucleophile.

The first evidence bearing on the stereochemistry of these reactions came from a remarkable series of investigations by Kenyon, Phillips, and their collaborators [1]. Recognizing the possibility that the optically active substances easily available from natural lactic or malic acids might offer especially complicated material, they undertook and solved the then difficult problem of preparing a series of optically active alcohols which contain no other functional group. Working with them, they found a number of clear and unambiguous cases of the following sort:

$$C_6H_5{-}CH_2(CH_3)C(H)OH \;(\alpha = +33.02) \xrightarrow{C_7H_7SO_2Cl} C_6H_5{-}CH_2(CH_3)C(H){-}O{-}SO_2C_7H_7 \;(\alpha = +31.11)$$

$$C_6H_5{-}CH_2(CH_3)C(H)OH \xrightarrow{(CH_3CO)_2O} C_6H_5{-}CH_2(CH_3)C(H)OCO{-}CH_3 \;(\alpha = +7.13)$$

$$C_6H_5{-}CH_2(CH_3)C(H){-}O{-}SO_2C_7H_7 \xrightarrow{C_2H_3O_2^-} C_6H_5{-}CH_2(CH_3)C(H)OCO{-}CH_3 \;(\alpha = -7.06) \xrightarrow{OH^-} C_6H_5{-}CH_2(CH_3)C(H)OH \;(\alpha = -32.18) \qquad \text{(VI)}$$

All the reactions can be carried out with high yields, and the magnitudes of the rotation of the two carbinols is nearly the same.

The step involving the inversion of configuration of the carbinol carbon can definitely be assigned as the displacement of toluenesulfonate ion by acetate ion through the following process of elimination. It cannot be the reaction of carbinol with sulfonyl chloride because this does not break any of the linkages of the asymmetric carbon. No inversion can conceivably occur unless one of these is broken and replaced by a new link in the opposite configuration. A displacement at another point in the molecule, in this case the displacement of hydrogen attached to oxygen by the toluenesulfonyl group, cannot invert. It seemed probable then (and has since been proved unambiguously by isotopic labeling) that the acetylation of the alcohol also leaves the carbon-oxygen link untouched. The consistency of this kind of behavior led Kenyon and Phillips to the conclusion that the displacement of toluenesulfonate ion by a carboxylate or alkyloxy ion is invariably accompanied by inversion of configuration and to the suggestion that any nucleophilic displacement on carbon inverts.

6.2 RACEMIZATION AND ISOTOPIC DISPLACEMENT

It has been known since 1913 [2] that alkyl bromides are racemized by bromide ion and alkyl iodides by iodide ion at a rate which is proportional to the concentration of the halide ion. It has also been found [3] that alkyl bromides undergo an exchange reaction with isotopically labeled bromide ion and alkyl iodides with iodide ion at a rate which is proportional to the concentration of the halide ion. The isotope exchange is a reversible process

$$RX + {}^*X^- \underset{k_1}{\overset{k_1}{\rightleftharpoons}} R^*X + X^- \tag{VII}$$

the asterisk designating the radioactive halogen, in which the specific rates of forward and reverse reactions are practically identical. The estimation of the exchange rate is complicated by the decay of the short-lived radioactivity of the halogen. If k_r is the specific rate of the decay, the rate equations are

$$\frac{d[R^*X]}{dt} = k_1[RX][{}^*X^-] - k_1[R^*X][X^-] - k_r[R^*X] \tag{1}$$

$$\frac{d[{}^*X^-]}{dt} = k_1[R^*X][X^-] - k_1[RX][{}^*X^-] - k_r[{}^*X^-] \tag{2}$$

If [A] represents the total concentration of alkyl halide and [B] that of halide ion, an experimentally determinable ratio γ may be defined as

$$\gamma = \frac{[R^*X]/[A]}{[{}^*X^-]/[B]} \tag{3}$$

From Eqs. (1) to (3) and the definitions of [A] and [B] it follows that

$$\frac{1}{k_1}\frac{d\gamma}{dt} = [\mathrm{B}] + ([\mathrm{A}] - [\mathrm{B}])\gamma - [\mathrm{A}]\gamma^2 \tag{4}$$

$$k_1 t = \frac{1}{[\mathrm{A}] + [\mathrm{B}]} \ln \frac{1 - ([\mathrm{A}]/[\mathrm{B}])\gamma}{1 - \gamma} \tag{5}$$

If the racemization involves the displacement of one X^- by another, with every such displacement inverting the configuration, the rate equation is

$$-\frac{d[d\mathrm{RX}]}{dt} = \frac{d[l\mathrm{RX}]}{dt} = k_1[d\mathrm{RX}][\mathrm{X}^-] - k_1[l\mathrm{RX}][\mathrm{X}^-] \tag{6}$$

The rotation α is given by

$$\alpha = m([d\mathrm{RX}] - [l\mathrm{RX}]) \tag{7}$$

from which

$$\frac{d\alpha}{dt} = -2k_1[\mathrm{X}^-]\alpha \tag{8}$$

and

$$\ln \alpha_0 - \ln \alpha = 2k_1[\mathrm{X}^-]t \tag{9}$$

For three different halides, *s*-octyl iodide, α-phenylethyl bromide, and α-bromopropionic acid, Hughes and his collaborators obtained k_1 values from the radioactive exchange which agreed with the k_1 values from the racemization to well within the 10 percent uncertainty in the exchange measurement. One such agreement might be attributed to coincidence; three such agreements point strongly to the conclusion that exchange and racemization are symptoms of a single process, the displacement with inversion of one halide ion by another.

One arrives therefore with considerable assurance at the picture of the transition state of these kinetically second-order displacements which is indicated in Fig. 6.2*b*. In this the bond to carbon of the nucleophilic atom being displaced has stretched somewhat, and the bond to carbon of the dis-

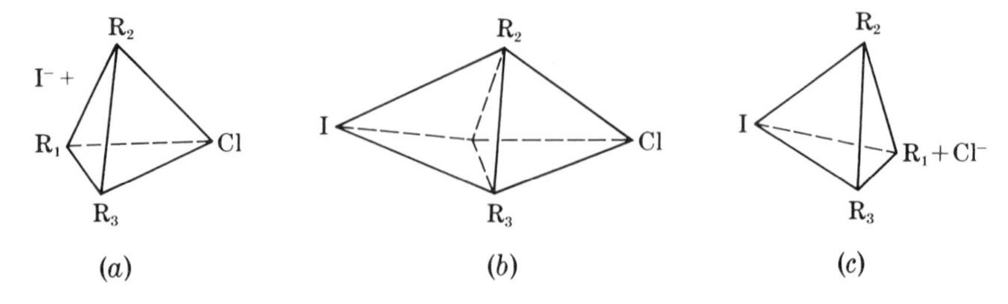

Fig. 6.2 Original (*a*), transition (*b*), and final (*c*) states in the displacement of chloride ion by iodide ion.

placing nucleophilic atom is not yet as short as it will be in the reaction product. The R groups lie much more nearly in a plane with the central carbon atom than they do either in the reactant or in the product. This is an adequate picture in terms of any information available if one keeps in mind the strong interactions which must exist with polar solvent molecules. The data do not exclude the possibility of a detailed mechanism involving additional intermediates, but there seems to be no reason to take the uncertainty very seriously.

6.3 THE SOLVOLYTIC REACTION

A solvolytic reaction is a kinetically first-order nucleophilic displacement in which the displacing nucleophile is a molecule of the solvent or of a solvent component. This process is so intimately related to a variety of other first-order reactions—such as inversion of configuration, allylic and other rearrangements, replacement of one nucleophile by another which is not a solvent component, and olefin formation—that the whole complex constitutes a single problem.

A solvolytic reaction always accompanies the second-order displacement of X in a substance RX by the lyate ion, namely, by OS^- when the solvent is HOS. On the other hand a first-order solvolysis is sometimes unaccompanied by any recognizable second-order reaction with the lyate ion.

The effect of the structure of RX on the rate of the solvolytic reaction is emphatically different from the effect on the second-order displacements which involve the same RX compounds. For the second-order reaction rates consistently decrease in the order $CH_3 > C_2H_5 > i\text{-}C_3H_7$. The rates of reaction of tertiary compounds are presumably even slower, but there is no direct evidence because the first-order rates are so fast. A survey by Streitwieser [4] lists values of the ratio of the specific rate of the reaction of a methyl derivative to that of the corresponding reaction of the isopropyl derivative which range from 18,600 for the reaction of alkyl bromide with iodide ion in acetone at 25°C to 230 for the reaction of alkyl iodide with pyridine in nitrobenzene at 50°, the average value being 1,200. It is significant that this sequence and roughly this range of rates apply when the displacing nucleophile is electrically neutral as well as when it is an anion and that the lyate ion occupies no special position.

By contrast, the rates of the first-order solvolysis of methyl, ethyl, and isopropyl derivatives are not very different from each other, and *t*-butyl derivatives react several orders of magnitude faster. With benzhydryl derivatives also solvolysis is very fast, and second-order reaction with lyate ions is undetectable.

These structural effects indicate strongly that the reactions of tertiary alkyl and benzhydryl derivatives do not involve the same kind of transition state as the second-order displacements do. One can reasonably account for the decrease in rate as alkyl groups replace hydrogen in such transition-state structures as A or B

$$\underset{\text{(A)}}{R_1R_2R_3N\cdots CH_2(H)\cdots X^-} \qquad \underset{\text{(B)}}{R{-}O\cdots CH_2(H)\cdots X} \qquad \underset{\text{(C)}}{(H)(R)O\cdots CH_2(H)\cdots X}$$

in terms of repulsions between these groups and the approaching nucleophile. It is very hard to see why the same structural effects should not apply to the solvolysis if the transition state were representable by C.

6.4 THE FREE-CARBONIUM-ION MECHANISM

In solvents which are favorable to the existence of free ions rather than of ion pairs or larger aggregates the solvolytic reactions of tertiary alkyl and benzhydryl derivatives are satisfactorily interpreted in terms of the free-carbonium-ion mechanism[1]

$$\begin{aligned} RX &\underset{k_{-1}}{\overset{k_1}{\rightleftharpoons}} R^+ + X^- \\ R^+ + HOS &\xrightarrow{k_2} ROS + H^+ \end{aligned} \qquad \text{(VIII)}$$

The mechanism is consistent with the effect of azide ion on rate and product composition. Azide ion is remarkable in being able to compete effectively with the solvent and in forming a reaction product which does not react further. The introduction of its use as a probe for carbonium-ion intermediates by Hughes and Ingold in 1940 constituted an important pioneering step in the study of the solvolytic reaction. In the typical case of the hydrolysis of *p,p*-dimethylbenzhydryl chloride in an 85% by volume mixture of acetone with water the addition of 0.05 *M* sodium azide increased the rate of disappearance of the chloride by 48 percent. This differs by only a few percent from the effect of added lithium chloride or tetramethylammonium nitrate. If the reaction with azide and the hydrolysis were independent processes, the ratio of the rates of production of benzhydryl azide and of benzhydrol would be 0.48/1.48, or 0.32. In fact the mole fraction of azide in the reaction product was 0.60 [6]. This can only be because the azide reacts with an intermediate which is produced from the benzhydryl chloride without the involvement of the azide.

The free-carbonium-ion mechanism is consistent with what is called the mass-law or the common-ion effect. For instance in an acetone-water mixture

[1] This mechanism appears to have been suggested at about the same time by Olivier and Berger; Ward; and Ingold [5].

containing 80% by volume acetone the rate of hydrolysis of benzhydryl chloride is decreased 13 percent by the addition of 0.1 *M* lithium chloride, and lithium bromide has the same effect on the rate of hydrolysis of benzhydryl bromide. Yet lithium bromide accelerates the hydrolysis of benzhydryl chloride by 17 percent, and lithium chloride accelerates that of benzhydryl bromide by 27 percent [7]. If one assumes the accelerations to be salt effects operating on the k_1 of reaction system (VIII), the retardations may reasonably be attributed to the term $k_{-1}[X^-]$ in the denominator of the Bodenstein steady-state equation for this system, namely,

$$k^{(p)} = \frac{k_1 k_2}{k_2 + k_{-1}[X^-]} \tag{10}$$

A similar situation is involved in the trapping of radioactive chlorine by unreacted alkyl chloride during the solvolysis of inactive alkyl chloride in the presence of active chloride ion [8] or in the release of active chloride ion when active aralkyl chloride R*Cl solvolyzes in the presence of inactive chloride ion [9]. In the latter case the specific rate k_r of formation of active chloride ion $^*Cl^-$ is given by

$$k_r = k_1 \left(1 - \frac{k_{-1}}{k_2 + k_{-1}[Cl^-]} \frac{[RCl][^*Cl^-]}{[R^*Cl]}\right) \tag{11}$$

while the specific rate k_h of the hydrolysis, with R*Cl present in tracer proportions, is given by Eq. (10). Consequently

$$\frac{k_r}{k_h} = 1 + \frac{k_{-1}}{k_2}\left([Cl^-] - \frac{[RCl][^*Cl^-]}{[R^*Cl]}\right) \tag{12}$$

In the hydrolysis of benzhydryl chloride and several substituted benzhydryl chlorides in a 70% by volume mixture of acetone with water the values of k_{-1}/k_2 derived from this equation were independent of the concentration of the added electrolyte within the experimental uncertainty of 5 percent over the range from 0.025 to 0.1 *M* and were the same when the added electrolyte was HCl as they were when it was NaCl. This is powerful evidence for the validity of the free-carbonium-ion mechanism in this case.

The free-carbonium-ion mechanism is consistent with the fact that when the carbonium ion can be converted to olefin as well as to carbinol, as in the *t*-butyl case,

$$(CH_3)C^+ \begin{cases} \xrightarrow{+\,HOS} (CH_3)_3COS + H^+ \\ \longrightarrow (CH_3)_2C{=}CH_2 + H^+ \end{cases} \tag{IX}$$

the proportion of olefin formed in the solvolysis in a strongly dissociating solvent is roughly independent of the nature of X, even though the total rate of reaction depends heavily on X. Thus the proportion of olefin formed in the solvolysis of *t*-butyl compounds in an 80% by volume mixture of ethanol with water at 25°C is 17 percent for the chloride and 13 percent for both bromide and iodide although the total rate of reaction varies in the ratio 1:44:105. And in the same solvent at 65° the elimination of $S(CH_3)_2$ from $(CH_3)_3CS(CH_3)_2^+$ yields the same proportion, 36 percent, of olefin as does the elimination of Cl^- from $(CH_3)_3CCl$, the rates being in the ratio 1:7.6 [10].

6.5 SALT EFFECTS IN STRONGLY DISSOCIATING SOLVENTS

It is obvious that electrolytes which are not stoichiometrically involved in a solvolytic reaction exert a considerable influence on the rate of the reaction. The effects are specific to the electrolyte, and they are large enough so that it is not easy to sweep the problem under the rug in considering mass-law effects or the diversion of the product from carbinol to azide. In the conversion of *t*-butyl nitrate to *t*-butanol in a 60% by weight mixture of dioxane with water the specific rate is decreased 4.3 percent by the addition of 0.108 *M* sodium hydroxide, although it is increased 16.5 percent by the addition of the same concentration of sodium perchlorate. In 75% dioxane the rate of the same reaction is increased 37 percent by sodium perchlorate or perchloric acid at 0.108 *M* concentration, 16 percent by potassium nitrate, and only 10 percent by sodium chloride or toluenesulfonate [11] (see also [7]). In mixed aqueous solvents such as 80% acetone [12], as well as in poorly dissociating solvents like acetic acid, the specific rate k is usually linear in salt concentration. In unmixed aqueous solution, however, $\log k$ instead of k is linear in salt concentration for the hydrolysis of *t*-butyl chloride [13]. When the effect is linear in k, the salt behaves like a typical catalyst (Sec. 5.26).

6.6 THE ROLE OF THE SOLVENT

The function of the solvent in the solvolytic reaction is illuminated by the effect of small concentrations of water in the alcoholysis of benzhydryl chloride [14].[1] As shown in Fig. 6.3, water increases the rate, linearly at concentrations below 1 *M*, yet the reaction product remains almost entirely benzhydryl ethyl ether. Thus 0.60 *M* water increases the rate by a factor of 1.38 while the fraction of benzhydryl in the reaction product is only 0.018. If the acceleration by water were due to the formation of a transition state similar to C, in which the water molecule is in the process of forming a carbon-oxygen bond, the mole fraction of benzhydryl in the product would be $0.38/1.38 = 0.27$ instead of the observed 0.018. It is reasonable therefore to

[1] Many of the data on the rate are from [15] and [16].

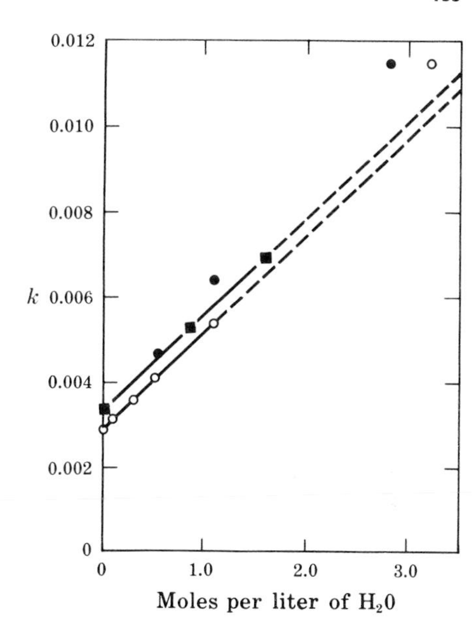

Fig. 6.3 Variation of specific rate with water content in the solvolysis of benzhydryl chloride. (○ = *data of Norris and Morton* [16]; ● = *data of Ward* [15]; ■ = *data of Farinacci and Hammett* [14].)

suppose that the water is hydrogen-bonded to the nascent chloride ion in a transition-state structure like D and that in the absence of water an alcohol molecule performs the same function but does it less effectively.

$$(C_6H_5)_2HC\cdots Cl---H\cdots OH$$

(D)

6.7 A MATTER OF NOMENCLATURE

In this field, as in so many others, it is difficult to give operational meaning to conceptual distinctions. Ingold [17] distinguishes between a unimolecular substitution, labeled S_N1, in which the solvent molecule is not in the process of forming an oxygen-carbon bond in the transition state, and a bimolecular substitution, labeled S_N2, in which the transition state looks like structure C.

With reactants for which mass-law effects or other characteristics of the free-carbonium-ion mechanism cannot be detected the primary evidence against the acceptance of a transition-state structure like C is the evidence from the effect of structure on reactivity, which in any case is ambiguous. In the extreme case of the primary RX compound the fact that the first-order reaction of methyl derivatives is faster than that of ethyl derivatives and that the first-order reaction inverts the configuration of *n*-butyl-1-*d*-bromobenzenesulfonate completely [18] argues strongly for a C type of transition state.

Because of the characteristic uncertainty of the concept of molecularity in this as in so many other cases, I shall use the term solvolysis to include all kinetically first-order reactions with solvent of an RX compound, regardless of any suspicions I may entertain about the detailed mechanism.

6.8 INADEQUACIES OF THE FREE-CARBONIUM-ION MECHANISM

The proportion of olefin formed in the solvolysis of $(CH_3)_3CX$ in ethanol or in acetic acid, instead of being independent of the nature of X, as it is in 80% aqueous ethanol (Sec. 6.4) or in water, becomes decidedly dependent on X, as shown in Table 6.1.

A similar difficulty appears in the allylic rearrangement. The two chlorides E and F should form the same carbonium ion, which may be represented as G.

$$CH_3{-}CH{=}CH{-}CH_2Cl \quad \text{(E)} \qquad CH_3{-}CHCl{-}CH{=}CH_2 \quad \text{(F)}$$

$$CH_3{-}CH\overset{\cdots}{=}CH\overset{\cdots}{=}CH_2 \quad \text{(G)}$$

$$CH_3{-}CH{=}CH{-}CH_2OC_2H_5 \quad \text{(H)} \qquad CH_3{-}CH(OC_2H_5){-}CH{=}CH_2 \quad \text{(I)}$$

Yet solvolysis in ethanol of E yields 8 percent of I while solvolysis of F yields 18 percent of this product. In both cases the remainder of the reaction product is H [21]. Here, as in the matter of the proportion of olefin, the composition of the reaction product depends more on the starting material than would be predicted from the free-carbonium-ion mechanism.

A large significance attaches to the wide variation in the extent of the racemization which often accompanies a solvolytic reaction when RX is optically active by virtue of the asymmetry of the carbonium carbon. For such reactions the configuration of the product may be anything from almost

Table 6.1 Mole percent of olefin from solvolysis of $(CH_3)_3CX$ in several solvents[a]

X	*Water* 25°	*Water* 75°	*Ethanol* 75°	*Acetic acid* 75°
Cl^-	5.0	7.6	44.2	73
Br^-	5.0	6.6	36.0	69.5
I^-	4.0	6.0	32.3	
$(CH_3)_2S$		6.5	17.8	11.7

[a] Data of Cocivera and Winstein [19]. See also [20].

complete inversion through complete racemization to a considerable measure of retention. Retention has been observed only in cases where suspicion that two successive inverting displacements may be involved seems justified (Sec. 6.11) [22, 23]. So far as it has been investigated, the degree of racemization is negligible for primary aliphatic compounds, and it appears to increase through secondary to tertiary, and to be greater with α-phenyl derivatives than with aliphatic compounds. It is, for instance, greater with $C_6H_5{\cdot}CHX{\cdot}CH_3$ than with $CH_3{\cdot}CH_2{\cdot}CHX{\cdot}CH_3$. It does, however, depend so much on the solvent that these generalizations are difficult to document.

There are theoretical reasons for expecting that a free carbonium ion is planar and that having a plane of symmetry it cannot transmit the asymmetry of a reactant to the reaction product. The idea is supported by the large measure of racemization observed in the solvolysis reaction under conditions most favorable to the formation of a free carbonium ion. For instance the solvolysis of α-phenylethyl chloride in water or aqueous acetone leads to phenylethyl alcohol which is from 83 to 98 percent racemized. It is also supported by the fact that trimethylborane, which is isoelectronic with *t*-butyl ion, is planar [24].

6.9 THE ION-PAIR HYPOTHESIS

It seems probable (Sec. 5.15) that the path downhill from a transition state does not fork so long as it continues downhill. That is, it appears likely that a group of systems which are on the summit of a barrier between reactant and product, which have similar composition and geometry, and which are alike in the nature of the bond-making and bond-breaking processes under way progress inevitably to a group of systems of similarly related composition and geometry from which escape is possible only at the expense of an increase in standard potential. The group of systems thus attained may be so stable toward other reactions as to be the final reaction product; it may also constitute a temporary halt on the way to the final product, i.e., an intermediate.

It also seems probable that when the conversion of a transition state to a reaction product requires a dissociation, there must be at least one intermediate followed by a barrier of a height at least as great as that required to overcome the forces which oppose the separation by diffusion of the dissociation fragments (Sec. 5.27).

Applied to the carbonium-ion mechanism, these considerations lead to the conclusion that the free carbonium ion must be preceded by an intermediate in which the spacing of the departing nucleophile from the carbon on which the displacement occurs is greater than it was in the reactant molecule and in which the internal electron distribution and the interaction with the solvent more nearly resemble those in the separated R^+ and X^- ions than they do those in the

RX molecule. Such a structure is reasonably called an ion pair. If the carbonium carbon is asymmetric, the ion pair as it is initially formed must also be asymmetric.

Conceivably the barrier against separation may be high enough, especially if the solvent is not one favorable to the existence of free ions, to allow other processes to compete with the separation. Thus an adjacent solvent molecule might form an oxygen-carbon bond on the side away from the X^- ion, losing a proton to another solvent molecule simultaneously or later but in any case inverting the configuration. Or a solvent molecule might simultaneously transfer a proton to the X^- ion and an OS^- to the carbonium carbon, leading probably to a product of the same configuration as the reactant. Or if the spacing of R^+ and X^- is large enough, the R^+ might rotate or the X^- slip around from one side to the other leading to partial or complete racemization. A mechanism involving the ion-pair intermediate can therefore account in a reasonable fashion for partial racemization of the solvolysis product.

The ion-pair hypothesis accounts for the incompleteness of the allylic rearrangement (Sec. 6.8) by supposing that there are two isomeric ion pairs and that the attachment of the solvent molecule to the carbon atom to which the X^- was originally attached is more likely than attachment to the other allylic carbon. It accounts for the dependence of the proportion of olefin formed on the nature of X^- by supposing that olefin formation competes with formation of alcohol or ether at the ion-pair stage and that the competition is influenced by the nature of X^-.

The idea of what amounts to the ion-pair mechanism as a way of accounting for partial racemization was suggested by Ogg and Polanyi in 1935 [25]. It was given a somewhat greater precision and the term ion pair was introduced in 1940 [26, p. 172]. The mechanism was applied to the allylic rearrangement by Young, Winstein, and Goering [27] in 1951, and it has since been developed and applied widely by Winstein and his collaborators.[1]

The adequacy of the ion-pair mechanism does not in itself exclude the possibility of a parallel-path mechanism in which the inverted or unrearranged product is formed by an S_N2 process while the racemized or rearranged product is formed by the free-carbonium-ion mechanism.

6.10 EVIDENCE FROM THE AZIDE PROBE

Very direct evidence for the operation of an ion-pair mechanism has been obtained by Sneen and coworkers [29, 30] in a study of the solvolysis of 2-octyl methanesulfonate in a 30% by volume mixture of dioxane with water. It was found that sodium azide increased the specific rate of disappearance of the

[1] See, for instance [28], p. 109.

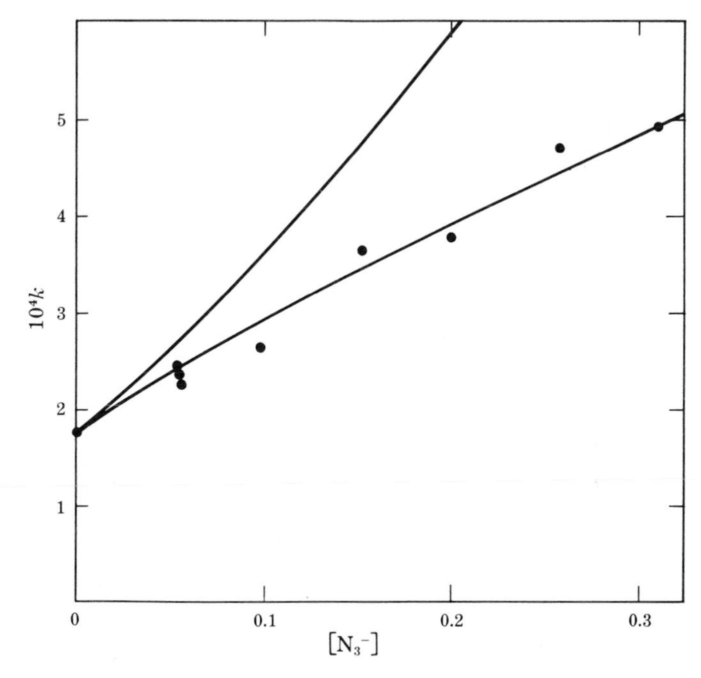

Fig. 6.4 Effect of azide ion on the reaction rate of 2-octyl methanesulfonate in 30% dioxane. (*Data of Sneen and Larsen* [30].)

reactant by the amounts shown by the circles in Fig. 6.4 and that the composition of the reaction product was adequately represented by the equation

$$\frac{[RN_3]}{[ROH]} = 9.04[N_3^-] \tag{13}$$

If the octyl azide had been formed by an independent second-order reaction of RX,with N_3^-, the specific rate would have been that indicated by the upper curve of the figure, assuming that the salt effect of sodium azide is the same as the small effect observed with a variety of other electrolytes in this medium. If, on the other hand, the mechanism is

$$\begin{aligned} &RX \underset{k_{-1}}{\overset{k_1}{\rightleftharpoons}} R^+X^- \\ &R^+X^- + H_2O \xrightarrow{k_s} ROH + H^+X^- \\ &R^+X^- + N_3^- \xrightarrow{k_N} RN_3 + X^- \end{aligned} \tag{X}$$

with $k_N/k_S = 9.04$ and $k_{-1}/k_S = 2.59$, the specific rate would be that given by the lower curve in the figure. Similar results were obtained in a 25% mixture of dioxane with water. The conclusion is inescapable that there is a reversibly formed intermediate which can react with water or with azide ion at competitive rates.

Both in the presence and in the absence of azide the octanol produced is about 95 percent inverted in configuration, and the octyl azide produced in the presence of sodium azide concentrations in the neighborhood of 0.04 *M* is 80 percent inverted. The intermediate is therefore asymmetric. The picture of a free carbonium ion which remains asymmetric long enough to form asymmetrical alcohol and azide and which forms them with inverted configuration may safely be rejected. The intermediate must therefore be something of the nature of what has been described as an ion pair.

The relatively slow conversion of this ion pair to its enantiomer is in striking contrast to the behavior of the *p*-chlorobenzhydryl–*p*-nitrobenzoate ion pair (Sec. 6.14), whose racemization is rapid compared with return to the covalent reactant or reaction with solvent or other nucleophile. The difference is perhaps determined by the considerably greater stability of the benzhydryl derivative. This might lower the standard potential of the ion pair with respect to the barrier against the return and the reaction with nucleophiles but not with respect to that against the internal inversion of configuration.

6.11 THE INVOLVEMENT OF NONHYDROXYLIC SOLVENT COMPONENTS

Weiner and Sneen [29] also report that the hydrolysis of optically active 2-octyl methanesulfonate in unmixed aqueous solution produces completely inverted octanol; that solvolysis of 2-octyl bromobenzenesulfonate in unmixed methanol produces completely inverted octyl methyl ether; but that solvolysis in mixtures of water or of methanol with dioxane produces partially racemized product, the extent of the racemization increasing with the dioxane content of the solvent. They conclude that an intermediate of structure J

(J)

and inverted configuration is formed in the presence of dioxane and that this intermediate reacts with water or methanol in an inverting displacement to produce octanol or octyl methyl ether of the same configuration as that of the reactant.

The solvolysis of optically active 2-octyl bromobenzenesulfonate in 75% dioxane in the absence of added azide yields octanol which is only 77 percent inverted, the remainder being racemic. The addition of 0.30 *M* sodium azide produces octanol of completely inverted configuration to the extent of 35 percent of the total reaction product, the remainder being completely inverted octyl azide. The racemized octanol must have been produced from an asymmetric intermediate whose formation is suppressed by the azide. It is hard to see how this intermediate can be anything but J.

Finally the solvolysis of 2-octyl bromobenzenesulfonate in an 80% by volume mixture of acetone with methanol yielded a product which contained 15% of octanol in addition to the octyl methyl ether. This can reasonably be attributed to the formation of a substituted oxonium ion analogous to J and the reactions

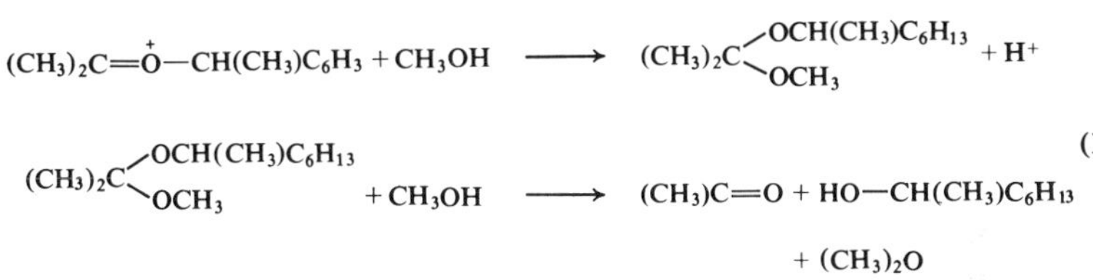

$$(CH_3)_2C{=}\overset{+}{O}{-}CH(CH_3)C_6H_3 + CH_3OH \longrightarrow (CH_3)_2C\begin{matrix}\diagup OCH(CH_3)C_6H_{13}\\ \diagdown OCH_3\end{matrix} + H^+$$

$$(CH_3)_2C\begin{matrix}\diagup OCH(CH_3)C_6H_{13}\\ \diagdown OCH_3\end{matrix} + CH_3OH \longrightarrow (CH_3)C{=}O + HO{-}CH(CH_3)C_6H_{13} + (CH_3)_2O \qquad \text{(XI)}$$

No octanol was formed when lutidine was added, presumably because this suppressed the acid-catalyzed ketal interchanges.

Weiner and Sneen conclude that all solvolytic reactions of 2-octyl derivatives, and presumably of other aliphatic secondary RX compounds, go by way of an inverting reaction of an ion pair which has the same configuration as the reactant and that racemization results only from two successive inverting reactions. This hypothesis accounts for the relatively low reactivity of lyate ions with secondary RX compounds by supposing that conversion of reactant to ion pair without the assistance of incipient bond formation between the oxygen of the solvent and the carbonium carbon is relatively easy with the secondary compound. The hypothesis can account for retention of configuration in the reaction product (Sec. 6.14). If a product of the structure of J or the like is formed from the ion pair at a rate greater than that of the formation of K or L and then reacts rapidly with water or hydroxyl ion by a second inverting process, the configuration of the alcohol produced will be that of the reactant.

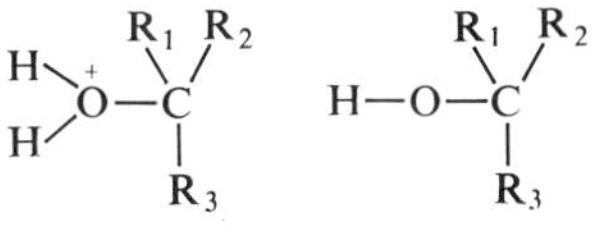

$$H_2\overset{+}{O}{-}C(R_1)(R_2)(R_3) \qquad H{-}O{-}C(R_1)(R_2)(R_3)$$

(K) (L)

6.12 THE ALLYLIC REARRANGEMENT

The solvolysis of M in acetic acid is accompanied by a considerable although transitory rearrangement to N [27].

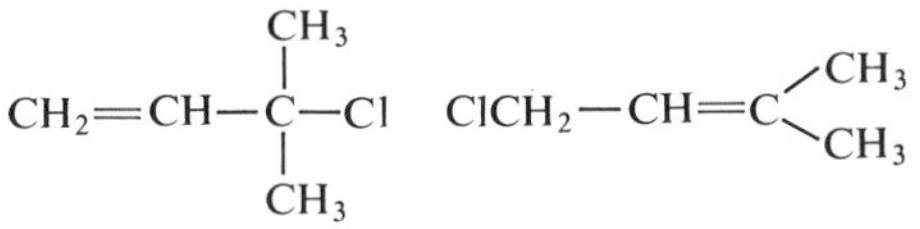

$$CH_2{=}CH{-}C(CH_3)_2{-}Cl \qquad ClCH_2{-}CH{=}C\begin{matrix}\diagup CH_3\\ \diagdown CH_3\end{matrix}$$

(M) (N)

In a system containing varying amounts of potassium chloride and potassium acetate at a constant value of the sum of these concentrations the rate of the rearrangement is independent of the concentration of potassium chloride. Young, Winstein, and Goering [27] proposed the hypothesis that the rate-determining process for both solvolysis and rearrangement is the formation of an ion pair or mixture of isomeric ion pairs, which can form N or react with solvent to form the allylic acetate at comparable rates. They called the process internal return.

The effect of a change in solvent is puzzling, as it often is. No rearrangement is observed in unmixed ethanol, but considerable rearrangement occurs in a 75% mixture of ethanol with water [31]. The solvolysis rate in ethanol is about the same as it is in acetic acid, but it is 45 times greater in the aqueous ethanol. In the aqueous ethanol the presence of radioactively labeled chloride ion in solution leads to some formation of labeled allylic halide but not enough to permit the conclusion that all the rearrangement takes place by way of free carbonium ion. It is intelligible that ethanol should react faster with the carbonium ion of the ion pair than acetic acid does thereby suppressing the formation of rearranged allylic chloride. But it is hard to see why this effect should not tend toward less rather than more rearrangement in aqueous ethanol than in the anhydrous solvent.

In the alternative picture [31] (that rearrangement and solvolysis are independent reactions) some of the systems which constitute the rate-determining transition state, in all of which the carbon-chlorine bond has been loosened by interaction of the solvent with the partially ionic chlorine, have a geometry which leads to a shift of the chlorine to the other allylic carbon. Others have a geometry which leads to the ion pair and thence to the solvolysis product. In terms of this hypothesis also the solvent effect is puzzling. One might expect the relative populations of the two groups of systems in the transition state to be independent of the nature of the solvent, unless one attributes significant S_N2 character to the systems which lead to the ion pair. Such a character seems unlikely for an unsaturated tertiary chloride.

6.13 RACEMIZATION OF REACTANT ACCOMPANYING SOLVOLYSIS

When the carbonium carbon of an RX compound is asymmetric, solvolysis is often, especially in poorly dissociating solvents like acetic acid, accompanied by considerable racemization of the unreacted RX. Regardless of mechanism, the specific rate k_t of conversion of RX to ROS, which Winstein calls the titrimetric constant, can be determined by acidimetric titration. If the ROS formed is optically inactive, the polarimetric constant k_α, defined as $-d\ln|\alpha|/dt$, where α is rotation, is given by

$$k_\alpha = k_t + 2k_{in} \tag{14}$$

where k_{in} is the specific rate of interconversion of d and l forms of RX.

If the ion-pair mechanism

$$\begin{array}{lcccc} d\text{-RX} & \underset{k_{-1}}{\overset{k_1}{\rightleftharpoons}} & d\text{-I} & \xrightarrow{k_2} & \text{ROS} \\ l\text{-RX} & \underset{k_{-1}}{\overset{k_1}{\rightleftharpoons}} & l\text{-I} & \xrightarrow{k_2} & \text{ROS} \end{array} \qquad \text{(XII)}$$

applies and the enantiomers of the ion pair I are in mobile equilibrium,

$$\begin{aligned} \frac{d[d\text{-RX}]}{dt} &= -k_1[d\text{-RX}] + k_{-1}[d\text{-I}] \\ \frac{d[l\text{-RX}]}{dt} &= -k_1[l\text{-RX}] + k_{-1}[l\text{-I}] \end{aligned} \qquad (15)$$

and since at equilibrium $[d\text{-I}] = [l\text{-I}]$, then,

$$\frac{d([d\text{-RX}] - [l\text{-RX}])}{dt} = -k_1([d\text{-RX}] - [l\text{-RX}]) \qquad (16)$$

from which, since α is proportional to $[d\text{-RX}] - [l\text{-RX}]$,

$$\frac{d \ln|\alpha|}{dt} = k_1 \qquad (17)$$

and since

$$[d\text{-I}] + [l\text{-I}] = \frac{k_1}{k_{-1} + k_2}([d\text{-RX}] + [l\text{-RX}]) \qquad (18)$$

it follows that

$$k_t = \frac{k_1 k_2}{k_{-1} + k_2} \qquad (19)$$

As Winstein and Robinson [32] point out, it is a remarkable and very general feature of this situation that the ratio k_α/k_t is nearly independent of the solvent and of the nature of X. Thus for the solvolysis of 3-phenyl-2-butyl bromobenzenesulfonate the values of this ratio are in the proportion 1.5:2.2:1 in the solvents formic acid, acetic acid, and ethanol, while the values of k_α are in the proportion 5,700:3.7:1. For the solvolysis of norbornyl bromobenzenesulfonate the ratio varies by a factor of only 4 in carboxylic acid–dioxane mixtures, while k_t varies by a factor of 10^4. In the acetolysis of norbornyl derivatives the ratio is nearly the same for the chloride, the bromide, the iodide, and the bromobenzenesulfonate.

If the ion-pair mechanism (XII) applies, this generalization means that the quantity $k_2/(k_{-1} + k_2)$ is nearly independent of the nature of the solvent and of X. This is possible only if the ratio $q_1^\ddagger/q_2^\ddagger$, where the subscripts refer to the first and the second transition states of mechanism (XII), and the difference

$\mu_1^\ddagger - \mu_2^\ddagger$ are similarly independent. The first transition state of this mechanism is clearly the optimum pass over the barrier between covalent RX and the ion pair; the second is not so certainly defined. It might involve the barrier against separation of the ion pair, or it might involve the barrier against bonding of an adjacent solvent molecule with the carbonium ion of the pair. But whatever the second barrier is, one would hardly have great a priori confidence that the difference in height of the two barriers would be almost unaffected by a change in the solvent or in the nature of X.

If, on the other hand, the racemization and the solvolysis are independent parallel reactions,

$$k_\alpha = k_t + k_r \tag{20}$$

where k_r is the specific rate of the racemization process. The condition that k_α/k_t be independent of solvent and of X is then that k_r/k_t be thus independent, i.e., that the difference in the standard potentials of the two parallel transition states be thus independent. Since both transition states require a loosening of the covalent C—X bond and both presumably are dependent on the interaction of the nascent X^- with the solvent, it is perhaps easier to accept the requirement for this mechanism than it is to accept the requirement for the ion-pair mechanism. The acceptance of either requires a considerable degree of willingness to reject the attitude that nature must always be complicated except when one can find a theoretical reason for supposing it to be otherwise.

6.14 MORE EVIDENCE FROM THE AZIDE PROBE

The ion-pair mechanism, or something very much like it, has been demonstrated by Goering and coworkers [22, 33] to apply to the racemization and hydrolysis of *p*-chlorobenzhydryl *p*-nitrobenzoate in 80 and in 90% by volume mixtures of acetone with water at 100°C. Isotopic labeling of the carboxylate oxygens demonstrates that the solvolysis goes entirely by rupture of the bond between the benzhydryl carbon and the ether oxygen. The chlorobenzhydryl produced by the hydrolysis is largely racemic, but there is 8 to 10 percent of retention of configuration (Sec. 6.11). By adding *p*-nitrobenzoic acid labeled with C^{14} it was shown that no important part of the racemization of the unreacted chlorobenzhydryl nitrobenzoate which accompanies the hydrolysis results from recombination of separated carbonium and nitrobenzoate ions or from reaction of separated nitrobenzoate with any intermediate.

When 0.141 *M* sodium azide was added, the racemization was completely suppressed. There can therefore be no doubt of the presence of an intermediate which can convert to its enantiomer, which in both enantiomeric forms can revert to the chlorobenzhydryl nitrobenzoate, and which in the presence of azide reacts more rapidly to form the chlorobenzhydryl azide than it rearranges. In the hydrolysis of *p*-chlorobenzhydryl chloride in 80%

acetone at 25° Winstein [28, p. 121] reports that sodium azide definitely decreases the racemization of the reactant during hydrolysis but does not suppress it completely.

Goering and coworkers also report on an oxygen-scrambling reaction of the chlorobenzhydryl nitrobenzoate during hydrolysis. Here the carbonyl oxygen of the reactant was isotopically labeled, and the rate of appearance of the label in the ether oxygen was determined. The reaction is appreciably faster than the racemization or the hydrolysis, and its rate is little if any affected by the addition of sodium azide. One can attribute these phenomena to the presence of two kinds of ion-pair intermediates, using an idea which was proposed by Winstein and coworkers in a different context [34]. In the present instance the ion pair first formed, called by Winstein an intimate ion pair, permits the rapid shift of the carbonium carbon from one oxygen atom to the other but does not permit either the slipping around of the anion from one side of the carbonium carbon to the other or the reaction with azide ion. The second, the solvent-separated ion pair, permits both the racemization and the reaction with azide ion. So far as the direct evidence goes, however, the oxygen scrambling might go by a parallel reaction independent of the formation of any ion pair, a transfer from one carboxylate oxygen to the other of carbonium carbon, its bonding to oxygen weakened in the transition state by interaction with the solvent.

6.15 THE SPECIAL SALT EFFECT

The picture of a succession of intermediates of the ion-pair type instead of a single one was proposed by Winstein and coworkers to account for an unusual effect of lithium perchlorate on the rate of solvolysis in acetic acid solution of a number of arenesulfonates which are expected to form relatively stable cationic intermediates. Figure 6.5 shows a typical example in the acetolysis of *threo*-3-*p*-anisyl-2-butyl *p*-bromobenzenesulfonate [32]. The ordinate in the lower plot is the specific rate k_t of the conversion of reactant to the corresponding acetate; in the upper one it is k_α, the polarimetric specific rate (Sec. 6.13).

The special salt effect is the sharp rise in k_t at low concentrations of lithium perchlorate, together with the fact that k_t ultimately becomes approximately parallel with, but still considerably smaller than, k_α. Winstein accounts for these phenomena in terms of the mechanism

$$
\begin{array}{lcl}
\mathrm{RX} & \underset{k_{-1}}{\overset{k_1}{\rightleftharpoons}} \; \mathrm{R^+X^-} \; \underset{k_{-2}}{\overset{k_2}{\rightleftharpoons}} & \mathrm{R^+\|X^-} \\
\mathrm{R^+\|X^- + HOS} & \xrightarrow{k_{sx}} & \mathrm{ROS + HX} \\
\mathrm{R^+\|X^- + LiClO_4} & \underset{k_{ey}}{\overset{k_{ex}}{\rightleftharpoons}} & \mathrm{R^+\|ClO_4 + LiX} \\
\mathrm{R^+\|ClO_4^- + HOS} & \xrightarrow{k_{sy}} & \mathrm{ROS + HClO_4}
\end{array}
\qquad \text{(XIII)}
$$

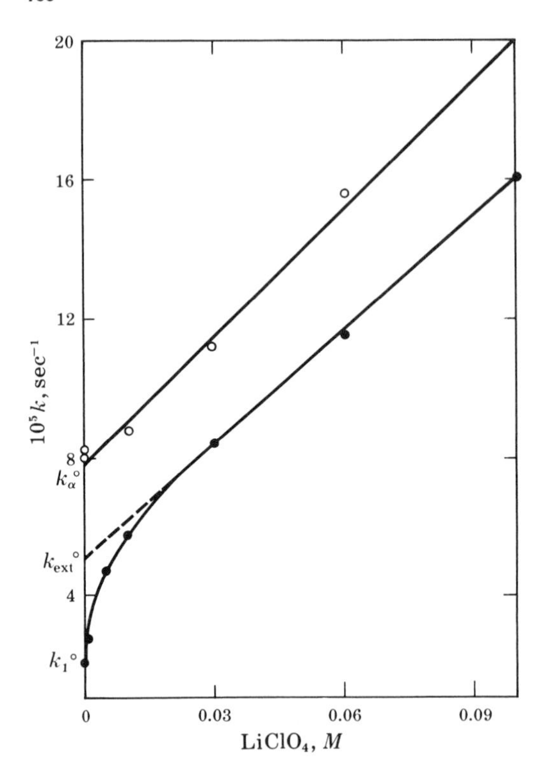

Fig. 6.5 Effect of lithium perchlorate on acetolysis of *threo*-3-*p*-anisyl-2-butyl *p*-bromobenzenesulfonate at 25.0°. [*By permission of S. Winstein and G. C. Robinson, J. Am. Chem. Soc.*, **80**:169 (1958).]

in which R^+X^- represents the intimate ion pair and $R^+\|X^-$ the solvent-separated ion pair. If k_{ex} and k_{sy} are large enough compared with k_{sx} the addition of lithium perchlorate will increase k_t, but the increase will stop when practically all the formation of ROS goes by the perchlorate route, except that a normal linear salt effect continues the increase. The crucial argument for the intervention of the intimate ion pair is the fact that k_α is always considerably larger than k_t. If the intimate pair racemizes rapidly and k_{-1} is not much smaller than k_2, racemization will be faster than conversion to ROS even when the catalytic effect of the lithium perchlorate causes every solvent-separated pair to go on to ROS.

The application of the Bodenstein steady-state approximation to this mechanism, assuming no accumulation of any intermediate, leads to the equation [35]

$$\frac{1}{k_t} = \frac{1}{k_{\text{ext}}}\left\{1 + \frac{1}{a + b_s[\text{LiClO}_4]/(1 + c[\text{LiX}])}\right\} \tag{21}$$

in which

$$k_{\text{ext}} = \frac{k_1 k_2}{k_{-1} + k_2} \tag{22}$$

and a, b_s, and c are functions of the specific rates of the various steps of the mechanism. It is further supposed that k_{ext} is a linear function of the concentrations s_i of the ionophores present, i.e.,

$$k_{ext} = k_{ext}^{\circ}\left(1 + \sum_i b_i s_i\right) \tag{23}$$

Equation (21) has been found to be in excellent agreement with experiment for a considerable number of RX compounds which exhibit the special salt effect. It not only represents closely the effect of the addition of lithium perchlorate, but it accounts for the fact that LiX, which in these cases exerts only a small positive salt effect in the absence of lithium perchlorate, decreases k_t substantially in the presence of the perchlorate.

There is, however, a difficulty in the near parallelism of the k_α plot with the linear portion of the k_t plot, a parallelism which in at least one case is very exact [36]. If mechanism (XIII) applies, $k_\alpha = k_1$; consequently the linearity of the k_α plot demonstrates that the derivative dk_1/ds, where s is salt concentration, is independent of s. The linear portion of the k_t plot is given by Eq. (22), from which

$$\frac{dk_{ext}}{ds} = \frac{k_2}{k_{-1} + k_2}\frac{dk_1}{ds} - \frac{k_1 k_2}{(k_{-1} + k_2)^2}\frac{dk_{-1}}{ds} + \frac{k_1 k_{-1}}{(k_{-1} + k_2)^2}\frac{dk_2}{ds} \tag{24}$$

Since k_1 is a function of s the linearity of the k_{ext} plot, is possible only if both k_{-1} and k_2 are independent of s. If they are, the right side of Eq. (24) reduces to the first term and

$$\frac{dk_{ext}/ds}{dk_\alpha/ds} = \frac{k_2}{k_{-1} + k_2} \tag{25}$$

From the intercepts in Fig. 6.5 the quantity $k_2/(k_{-1} + k_2)$ is 0.67 for the reaction represented in that figure, whereas the ratio of the slopes is 0.88. The difference in these values is well beyond any reasonable estimate of experimental uncertainty.

If, however, there is only one kind of ion pair but an independent parallel process with a specific rate k_r racemizes the reactant, Eq. (21) still applies to k_t but the value of k_{ext} is k_1', the specific rate of the conversion of RX to the ion pair. The polarimetric constant is given by

$$k_\alpha = k_1' + k_r \tag{26}$$

If k_r is independent of salt concentration, which might well be the case for an internal rearrangement, the slopes of the k_α and the k_{ext} plots would be the same.

6.16 DOUBLE INVERSIONS OF CONFIGURATION

Nothing has done more to dispell the veil of confusion which once covered the Walden inversion phenomena than an investigation by Cowdrey, Hughes, and Ingold [37]. This showed typically that a solution of α-bromopropionic acid in methanol reacts by two kinetically distinguishable paths, one a first-order reaction of bromopropionate ion, the other a second-order reaction of bromopropionate ion with methoxyl ion. The relative values of the specific rates are such that the second-order reaction predominates at sodium methylate concentrations from 0.5 to 1 M, and the first-order reaction in the region from 0.03 to 0.06 M. In the presence of 1 M base the ion of *d*-bromopropionic acid yields *l*-methoxypropionic acid; in the presence of 0.077 M base it yields the *d*-methoxy acid. This single experiment explained the classical difficulty that a small change in concentration of reagent leads to a change in the sign of the rotation of the reaction product. The supposedly small change involves in fact a complete overturn in the reaction mechanism.

In the methyl ester of bromopropionic acid both first- and second-order reactions are detectable, but both yield products of the same sign of rotation. These reactions are obviously the solvolysis and the second-order displacement of bromide ion by methoxyl ion, and the latter must surely invert the configuration of the α carbon. Since the bromo and methoxy esters can be obtained from the corresponding acids or converted to them by reactions which do not involve the asymmetric carbon, the knowledge thus gained of the configurations of the two esters permits the proof that the second-order reaction of bromopropionate ion inverts the configuration of the α carbon and that the first-order reaction is accompanied by retention of configuration.

The obvious interpretation of these phenomena is the one first proposed by Bean, Kenyon, and Phillips [1] in which an α-lactone is formed by an inverting displacement of bromide ion by one of the oxygens of the carboxylate group, followed by a likewise inverting displacement of this oxygen by a solvent molecule or by a lyate ion.

$$CH_3-CH(Br)-CO_2^{\ominus} \rightleftharpoons CH_3-\overset{O}{\overbrace{CH-C}}=O + Br^- \tag{XIV}$$

$$CH_3-\overset{O}{\overbrace{CH-C}}=O + HOCH_3 \rightleftharpoons CH_3-CH(OCH_3)-CO_2^{\ominus} + H^+$$

This interpretation is strengthened by the discovery by Grunwald and Winstein [38] that although the reaction is accelerated by the addition of perchlorates, it is retarded by the addition of bromides, presumably because the first step is reversible.

At the time of the Cowdrey, Hughes, and Ingold experiments there was a certain difficulty because the only available oxygen-labeling experiment on ester hydrolysis was that of Polanyi and Szabo on amyl acetate [39]. In this it was found that the ether oxygen of the ester remained attached to the alkyl group, which meant that the process could not invert the configuration of the alkyl group. There was, however, certainty that the hydrolysis of β-lactones under some conditions inverts the configuration of the alkyl group [40], and since that time it has been found that many ester hydrolyses go by way of alkyl-oxygen rupture and may therefore invert.

6.17 THE BROMONIUM-ION INTERMEDIATE

Winstein and Lucas [41] found that in the reaction with strong hydrobromic acid optically active *erythro*-3-bromo-2-butanol O yielded *meso*-2,3-dibromobutane Q, whereas active *threo*-3-bromo-2-butanol yielded racemic 2,3-dibromobutane.

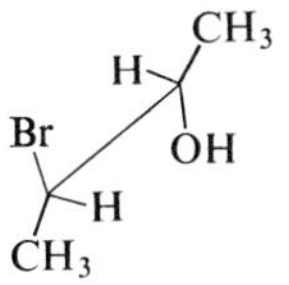

(O) 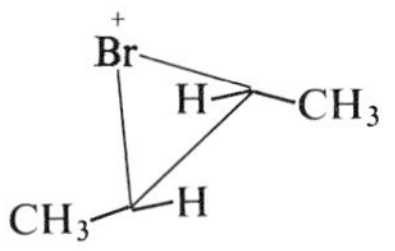 (P) 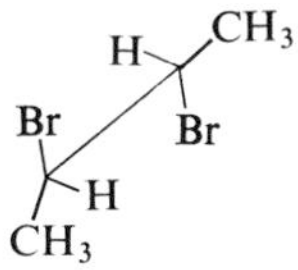 (Q)

They attributed this stereochemistry to the addition of a hydrogen ion to the oxygen, followed by the inverting displacement of water by the neighboring bromine to form the cyclic bromonium ion P, and finally by the inverting displacement of the ring bromine by an external bromide ion. The bromonium ion is the same intermediate as the one suggested by Roberts and Kimball (Sec. 5.17) to account for the stereospecificity of the addition of bromine to olefin.

If there is indeed a bromonium-ion intermediate, one would expect the energy of formation of this intermediate to contribute toward a reduction of the energy of the transition state. The rate of the solvolysis should therefore be greater when this intermediate can be formed than it would be if the formation of the intermediate could be excluded without the exertion of any other influence on the rate of the solvolysis. Winstein, Grunwald, and Ingraham [42] tested this conclusion by a study of the cis and trans 1,2-cyclohexane derivatives R and S, in which OBs represents the *p*-bromobenzenesulfonate group.

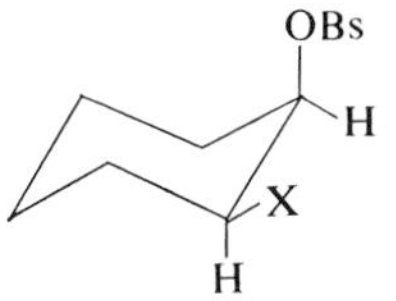

(R) 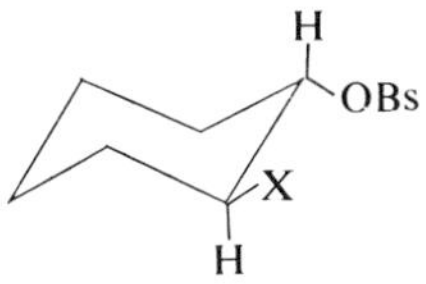 (S)

In the cis compound R the X group and the OBs are constrained by the ring to a geometry in which it is impossible for X to approach the carbon to which the OBs group is attached on the side away from the latter. An inverting displacing of OBs by X to form a three-membered ring should therefore be difficult or impossible for the cis compounds, whereas there is no difficulty of this kind for the trans compounds S. Experimentally it was found in the solvolysis in acetic acid that the ratio of the specific rate of the trans compound to that of the cis compound is 1.12 when X is bromobenzenesulfonate, 3.8 when it is chlorine, 810 when it is bromine, and 2.7×10^6 when it is iodine. Clearly something of the nature of the three-membered ring formation has a large influence on the standard potential of the transition state for the solvolysis in the bromine case, and an even larger effect in the iodine case, but little if any influence in the chlorine and arenesulfonate cases.

The bromonium-ion hypothesis possesses therefore the highest virtue a theory can have, namely, accounting by a single hypothesis for phenomena which without it seem entirely unrelated. In this case these are the stereochemistry of the addition of halogen to olefin, the stereochemistry of the solvolysis when bromine is attached to the carbon α to one which carries a nucleophile, and a profound influence on solvolysis rate exerted by bromine in this position. The effect exerted by neighboring bromine on solvolysis rate is called by Winstein anchimeric assistance [43].

6.18 THE QUESTION OF PHENONIUM ION

The solvolysis of 3-phenyl-2-butyl toluenesulfonate has been investigated with striking results by Cram [44]. There are two stereoisomers of this substance, threo T and erythro V.

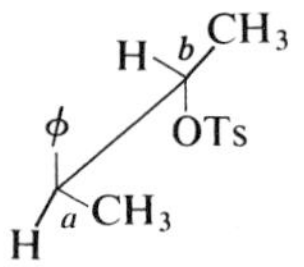

(T) 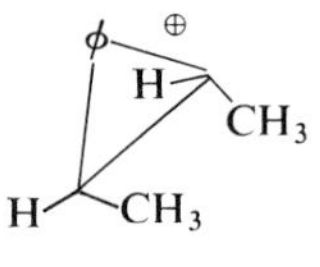 (U)

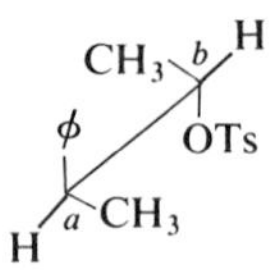

(V) 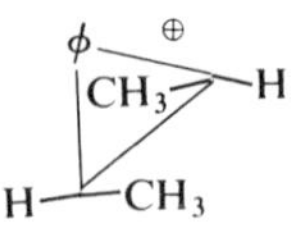 (W)

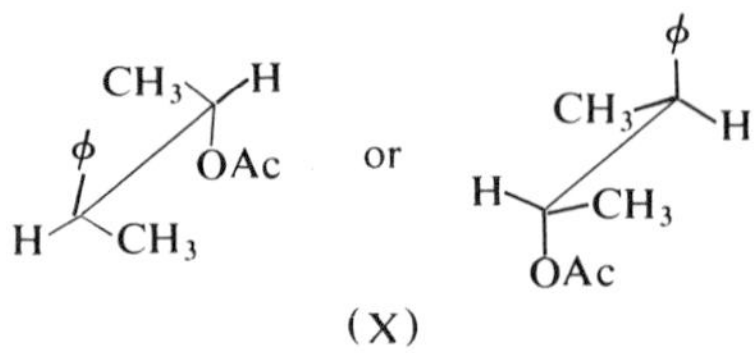

or

(X)

Both are solvolyzed in acetic or formic acid solution with a yield of acetate or formate ester of from 50 to 70 percent, the rest of the reaction product being mostly olefins. The ester from the optically active threo compound is better than 95 percent racemic threo; that from the active erythro compound is better than 94 percent active ester formed with retention of configuration. Isotopic labeling experiments show that when the phenyl is initially attached to carbon *a* the ester formed is a 1:1 mixture of substances in which the phenyl group is attached to carbons *a* and *b*, respectively [45].

Because configuration is retained, not inverted, the intervention of an intermediate is indicated. This must be one which, on the average, reacts with solvent equally at carbons *a* and *b*. It must also be one in which there is decided interference with the rotation about the *a*—*b* bond which would interconvert the threo and erythro structures. There is some interconversion, but it involves only about 5 percent of the product in the acetolysis and much less in the formolysis. These requirements are satisfied by the assignment of structures U and W, which Cram calls phenonium ions, to the intermediates formed from the threo and erythro reactants. Structure U has a plane of symmetry, and an inverting reaction with the solvent can lead only to racemic product with the threo configuration. An inverting reaction with structure W at either carbon *a* or carbon *b* would lead to the same product, active erythro X with retained configuration.

In terms of this picture one would expect, as Brown [46] has emphasized, an anchimeric assistance of the kind observed in the bromonium-ion case. Opinions of those skilled in the art differ emphatically on the question whether or not such assistance is present [47]. The elegance of the theory of the bromonium-ion intermediate, a theory which accounts decisively for otherwise unrelated phenomena, is therefore present somewhat uncertainly in the phenonium-ion hypothesis.

6.19 REARRANGEMENTS

"All rearrangements involving a change in the carbon skeleton may be accounted for by a hypothesis of Whitmore [48] as follows: a carbonium ion is formed, and an alkyl group together with its bonding pair shifts from a neighboring carbon atom to the carbonium carbon. . . . The group that shifts may be a hydrogen atom with its bonding pair, i.e., a hydride ion." [26, p. 317] Since this was written detailed information about rearrangements of this sort has accumulated in very large amount. So also have problems of mechanistic detail of the kind involved in the phenonium-ion question.[1] I shall make no attempt to survey this extensive material. My comment of 1940 should be amplified to include under the heading of neighboring carbon atoms in the

[1] There are excellent summaries in [4], pp. 126–157 and 181–187, and in [49], chap. 14.

5 and 6 positions in 8- to 12-membered rings, at least so far as hydride shifts are concerned [50].

In the interest of historical accuracy it should be noted that Whitmore explicitly denied that the intermediate he assumed was a carbonium ion; it was a carbon atom with a sextet of electrons. The climate of opinion in the Establishment in the early 1930s was decidedly unfavorable toward ions as reaction intermediates. In view of the importance of ion pairs in current thinking Whitmore's conservatism was perhaps foresighted.

6.20 ELECTROPHILIC AROMATIC DISPLACEMENT

There is a familiar group of reactions in which a ring hydrogen in an aromatic compound, or sometimes an SO_3 or NO_2 group or a halogen, is replaced by another atom or group and for which the effect of changes in the structure of the aromatic compound have a common pattern. The group includes Friedel-Crafts reactions, hydrogen isotope exchange, sulfonation, most types of nitration, some kinds of halogenation, and diazo coupling.[1] Since the reactions all appear to involve the displacement of one electron-deficient entity by another, they are suitably called electrophilic aromatic displacements. The Ingold symbol is S_E.

The diazo-coupling reaction of phenols and aromatic amines can be carried out in dilute aqueous solution and has been an important technical process for a long time. Consequently a large background of both theoretical and empirical nature is available. Both kinds of background have been utilized by Zollinger and his collaborators in a series of very illuminating studies of the reaction.

6.21 THE DIAZO-COUPLING REACTION

Aromatic diazonium salts are strong electrolytes in aqueous solution. The two nitrogen atoms are not interchangeable.[2] A satisfactory representation of the structure of the diazonium ion is the resonance hybrid Y.

$$C_6H_5-\overset{+}{N}\equiv\overset{-}{N} \longleftrightarrow C_6H_5-\overset{-}{N}=\overset{+}{N}$$

(Y)

Both by electrometric pH titrations [53] and by spectrophotometric methods [54] the diazonium ion can be shown to be involved in a mobile reversible reaction

$$ArN_2^+ + H_2O \rightleftharpoons ArN_2O^- + 2H^+ \qquad (XV)$$

[1] There is an excellent review in [51].

[2] This background is summarized in [52], p. 40.

These experiments furnish no evidence for the presence of the diazonium hydroxide, ArN_2OH, and indeed exclude its presence to the extent of as much as 1 percent of the total diazonium substance present under any conditions of acidity. The pK_D value, i.e., the value of $-\log K_D$ for the dibasic acid ArN_2^+ runs from 18.88 for *p*-nitrobenzene diazonium ion to 25.18 for the *p*-methyl derivative [54].

The primitive value $k^{(p)}$ of the specific rate of the coupling of diazonium compound and phenol, defined as

$$k^{(p)} = \frac{v}{c_d\, c_p} \tag{27}$$

where v is reaction rate and

$$c_d = [Ar_d\, N_2^+] + [Ar_dN_2O^-] \tag{28}$$

$$c_p = [Ar_pOH] + [Ar_pO^-] \tag{29}$$

increases with increasing pH in the region from 4.5 to 9.2 [55], but Wittwer and Zollinger [53] found that it decreases with increasing pH in the region of 12 to 13. This is illustrated by Fig. 6.6, in which the experimental points represent the data of Wittwer and Zollinger for the reaction

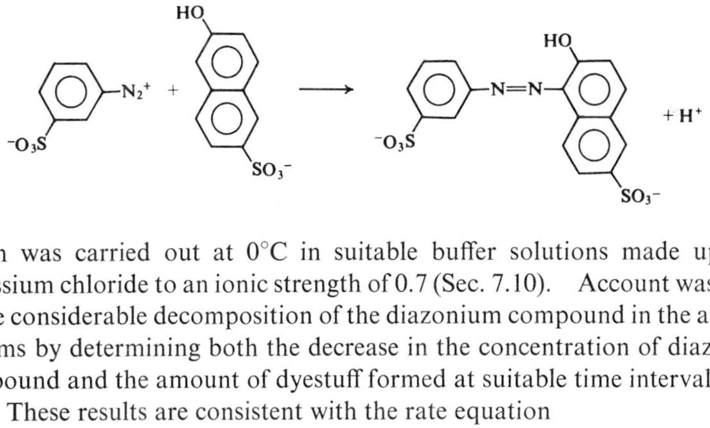

^-O_3S–C_6H_4–N_2^+ + HO–$C_{10}H_5$–SO_3^- → ^-O_3S–C_6H_4–N=N–$C_{10}H_4$(HO)–SO_3^- + H^+ (XVI)

which was carried out at 0°C in suitable buffer solutions made up with potassium chloride to an ionic strength of 0.7 (Sec. 7.10). Account was taken of the considerable decomposition of the diazonium compound in the alkaline systems by determining both the decrease in the concentration of diazonium compound and the amount of dyestuff formed at suitable time intervals.

These results are consistent with the rate equation

$$v = k[Ar_dN_2^+]\,[Ar_pO^-] \tag{30}$$

For it follows from

$$\frac{[Ar_dN_2O^-]\,[H^+]^2}{[Ar_dN_2^+]} = K_d \tag{31}$$

that

$$c_d = [Ar_dN_2^+]\left(1 + \frac{K_d}{[H^+]^2}\right) \tag{32}$$

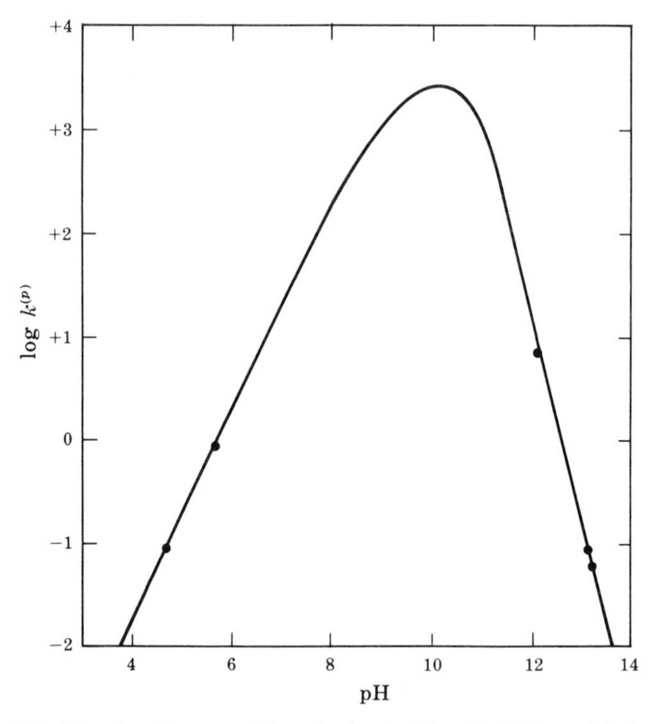

Fig. 6.6 Coupling rate of diazotized metanilic acid with 2-naphthol-6-sulfonic acid. (*Data of Wittwer and Zollinger* [53].)

Similarly

$$c_p = [\mathrm{Ar}_p\mathrm{O}^-]\left(1 + \frac{[\mathrm{H}^+]}{K_p}\right) \tag{33}$$

Consequently

$$k^{(p)} = \frac{k}{(1 + [\mathrm{H}^+]/K_p)(1 + K_d/[\mathrm{H}^+]^2)} \tag{34}$$

The relation between $\log k^{(p)}$ and pH which corresponds to Eq. (34) is plotted in Fig. 6.6 and is clearly in agreement with the observations. It is significant that the values $K_d = 2.1 \times 10^{-22}$ and $K_p = 6.3 \times 10^{-10}$ used in constructing this plot were not obtained from the kinetic data but came from electrometric pH measurements on the diazonium compound and the phenol.

Values of K_d and K_p could be derived from the kinetic measurements alone, although not with high precision. For large hydrogen-ion concentrations Eq. (34) reduces to $k^{(p)} = kK_p/[\mathrm{H}^+]$, that is, to $\log k^{(p)} = \log(kK_p) + \mathrm{pH}$; consequently the value of the product kK_p can be obtained from the linear portion of the plot to the left of the maximum. Similarly the equation of the linear portion of the plot to the right of the maximum is $\log k^{(p)} = \log(k/K_d) - 2\mathrm{pH}$, and the value of the ratio k/K_d is therefore easily obtained. Individual values of the three parameters can be obtained, however, only from the behavior of the plot near the maximum.

6.22 THE QUESTION OF THE APPROACH TO THE TRANSITION STATE

It is not possible to exclude the presence of the diazonium hydroxide in mobile equilibrium with the diazonium ion, even though there is no direct evidence for its existence. If there is a mobile equilibrium,

$$\frac{[H^+][Ar_dN_2OH]}{[Ar_dN_2{}^+]} = K_i \tag{35}$$

from which with the equilibrium relation for the ionization of the phenol

$$[Ar_dN_2OH][Ar_pOH] = \frac{K_i}{K_p}[Ar_dN_2{}^+][Ar_pO^-] \tag{36}$$

Consequently any experimental data that are consistent with a rate proportional to $[Ar_dN_2{}^+][Ar_pO^-]$ and with a mechanism involving the direct combination of the diazonium ion with the phenolate ion are equally consistent with a rate proportional to $[Ar_dN_2OH][Ar_pOH]$ and with a mechanism involving the direct combination of the diazohydroxide with phenol. Indeed they are equally consistent with a mechanism involving the reaction of the diazotate anion with the conjugate acid of the phenol.

Here, as in so many cases in which a reactant is involved in a mobile equilibrium, the effort to derive a detailed mechanism has been painful

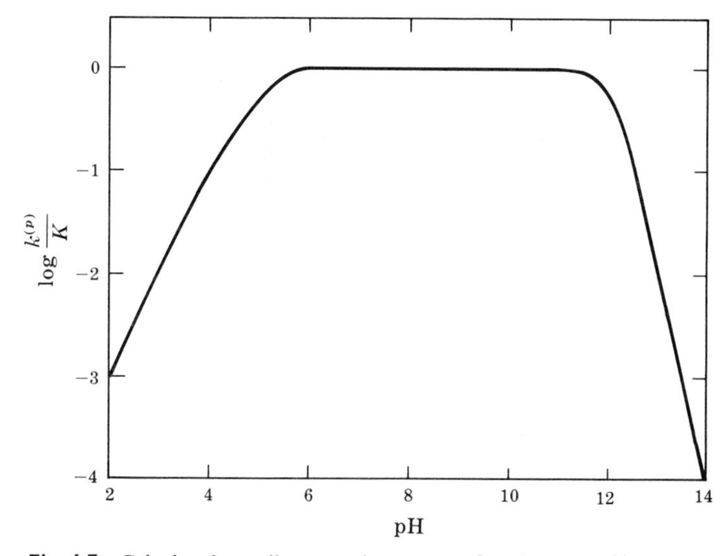

Fig. 6.7 Calculated coupling rates for $K_p = 10^{-5}$ and $K_d = 10^{-24}$.

(Sec. 5.18). The appearance can be deceptive. If in the diazo-coupling reaction K_p is considerably larger than $K_d^{1/2}$, there will be a significant region of pH in which both $[H^+]/K_p$ and $K_d/[H^+]^2$ are much smaller than unity and for which Eq. (34) reduces to $k^{(p)} = k$. Under these conditions the picture of Fig. 6.6 changes to one in which there is a broad flat top to the plot, as in Fig. 6.7, which is calculated for $K_d = 10^{-24}$ and $K_p = 10^{-5}$. Measurements made only in the pH range below 10 will be representable by

$$k^{(p)} = k \frac{K_p}{K_p + [H^+]} \tag{37}$$

a relation whose resemblance to

$$\frac{[Ar_pO^-]}{c_p} = \frac{K_p}{K_p + [H^+]} \tag{38}$$

makes it natural to interpret the reaction as one in which the phenolate ion Ar_pO^- is a direct participant [56].

6.23 THE NATURE OF THE TRANSITION STATE IN THE DIAZO-COUPLING REACTION

The diazo-coupling reaction requires both the formation of a bond between the diazo nitrogen and the carbon atom of the phenol and the removal of a hydrogen ion from that carbon. A mere ejection of the hydrogen ion would require an impossibly high energy; it must be removed by combination with a base, which may be but need not be the solvent water. If the bond to the base is formed to a significant extent in the rate-determining transition state, the substitution of D or T for this H would be expected to reduce the rate substantially, by a factor of as much as 12 for deuterium (Sec. 5.22). It would also be likely that solute bases, especially hydroxyl ion, would participate in place of water, a process which would produce measurable deviations from Eq. (34) in alkaline solutions.

6.24 THE PYRIDINE CATALYSIS

An important feature of the situation is the fact, which has been known for many years in the dyestuff industry and has important practical applications, that some diazo-coupling reactions which are otherwise sluggish are strongly catalyzed by pyridine. A pronounced effect of this sort seems to exist only in cases in which the coupling site in the phenolic component is severely crowded by neighboring substituents [56]. Thus 1-naphthol-4-sulfonic acid Z

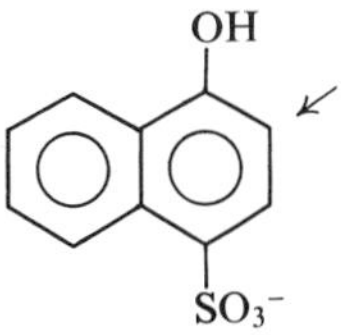

(Z) 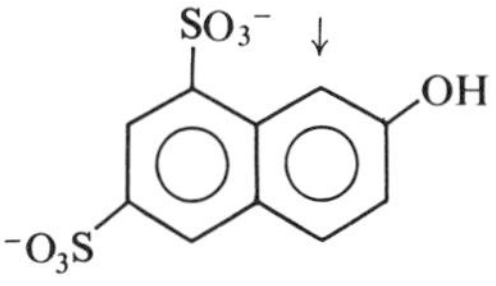 (AA)

which couples at the 2 position indicated by the arrow shows no catalysis by pyridine in the coupling reaction [56] and the rate agrees with Eq. (34) at pH values up to 10 [57, 58]. The replacement of H by D in the 2 position has no significant effect on the rate of coupling. The ratio k_H/k_D is 0.97 for coupling with *o*-methoxybenzenediazonium ion and 1.04 for coupling with *p*-chlorobenzenediazonium ion [59]. In this case, which appears to be typical for nonhindered coupling, the reaction resembles a wide variety of electrophilic aromatic displacement reactions, notably nitration and halogenation, which show no hydrogen isotope effect [60].

By contrast 2-naphthol-6,8-disulfonic acid (AA), which couples in the 1 position which is crowded by the peri sulfonic group, reacts only 0.018 times as fast with *p*-chlorobenzenediazonium ion as the 1-naphthol-4-sulfonic acid does [59]. There is pronounced catalysis by pyridine, a hundredfold by 0.25 *M* pyridine, and the rate in strongly alkaline solution is greater than that predicted by Eq. (34). Replacement of H in the 1 position by D decreases the rate of coupling with *p*-chlorobenzenediazonium ion by a factor of 6.55 [57].

The catalysis by pyridine is not only large, it is far from linear. In the experiments represented by Fig. 6.8 varying amounts of pyridine plus one-tenth of an equivalent of HCl together with enough KCl to maintain an ionic strength of 0.2 were added to a phosphate buffer of pH 6.68. At the lower pyridine concentrations the effect on the electrometric pH was small, and even with 1 *M* pyridine it dropped only to 6.5. The ordinate in the figure is the k of Eq. (34) not the $k^{(p)}$, the abscissa is the concentration of pyridine base, and the points are experimental.

This behavior is quantitatively consistent with a two-step mechanism involving transition states of structures BB and DD and an intermediate of structure CC.

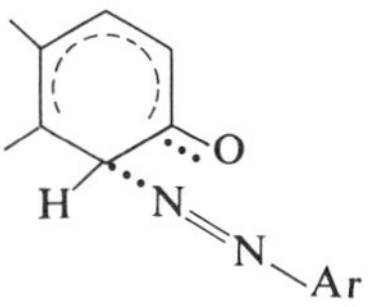

(BB) 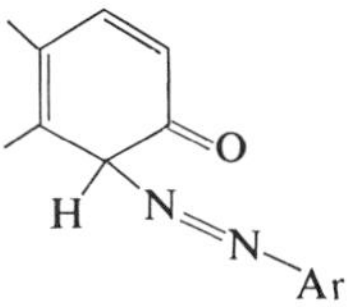 (CC) 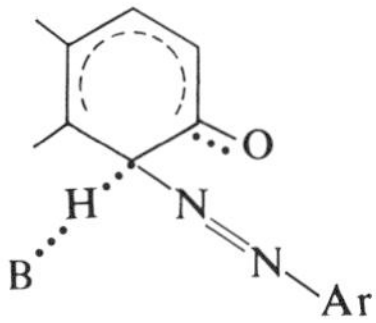 (DD)

The base B may be water, the HPO_4^{--} of the buffer, or pyridine. Since the reaction rate is proportional to the product [D][N], where D is diazonium ion and N is naphtholate ion, the Bodenstein approximation may be used. This leads to [61]

$$\frac{1}{k^{(p)}} = \frac{1}{k_1}\left\{1 + \frac{1}{k_w/k_{-1} + (k_2/k_{-1})\,[\mathrm{P}]}\right\} \tag{39}$$

where P = pyridine base

k_1 = specific rate of formation of intermediate from D and N

k_w = specific rate of reaction of intermediate with water or HPO_4^{--} or both

k_2 = specific rate of reaction of intermediate with pyridine

This equation is plotted in Fig. 6.8 with $k_1 = 244$, $k_w/k_{-1} = 0.00248$, and $k_2/k_{-1} = 0.987$. The rms deviation of the experimental points is 3 percent, and positive and negative deviations show a random scatter.

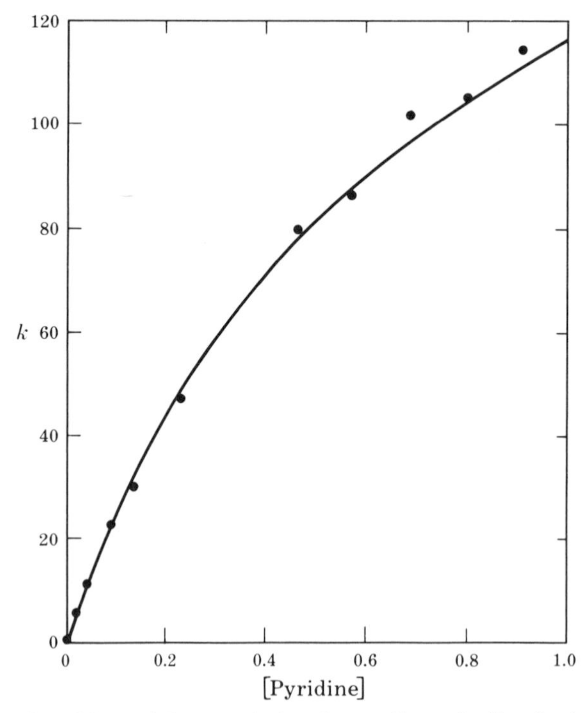

Fig. 6.8 Pyridine catalysis of coupling of diazotized *p*-chloroaniline with 2-naphthol-6;8-disulfonic acid. [*Data of R. Ernst, O. A. Stamm, and H. Zollinger, Helv. Chim. Acta,* **41**: 2274 (1958).]

6.25 HYDROGEN ISOTOPE EFFECTS IN THE DIAZO COUPLING

If the H in the 1 position of 2-naphthol-6,8-disulfonic acid is replaced by D, the ratio k_H/k_D for coupling with *p*-chlorobenzenediazonium ion is 6.55 in the absence of pyridine, 6.01 with 0.232 *M* pyridine, and 3.62 with 0.905 pyridine [58]. This is intelligible in terms of the two-step mechanism. The addition of pyridine increases the rate of the second step, and this makes the overall rate more dependent on the first step, in which there is no primary isotope effect.

If one neglects possible secondary isotope effects, k_1 and k_{-1} should be unaffected by substitution of D for H. On this basis

$$\frac{k_H}{k_D} = x \frac{1 + (k_2/k_w)[P]}{1 + (x/y)(k_2/k_w)[P]} \frac{1 + (1/x)(k_w/k_{-1}) + (1/y)(k_2/k_{-1})[P]}{1 + (k_w/k_{-1}) + (k_2/k_{-1})[P]} \tag{40}$$

where

$$x = \frac{k_{w(H)}}{k_{w(D)}} \tag{41}$$

and

$$y = \frac{k_{2(H)}}{k_{2(D)}} \tag{42}$$

and the k's on the right side of Eq. (40) all apply to the hydrogen compound. From the observed value of k_H/k_D in the absence of pyridine the value of x is 6.57, and from the value of k_H/k_D at high concentrations of pyridine the value of y is 5.97. From these values of x and y the k_H/k_D value for 0.0232 *M* pyridine should be 6.01, which is in good agreement with the observed value.

Another revealing isotope effect appears when the same naphthol disulfonic acid is coupled with *p*-chloro-, *m*-chloro-, and *p*-nitrobenzene-diazonium ion [58]. The specific rates for the H compound in a phosphate buffer increase in this sequence in the ratio 1:12.3:1,780, while the k_H/k_D values are 6.55, 5.48, and 4.78. If k_1 and k_{-1} are not subject to an isotope effect,

$$\frac{k_H}{k_D} = \frac{(k_w/k_{-1}) + x}{(k_w/k_{-1}) + 1} \tag{43}$$

Since x is considerably greater than unity and should be little (if any) dependent on the substituents in the diazonium ion, the ratio k_w/k_{-1} must increase in the above sequence, i.e., the standard potential of the second transition state decreases more rapidly than that of the first transition state.

These various phenomena supply convincing evidence against a concerted mechanism, i.e., one in which there is a single transition state instead of two, a state in which both the removal of the hydrogen ion and the formation of the carbon-nitrogen bond are under way. In order to accept the concerted mechanism one must suppose that the water reaction and the pyridine reaction are independent parallel reactions. One must admit that a nonlinear-medium effect quantitatively simulates the effect of a two-step reaction. One must make the unlikely assumption that the isotope-effect ratio for the pyridine reaction is only 3.62 while that for the water reaction is 6.55—unlikely because pyridine reacts faster than water does and ought to have a larger not a smaller effect on the vibration frequency of the transition state. If there were independent parallel processes, the reaction in the presence of 0.0232 M pyridine, which is 9.7 times faster than the reaction in the absence of pyridine, would go 90 percent by the pyridine route, and the isotope effect should be 3.83 instead of the 6.01 observed. Finally one must make the unlikely assumption that lowering the standard potential of the transition state by a change in the structure of the diazonium ion decreases the isotope effect.

On the other hand, the two-step mechanism is quantitatively as well as qualitatively in agreement with the varied phenomena with which the concerted mechanism disagrees. The natural conclusion that the coupling reaction also goes by the two-step mechanism in those cases in which catalysis by pyridine and hydrogen isotope effects cannot be detected is an extrapolation. Like any extrapolation it involves some uncertainty.

6.26 STERIC INFLUENCES IN THE DIAZO COUPLING

The value of k_1 for the coupling with *p*-chlorobenzenediazonium ion of the sterically hindered 2-naphthol-6,8-disulfonic acid is 244 liters/mole-sec. If the reaction of the unhindered 1-naphthol-4-sulfonic acid goes by the same mechanism, the value of k_1 is the value of k, which is 404 [59]. It appears therefore that crowding in the neighborhood of the reaction zone has little effect on the difference in the standard potentials of the reactants and the first transition state, for example BB; that is, that there is little hindrance to the approach of the azo nitrogen to the naphthol carbon. But the crowding has a large effect on the difference in standard potential between the first and the second transition states. For the water reaction $\mu_w^\ddagger$ in the unhindered case must be at least 2 kcal lower than $\mu_1^\ddagger$, otherwise the kinetics would be observably complex. In the hindered case $\mu_w^\ddagger$ is 3.5 kcal higher than $\mu_1^\ddagger$, since k_w/k_{-1} is 0.0025. The steric effect is therefore determined by the difference between the standard potentials of transition states of type BB and DD; that is, it involves interference with the approach of the base in DD.

So far as the phenolic component is concerned the effects of changing structure are in line with predictions from models. The k_H/k_D values for coupling with *p*-chlorobenzenediazonium ion in the position marked by the arrow are 1.04 for EE, 3.10 for FF, 6.2 for GG, and 6.55 for HH [59]. As expected, the SO_3^- group in the peri position in GG and HH has a bigger effect than the one in the ortho position in FF. Catalysis by bases has been observed in the coupling of II. This indicates that the steric effect is not limited to the negatively charged SO_3^- group.

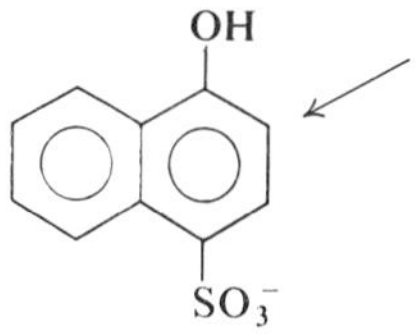

(EE) 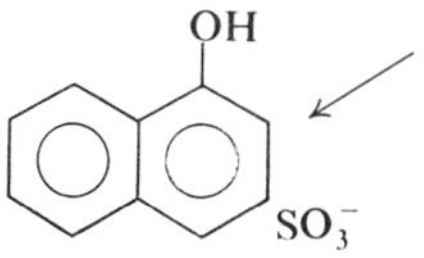 (FF) 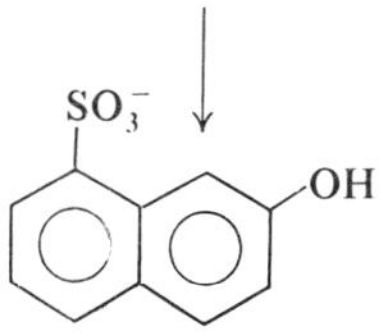 (GG)

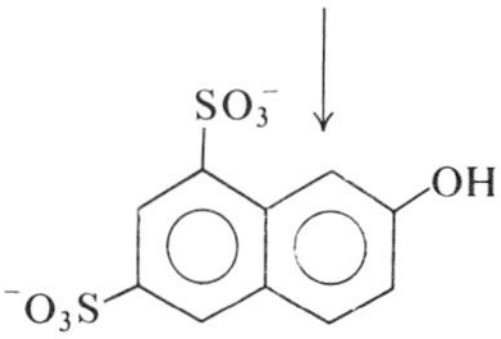

(HH) 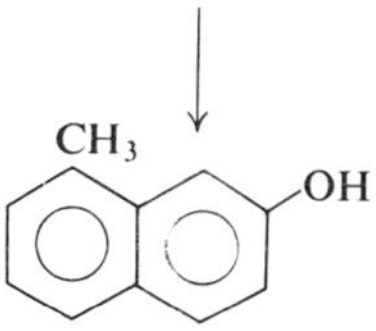 (II)

With respect to the nature of the base, pyridine, although a weaker base than tertiary alkylamines, is a more effective catalyst, but quinuclidine is more effective than triethylamine [62, 63]. The k_2/k_{-1} values for some methyl-substituted pyridines are listed in Table 6.2 along with the pK values of the bases. In the absence of a steric influence the stronger base is a more effective catalyst, but bases substituted in the 2 position are less effective than their strength would predict.

These results are important because they place the position of the base in the second transition state at the point where the crowding exists. Without this evidence one could not exclude the structure

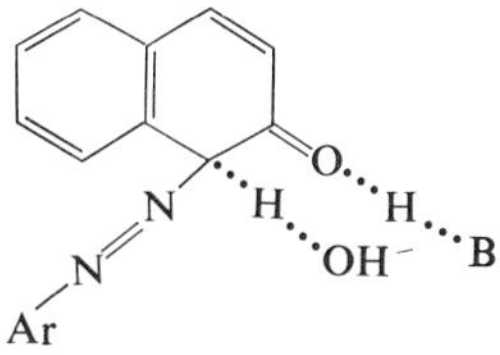

(JJ)

Table 6.2 Effect of pyridine derivatives on diazo-coupling rate[a]

	Pyridine	α-CH_3	β-CH_3	γ-CH_3	2,6-*dimethyl*
$\frac{k_2}{k_{-1}}$	1.30	0.65	1.60	2.50	0.20
pK	5.50	6.37	6.12	6.43	7.09

[a] Data of Zollinger [62].

in which the ring hydrogen is being removed by a hydroxyl ion while pyridinium ion simultaneously transfers a proton to the phenolic oxygen. If this were the transition state of the second step, its rate would be proportional to the product $[C_5H_5NH^+][OH^-]$, which is proportional to the concentration of pyridine, in agreement with the observed kinetics.

This kind of problem in connection with the structure of the transition state is a common one in reactions which exhibit general acid or base catalysis [64]. It has been approached in other cases than this [65] through a study of steric effects on reaction rate.

6.27 AN ENTROPY PHENOMENON

o-Nitrobenzenediazonium ion couples with 1-naphthol-3-sulfonic acid FF both in the ortho, or 2, position and in the para, or 4, position [66]. The specific rate, the k of Eq. (34), varies with the kind and concentration of the buffer solution in which the reaction takes place even at constant pH. This is the characteristic feature of a reaction subject to general acid or base catalysis (Sec. 10.1). Data on the two reactions in a 1:1 sodium acetate–acetic acid buffer are plotted against acetate-ion concentration in Fig. 6.9. For ortho coupling, the upper plot, the picture is that of a reaction which is only slightly

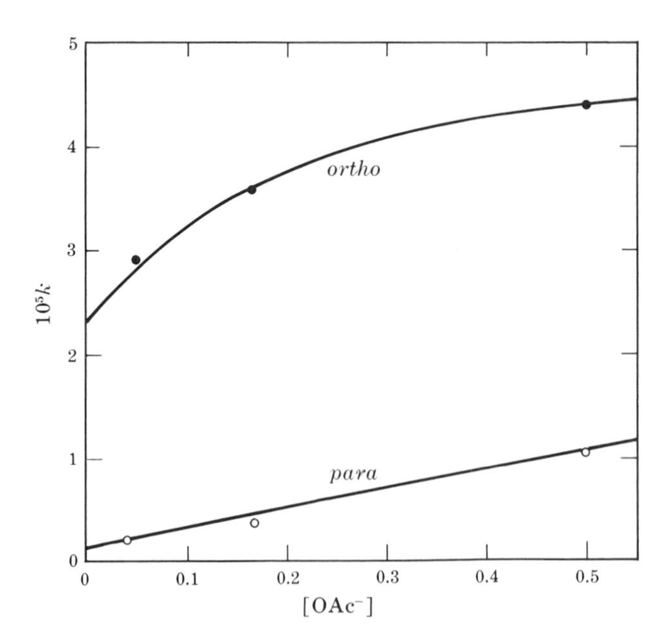

Fig. 6.9 Coupling rate of diazotized *o*-nitroaniline with 1-naphthol-3-sulfonic acid in the ortho and para positions. [*Data of O. A. Stamm and H. Zollinger, Helv. Chim. Acta,* **40**: 1955 (1957).]

accelerated by bases and is rapidly approaching the upper limit of this acceleration. The curve drawn is based on Eq. (39) with $k_1 = 5.5 \times 10^{-5}$, $k_w/k_{-1} = 0.7$, and $k_2/k_{-1} = 6.0$; k_2 is the specific rate of the reaction of acetate ion with the intermediate. From these values the specific rate of the coupling in the ortho position in the 0.5 *M* acetate buffer is 80 percent of k_1, that is, the first step is essentially rate-determining. For coupling in the para position the picture corresponds to considerable steric hindrance. There is a strong catalysis by the base acetate ion, and the rate in the absence of catalyst is over an order of magnitude smaller than the rate in the ortho position. The hindrance is presumably due to the hydrogen in the peri position.

From the effect of temperature on the rates of coupling in the two positions in a 0.5 *M* acetate buffer it is found that the entropy of activation is 28 ± 8 cal/deg more positive for ortho coupling than for para coupling. It is possible that this derives from the difference in the composition of the effective transition states in the two cases. For ortho coupling the observed specific rate is essentially equal to k_1 and is therefore determined by the change in standard potential involved in bringing together two solute entities, the diazonium and the naphtholate ions, to form the rate-determining transition state. For para coupling at high concentrations of catalyst the specific rate is essentially determined by the standard potential of the second transition state, which is formed by bringing together three solute entities, the diazonium, the naphtholate, and acetate ions. This might well lead to a lower entropy of activation for the para than for the ortho coupling, even though solvation effects may complicate the situation (Sec. 5.21).

REFERENCES

1. Phillips, H.: *J. Chem. Soc.*, **123:** 44 (1923); J. Kenyon, H. Phillips, and H. G. Turley: *ibid.*, **127:** 399 (1925); H. Phillips: *ibid.*, **127:** 2552 (1925); G. A. C. Gough, H. Hunter, and J. Kenyon: *ibid.*, 2052 (1926); J. Kenyon, H. Phillips, and V. P. Pittman: *ibid.*, 1072 (1935); C. M. Bean, J. Kenyon, and H. Phillips: *ibid.*, 303 (1936).
2. Holmberg, B.: *J. Prakt. Chem.*, (2) **88:** 553 (1913).
3. Hughes, E. D., F. Juliusberger, S. Masterman, B. Topley, and J. Weiss: *J. Chem. Soc.*, **1935:** 1525; E. D. Hughes, F. Juliusberger, A. D. Scott, B. Topley, and J. Weiss: *ibid.*, **1936:** 1173; W. A. Cowdrey, E. D. Hughes, T. P. Nevell, and C. L. Wilson: *ibid.*, **1938:** 209.
4. Streitwieser, A., Jr.: "Solvolytic Displacement Reactions," McGraw-Hill Book Company, New York, 1962.
5. Olivier, S. C. J., and G. Berger: *Rec. Trav. Chim.*, **45:** 712 (1926); A. M. Ward: *J. Chem. Soc.*, **1927:** 2285; C. K. Ingold: *Ann. Rept. Progr. Chem.* (*Chem. Soc., London*), **24:** 156 (1927).
6. Bateman, L. C., E. D. Hughes, and C. K. Ingold: *J. Chem. Soc.*, **1940:** 974.
7. Benfey, O. T., E. D. Hughes, and C. K. Ingold: *J. Chem. Soc.*, **1952:** 2488.
8. Bunton, C. A., and B. Nayak: *J. Chem. Soc.*, **1959:** 3854.
9. Bailey, T. H., J. R. Fox, E. Jackson, G. Kohnstam, and A. Queen: *Chem. Commun.*, **1966:** 122.

10. Cooper, K. A., E. D. Hughes, and C. K. Ingold: *J. Chem. Soc.*, **1937:** 1280; K. A. Cooper, E. D. Hughes, C. K. Ingold, and B. J. MacNulty: *ibid.*, **1948:** 2038.
11. Lucas, G. L., and L. P. Hammett: *J. Am. Chem. Soc.*, **64:** 1938 (1942).
12. Winstein, S., M. Hojo, and S. Smith: *Tetrahedron Letters*, **1960:** 12.
13. Clarke, G. A., and R. W. Taft: *J. Am. Chem. Soc.*, **84:** 2295 (1962).
14. Farinacci, N. T., and L. P. Hammett: *J. Am. Chem. Soc.*, **59:** 2542 (1937); **60:** 3097 (1938).
15. Ward, A. M.: *J. Chem. Soc.*, **1927:** 2285.
16. Norris, J. F., and A. A. Morton: *J. Am. Chem. Soc.*, **50:** 1795 (1928).
17. Ingold, C. K.: "Structure and Mechanism in Organic Chemistry," pp. 310ff, Cornell University Press, Ithaca, N.Y., 1953.
18. Streitwieser, A., Jr.,: *J. Am. Chem. Soc.*, **77:** 1117 (1955).
19. Cocivera, M., and S. Winstein: *J. Am. Chem. Soc.*, **85:** 1702 (1963).
20. Cram, D. J., and M. R. V. Sahyun: *J. Am. Chem. Soc.*, **85:** 1257 (1963).
21. Catchpole, A. G., and E. D. Hughes: *J. Chem. Soc.*, **1948:** 1.
22. Goering, H. L., E. G. Briody, and J. F. Levy: *J. Am. Chem. Soc.*, **85:** 3059 (1963).
23. Goering, H. L., and S. Chang: *Tetrahedron Letters*, **1965:** 3607.
24. Lévy, H. A., and L. O. Brockway: *J. Am. Chem. Soc.*, **59:** 2085 (1937).
25. Ogg, R. A., Jr., and M. Polanyi: *Trans. Faraday Soc.*, **31:** 604 (1935).
26. Hammett, L. P.: "Physical Organic Chemistry," 1st ed., McGraw-Hill Book Company, New York, 1940.
27. Young, W. G., S. Winstein, and H. L. Goering: *J. Am. Chem. Soc.*, **73:** 1958 (1951).
28. Winstein, S., B. Appel, R. Baker, and A. Diaz: *Chem. Soc. (London) Spec. Pub.* 19, 1965.
29. Weiner, H., and R. A. Sneen: *J. Am. Chem. Soc.*, **87:** 287, 292 (1965).
30. Sneen, R. A., and J. W. Larsen: *J. Am. Chem. Soc.*, **88:** 2593 (1966).
31. de la Mare, P. D. B., and C. A. Vernon: *J. Chem. Soc.*, **1954:** 2504.
32. Winstein, S., and G. C. Robinson: *J. Am. Chem. Soc.*, **80:** 169 (1958).
33. Goering, H. A., and J. F. Levy: *J. Am. Chem. Soc.*, **86:** 120 (1964).
34. Winstein, S., E. Clippinger, A. H. Fainberg, and G. C. Robinson: *J. Am. Chem. Soc.*, **76:** 2597 (1954).
35. Winstein, S., P. E. Klinedienst, Jr., and G. C. Robinson: *J. Am. Chem. Soc.*, **83:** 885 (1961). In this article k_1 is erroneously substituted for k_{-1} in the denominator of Eq. (22).
36. Allred, E. L., and S. Winstein: *J. Am. Chem. Soc.*, **89:** 3998 (1967).
37. Cowdrey, W. A., E. D. Hughes, and C. K. Ingold: *J. Chem. Soc.*, **1937:** 1208; **1938:** 1243.
38. Grunwald, E., and S. Winstein: *J. Am. Chem. Soc.*, **70:** 841 (1948).
39. Polanyi, M., and A. L. Szabo: *Trans. Faraday Soc.*, **30:** 508 (1934).
40. Olson, A. R., and R. J. Miller: *J. Am. Chem. Soc.*, **60:** 2687 (1938).
41. Winstein, S., and H. J. Lucas: *J. Am. Chem. Soc.*, **61:** 1575, 2845 (1939).
42. Winstein, S., E. Grunwald, and L. L. Ingraham: *J. Am. Chem. Soc.*, **70:** 821 (1948); E. Grunwald: *ibid.*, **73:** 5458 (1951).
43. Winstein, S., C. R. Lindegren, H. Marshall, and L. L. Ingraham: *J. Am. Chem. Soc.*, **75:** 147 (1953).
44. Cram, D. J.: *J. Am. Chem. Soc.*, **71:** 3863, 3975 (1949); **86:** 3767 (1964).
45. Smith, W. B., and M. Showalter: *J. Am. Chem. Soc.*, **86:** 4136 (1964).
46. Brown, H. C.: *Chem. Soc. (London) Spec. Pub.* 16, p. 140, 1962.
47. Brown, H. C., K. J. Morgan, and F. J. Chloupek: *J. Am. Chem. Soc.*, **87:** 2137 (1965); D. J. Cram and J. A. Thompson, *ibid.*, **89:** 6766 (1967).
48. Whitmore, F. C.: *J. Am. Chem. Soc.*, **54:** 3274 (1932).
49. Hine, J.: "Physical Organic Chemistry," 2nd ed., McGraw-Hill Book Company, New York, 1962.

50. Cope, A. C., S. W. Fenton, and C. F. Spencer: *J. Am. Chem. Soc.*, **74:** 5884 (1952); H. J. Urech and V. Prelog: *Helv. Chim. Acta*, **40:** 477 (1957); J. D. Dunitz and V. Prelog: *Angew. Chem.*, **73:** 896 (1960).
51. Berliner, E.: *Progr. Phys. Org. Chem.*, **2:** 253 (1964).
52. Zollinger, H.: "Diazo and Azo Chemistry," p. 40, trans. H. E. Nursten, Interscience Publishers, Inc., New York, 1961.
53. Wittwer, C., and H. Zollinger: *Helv. Chim. Acta*, **37:** 1954 (1954).
54. Lewis, E. S., and H. Suhr: *Ber.*, **91:** 2350 (1858).
55. Conant, J. B., and W. D. Peterson: *J. Am. Chem. Soc.*, **52:** 1220 (1930); R. Wistar and P. D. Bartlett: *ibid.*, **63:** 413 (1941).
56. Pütter, R.: *Angew. Chem.*, **63:** 188 (1951).
57. Zollinger, H.: *Helv. Chim. Acta*, **38:** 1597 (1955).
58. Zollinger, H.: *Helv. Chim. Acta*, **38:** 1617 (1955).
59. Ernst, R., O. A. Stamm, and H. Zollinger: *Helv. Chim. Acta*, **41:** 2274 (1958).
60. Melander, L.: *Arkiv. Kemi*, **2:** 213 (1950); *Chem. Soc. (London) Spec. Pub.* 16, p. 77, 1962; "The Use of Nuclides in the Determination of Organic Reaction Mechanisms," University of Notre Dame Press, Notre Dame, Ind., 1965.
61. Zollinger, H.: *Chem. Ind. (London)*, **1965:** 885.
62. Zollinger, H.: *Helv. Chim. Acta*, **38:** 1623 (1955).
63. Zollinger, H.: *Angew. Chem.*, **70:** 204 (1958).
64. Pedersen, K. J.: *J. Phys. Chem.*, **38:** 581 (1934).
65. Zucker, L., and L. P. Hammett: *J. Am. Chem. Soc.*, **61:** 2785 (1939).
66. Stamm, O. A., and H. Zollinger: *Helv. Chim. Acta*, **40:** 1955 (1957).

7
Salt Effects

7.1 THE BRØNSTED EQUATION

The salt effect occupies a key position in the theory of reaction rates in solution because the only quantitatively predictable effect of medium on rate is that described by the Brønsted equation

$$k = k^{\circ} \frac{\gamma_{A} \gamma_{B}}{\gamma_{\ddagger}} \tag{1}$$

This is concerned with the effect of the kind and concentration of the ions present in a solution on the specific rate k of a reaction between ions A and B. k° is the limiting value of the specific rate for zero value of all ion concentrations, γ_{A} and γ_{B} are the activity coefficients of A and B, and $\gamma_{\ddagger}$ is the activity coefficient of a molecular species whose charge is the algebraic sum of the charges on A and B. $\gamma_{\ddagger}$ may therefore be interpreted as the activity coefficient of the transition state.

7.2 THE LIMITING LAW

The Debye-Hückel theory predicts that the assigned activity coefficient (Sec. 2.18) of an ionic species i will satisfy the relationship

$$\lim_{I\to 0} \frac{d\log\gamma_i}{dI^{1/2}} = -Az_i^2 \tag{2}$$

Here I is the ionic strength of the solution, given by

$$I = \frac{1}{2}\sum_j c_j z_j^2 \tag{3}$$

with the summation taken over all the ions present in the solution including i, c_j being the concentration and z_j the number of unit charges on ion j. The value of A is given by

$$A = 0.4343\frac{(2\pi N_0)^{1/2}\mathbf{e}^3}{(10\epsilon\mathbf{k}T)^{3/2}} = 1.825\times 10^6(\epsilon T)^{-3/2} \tag{4}$$

in which ϵ is the dielectric constant of the solvent. For water the value of A is 0.512 at 25°C, 0.492 at 0°, and 0.608 at 100°.

The prediction is therefore that the slope of a plot of $\log\gamma$ against $I^{1/2}$ will approach $-Az^2$ as $I^{1/2}$ goes to zero. This prediction has been overwhelmingly verified from measurements of mean ionic-activity coefficients, from measurements of the activity of the solvent (cf. Sec. 2.16), and from observations of the effect of ionic strength on the solubility of strong electrolytes and on other equilibria involving ions.[1] It has been found to be valid not only for aqueous solutions but also for solvents of considerably lower dielectric constant. A related prediction about the conductance-concentration relationship has been even more thoroughly verified.[2]

Combination of the Brønsted equation with the Debye-Hückel limiting law leads to

$$\lim_{I\to 0} \frac{d\log k}{dI^{1/2}} = 2z_A z_B A \tag{5}$$

The factor $2z_A z_B$ enters because $z_{\ddagger} = z_A + z_B$; hence $z_A^2 + z_B^2 - z_{\ddagger}^2 = -2z_A z_B$. Because the z's are algebraic numbers, the equation predicts a positive slope for a plot of $\log k$ against $I^{1/2}$ if A and B have the same sign of charge and a negative slope if they have opposite signs. In either case the magnitude of the limiting slope at low ionic strength should be $2z_A z_B A$. If either A or B is a neutral molecule, the prediction is that the slope will be zero.

[1] See for instance [1] or [2].

[2] See for instance [3].

7.3 SALT EFFECTS ON THE DIAZO-COUPLING REACTION

The validity of these predictions is well illustrated by the data of Zollinger [4] on the diazo-coupling (Sec. 6.21) reactions of 2-naphthylamine-6-sulfonic acid A.

NH_2 $^{-}O_3S$ (A) CH_3—N_2^+ (B)

$^{-}O_3S$—N_2^+ (C) SO_3^- N_2^+ $^{-}O_3S$ (D)

The reactions were carried out at 10°C in a 0.005 *M* acetate buffer in which essentially all the naphthylamine derivative was in form A, which carries a single negative charge. The reactant concentrations were in the range 10^{-3} to 10^{-5}, and the ionic strength was fixed by the addition of suitable amounts

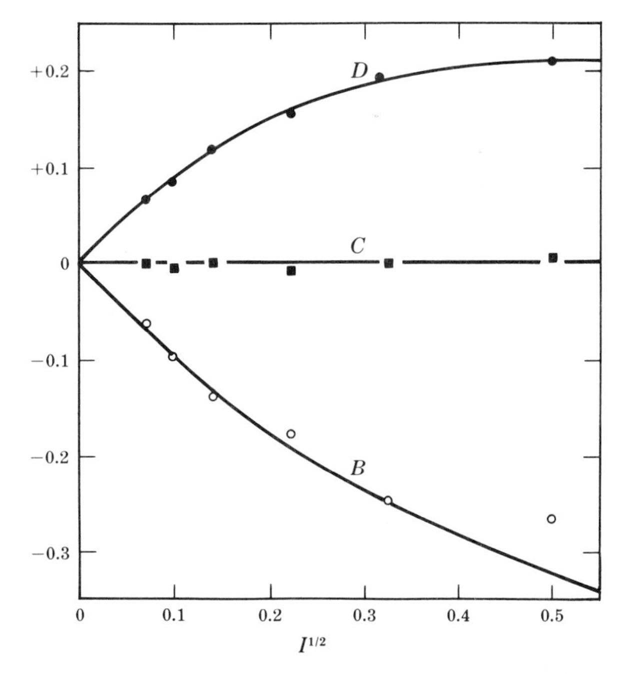

Fig. 7.1 Diazo-coupling rates of amine *A* with *B* (○ = log*k* + 0.532); *C* (■ = log*k* − 1.835); *D* (● = log*k* − 1.586). (*Data of Zollinger* [4].)

of potassium chloride. For reaction with the positively charged 4-diazotoluene B (Fig. 7.1), the slope is negative ($z_A z_B = -1$); for reaction with the electrically neutral diazobenzene-4-sulfonic acid C the specific rate is essentially independent of ionic strength; and for the negatively charged diazobenzene-2,5-disulfonic acid D the slope is positive.

The agreement is satisfactorily quantitative as well as qualitative. Except for the deviant point at $I^{1/2} = 0.5$, the points for the positively charged diazo compound are closely represented by the equation

$$\log k = -0.532 - 1.016 I^{1/2} + 0.73 I \tag{6}$$

which is plotted as curve B in the figure. The data are therefore consistent with a limiting slope of -1.016, which is the value of the quantity $2 z_A z_B A$ at the temperature of the experiments. Similarly the points for the negatively charged diazo compound are closely represented by the equation

$$\log k = 1.586 + 1.016 I^{1/2} - 1.46 I + 0.53 I^{3/2} \tag{7}$$

which is plotted as curve D in the figure. Again the data are consistent with a limiting slope of $2 z_A z_B A$.

7.4 THE APPLICABILITY OF THE LIMITING LAW TO UNSYMMETRICAL IONS

The Debye-Hückel theory is based on a model in which spherically symmetrical charged bodies are immersed in a medium whose dielectric constant is everywhere that observed in macroscopic measurements on the solvent. It is obvious that ions whose structure is of the kind represented by A, B, C, and D are not spheres and that the charge is not symmetrically distributed. Yet the theory is consistent with the observed behavior of these ions, presumably because in very dilute solution most of the ions are far enough apart to make the interaction between them close to that between charged spheres.

The charges must be even more highly localized in specific portions of the ions in the alkaline hydrolysis of aliphatic monoester ions

$$OH^- + C_2H_5OOC(CH_2)_xCOO^- \rightarrow {}^-OOC(CH_2)_xCOO^- + C_2H_5OH \tag{I}$$

In any reasonable picture of the transition state for these reactions two distinct unit charges are present, which are separated by a distance which increases with x. It is of the order of 4 Å for oxalate ($x = 0$) and of the order of 7 for adipate ($x = 3$). The salt effect was studied by Nielsen [5] for x equal to 0, 1, 2, and 3. The reactant concentrations were in the range from 0.0009 to 0.011, and the ionic strength was adjusted to values in the range from 0.05 to 0.25 by the addition of potassium chloride. Nielsen's values of $\log k$ for three of these reactants are plotted against the value of $I^{1/2}$ at the start of the reaction in Fig. 7.2. The behavior of oxalate is similar. The ionic strength of the solution

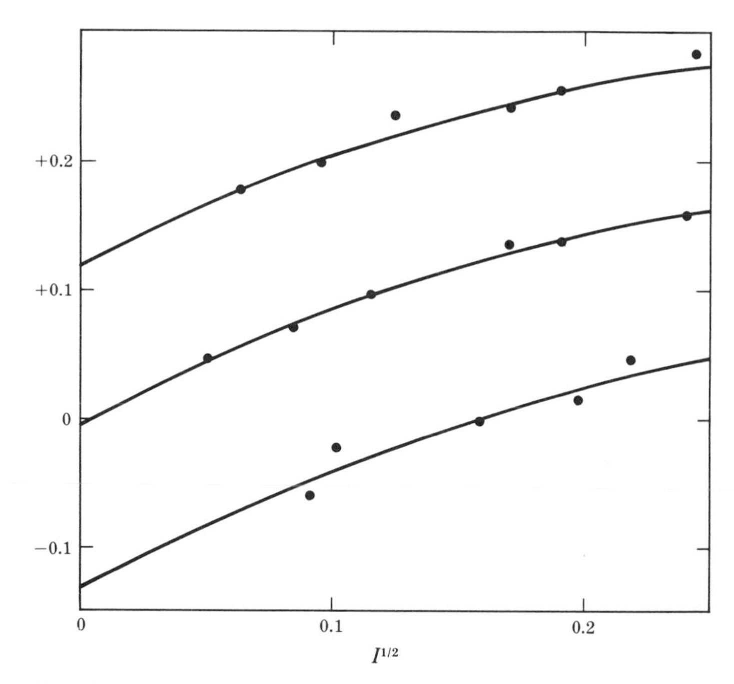

Fig. 7.2 Alkaline hydrolysis of monoester anions: (*lower plot*) $\log k + 0.1$ for malonate; (*middle plot*) $\log k$ for succinate; (*upper plot*) $\log k$ for adipate. (*Data of Nielsen* [5].)

increases as the reaction proceeds, but the specific rate is unchanged, presumably because it depends only on the kind and concentrations of the cations present (Sec. 7.9). The curves in the figure are plots of the equation

$$\log k = \log k^\circ + 1.012 I^{1/2} - bI \tag{8}$$

with b values of 1.2, 1.4, and 1.6 for malonate, succinate, and adipate, respectively. The coefficient 1.012 is the value of $2z_A z_B A$ for the 20° temperature of the experiments. All the ester ions have the same dependence on salt concentration at low salt concentrations, and the dependence is consistent with the Debye-Hückel limiting law.

7.5 THE LIMITING LAW FOR MULTIPLY CHARGED IONS

Data of Barrett and Baxendale [6] on the reaction of $Cr(C_2O_4)_3^{3-}$ with Fe^{++} in very dilute solutions, the maximum ionic strength being 0.006, are presented in Fig. 7.3. Salts of a wide variety of valence types have effects on the specific rate of this reaction between multiply charged ions which approach closely to the Debye-Hückel limiting slope in these very dilute solutions. This is particu-

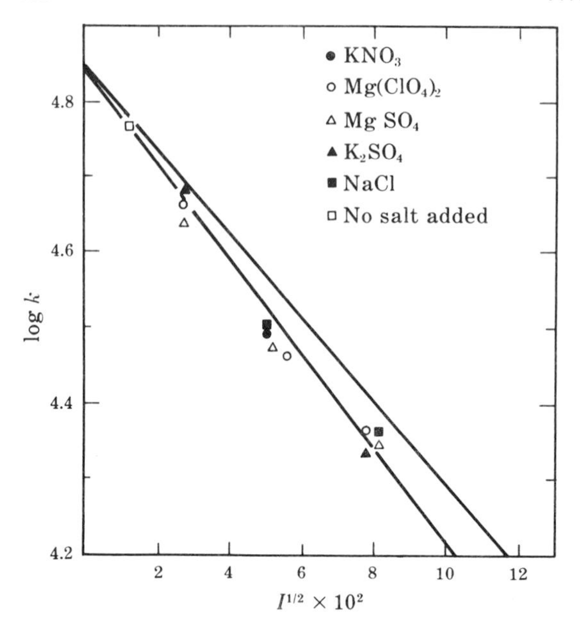

Fig. 7.3 Rate of reaction of Fe^{++} with $Cr(C_2O_4)_3{}^{3-}$. The lower line represents the Debye–Hückel limiting slope; the upper line closely represents many data on the effect of $KClO_4$ and $HClO_4$. (*From Barrett and Baxendale* [6].)

larly significant because abrupt deviations from the limiting slope appear at only slightly higher ionic strengths, when multiply charged ions of both signs are present.

7.6 SALT EFFECTS ON ACTIVITY COEFFICIENTS AT MODERATE SALT CONCENTRATIONS

If the Debye-Hückel limiting law were valid at finite concentrations and not merely as a limit, the relation $\log\gamma = -Az^2$ would apply at concentrations which are of practical as well as of theoretical interest. But even when only singly charged ions are present, the deviations from this equation are considerable at an ionic strength of 0.1 and are appreciable at one of 0.01. When multiply charged ions are present, the deviations are even larger.

Because the activity coefficient of an ion is no longer the same in two solutions which are of the same ionic strength but contain different electrolytes, it is desirable to work with systems in which all or nearly all the ions present derive from a single electrolyte. For this purpose one can suitably study the effect of varying concentrations of a single soluble electrolyte on the solubility of a difficultly soluble salt. The concentration of the ions derived from the saturating salt is so small that their effect may reasonably be expected to be that given by the limiting law, and the characteristic specificities of the effects of the added salts are clearly evident.

In such studies two contrasting types of behavior are observed. One, which may suitably be called the case of weak interactions, appears in aqueous solutions which do not contain both multiply charged cations and multiply charged anions. The observed value of $\log \gamma$ deviates only gradually from the limiting law, and the deviation is in the direction of a value of γ greater than that predicted by the limiting law. Experimental data are well represented by an alternating power series in $I^{1/2}$; thus

$$\log \gamma_i = -z_i^2 A I^{1/2} + BI - CI^{3/2} \tag{9}$$

at least up to ionic strengths of several tenths molar. But when in aqueous systems multiply charged ions of both signs are present, the deviation from the limiting law is abrupt, it appears at low ionic strengths, and it is in the direction initially of an activity coefficient less than that predicted by the limiting law. This behavior may suitably be called the case of strong interactions. It is also referred to as symptomatic of considerable ion association.

Both cases are well illustrated by Fig. 7.4, which is based on the work of LaMer and Mason [7]. In this the saturating salt consists of the triply charged cation $Co(NH_3)_6{}^{3+}$ and the singly charged anion $Co(NH_3)_2(NO_2)_4{}^-$. Its

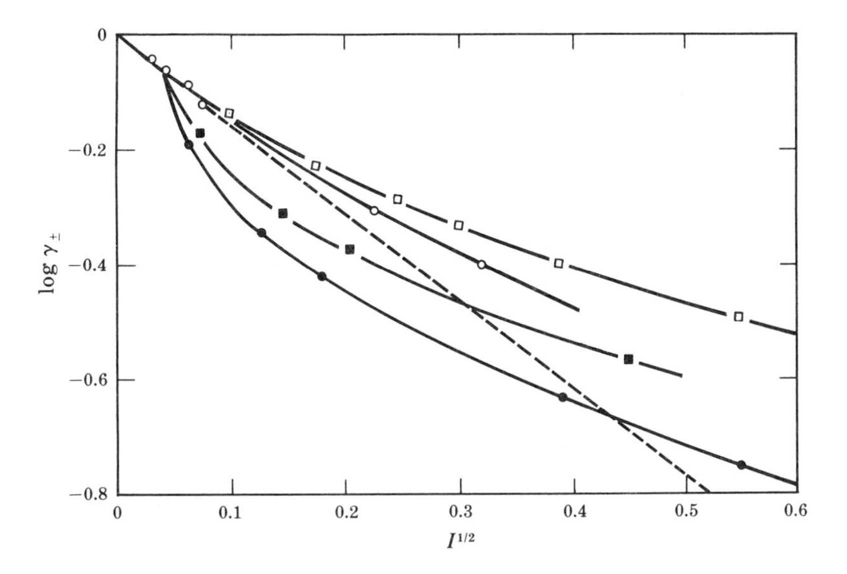

Fig. 7.4 Effect of various salts on the mean ionic-activity coefficient of $[Co(NH_3)_6]^{3+}[Co(NH_2)_2(NO_2)_4]_3{}^-$. ○ = KNO_3; □ = $BaCl_2$; ■ = $MgSO_4$; ● = K_2SO_4. (*Data of LaMer and Mason* [7].)

solubility in water at 25°C is 1.651×10^{-4} mole/liter. For a salt of this valence type the mean ionic-activity coefficient (Sec. 2.18) is given by

$$\log \gamma_{\pm} = \tfrac{1}{4}(\log \gamma_{+} + 3 \log \gamma_{-}) \tag{10}$$

The ratio of the $\gamma_{\pm}$ values in any two saturated solutions equals the inverse ratio of the solubilities, and the absolute value of the activity coefficient is obtained by extrapolation to zero ionic strength for the case of weak interactions.

From Eqs. (9) and (10)

$$\log \gamma_{\pm} = -1.536 I^{1/2} + \tfrac{1}{4}(B_{+} + 3B_{-})I - \tfrac{1}{4}(C_{+} + 3C_{-})I^{3/2} \tag{11}$$

The limiting law with the slope −1.536 is plotted in the figure as a dashed line. When the added salt is potassium or sodium nitrate, the behavior is that corresponding to weak interactions. The experimental data are well represented by the equation

$$\log \gamma_{\pm} = -1.536 I^{1/2} + 0.88 I \tag{12}$$

which is plotted in the figure. The data for systems which contain barium chloride as the added salt, in which again only singly charged anions are present, are in good agreement with the equation

$$\log \gamma_{\pm} = -1.536 I^{1/2} + 1.76 I - 1.1 I^{3/2} \tag{13}$$

which is also plotted in the figure.

But when the solutions contain the doubly negative sulfate ion as well as the triply negative hexammine cobaltic ion, the behavior is typically that of strong interaction. An abrupt break to low values of the activity coefficient appears at a low ionic strength. At ionic strengths in the region of 0.02 the plot has roughly the limiting-law slope, but the magnitude of the activity coefficient is about 20 percent less than that predicted by the limiting law. At still higher ionic strengths the plot crosses the limiting-law line, and the activity coefficient becomes greater than the limiting-law prediction. The contrast between the effect at a given ionic strength of the 2:1 salt barium chloride and the 1:2 salt potassium sulfate is striking and typical.

7.7 SALT EFFECTS ON THE RATES OF REACTIONS BETWEEN IONS AT MODERATE SALT CONCENTRATIONS

The same contrast between strong and weak interactions appears in the effect of added electrolyte on the specific rates of reaction between ions. Figure 7.5 presents a typical case from the work of LaMer and Fessenden [8]. The reaction is

$$S_2O_3^{--} + BrCH_2CO_2^{-} \rightarrow {}^{-}S_2O_3CH_2CO_2^{-} + Br^{-} \tag{II}$$

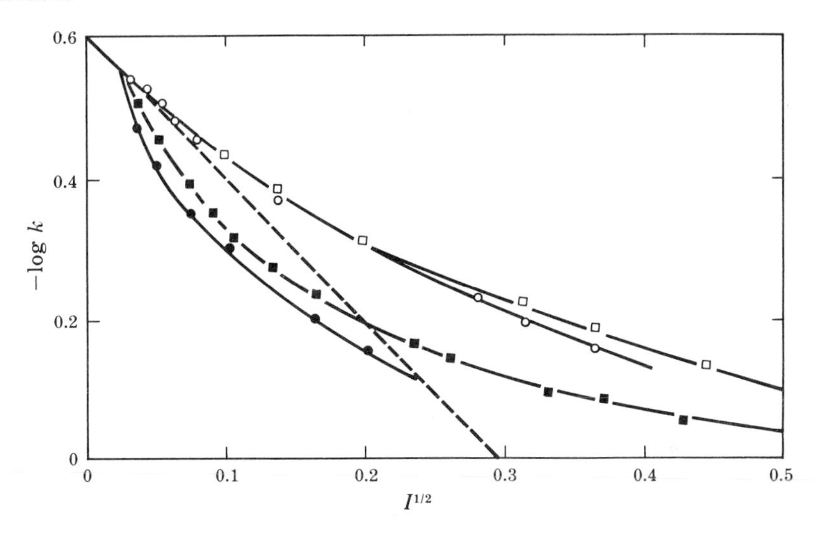

Fig. 7.5 Salt effect on the rate of the bromacetate-thiosulfate reaction. □ = Na^+; ○ = K^+; ■ = Mg^{++}; ● = Ba^{++}. (*Data of LaMer and Fessenden* [8].)

and the reaction mixtures were prepared in such a way that only one cation was present. For the reaction of a doubly charged anion with a singly charged anion the limiting-law slope at 25° is 2.048. The data for potassium salts are well represented by the power series

$$\log k = -0.606 + 2.05I^{1/2} - 3.2I + 2.6I^{3/2} \quad (14)$$

and the data for sodium salts by the equation

$$\log k = -0.606 + 2.05I^{1/2} - 3.91I + 3.86I^{3/2} \quad (15)$$

But when the cation is the doubly charged magnesium, calcium, or barium, the deviation from the limiting slope is abrupt, occurs at low ionic strength, and is in the direction opposite from the deviation observed when the only cation present is singly charged. There is therefore an exact parallelism between the effects observed with reaction rates and those observed in such equilibrium phenomena as the solubility of salts. Both strong and weak interaction effects appear in both cases, and the nature of the effect is closely the same in the rate and in the equilibrium case.

7.8 SALT EFFECTS AS EVIDENCE FOR TRANSITION-STATE THEORY

All the phenomena associated with salt effects on reaction rate indicate that the rate of a reaction responds to variations in the medium in which the reaction occurs in the same way that the equilibrium of an association reaction involving the reactants does. The limiting law for zero ionic strength is quantitatively the same for the rate and for the equilibrium, and the deviations from the limiting law corresponding both to strong and to weak interactions appear under identical conditions and have the same form for the rate as they do for the equilibrium.

This identity of effects on rate and on equilibrium argues strongly for the validity of general transition-state theory. More specifically it demonstrates that an electrically charged transition state is subject to the same kind of interaction with the ions present in the solution as a stable charged molecule is and that this is as true when there is what is called ion association as it is when there are only weak interactions.

7.9 THE OLSON-SIMONSON RULE

Olson and Simonson [9] showed that in a reaction involving ions of the same sign of charge the rate in an aqueous solution at ionic strengths in the neighborhood of 0.01 to 0.1 M is consistently independent of the charge on the ions of the same sign as that of the reactants. An isolated example of this effect had been reported earlier by Brønsted and Delbanco [10] in the reaction of nitrourethane anion with hydroxyl ion

$$C_2H_5OOCNNO_2^- + OH^- \rightarrow N_2O + CO_3^{--} + C_2H_5OH \qquad \text{(III)}$$

For solutions 0.00581 M in the nitrourethane anion and 0.0250 M in hydroxyl ion the specific rates, as shown in Table 7.1, are close to the same for systems with the same potassium-ion concentration even though the ionic strength varies from 0.101 to 0.171.

Olson and Simonson found that in the reaction

$$Co(NH_3)_5Br^{++} + Hg^{++} + H_2O \rightarrow Co(NH_3)_5(H_2O)^{3+} + \tfrac{1}{2}HgBr_2 + \tfrac{1}{2}Hg^{++} \qquad \text{(IV)}$$

with reactant concentrations of 5×10^{-6} M and 2.50×10^{-4} M the rate in the presence of added $NaClO_4$ agrees with that in the presence of $La(ClO_4)_3$ at the same perchlorate-ion concentration in spite of the large difference in ionic

Table 7.1 Salt effects in the nitrourethane reaction[a]

Added salt	*Molarity salt*	$[K^+]$	I	k
KCl	0.07	0.101	0.101	0.242
K_2SO_4	0.035	0.101	0.136	0.243
$K_3Co(CN)_6$	0.0233	0.101	0.171	0.247
$Pt(NH_3)_4Cl_2$	0.035		0.136	0.306
$Co(NH_3)_6Cl_3$	0.0233		0.171	0.586

[a] Data of Brønsted and Delbanco [10].

Table 7.2 Salt effects in the reaction of bromopentammine cobaltic ion with mercuric ion[a]

Added salt	*Molarity salt* $\times 10^3$	$10^3[ClO_4^-]$	$10^3 I$	k
None		0.25	1.75	103.8
$NaClO_4$	7.06	7.31	8.81	145.0
$La(ClO_4)_3$	2.35	7.30	15.85	146.7
$NaClO_4$	11.70	11.95	13.45	162.2
$La(ClO_4)_3$	3.90	11.95	25.25	164.2
$NaClO_4$	23.56	23.81	25.31	200.4
$La(ClO_4)_3$	7.85	23.80	48.85	200.4

[a] Data of Olson and Simonson [9].

strength. The data are presented in Table 7.2. For reaction (II) the specific rates with reactant concentrations of 0.001 M in the presence of 0.02 M KNO_3, of 0.01 M K_2SO_4, and of 0.0067 M $K_3Co(CN)_6$ are 0.472, 0.472, and 0.462 respectively [9]. All these solutions have the same potassium-ion concentration, but the ionic strengths are 0.0240, 0.0340, and 0.0440, respectively. For the same reaction the data of von Kiss and Vass [11] show that the specific rate is the same with added $MgSO_4$ as with added $Mg(NO_3)_2$ when the magnesium-ion concentration is the same.

The rates of reaction with hydroxyl ion in water of the doubly charged anions of bromophenol blue and of bromophenol red are the same at the same cation concentration for KCl, K_2SO_4, $K_3Fe(CN)_6$, and $K_4Fe(CN)_6$ at salt normalities from 0.02 to 0.2 [12]. The rate of the alkaline hydrolysis in water of the monoethylmalonate ion is closely the same for NaCl, Na_2SO_4, $Na_3P_3O_9$, $Na_4P_4O_{12}$, and $Na_5P_3O_{10}$ at the same salt normality at values up to 0.08 [13]. But while the Olson-Simonson rule holds for the alkaline hydrolysis in water of the monoethyloxalate ion as well as for the monoethylmalonate ion, K_2SO_4 and KNO_3 have the same effect at the same ionic strength for the hydrolysis of the monoethyladipate and the monoethylsebacate ions [14]. In 70% aqueous ethanol the alkaline hydrolysis of the monoethylsuccinate ion is the same when the doubly charged succinate ion is present as it is when only singly charged anions are present, provided the concentration of the cation is the same [15].

7.10 THE SUPPRESSION OF SALT EFFECTS IN THE INVESTIGATION OF REACTION ORDER

When the order of a reaction involving ions is to be investigated it is desirable to operate at the lowest possible concentrations of the reactant ions but in the presence of several tenths of a mole per liter of a uni-univalent salt which is not

Table 7.3 Equilibrium constant at 25°C of reaction (V) in solutions all of which are 1.65 *M* in KCl and 0.1 *M* in HCl[a]

$10^3[Fe^{++}]$	$10^3[Fe^{3+}]$	$10^3[I_2]$	$10^3[I^-]$	K
1.257	1.223	5.3	1.14	20.7
3.536	2.644	1.29	2.24	21.4
7.535	4.83	2.38	3.58	21.3
15.74	9.00	4.15	5.49	20.5
3.856	1.104	1.04	5.26	21.4
0.804	0.436	0.32	1.61	20.5
10.45	1.92	1.85	10.17	21.0
5.752	0.43	0.76	17.13	21.6

[a] Data of Brønsted and Pedersen [17].

involved in the reaction. Otherwise serious misinterpretation of the reaction order can occur because the changes in the concentrations of the reactants which are needed for the determination of the order may produce large changes in the activity coefficients of the reactants and of the transition state and thereby change the rate in a way which has nothing to do with the order of the reaction. Because ionic activity coefficients change less rapidly with changing total ion concentration at high ion concentrations than they do at low ones, the large excess of inert salt tends to suppress these changes in the activity coefficients.

An essentially equivalent technique involves keeping the ionic strength of the solution constant by varying the concentration of the inert salt as the concentrations of the reactants are varied. The device of using a large excess of inert salt to suppress salt effects on the equilibria and on the rates of reactions involving ions was proposed by Brønsted [16]. How effective it is is shown by the data of Table 7.3 on the equilibrium of the reaction

$$Fe^{3+} + I^- \rightleftharpoons Fe^{++} + \tfrac{1}{2}I_2 \qquad \text{(V)}$$

in the presence of 1.65 *M* KCl and 0.1 *M* HCl. The equilibrium constant K

$$K = \frac{[Fe^{++}][I_2]^{1/2}}{[Fe^{3+}][I^-]} \qquad (16)$$

is satisfactorily constant even though the individual reactant concentrations vary by factors of more than 10.

7.11 THE NATURE OF THE DEBYE-HÜCKEL THEORY

Starting from the model of a conducting sphere in a continuous medium of constant dielectric constant, the Debye-Hückel theory uses the Boltzmann equation of statistical mechanics and the Poisson equation of electrostatics to obtain the differential equation

$$\frac{1}{r^2}\frac{d}{dr}\left(r^2\frac{d\phi}{dr}\right) = -\frac{4\pi}{\epsilon}\sum_j c_j z_j \exp\left(\frac{-z_j \mathbf{e}\phi}{\mathbf{k}T}\right) \tag{17}$$

in which the distance r is measured from the center of a particular ion which is taken as the origin of coordinates, ϕ is the electric potential at r, ϵ is the dielectric constant, taken to be that observed in macroscopic measurements on the solvent, c_j is the concentration of ions of kind j, and z_j, an algebraic number, is the number of unit positive charges on an ion of kind j. The summation is taken over all the kinds of ion present. There seems to be no doubt of the theoretical validity of this relationship for very dilute solutions, especially when the z's are small and ϵ is large, but there are difficulties when these conditions are not satisfied.[1]

When the conditions are satisfied, Eq. (17) can be considerably simplified by neglecting all but the first two terms in the expansion

$$\exp\left(-\frac{z_j \mathbf{e}\phi}{\mathbf{k}T}\right) = 1 - \frac{z_j \mathbf{e}\phi}{\mathbf{k}T} \tag{18}$$

of the exponential. Debye and Hückel thus reduced the nonlinear differential equation, Eq. (17), to a linear one, which when integrated over the range from $r = a$, the diameter of the ion which is situated at the origin, to $r = \infty$ leads to the familiar equation

$$\log \gamma_i = -\frac{A z_i^2 I^{1/2}}{1 + bI^{1/2}} \tag{19}$$

The coefficient b is defined as

$$b = \frac{50.3}{(\epsilon T)^{1/2}} a \tag{20}$$

with the diameter a in angstrom units. This amounts to $b = 0.328a$ for water at 25°C [18].[2]

7.12 ADAPTIONS OF THE THEORY FOR THE CASE OF WEAK INTERACTIONS

Neither in theory nor in practice is there any reason to question the limiting law, Eq. (2), to which Eq. (19) reduces at low ionic strengths, but neither in

[1] See for instance the discussion in [18], pp. 515–520.

[2] The details of this development may be found in [18], chap. 21, in [1] and [2], and indeed at various levels of sophistication in almost any modern text on physical chemistry.

theory nor in practice can Eq. (19) be taken very seriously. It does not reproduce the observed variation of activity coefficient with ionic strength very well, and insofar as it can be adjusted to the data, the *a* values required to make it fit are only very roughly predictable, if indeed one knows at all how to predict the diameter even of a spherical ion in solution. The fit may be considerably improved by adding a term linear in concentration

$$\log \gamma_i = -\frac{Az_i^2 I^{1/2}}{1 + bI^{1/2}} + \sum_j \beta_j c_j \tag{21}$$

with the summation taken only over ions of sign opposite to that of i. For the mean ionic-activity coefficient of a single electrolyte and for a number of other useful applications this is equivalent to

$$\log \gamma_i = -\frac{Az_i^2 I^{1/2}}{1 + bI^{1/2}} + \beta I \tag{22}$$

Guggenheim [19] found that the available data on the mean ionic-activity coefficient of the common inorganic strong electrolytes in water are adequately represented by the equation

$$\log \gamma_i = -\frac{Az_i^2 I^{1/2}}{1 + I^{1/2}} + \beta I \tag{23}$$

i.e., by Eq. (22) with a b value of unity. Scatchard [20] finds the fit better with a b value of 1.5, while Pitzer and Brewer [21] report that their review of the data indicates little basis for preference since some substances are slightly better fitted with one coefficient and some with the other.

Since

$$\frac{1}{1 + I^{1/2}} = 1 - I^{1/2} + I - I^{3/2} \cdot \cdot \cdot \tag{24}$$

so long as $I^{\frac{1}{2}} < 1$, the Guggenheim equation is equivalent to

$$\log \gamma_i = -Az_i^2 I^{1/2} + (\beta + Az_i^2)I - Az_i^2 I^{3/2} \tag{25}$$

and the Scatchard equation to

$$\log \gamma_i = -Az_i^2 I^{1/2} + (\beta + 1.5Az_i^2)I - 1.5Az_i^2 I^{3/2} \tag{26}$$

The adequacy of these equations means therefore only that the experimental data can be fitted by a power series in $I^{1/2}$ with the coefficient of the first term predictable from theory and with the coefficient of the third term, which depends on the second derivative of the experimental data, fixed only to so meager a precision that one cannot tell reliably whether or not it has the same value for all electrolytes. The ability to represent experimental data by a power series does not of course constitute any advance in theory, although the fact that it is a power series in $I^{1/2}$ not in I is extremely significant. It shows that the actual behavior of low-valence electrolytes in a solvent of high dielectric constant is consistent with the Debye-Hückel approximation, Eq. (18).

7.13 THE BJERRUM APPROXIMATION

For strong interactions, on the other hand, the facts are completely inconsistent with the Debye-Hückel approximation, but they can be accounted for by a different approximation to a solution of the Poisson-Boltzmann equation, Eq. (17), which was proposed by Bjerrum [22]. This may be based on the following considerations: (1) those ions which are at large distances from the origin have a considerable effect on the energy of the ion at the origin because the number of ions which are at a distance r is proportional to r^2; (2) the close-in ions of sign opposite to that of the ion at the origin have a large effect because the strength of the interaction varies as $1/r$; (3) the number of close-in ions of the same sign as that of the one at the origin is so small because of the mutual repulsion that their effect is negligible; (4) the effect of ions of both signs at intermediate distances is small because neither the number nor the interaction energy is large.

It is therefore a reasonable approximation to divide the total effect into two parts. The part due to ions more distant than some value d is then given by Eq. (19) with

$$b = \frac{50.3}{(\epsilon T)^{1/2}} d \tag{27}$$

The part due to close-in ions is accounted for in the same way that one accounts for any close association of the molecules of two different species, i.e., by writing an equilibrium constant K_j for the association of the kind of ions i, one of which is at the origin, with each kind j of ions of sign opposite to that of the one at the origin. Like any equilibrium constant for a reaction involving ions, K is subject to a salt effect.

In these terms the primitive value $\gamma_i^{(p)}$ of the activity coefficient of species i is given by

$$\gamma_i^{(p)} = \alpha_i \gamma_i^{(s)} \tag{28}$$

in which α_i is the fraction of the total i content of the system which is free, i.e., not involved in the formation of association products with ions j, and

$$\log \gamma_i^{(s)} = -\frac{A z_i^2 I^{1/2}}{1 + b I^{1/2}} \tag{29}$$

with I calculated in terms only of free ions and b based on the Bjerrum distance d. The mean ionic-activity coefficient $\gamma_\pm^{(p)}$ at the primitive concentration c of a symmetrical electrolyte in the absence of other electrolytes is then given by solution of the equations

$$\gamma_\pm^{(p)} = \alpha\gamma_\pm^{(s)} \tag{30}$$

$$\frac{c\alpha^2}{1-\alpha} = \frac{1}{K^\circ(\gamma_\pm^{(s)})^2} \tag{31}$$

$$\log\gamma_\pm^{(s)} = -\frac{Az^2 I^{1/2}}{1+bI^{1/2}} \tag{32}$$

$$I = z^2\alpha c \tag{33}$$

Bjerrum proposed that the distance d be set at the value at which the probability of finding a j ion within a spherical shell of thickness dr is a minimum [18, p. 511]. This is

$$d = -\frac{z_i z_j \mathbf{e}^2}{2\epsilon\mathbf{k}T} \tag{34}$$

For water at 25°C the distance is 3.57 Å for a 1:1 electrolyte, leading to a b value of 1.17. The corresponding values for a 2:2 electrolyte are 14.28 for d and 4.68 for b.

Equations (30) to (33) constitute a functional relationship between γ and c which contains two adjustable parameters and which is therefore very adaptable. Davies [23] has found, however, that many data on higher-valence electrolytes in water can be accounted for by what amounts to a choice of a Bjerrum distance of 3.7 Å for all ions and that the K values calculated for a given salt are consistently the same as those obtained from a somewhat simplified theory of the conductance-concentration relationship. The Davies choice of a Bjerrum distance is not, however, consistent with the interpretation of Eqs. (30) to (33) as an approximation to the solution of the Poisson-Boltzmann equation.

That the Bjerrum approach can be such an approximation provided a proper choice of d is made has been demonstrated by Guggenheim [24] by comparing its results with those of exact numerical solutions of the equation for 1:1 and 2:2 electrolytes of various ionic diameters. By the same method he showed that an equally good agreement can be obtained with a considerable range of pairs of values of the parameters d and K. The agreement is as good for a 2:2 electrolyte in water with a d value of 10 Å as with the 14.3 given by Eq. (34), but a smaller value of d leads to significant disagreement. The K° value which corresponds to the 10 Å value of d is 20 percent greater than the one which corresponds to the 14.3 value. With the smaller value of d one counts fewer j ions as close in and gets an increased value of α but counts more as far out and gets a decreased value of γ. The $\alpha\gamma$ product is nearly unchanged. The study of activity coefficients or of conductance phenomena cannot therefore be a very precise way of determining the extent of ion association. This is of course characteristic of the situation in which a two-parameter function is fitted to experimental data.

Bjerrum obtained a functional relationship involving a single parameter, the ionic diameter a, which is adjustable within limits, by calculating the partition function of the pairs of ions for which r is between a and d as a harmonic vibrator. Fuoss [3, p. 210] has proposed a different one-parameter relationship which frequently accounts satisfactorily for the observed conductivity-concentration relationship in the case of electrolytes composed of large symmetrical ions in solvents of low to moderate dielectric constant. Both the Bjerrum and the Fuoss relationships constitute in effect ways of establishing a criterion of purely electrostatic interactions, deviations from which can be assigned to specific forces between the ions or between the ions and solvent molecules.

7.14 ION PAIRS IN CHEMICAL REACTIONS

The ion-pair idea has been applied by Davies and Williams [25] to an analysis of the LaMer and Fessenden data (Sec. 7.7) on the rate of the reaction of magnesium thiosulfate with magnesium bromacetate. The Brønsted equation for the reaction is

$$k = k^\circ \frac{\gamma_B{}^{(p)} \gamma_T{}^{(p)}}{\gamma_\ddagger{}^{(p)}} \tag{35}$$

in which T refers to thiosulfate, B to bromacetate, and $\ddagger$ to the transition state. By ion-pair theory each γ is set equal to an $\alpha\gamma^{(s)}$ product. For $\gamma^{(s)}$ the relation

$$\gamma^{(s)} = -Az^2\left(\frac{I^{1/2}}{1 + I^{1/2}} - 0.2I\right) \tag{36}$$

was used, which is experimentally indistinguishable from

$$\gamma^{(s)} = -\frac{Az^2 I^{1/2}}{1 + 1.2I^{1/2}} \tag{37}$$

and amounts therefore to the choice of a Bjerrum distance of 3.7 Å. This is a small fraction of the 14.3 given for a 2:2 electrolyte by Eq. (34). The validity of the conclusions should not, however, be seriously impaired because the same relationship was used in deriving the K_B and K_T values from conductance and solubility data [26]. These values were 3.57 and 69.

With $[T^{--}]$ for the concentration of free thiosulfate ions, $[M^{++}]$ for that of free magnesium ions, and [MT] for the concentration of the magnesium thiosulfate ion pair,

$$\frac{[MT]}{[T^{--}][M^{++}]} = K_T^\circ \gamma_2{}^2 \tag{38}$$

in which γ_2 is the value of $\gamma^{(s)}$ given by Eq. (36) for a doubly charged ion. With c for the primitive concentration of thiosulfate, which was the same as that of bromacetate,

$$\frac{[\mathrm{T}^{--}]}{c} = \alpha_{\mathrm{T}} = \frac{1}{1 + K_{\mathrm{T}}^{\circ}\gamma_2{}^2[\mathrm{M}^{++}]} \tag{39}$$

Similarly from

$$\frac{[\mathrm{MB}^{+}]}{[\mathrm{B}^{-}][\mathrm{M}^{++}]} = K_{\mathrm{B}}^{\circ}\frac{\gamma_1\gamma_2}{\gamma_1} \tag{40}$$

$$\alpha_{\mathrm{B}} = \frac{1}{1 + K_{\mathrm{B}}^{\circ}\gamma_2[\mathrm{M}^{++}]} \tag{41}$$

By the same token

$$\alpha_{\ddagger} = \frac{1}{1 + K_{\ddagger}^{\circ}(\gamma_2\gamma_3/\gamma_1)[\mathrm{M}^{++}]} \tag{42}$$

in which $K_{\ddagger}^{\circ}$ is the equilibrium constant (cf. Sec. 5.26) for the association of the triply negative free transition state with magnesium ion to form a singly negative ion-pair transition state. From Eqs. (39), (41), and (42) and the material- and electric-balance relations it follows that

$$\frac{1}{c} = \frac{3/2}{[\mathrm{M}^{++}]} - \frac{K_{\mathrm{T}}^{\circ}\gamma_2{}^2}{1 + K_{\mathrm{T}}^{\circ}\gamma_2{}^2[\mathrm{M}^{++}]} - \frac{K_{\mathrm{B}}\gamma_2}{1 + K_{\mathrm{B}}\gamma_2[\mathrm{M}^{++}]} \tag{43}$$

From this, the concentration of free magnesium ions in any reaction system can be calculated. From Eq. (35)

$$k = k^{\circ}\frac{\alpha_{\mathrm{B}}\,\alpha_{\mathrm{T}}}{\alpha_{\ddagger}}\frac{\gamma_1\gamma_2}{\gamma_3} \tag{44}$$

and with Eq. (43)

$$k^{(p)} = k^{\circ}\frac{\{1 + K_{\ddagger}^{\circ}(\gamma_2\gamma_3/\gamma_1)[\mathrm{M}^{++}]\}\gamma_1\gamma_2/\gamma_3}{(1 + K_{\mathrm{B}}^{\circ}\gamma_2[\mathrm{M}^{++}])(1 + K_{\mathrm{T}}^{\circ}\gamma_2{}^2[\mathrm{M}^{++}])} \tag{45}$$

Since k° is known from extrapolation of the data for the reaction of the sodium and potassium salts for which ion pairing is presumably negligible, and since the γ's can be calculated from Eq. (36) the equation contains only one adjustable parameter $K_{\ddagger}^{\circ}$. The equation can be put in the form

$$\log\frac{k^{(p)}(1 + K_{\mathrm{B}}^{\circ}\gamma_2[\mathrm{M}^{++}])\{1 + K_{\mathrm{T}}^{\circ}\gamma_2{}^2[\mathrm{M}^{++}] - k^{\circ}(\gamma_1\gamma_2/\gamma_3)\}}{[\mathrm{M}^{++}]} = \log k^{\circ}K_{\ddagger}^{\circ} - 2\log\gamma_2 \tag{46}$$

which predicts that the known quantity y, given by the left side, should be linear in

$$x = \frac{I^{1/2}}{1 + I^{1/2}} - 0.2I \tag{47}$$

with a slope of –4.07. Figure 7.6 is the Davies and Williams plot of y against x, not only for the LaMer and Fessenden data on magnesium salts but also for their data on calcium and barium salts and for some values of von Kiss and Vass [11] in which magnesium nitrate or sulfate was added to the reaction of sodium thiosulfate with sodium bromacetate. The lines have the predicted slope of –4.07.

The rate equation used by Davies and Williams was

$$-\frac{d[\mathrm{T}^{--}]}{dt} = k_1[\mathrm{T}^{--}][\mathrm{B}^{-}]\frac{\gamma_1\gamma_2}{\gamma_3} + k'[\mathrm{M}^{++}][\mathrm{T}^{--}][\mathrm{B}^{-}]\gamma_2^{\,2} \tag{48}$$

If their k_1 and k' are identified with the k° and $k^\circ K^\circ_\ddagger$ of the above discussion, the two equations are identical.

From the intercept of the plot of Eq. (46) the value of 450 is found for $K^\circ_\ddagger$ in the magnesium salt reaction. This is larger than the 69 of K_T, which is in

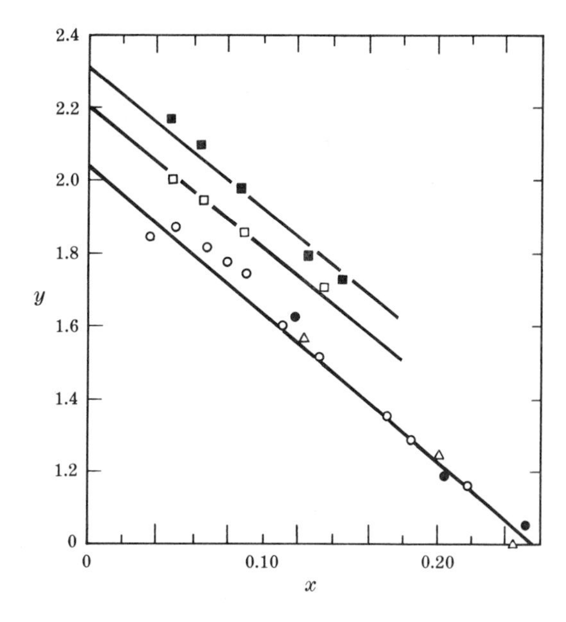

Fig. 7.6 Data of LaMer and Fessenden [8]: ■ = Ba; □ = Ca; ○ = Mg. Data of von Kiss and Vass [11]: ● = $Mg(NO_3)_2$ added; △ = $MgSO_4$ added. [*From C. W. Davies and I. W. Williams, Trans. Faraday Soc.,* **54**: 1547 (1958).]

turn larger than the 3.57 of K_B. It is in fact reasonable that the association should be larger for the triply charged transition state than it is for the doubly charged thiosulfate ion just as it is larger for thiosulfate than for the singly charged bromacetate ion.

7.15 ION PAIRING AND THE OLSON-SIMONSON RULE

Davies and Williams calculated the concentration of free magnesium ion and the ionic strength for some systems which had been investigated by von Kiss and Vass in terms of the K_B and K_T values used in the previous section and independently determined K° values of 143 for $MgSO_4$ and of 5.3 for $NaSO_4^-$. Table 7.4 presents some quantities based on these calculations for the reaction of 0.00125 *M* sodium thiosulfate with 0.00125 *M* sodium bromacetate in the presence of 0.05 *M* magnesium nitrate and in the presence of 0.05 *M* magnesium sulfate. As the last column shows, the ratio of the rate in the presence of magnesium sulfate to that in the presence of the nitrate is 0.95, which agrees exactly with the experimental value of the ratio and is essentially in agreement with the Olson-Simonson rule.

According to this analysis, the concentration of magnesium ion is significantly less in the sulfate solution than in the nitrate solution, but the ionic strength is only 8 percent less because one sulfate contributes twice as much to the ionic strength as two nitrate ions do. The γ ratio is not therefore very different in the two solutions. Although $K^\circ_\ddagger$ has the large value of 450, the quantity $K^\circ_\ddagger \gamma_2 \gamma_3 / \gamma_1$ is only 13 at ionic strengths in the neighborhood of 0.15. By Eq. (42) the quantity $\alpha_\ddagger$ is not therefore very sensitive to the magnesium-ion concentration in the region of 0.05 *M*. The values of α_B and α_T are even less sensitive, and insofar as they are changed by the substitution of sulfate for nitrate, the changes tend to compensate the change in $\alpha_\ddagger$. This analysis goes far toward making the Olson-Simonson rule intelligible.

7.16 THE SEMANTICS OF ION PAIRING

The terms ion pair and ion association carry the connotation of two ions of opposite sign which are in contact but which retain essentially the same in-

Table 7.4 Effects of added magnesium salts on the thiosulfate–bromacetate reaction[a]

Added	$[Mg^{++}]$	I	α_B	α_T	$\alpha_\ddagger$	$\frac{\alpha_B \alpha_T}{\alpha_\ddagger}$	$\frac{\gamma_B \gamma_T}{\gamma_\ddagger}$	$\frac{k}{k^\circ}$
$Mg(NO_3)_2$	0.0496	0.150	0.94	0.75	0.60	1.17	3.24	3.80
$MgSO_4$	0.0330	0.138	0.93	0.81	0.67	1.16	3.11	3.60

[a] Data of Kiss and Vass [11].

ternal electronic structure as the separated ions. As with many scientific classifications, it is difficult to give this one an operational definition. Fortunately or unfortunately the form of the relation between the primitive value of the activity coefficient and the composition of the solution which results from the Bjerrum approximation is the same as that which applies to the ionization of a weak electrolyte in which covalent linkages are heavily involved. The Davies treatment preserves the form of the Bjerrum equations, but it requires a value of the parameter d which, as Guggenheim showed (Sec. 7.13), is inconsistent with the Poisson-Boltzmann equation.

This is not really surprising. Two oppositely charged bodies having the properties of real ions cannot be brought close together without a certain amount of alteration of the charge distributions within the ions, an alteration which if continued to the limit would lead to a covalent linkage. When a cesium ion and a fluoride ion come together in the gas phase, this alteration appears to be so small that in Pauling's [27] terms the bond between cesium and fluorine is "essentially ionic with only a small amount of covalent character." But when a hydrogen ion and an iodide ion come together in the gas phase, the resulting hydrogen iodide molecule can be adequately pictured as having two electrons in an orbital which is concentrated between the hydrogen and the iodine nuclei. Nevertheless the molecule retains a small excess of negative charge on the iodine side and an equivalent excess of positive charge on the hydrogen side, and it has therefore a dipole moment. It is "essentially covalent with only a small amount of ionic character." No matter how large or how small the shift in the electron structure produced by the proximity of the ions, it is necessarily in the direction of a structure of lower energy. Consequently the work required to separate the ions is greater the greater the degree of covalence.

Even in what might still be called an ion pair the work required to separate the ions is greater when the free ions have an unsymmetrical distribution of charge than it is when the distribution is spherically symmetrical. The dissymmetry of charge which exists in most of the ions of interest in organic chemistry may lead to a change of many orders of magnitude in the equilibrium constant of the ion association. This is notably true when effects classifiable as hydrogen bonding are present.

Thus in the solvent nitrobenzene Wynne-Jones [28] obtained from conductance measurements association constants of from 5 to 7×10^2 for piperidinium and dipropylammonium perchlorates, 6×10^3 for piperidinium and dipropylammonium picrates, and 5×10^4 for diphenylguanidinium picrate, whereas the association in the case of tetraethylammonium picrate is too small to be detected. The conductance of piperidinium picrate is not affected by the addition of small amounts either of piperidine or of picric acid; consequently the effect is not due to incompleteness of the proton transfer from picric acid to piperidine. The effects are consistent with hydrogen bonding between the acidic hydrogen in the substituted ammonium ions and the oxygens of the anion. This is stronger with the more acidic diphenylguanidinium ion than with the less acidic piperidinium or dipropylammonium ions, it is stronger with the more basic picrate ion than with the less basic perchlorate ion, and it does not exist with the quaternary ammonium ion, which has no acidic hydrogen. Finally the conductance of the secondary ammonium salts is materially increased by the addition of small proportions of ethanol, which should compete with the ammonium ion in hydrogen bonding with the anion.

One can expect ion pairing to conform to the model of the interaction of charged spheres in a continuous dielectric only under especially favorable circumstances. Pairing should be less when the charge on an ion is widely distributed than when it is concentrated on a single atom. When the charge is concentrated, the structure in the neighborhood of the concentration may have a considerable effect on the closeness to which another ion can approach; there may be steric hindrance to ion pairing. There may be charge-transfer (Sec. 8.29) coupling between ions as well as hydrogen bonding. There may be multipolar complexing (Sec. 8.30) of an ion pair with another ion pair or with any polar molecule. In water, and perhaps in other solvents, the presence of a solute molecule, charged or uncharged, disturbs the highly structured liquid system. An ion pair has no doubt a different effect on the structure from that of the separated ions. All these factors may influence the energy change which accompanies ion pairing and hence the extent of the pairing.

7.17 ON WEAK ION PAIRING

The absence of the strong interaction phenomenon (Sec. 7.6) does not prove that ion pairing is absent. The relationship represented by Eqs. (30) to (33) can be expanded in a MacLaurin's series, leading to

$$\log \gamma^{(p)} = -Az^2 y + (Az^2 b - 0.43K^\circ) y^2 - Az^2 b^2 y^3 \tag{49}$$

in which y, defined as $(cz^2)^{1/2}$, is the square root of the primitive value of the ionic strength. So long therefore as K° is less than 2.3 Ab, the characteristic weak-interaction picture of an alternating power series in the square root of the ionic strength will prevail even though there is some ion pairing. But since the quantity Ab is inherently positive, and since most data on 1:1 electrolytes in water indicate that the coefficient of y^2 is more positive than any reasonable value of the quantity $Az^2 b$, there must be influences other than those accounted for by the $Az^2 b$ and the 0.43 K° terms which affect that coefficient. These influences cannot be accounted for in terms of the model on which the Poisson-Boltzmann equation is based.

7.18 SALT EFFECTS ON NONELECTROLYTES IN AQUEOUS SOLUTION[1]

If the effect of the charge of an ion on the interaction of the ion with the medium is superimposed on the effect a similar uncharged molecule would have, there should be an additional term in the coefficient of y^2 in Eq. (49); for the variation of the activity coefficient of a nonelectrolyte with electrolyte concentration in aqueous solution is of this form, namely,

$$\log \gamma_i = \varkappa_{ij} c_j \tag{50}$$

where γ_i is the activity coefficient of nonelectrolyte i and c_j is the concentration of electrolyte j. The equation is in excellent agreement with the facts at low to moderate electrolyte concentration. For nonelectrolytes of low solubility Eq. (50) is equivalent to the Setschenov equation [30]

$$\log \frac{s_0}{s} = Kc \tag{51}$$

where s_0 is solubility in water and s is solubility at electrolyte concentration c.

Like most properties of strong electrolytes in dilute aqueous solution, the values of $\varkappa$ are decidedly additive. Thus for a given nonelectrolyte the difference between the $\varkappa$ values for a chloride and a bromide is essentially independent of the cation, and the difference between the values for a sodium and a potassium salt is similarly independent of the anion. With the exception of acidic and basic nonelectrolytes like aniline and benzoic acid, the order of the effect of different electrolytes is nearly the same for all nonelectrolytes. Some $\varkappa$ values for benzene are NaCl, +0.195; KCl, +0.166; LiCl, +0.141; RbCl, +0.141; NH_4Cl, +0.103; CsCl, +0.088; HCl, +0.048; Na_2SO_4, +0.548; NaF and NaOH, +0.255; NaBr, +0.155; $NaClO_4$, +0.106; $HClO_4$, −0.041; potassium benzoate, −0.01; $(CH_3)_4NBr$, −0.24. The negative value for the quaternary ammonium salt is characteristic of the effect of electrolytes which contain large ions, whether they are cations or anions. The phenomenon has been called hydrotropism [31].

The order of the effect of various electrolytes is much the same for polar nonelectrolytes as it is for nonpolar ones like benzene, but the values are consistently more negative. Thus for sulfur dioxide the $\varkappa$ for NaCl is only +0.01, while that for NaBr is −0.05 and that for KI is −0.13.

The order of the $\varkappa$ values is similar to the order observed with many properties of aqueous electrolytes. To the classical colloid chemist[2] it is the Hofmeister series, which applies to the salting out of a number of proteins. As Traube [33] showed, it is the order of the effect of salts on the compressibility and the surface tension of water as well as on a large variety of properties of biological interest. Traube called it the order of the *Haftdruck* of the

[1] This section derives largely from the critical discussion by Long and McDevit [29].

[2] See for instance [32].

solution, i.e., of what others have called the internal pressure or the effective pressure. The measure of this pressure, which has been developed by Tamann [34] and by Gibson [35], bases on the fact that the compressibility of a salt solution at low pressure is the same and varies with pressure in the same way as that of water at a higher pressure. The additional pressure which must be applied to water to make its compressibility the same as that of a salt solution at low pressures is called by Gibson the effective pressure P_e exerted by the salt. Long and McDevit find that the quantity dP_e/dc_s, where c_s is salt concentration, parallels closely the $\varkappa$ values for the effects of various salts on the activity coefficient in aqueous solution of benzene, of oxygen, and of hydrogen.

These effects may be satisfactorily interpreted in the following terms. Water is a highly structured liquid in which there are strong and highly directed forces between the molecules. The introduction of a nonpolar molecule requires the performance of work against these forces. Most electrolytes decrease volume and compressibility and consequently increase the work required to introduce the nonpolar molecule. As a result the standard potential and the activity coefficient of the nonelectrolyte are increased by the presence of the electrolyte. If the effect of the electrolyte were solely what Frank and Evans [36] call structure breaking, i.e., a collapse in the neighborhood of the ion of the open, icelike structure of water, the effect would decrease with increasing ion size, because the electric field in the neighborhood of a large ion is less intense than that in the neighborhood of a small one. It does decrease in the sequence Na^+, K^+, Rb^+, Cs^+, and in the sequence F^-, Cl^-, Br^-, I^-. But Li^+ is way out of line, lying between K^+ and Cs^+; and NH_4^+, OH_3^+, and OH^- are far from the positions indicated by crystallographic data. The small cations and anions must therefore be assigned what Frank and Evans call a structure-making quality, which works against the normal structure-breaking quality of an ion. A plausible picture makes the coordination of water molecules around the small ions approach the same fourfold one which tends to exist around any individual water molecule. These ions have therefore a relatively small disturbing effect on the normal water structure. The specialized position of the small ions appears to be specific to aqueous solutions; it is not present in methanol or in ethylene glycol [37].

Basic nonelectrolytes tend to show an increased sensitivity to changes in the anion of the salt. Thus the $\varkappa$ values for aniline are KOH, +0.22; KCl, +0.13; KBr, +0.07; KI, 0.00. Further the values for lithium and sodium salts tend to become more negative relative to potassium salts. The $\varkappa$ values for ammonia are KCl, +0.057; NaCl, +0.033; LiCl, −0.024. With acidic nonelectrolytes the values for lithium salts become relatively more positive, and the anion has relatively little effect. The $\varkappa$ values for benzoic acid are LiCl, +0.189; NaCl, +0.182; KCl, +0.144; $NaNO_3$, +0.075; $NaClO_4$, +0.052; KBr, +0.109; KI, +0.049.

A plausible interpretation of these effects may be based on the idea [1, 38] that with cations, and particularly with small cations and with onium ions like NH_4^+ and OH_3^+, the neighboring water molecules tend to be oriented with the protons outward and have an attracting interaction with basic nonelectrolyte molecules. With small anions the orientation of the adjacent water molecules is with oxygen outward, and the effect on acidic and basic nonelectrolytes is the reverse of the effect of the cations.

7.19 SALT EFFECTS ON REACTIONS INVOLVING AN ION AND A NEUTRAL MOLECULE IN AQUEOUS SOLUTION

When an ion reacts with a neutral molecule, the transition state has the same charge as the reactant ion. If $\log\gamma$ for the nonelectrolyte is linear in the ionic strength, the limiting slope of the plot of $\log k$ against $I^{1/2}$ will be zero. In many cases the deviations from the limiting slope cancel between transition state and reactants, and the specific rate is independent of ionic strength over a considerable range. The reaction of the anion of 2-naphthylamine-6-sulfonic acid with the neutral 4-sulfodiazobenzene (Fig. 7.1) is a case in point. Many other examples of this kind of behavior are cited in Brønsted's classical paper [39] of 1922, in which Eq. (1) was first proposed.

This cancellation of activity coefficients between transition state and reactants sometimes extends to surprisingly high salt concentrations. The specific rate of the hydrolysis of ethyl acetate is unaffected by added sodium chloride up to 0.5 M [40]. The transition state is a bulky molecule with a localized charge, and it is not surprising that the logarithm of its activity coefficient should equal the sum of the corresponding quantities for a similar uncharged molecule, ethyl acetate, and for a small charged body, hydroxyl ion. In solutions which contain both calcium chloride and sodium chloride at a constant ionic strength the specific rate of this reaction is independent of the calcium chloride concentration up to 0.16 M. Yet it is known from the effect of calcium hydroxide on the solubility of calcium iodate that there is strong interaction between calcium ion and hydroxyl ion with an association constant around 20. There appears therefore to be a strong specific interaction of calcium ion with the transition state which is of about the same intensity as that of calcium ion with hydroxyl ion. With barium chloride instead of calcium chloride the rate is increased 10 percent by 0.0592 M barium salt. This indicates a stronger interaction of barium ion with the transition state than with hydroxyl ion.

On the other hand, the hydroxyl-ion–catalyzed depolymerization of diacetone alcohol

$$(CH_3)_2C(OH)CH_2COCH_3 \rightarrow 2CH_3COCH_3 \qquad \text{(VI)}$$

is strongly and specifically retarded by calcium or barium ion [41]. For potassium and rubidium hydroxides the specific rate $k = v/c_a c_{OH^-}$, in which c_a is the concentration of diacetone alcohol and c_{OH^-} the primitive value of the concentration of hydroxyl ion, is independent of c_{OH^-} over a wide range. For sodium hydroxide it decreases only by 7 percent from zero to 0.4 M. But for calcium hydroxide the decrease is 12 percent at only 0.036 M, and for barium hydroxide the decrease is somewhat larger than for calcium hydroxide. There would appear therefore to be negligible interaction between the negatively charged transition state of this reaction and the alkaline-earth ions.

The value of log k for the hydrolysis of acetylimidazolium ion

$$CH_3CO{-}N\overset{+}{\bigcirc}N{-}H + H_2O \longrightarrow CH_3COOH + H{-}N\overset{+}{\bigcirc}N{-}H \quad \text{(VII)}$$

on 0.1 M aqueous hydrochloric acid is decreased linearly up to 4 M salt concentration by a wide variety of 1:1 salts [42]. For sodium perchlorate the data extend to 8 M salt, at which point the linearity still holds and the rate is one five-hundredth of that in the absence of salt. Sulfate increases the rate a little, but the effect soon flattens off. Magnesium, calcium, and lanthanum retard strongly and nonlinearly. The effect of various salts bears no relation to their effect on the activity of water. Differences between the effect of cations is small, but $d \log k/dc_s$ is –0.301 for $NaClO_4$, –0.240 for sodium toluenesulfonate, –0.255 for NaBr, –0.150 for NaCl, and –0.141 for $NaNO_3$. Clearly the terms in $I^{1/2}$ and in $I^{3/2}$ in Eq. (9) are effectively equal for the positively charged transition state and for the reactant ion, but the coefficient of the linear term is much more positive for the transition state than for the reactant.

7.20 SALT EFFECTS ON A REACTION INVOLVING AN ION AND A NEUTRAL MOLECULE IN SULFUR DIOXIDE SOLUTION

Sulfur dioxide at 0°C is a weakly dissociating solvent with a dielectric constant of 15.6, in which the dissociation constants of typical ion pairs are 2.14×10^{-3} for tetraethylammonium bromide, 1.43×10^{-4} for potassium bromide, and 2.7×10^{-5} for lithium bromide. Lichtin and Rao [43] find that the specific rate v/c_s[RBr] of the exchange reaction of p-nitrobenzyl bromide with alkali and quaternary ammonium bromides decreases by a factor of 3.6 in the range of salt concentrations from 10^{-4} to 5×10^{-2}. The variation can be quantitatively accounted for by the equation

$$v = [\mathrm{RBr}](k_f[\mathrm{Br}^-] + k_p[\mathrm{MBr}]) \tag{52}$$

in which k_f and k_p are independent of salt concentration, the equilibrium constant

$$\frac{[\mathrm{MBr}]}{[\mathrm{M}^+][\mathrm{Br}^-]} = K^\circ \gamma_\pm^2 \tag{53}$$

is estimated from conductance data, and

$$\log \gamma_{\pm} = -\frac{AI^{1/2}}{1 + bI^{1/2}} \tag{54}$$

The fit to the data improves somewhat with larger b values and is about twice as good with one corresponding to a Bjerrum distance of 30 Å as it is for one corresponding to 3.28 Å.

Equation (52) can be put in the form

$$k^{(p)} = k_f \frac{1 + (k_p/k_f)\, K^{\circ} \gamma_{\pm}^2 [\mathrm{M}^+]}{1 + K^{\circ} \gamma_{\pm}^2 [\mathrm{M}^+]} \tag{55}$$

In terms of transition-state theory it can also be written

$$k^{(p)} = k_f \frac{1 + K^{\ddagger} \gamma_{\pm}^2 [\mathrm{M}^+]}{1 + K^{\circ} \gamma_{\pm}^2 [\mathrm{M}^+]} \tag{56}$$

where $K^{\ddagger}$ is the limiting value of the equilibrium constant for the conversion of the transition state which does not contain M^+ to the one which does contain M^+ (Sec. 5.26). The quantity $(k_p/k_f)K^{\circ}\gamma_{\pm}^2$ measures therefore the ion-pairing tendency of the transition state. Since the ion pair and the free ions are in mobile equilibrium, the question of the mechanism by which the transition state which contains M^+ is formed is irrelevant.

The k_f values are independent of the cation, but the k_p values and consequently the $K^{\ddagger}$ values increase in the same order Li^+, K^+, $(CH_3)_4N^+$, $(C_2H_5)_4N^+$ as the K° values, but less rapidly.

7.21 SALT EFFECTS ON THE SOLVOLYTIC REACTION IN AQUEOUS SOLUTION

Clarke and Taft [44] have studied the effect of electrolytes on the activity coefficient γ_b of *t*-butyl chloride in aqueous solution and on the activity coefficient of the transition state for the hydrolysis of that substance. This was accomplished by determining the quantity $k_p = v/P_b$, where v is rate of hydrolysis and P_b is the limiting value for zero time of the partial pressure of butyl chloride from the solution. The variation of P_b with salt concentration measures the value of γ_b, while the variation of k_p measures $\gamma_{\ddagger}$. As shown in Fig. 7.7, both log γ_b and log $\gamma_{\ddagger}$ are linear in salt concentration. For γ_b the $\varkappa$ values correlate rather well with those for benzene except that tetramethylammonium bromide and sodium benzoate have considerably more positive values than would be predicted from this correlation. Table 7.5 shows the effects on $\varkappa_b$ and on $\varkappa_{\ddagger}$ of various cations relative to that of sodium ion and on various anions relative to that of chloride ion.

For sodium, potassium, and lithium salts the effects on $\varkappa_b$ and $\varkappa_{\ddagger}$ are so nearly parallel for salts of a given valence type that for 12 salts of the 1:1 type the quantity $d \log k/dc_s$ is 0.24 with a rms deviation of 0.05, which is less than the estimated uncertainty in the individual values. This cancellation between

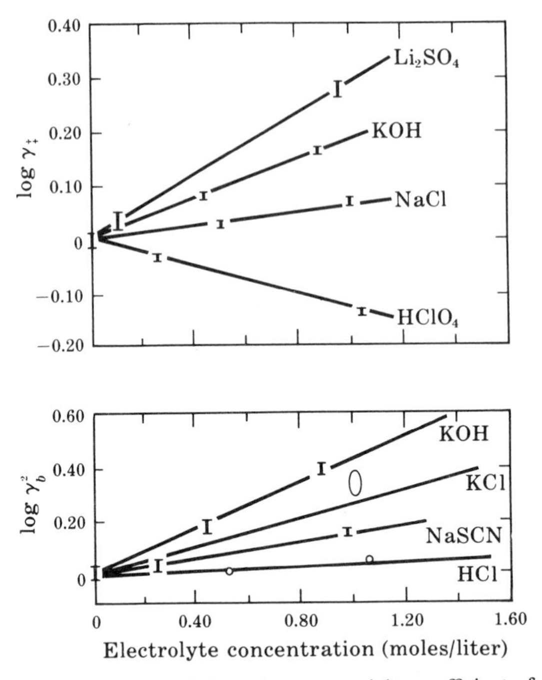

Fig. 7.7 Effect of electrolytes on activity coefficient of *t*-butyl chloride in aqueous solution and on activity coefficient for its hydrolysis. (*From Clarke and Taft* [44].)

transition state and reactant fails, however, for acids, for ammonium salts, and for organic electrolytes. The value is –0.05 for HNO_3, +0.14 for $HClO_4$, +0.16 for NH_4Cl, +0.08 for sodium acetate, and +0.02 for tetramethylammonium bromide. For five 1:2 salts the value is 0.63 with an rms deviation of 0.06.

7.22 SALT EFFECTS ON NONELECTROLYTES IN NONAQUEOUS SOLUTION

Salt effects on the activity coefficient of nonelectrolytes in aqueous solution and on the k/k° values for the solvolytic reaction are exponential, i.e.,

$$\gamma = e^{2.3\varkappa c_s} \tag{57}$$

The $\varkappa$ values are so small that the curvature of a plot of γ against c_s or k/k° against c_s is unrecognizable at salt concentrations below 0.1 M. The slope of the apparently linear portion of such plots is 2.3 $\varkappa$ and lies in the range from –0.5 to +0.5.

Table 7.5 Relative effects of various ions on the activity coefficient of *t*-butyl chloride and of the transition state for the hydrolysis of *t*-butyl chloride[a]

	$\varkappa_b$	$\varkappa_{\ddagger}$
Na^+	(0)	(0)
OH_3^+	−0.28	−0.09
Li^+	−0.06	−0.03
K^+	+0.06	−0.01
NH_4^+	−0.21	−0.05
$(CH_3)_4N^+$	−0.17	0.00
Cl^-	(0)	(0)
F^-	+0.25	+0.15
OH^-	+0.12	+0.14
Br^-	−0.07	−0.07
I^-	−0.14	−0.15
NO_3^-	−0.04	−0.02
ClO_4^-	−0.08	−0.11
SCN^-	−0.18	−0.16
$CH_3CO_2^-$	−0.06	+0.15
SO_4^{--}	+0.6	+0.2

[a] Data of Clarke and Taft [44.]

In the solvent acetic acid the effect of lithium perchlorate, toluenesulfonate, and acetate, of diphenylguanidine perchlorate and acetate, and of toluenesulfonic acid on the solvolysis of a variety of reactants is unmistakably linear, except when the special salt effect appears (Sec. 6.15), and is unmistakably not exponential [45]. The slopes of the plots of (k/k°) against c_s run from +0.5 to +34; that is, they are orders of magnitude larger than they are for solvolysis in water.

There is no reason to believe that these phenomena in acetic acid and in water are related in any way except for the unfortunate fact that they are both called salt effects. Ion concentrations are large in aqueous salt solutions; they are extremely small in the acetic acid solutions. The salt effects in water are intelligible in terms of the effect of the ions of the salt on the work required to find room for the nonelectrolyte molecule. The salt effects in acetic acid are intelligible in terms of an association of a salt molecule (or of an ion pair if one prefers the term) with the transition state of the solvolysis (Sec. 5.26).

The effect of lithium perchlorate on the polarimetric constant k_α (Sec. 6.13) of E

$$CH_3O-C_6H_4-C(CH_3)_2-OTs$$

is linear for salt concentrations up to 0.06 or 0.1 M [46]. The slope b is 12.2 for acetic acid and 13.1 for 50% acetic acid–water. It is negligible in dimethylsulfoxide and only 1.4 in dimethylformamide, but it reaches the height of 482 in tetrahydrofuran and 553 in ethyl acetate.

In 50% by weight dioxane-water log γ for naphthylene and for 1-naphthoic acid is linear in salt concentration for many salts [47] with slopes comparable to those typical for aqueous solutions. For other salts there is a curvature of the same sign as the slope. Salt effects on solvolysis of E and on racemization of *threo*-3-phenyl-2-butyl tosylate in this solvent show a behavior similar to those on the activity coefficients of the naphthylene compounds [48].

7.23 A HISTORICAL NOTE

Although Lewis invented the activity function in 1907, its use as a tool for the exact thermodynamic study of electrolyte solutions was still in its infancy in the early 1920s. The idea that strong electrolytes are completely ionized was, however, in the air, and activity coefficients were being expressed in terms of the total concentration of the ion constituent rather than in terms of what in the Arrhenius theory was supposed to be the true concentration of the ion. It was recognized that in dilute aqueous solution activity coefficients defined in this way always decrease with increasing electrolyte concentration.

Since in thermodynamic terms the condition for equilibrium in the reaction

$$A + B \rightleftharpoons C + D \tag{VIII}$$

is

$$\frac{[C]\,[D]}{[A]\,[B]} = K^{\circ}\frac{\gamma_A\,\gamma_B}{\gamma_C\,\gamma_D} \tag{58}$$

any expression for reaction rate consistent with thermodynamics must contain the activity coefficients of the reactants. The obvious way to attain this consistency was to write for the rate v

$$v = k_1^{\circ}[A]\,[B]\,\gamma_A\,\gamma_B - k_1^{\circ}[C]\,[D]\,\gamma_C\,\gamma_D \tag{59}$$

There was little if any information on the activity coefficients of nonelectrolytes by which this idea could be tested, and most chemists accepted the dogma that all reactions involving ions are "instantaneous." But Brønsted had been an assistant of Jörgensen, and under Jörgensen, Copenhagen had been a center for the investigation of cobaltammines. Nobody familiar with the reactions of cobaltammines could possibly accept the dogma of instantaneity. In 1922 Brønsted [39] pointed out that if Eq. (59) were valid, the known facts about activity coefficients would require that all reactions in which even one ion is involved be retarded by an increase in electrolyte concentration. He cited many reactions which involved an ion and a nonelectrolyte and in which there is essentially no salt effect on the reaction rate, and also several cases of reactions involving two ions of the same sign of charge in which added electrolytes substantially increase the rate.

Consistency between the rate equation and the equilibrium one requires, indeed, only that the rate equation have the form

$$v = k_1^\circ [\mathrm{A}][\mathrm{B}]\frac{\gamma_\mathrm{A}\gamma_\mathrm{B}}{\phi} - k_1^\circ [\mathrm{C}][\mathrm{D}]\frac{\gamma_\mathrm{C}\gamma_\mathrm{D}}{\phi} \tag{60}$$

in which ϕ can have any value or be any function of the composition of the system. Brønsted proposed that ϕ be assigned the value of the activity coefficient of an ion whose charge is the algebraic sum of the charges on A and B, which is also the sum of the charges on C and D. He rationalized the proposal in the terms: "The probability of a molecular system passing from its normal state into a state characterized by great improbability is proportional to the ratio between the activity coefficients in the normal and the improbable state."

This proposal about the nature of the kinetic salt effect was reported a year before the appearance of the Debye-Hückel theory. It came from a laboratory in which detailed study of the effect of added salts on the solubility of cobaltammine salts had shown that (1) the logarithm of the assigned activity coefficient of an ion i is almost completely determined by the kind and concentration of the ions of sign opposite to that of i; (2) over the range readily accessible to measurement the activity logarithm varies pretty closely as the cube root of the electrolyte concentration; (3) the effect of an ion j of sign opposite to that of i increases rapidly with the charge on either ion, and the equivalent concentration of j is a better measure of its effect than the molar concentration; (4) superimposed on the effect of ionic charge there are smaller effects specific both to i and to j; (5) the ionic-strength principle, which had been proposed empirically by Lewis and Randall in 1921, is not therefore universally applicable.

When in 1923 the Debye-Hückel theory appeared, Brønsted immediately applied it to the rate problem and showed [10] that the salt effect on the rate of reaction (III) is in good agreement with the theory so long as only singly charged ions are present but that it definitely does not agree when multiply charged ions are present (Table 7.1). The phenomena, he said, are in accordance with the principle of the specific interaction of ions which he had proposed in 1922, in that the reacting ions and the critical complex formed from them are all negatively charged and are therefore especially dependent on the nature and the valence of the positively charged ions.

All of this was rapidly forgotten in the enthusiasm for the Debye-Hückel theory. In 1930 Livingston [49] published a now familiar diagram in which the theoretical limiting-law lines are drawn for reactions of six charge types varying from $Co(NH_3)_5Br^{++} + Hg^{++}$ to $Co(NH_3)_5Br^{++} + OH^-$. Points representing experimental data for examples of each type were attached to the lines. The diagram has been copied and recopied and appears in many general texts on physical chemistry and even in some texts on reaction kinetics. Livingston stated that "The points represent all the experiments in which the added salts were of the uni-univalent type" but did not explain why data on other salts were omitted. In the textbooks even this caution is often left out.

With this background the Olson-Simonson paper aroused something like shocked horror. There were those who called it revolutionary, which may or may not have been praise. There were others who said that the paper contained nothing new in principle. There seemed to be a rather widespread feeling that it was not really in very good taste to bring such matters up. At any rate, the important positive contribution made by Olson and Simonson was largely lost sight of. The whole commotion is an example of the unpleasant results of the common pedagogic error of minimizing or concealing the limitations of a theory.

REFERENCES

1. Harned, H. S., and B. B. Owen: "The Physical Chemistry of Electrolyte Solutions," 3rd ed., Reinhold Publishing Corporation, New York, 1958.
2. Robinson, R. A., and R. H. Stokes: "Electrolyte Solutions," 2nd ed., Academic Press Inc., New York, 1959.
3. Fuoss, R. M., and F. Accascina: "Electrolyte Conductance," Interscience Publishers, Inc., New York, 1959.
4. Zollinger, H.: *Helv. Chim. Acta*, **36:** 1723 (1953).
5. Nielsen, R. F.: *J. Am. Chem. Soc.*, **58:** 206 (1938).
6. Barrett, J., and J. E. Baxendale: *Trans. Faraday Soc.*, **52:** 210 (1958).
7. LaMer, V. K., and C. F. Mason: *J. Am. Chem. Soc.*, **49:** 410 (1927).
8. LaMer, V. K., and R. W. Fessenden: *J. Am. Chem. Soc.*, **54:** 2351 (1932).
9. Olson, A. R., and T. R. Simonson: *J. Chem. Phys.*, **17:** 1167 (1949).
10. Brønsted, J. N., and A. Delbanco: *Z. Anorg. Allgem. Chem.*, **144:** 248 (1925).
11. von Kiss, A., and P. Vass: *Z. Anorg. Allgem. Chem.*, **217:** 305 (1934)..
12. Rudra, L., and M. N. Das: *J. Chem. Soc.*, **A1967:** 1167.
13. Indelli, A., G. Nolan, Jr., and E. S. Amis: *J. Am. Chem. Soc.*, **82:** 3237 (1960).
14. Indelli, A.: *Trans. Faraday Soc.*, **59:** 1827 (1963).
15. Burnett, R. L., and L. P. Hammett: *J. Am. Chem. Soc.*, **80:** 2415 (1958).
16. Brønsted, J. N.: *Medd. Kgl. Vetenskapsakad. Nobelinst.*, **5:** 1 (1919).
17. Brønsted, J. N., and K. Pedersen: *Z. Physik. Chem.*, **103:** 307 (1923).
18. Davidson, N.: "Statistical Mechanics," McGraw-Hill Book Company, New York, 1962.

19. Guggenheim, E. A.: *Phil. Mag.*, **19:** 588 (1935); E. A. Guggenheim and J. C. Turgeon: *Trans. Faraday Soc.*, **51:** 747 (1955).
20. Scatchard, G.: in W. J. Hamer (ed.), "The Structure of Electrolyte Solutions," p. 9, John Wiley & Sons, Inc., New York, 1939.
21. Lewis, G. N., and M. Randall: "Thermodynamics," 2nd ed., p. 327, rev. by K. S. Pitzer and L. Brewer, McGraw-Hill Book Company, New York, 1961.
22. Bjerrum, N.: *Kgl. Danske Videnskab. Selskab Mat.-Fys. Medd.*, 7(**9**): (1926).
23. Davies, C. W.: *J. Chem. Soc.*, **1938:** 2093; *Discussions Faraday Soc.*, **24:** 83 (1957).
24. Guggenheim, E. A.: *Discussions Faraday Soc.*, **24:** 53 (1957).
25. Davies, C. W., and I. W. Williams: *Trans. Faraday Soc.*, **54:** 1547 (1958).
26. Denney, T. O., and C. B. Monk: *Trans. Faraday Soc.*, **47:** 992 (1951); C. W. Davies and P. A. H. Wyatt: *ibid.*, **45:** 770 (1949).
27. Pauling, L.: "The Nature of the Chemical Bond," Cornell University Press, Ithaca, N.Y., 1936.
28. Wynne-Jones, W. F. K.: *J. Chem. Soc.*, **1931:** 785. See also the summary in M. M. Davis, Acid-Base Behavior in Aprotic Organic Solvents, *Natl. Bur. Std. U.S. Monograph* 105, pp. 41ff, 1968.
29. Long, F. A., and W. F. McDevit: *Chem. Rev.*, **51:** 119 (1952).
30. Setschenov, J.: *Z. Physik. Chem.*, **4:** 117 (1889).
31. Neuberg, C.: *Biochem. Z.*, **76:** 107 (1916).
32. Thomas, A. W.: "Colloid Chemistry," p. 344, McGraw-Hill Book Company, New York, 1934.
33. Traube, J.: *J. Phys. Chem.*, **14:** 452 (1910).
34. Tamaan, G.: "Aggregatzustande," Voss, Leipzig, 1923.
35. Gibson, R. E.: *J. Am. Chem. Soc.*, **56:** 4, 865 (1934); **57:** 284 (1935).
36. Frank, H. S., and M. W. Evans: *J. Chem. Phys.*, **13:** 507 (1945).
37. Gibson, R. E.: *J. Am. Chem. Soc.*, **59:** 1521 (1937).
38. Kruyt, H. R., and C. Robinson: *Proc. Acad. Sci. Amsterdam*, **29:** 1244 (1926); K. H. Meyer and M. Dunkel, *Z. Physik. Chem.* (Bodenstein Festband), **1931:** 553.
39. Brønsted, J. N.: *Z. Physik. Chem.*, **102:** 169 (1922).
40. Bell, R. P., and G. M. Waind: *J. Chem. Soc.*, **1950:** 1979.
41. Bell, R. P., and J. E. Prue: *J. Chem. Soc.*, **1949:** 362.
42. Marburg, S., and W. P. Jencks: *J. Am. Chem. Soc.*, **84:** 232 (1962).
43. Lichtin, N. N., and K. N. Rao: *J. Am. Chem. Soc.*, **83:** 2417 (1961).
44. Clarke, G. A., and R. W. Taft: *J. Am. Chem. Soc.*, **84:** 2295 (1962).
45. Fainberg, A. H., and S. Winstein: *J. Am. Chem. Soc.*, **78:** 2763, 2780 (1956).
46. Winstein, S., S. Smith, and D. Darwish: *J. Am. Chem. Soc.*, **81:** 5511 (1959).
47. Grunwald, E., and A. F. Butler: *J. Am. Chem. Soc.*, **82:** 5647 (1960).
48. Duynstee, E. F. J., E. Grunwald, and M. L. Kaplan: *J. Am. Chem. Soc.*, **82:** 5654 (1960).
49. Livingston, R.: *J. Chem Educ.*, **7:** 2887 (1930).

8
Effect of Solvent on Reactivity

8.1 THE FUNDAMENTAL PRINCIPLE

The effect of a change in solvent on the equilibrium of a chemical reaction is determined by the difference between the effects on the standard potentials of reactants and products. The salt-effect phenomena supply emphatic evidence that the effect of a change in reaction medium on reaction rate is determined by the difference between the effects on the standard potentials of the reactants and the standard potential of the transition state, a quantity whose response to a change in medium is identical with that of a stable molecular species. Both in the rate and in the equilibrium case, therefore, the problem of the effect of solvent on reactivity resolves itself largely into questions about the effect of the solvent on the standard potential of a solute species. A relatively intelligible effect of this sort appears when the solute species is electrically charged.

8.2 THE ELECTROSTATIC CONTRIBUTION TO THE CHEMICAL POTENTIAL OF AN IONIC SPECIES

In order to establish a charge Q on an isolated body of macroscopic dimensions immersed in a medium of dielectric constant ϵ it is necessary to do work. If the body is spherical and its radius is a, this work is $Q^2/2a\epsilon$.[1] If one takes this macroscopic system as a model for the behavior of an ion of charge $z\mathbf{e}$, there will be an electrostatic contribution of $N_0 z^2 \mathbf{e}^2/2a\epsilon$ to the chemical potential of the ionic species. It is a contribution to the chemical potential because the quantity represents reversible work; i.e., it measures free energy. Because ϵ depends on temperature, the free energy is not equal either to potential energy or to enthalpy.

For a binary electrolyte the electrostatic contribution μ°_{el} is given by

$$\mu^\circ_{\mathrm{el}} = \frac{N_0 z^2 \mathbf{e}^2}{2\epsilon}\left(\frac{1}{a_+} + \frac{1}{a_-}\right) \tag{1}$$

Because the theory on which this equation is based involves the assumption that only a small fraction of the solvent molecules are oriented in the electric field of the ions, the equation is most likely to apply if ϵ and the a's are large and z small.

Even for very unsymmetrical ions like acetate or methylammonium one might perhaps hope that Eq. (1) would represent a useful approximation if one takes for a the radius of the CO_2 or NH_3 structure on which the charge is concentrated. It would, however, be expected that the methyl group would increase the energy over that predicted on this basis because it excludes solvent molecules from part of the volume close to the charge. On the other hand, one might expect the charge on picrate ion to be distributed over the structure in such a way that the ion would behave like a large and not very unsymmetrical ion.

8.3 ION PAIRING: THE IDEAL ELECTROSTATIC CASE

When two ions of opposite charge form an ion pair, the resulting structure has a dipole moment, and an electric dipole has an electrostatic energy which is a function of the dielectric constant of the surrounding medium.[2] According to Geddes and Kraus [3], the dipole moment of the ion pair of the typical quaternary ammonium picrate is about one-half of what it would be if there were no charge distortion; i.e., it is about $a\mathbf{e}$ instead of $2a\mathbf{e}$. In terms of any reasonable model the quantity $d\mu^\circ_{\mathrm{el}}/d(1/\epsilon)$ for such a dipole is a small fraction of the quantity

$$\frac{d\mu^\circ_{\mathrm{el}}}{d(1/\epsilon)} = \frac{N_0 z^2 \mathbf{e}^2}{a_\pm} \tag{2}$$

[1] For an excellent discussion see [1].

[2] See for instance [2].

where μ_{el}° is the electrostatic contribution to the standard potential of the separated ions and $1/a_{\pm} = 1/a_{+} + 1/a_{-}$. If it is not only small but negligible, then

$$\frac{d \ln K}{d(1/\epsilon)} = \frac{N_0 z^2 \mathbf{e}^2}{a_{\pm} \mathbf{R} T} \tag{3}$$

where K is the equilibrium constant for the ion pairing. Equation (3) also results from the theoretical treatments of Denison and Ramsey [4] and of Fuoss [5].

8.4 ION ASSOCIATION IN QUATERNARY AMMONIUM SALTS

Much important information on ion association has been obtained from conductance studies on quaternary ammonium salts in a variety of solvents, work in which Kraus[1] and Fuoss have been leaders and pioneers.

The matter is somewhat complicated by the fact that conductance theory has been going through a succession of refinements [7]. Consequently the values of the association constant reported from a given set of conductance data change by a factor of as much as 1.5 with the degree of sophistication used in the analysis of the data [8], and therefore with the date of publication.

In spite of such difficulties as this, $\log K$ is frequently found to be linear in $1/\epsilon$ for quaternary ammonium salts of not highly unsymmetrical anions in a series of solvents, especially if these are not of the strong hydrogen-bonding or strong cation-solvating type. A typical case is shown in Fig. 8.1. The solvents involved range from *m*-dichlorobenzene, with a dielectric constant of 5.04, to nitrobenzene, with one of 34.69. The line plotted represents the relation

$$\log K = -0.470 + \frac{46}{\epsilon} \tag{4}$$

The slope leads to an a value of 5.3×10^{-8} by way of Eq. (3), which is reasonable in terms of known molecular dimensions.

As would be expected from Eq. (3), ion association is more extensive the smaller the ions. In nitrobenzene Witschonke and Kraus [10] found the association of tetra-*n*-butylammonium picrate too small to be detected by the method they used at that time for the analysis of the conductance data. For tetraethylammonium picrate they obtained the value of 7 for the equilibrium constant K of the ion pairing, and the K values were 80 for tetraethylammonium chloride and 62 for tetraethylammonium bromide.

[1] There is an excellent review by Kraus [6].

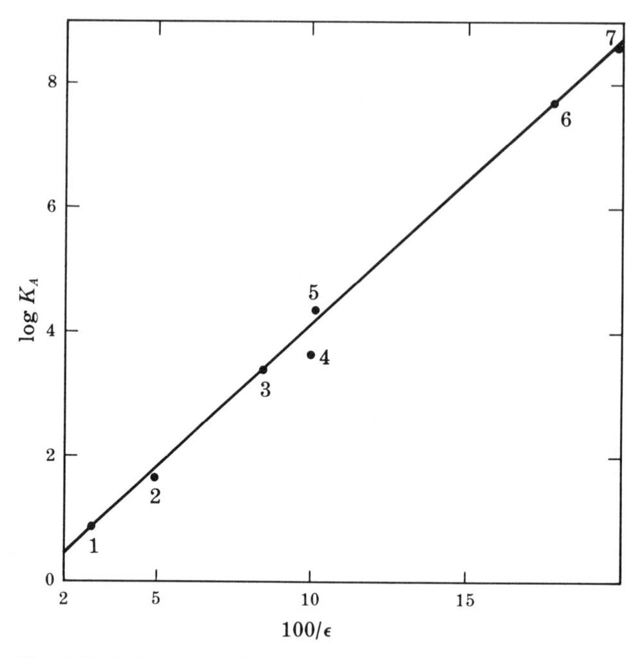

Fig. 8.1 Relation of the association constant of tetra-*n*-butylammonium picrate to the dielectric constant ϵ of the solvent. [*By permission of Y. H. Inami, H. K. Bodenseh, and J. B. Ramsey, J. Am. Chem. Soc.*, **83**: 4745 (1961); *the data were taken from a variety of sources.*]

8.5 ION TRIPLETS AND SALT POLYMERS

An ion pair is an electric dipole, and its association with a third ion of either sign is necessarily accompanied by a decrease in electrostatic energy. Ion triplets play an important role in the conductance of quaternary ammonium salts and of other electrolytes in solvents of dielectric constant less than 12. By the same token the association of two ion pairs to a salt dimer is accompanied by a decrease in electrostatic energy, and there is a further decrease when either ions or other ion pairs are added to the dimer. In the end the process leads to a crystal of the salt. In benzene ($\epsilon = 2.3$) the cryoscopically determined degree of association, the ratio of the average molecular weight to the molecular weight of the salt monomer, runs from 2.4 to 3.2 at a salt concentration of 0.001 formula weights per 1,000 g solvent for bulky quaternary ammonium iodides, perchlorates, and thiocyanates [11]. The value increases steadily with salt concentration to as much as 32 for tetra-*n*-butylammonium thiocyanate at 0.3 formal but decreases at higher salt concentrations, perhaps because at this point the volume concentration of salt is about 0.1. The solute particles in such solutions more nearly resemble fragments of the crystalline substance than they do free ion or ion pairs, and the medium is well on its way toward being a moderately diluted fused salt.

8.6 ON HYDROGEN BONDING

The extent of ion pairing may be greatly influenced by the unevenness of charge distribution which so commonly exists in the ions of organic chemistry. These lead to localized regions of high potential gradient in the neighborhood of the ion which can result in strong attractive interactions between cation and anion. Hydrogen bonding is a case in point. Conditions favorable to such bonding between cation and anion lead to increases of several orders of magnitude in the association constant (Sec. 8.7).

When a hydrogen atom is covalently bonded to a strongly electronegative atom, such as fluorine, oxygen, or nitrogen, or even to a carbon atom in such molecules as chloroform and acetylene, the hydrogen nucleus is embedded not far from the surface in a system of electrons whose distribution is largely controlled by the electronegative atom. The region of the surface of the molecule near the hydrogen nucleus then becomes one in which the potential gradient is very steep. On the other hand, large gradients of opposite sign exist at the surface of electronegative atoms which possess unshared electron pairs. If two regions of this kind of opposite sign can be brought together either in the same molecule or in different molecules, the process will be accompanied by a considerable decrease in energy, apparently by as much as 9 kcal. This kind of interaction between two molecules or between two structural groups within a single molecule is called hydrogen bonding. The molecule or group which supplies the hydrogen atom may reasonably be called the hydrogen-bond donor, although other conventions are sometimes used; the molecule or group to which the hydrogen is attached is then the acceptor. The hydrogen bond is often represented by a dashed line in structural formulas.

Direct evidence for hydrogen bonding comes from negative deviations from ideality in more or less equimolar mixtures of donor and acceptor, i.e., from potentials or molal enthalpies of the components in such mixtures which are considerably lower than those predicted from ideal-solution laws. Important evidence also comes from shifts toward lower frequencies in the stretching vibration of the O—D bond in a deuterated alcohol or from similar infrared absorption phenomena.

The shift in the infrared indicates a decrease in the force constant for the vibration. For a series of not too dissimilar substances this decrease in force constant might be expected to be related to the increase in the energy of formation of the bond with the acceptor. And indeed there is a good linear correlation between the shift produced by mixing CH_3OD with various nitrogen and oxygen bases and the conventional pK of the base [12]. A recent review by Arnett [13] shows that over a range of 22 pK units all but one of the 42 points lie within 1 unit on either side of the best straight line. The plot deliberately and explicity excludes pyridine and quinoline, which for a given shift are about 4 pK units weaker bases than aliphatic amines [14]. There are undoubtedly many cases in which steric repulsions have an important effect on hydrogen bonding, but this should not be the case when the donor has the kind of exposed proton that methanol has.

There is qualitative evidence of a relation between the intensity of hydrogen bonding and the acid strength of the donor, but there does not appear to be much quantitative evidence. Such a relation would be expected.

8.7 ON HYDROGEN-BONDED ION PAIRS

Some of the evidence for hydrogen bonding between anions and incompletely substituted ammonium ions was presented in the previous chapter (Sec. 7.16). There is an impressive amount of additional evidence, involving dipole moments, infrared and ultraviolet absorption, and colligative properties. This has recently been surveyed thoroughly and critically by Davis [15, pp. 41ff]. In solvents like benzene, chlorobenzene, and nitrobenzene, which are relatively inert with respect to hydrogen bonding, the work of Kraus and coworkers [6, 10, 11] shows that the association constants of the picrates of ammonia and of primary, secondary, and tertiary amines are of the order of 10^3 times the constant for similar quaternary ammonium picrates. Association with iodide ion is a little larger than with picrate ion, association with perchlorate ion an order of magnitude smaller.

In general, ion pairs in which there is strong hydrogen bonding show relatively little tendency toward polymerization. The association numbers of tri-*n*-butylammonium and tri-*i*-amylammonium picrates in benzene are only 1.01 at 0.001 formal salt concentration and rise only to 2.2 at 0.3 concentration [11] (cf. Sec. 8.5).

The behavior of the intensely colored salts of the phenol bromophthalein magenta, A

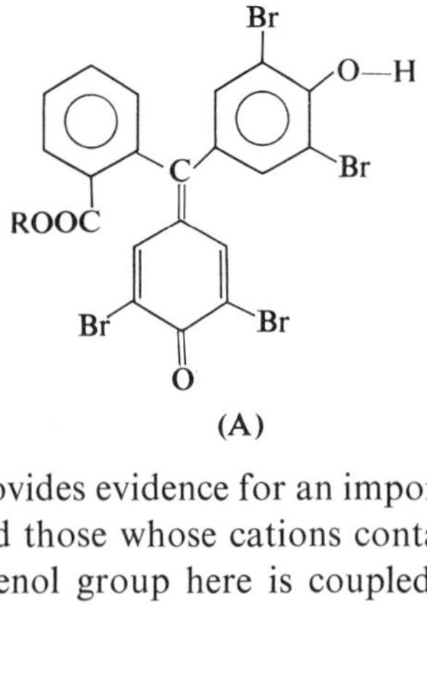

(A)

provides evidence for an important difference between salts of tertiary amines and those whose cations contain more than one acidic hydrogen [16]. The phenol group here is coupled to an extensive unsaturated system, and the visible and ultraviolet spectra are very sensitive to the environment of the group. The phenol itself is yellow, with an absorption maximum at 4000 Å. The tetrabutylammonium salt is blue in a variety of solvents, with a maximum near 6050. But the triethylammonium salt is magenta, with a maximum near 5400 in hydrocarbons, halogenated hydrocarbons, ethers, and esters, although the color changes to blue in solvents more favorable to ionic dissociation. Salts with secondary amines are blue of a different hue from that of the quaternary salts. The maximum is near 5750. Davis proposes a dimeric structure B for the secondary salts.

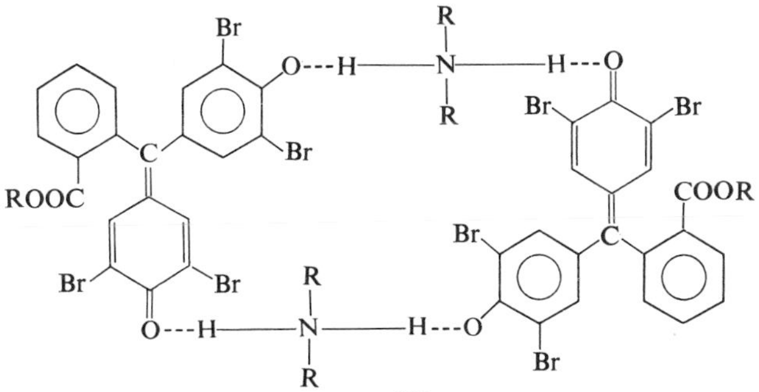

(B)

There is evidence from infrared absorption [17; 15, pp. 66–67, 94] that diethylammonium acetate is more extensively dimerized than triethylammonium acetate, presumably by way of a cyclic structure involving both of the protons in diethylammonium ion.

The characterization of the 1:1 compounds of a neutral base B with a neutral acid HA as hydrogen-bonded ion pairs has given rise to considerable discussion. Barrow [18] supposes on the basis of infrared studies that hydrogen-bonded ion pairs BH^+---A^- in which the proton has been transferred from the acid to the base are in mobile equilibrium with an isomeric structure B---HA in which the proton is still covalently attached to A^-. The stronger the base and the weaker the acid, the more the equilibrium will favor the ion pair. Davis [15, p. 72] doubts the validity of the evidence and supposes that a single compound is formed in every case but that the position of the proton shifts from close association with A^- to close association with B as the strength of the base increases or that of the acid decreases.

8.8 INTERACTION OF HYDROGEN-BOND DONORS WITH ANIONS

There is an impressive mass of evidence that hydrogen-bond donors form compounds with anions, both when the anion is free and when it is part of an ion pair; further that this compound formation shifts the ion-pair equilibrium in favor of free ions.[1] Very thorough investigations of these phenomena have

[1] Reviewed in [15], pp. 88–112.

been carried out by Kolthoff and coworkers and by Coetzee and coworkers in the solvent acetonitrile. The dielectric constant is 37.5 at 20°C, and such typical quaternary ammonium salts as the perchlorate, the salicylate, and the *p*-nitrophenolate show little if any ion pairing [19]. Figure 8.2 shows conductivity titration plots obtained by Kolthoff and Chantooni [20] for the addition of triethylamine to 3,5-dinitrobenzoic acid in acetonitrile. Not only qualitatively but quantitatively these can be accounted for in terms of the complete transfer of a proton from the acid to the base and the reactions

$$BH^+\text{---}A^- \rightleftharpoons BH^+ + A^- \qquad \text{(I)}$$

$$A^- + HA \rightleftharpoons A^-\text{---}HA \qquad \text{(II)}$$

$$BH^+\text{---}A^-\text{---}HA \rightleftharpoons BH^+ + A^-\text{---}HA \qquad \text{(III)}$$

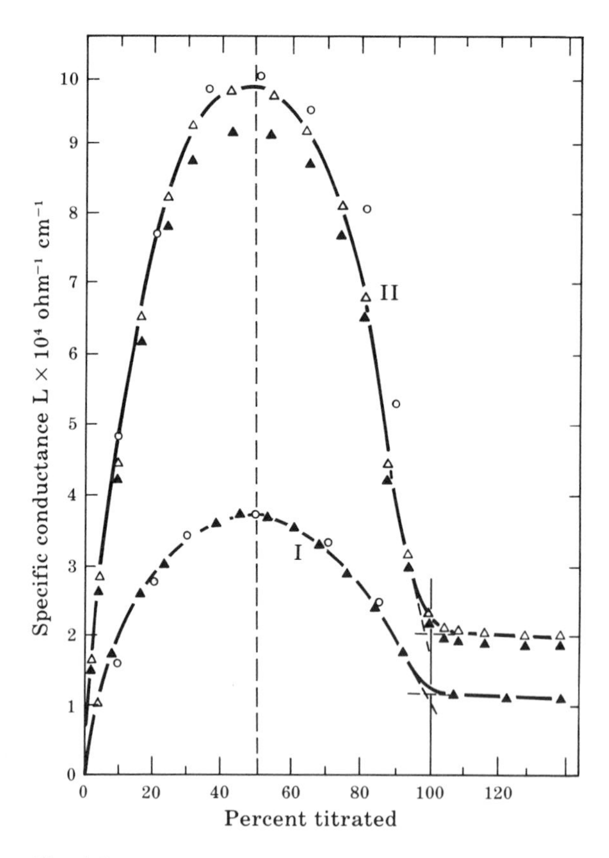

Fig. 8.2 Conductance titration of 3,5-dinitrobenzoic acid with triethyl amine: ▲ = experimental points; △ = experimental points corrected for viscosity; ○ = calculated points. (*By permission of Kolthoff and Chantooni* [20].)

The dissociation constant K_I of the simple salt BH^+---A^- and the limiting conductance of the ions were determined from the conductance-concentration behavior of the salt, the conjugation constant K_{II} was determined from the effect of the acid on the solubility of potassium dinitrobenzoate, and the ionic dissociation constant K_{III} of the conjugate salt BH^+---A^----HA and the limiting conductance of its ions were determined from the conductance behavior of solutions of the amine in a large excess of acid. The values used in constructing the calculated curves in the figure are $K_I = 1.2 \times 10^{-5}$, $K_{II} = 1.7 \times 10^4$, $K_{III} = 3.0 \times 10^{-2}$. It is clear that there is a rather stable A^----HA compound, one which would be only 5 percent dissociated to A^- and HA at 0.1 *M* concentration, further that the constant for the ionic dissociation of the conjugate salt is 400 times greater than that for the simple salt. This is a typical example of the general rule that the strength of a given hydrogen bond is weakened by the formation of an additional hydrogen bond to the same acceptor molecule.

Kolthoff calls the association of an acid HA with anion A^- homoconjugation, and he calls association of an acid HR with anion A^- heteroconjugation. In a detailed study of heteroconjugation Kolthoff and Chantooni [21] derive values of 3.4×10^2 and 5.1×10^3 for the equilibrium constants in acetonitrile of the reactions

$$A^- + HR \rightleftharpoons A^- \text{---} HR \qquad \text{(IV)}$$

$$A^- + 2HR \rightleftharpoons A^- \text{---} (HR)_2 \qquad \text{(V)}$$

in which A^- is 3,5-dinitrobenzoate ion and HR is resorcinol, from the effect of resorcinol on the solubility of potassium dinitrobenzoate. They then find that the effect of resorcinol on the conductimetric titration of dinitrobenzoic acid with triethylamine can be quantitatively accounted for by the additional assumption that the equilibrium constant is 0.01 for the ionic dissociation both of A^----HR and of A^----$(HR)_2$. Very similar results are obtained with *p*-bromophenol instead of resorcinol. That the phenol is a hydrogen-bond donor in these systems is strongly indicated by infrared absorption data. The standard potentials of the various hydrogen-bonded compounds relative to unbonded $A^- + HA + 2HR$ are indicated in Fig. 8.3, HR being resorcinol.

In the compound BH^+---A^----$(HR)_2$ the acceptor dinitrobenzoate ion is bonded to three donors. There are two especially favorable sites in the ion for the bonding, namely, the two carboxylate oxygens, and the possibility of bonding to a nitro group cannot surely be rejected. It is, however, possible for more than one donor to be strongly bonded to a single acceptor atom. Agarwal and Diamond [22] find from experiments involving the distribution of tetrapentyl- or tetrahexylammonium hydroxide between water and benzene containing varying amounts of benzyl or decyl alcohol that the hydroxide is present in the benzene solution chiefly as an ion pair to which three alcohol molecules are attached. In similar experiments involving the distribution of tetrapropyl- or tetrabutylammonium hydroxide between water and nitro-

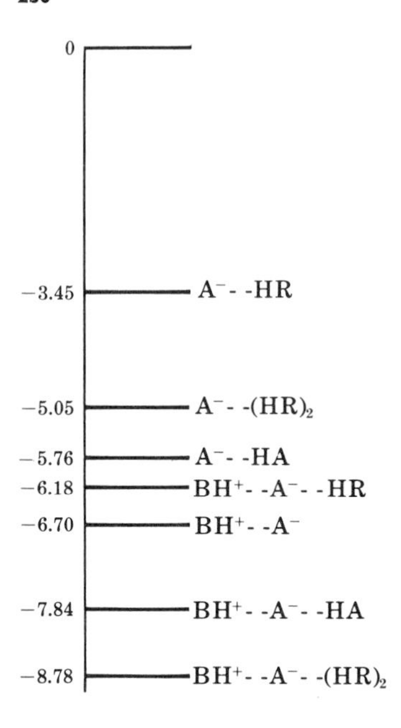

Fig. 8.3 Standard potentials in system triethyl amine (B), 3,5-dinitrobenzoic acid (HA), and resorcinol (HR). (*Based on data of Kolthoff and Chantooni* [21].)

benzene containing benzyl or 4-methylhexyl alcohol the hydroxide is present chiefly as free ions carrying three alcohol molecules. These are rather certainly attached to the hydroxyl ion, not to the cation.

That alcohols can serve as hydrogen-bond donors to anions is clearly shown by infrared evidence of Bufalini and Stern [23]. Solutions of methanol in benzene of concentrations less that 0.03 M show an absorption at 2.75 μ, which is attributable to the O—H stretching vibration. At higher concentrations another band appears at 3.0 μ, and the variation of the relative intensities of the two bands with methanol concentration is consistent with its assignment to a methanol dimer. At methanol concentrations at which the 3.0 band is negligible the addition of tetrabutylammonium bromide leads to the appearance of a band at 2.98 μ. Quantitative interpretation is difficult because much of the salt is present as dimer, but the indications are that one alcohol molecule is associated with one molecule of the ion pair at low alcohol concentrations and that the salt dimers also combine with the alcohol. Combination of methanol with tetrabutylammonium picrate is too small to be detected in this way, and with other tetrabutylammonium salts the extent of combination increases in the order formate, nitrate, bromide, and chloride.

Bonding of methanol to dimethylanilinium chloride is less extensive than to tetrabutylammonium chloride, presumably because the chloride ion in the former, already hydrogen-bonded to the cation, is less available for the formation of an additional hydrogen bond. Normal and tertiary butyl alcohols and N-methylacetamide also bond to tetrabutylammonium bromide, the tertiary alcohol somewhat less than the primary and both considerably less than methanol.

Hydrogen bonding to anions by donors has been investigated in a variety of other ways. The extent of proton transfer from HCl to an indicator base in dioxane is increased by such donors as alcohols, phenols, and acetic acid [24]. Presumably the hydrogen bonding shifts the electron system of the acid in a direction which facilitates the transfer of the proton to a base.

The frequencies of the O—H, N—H, and C—H stretching vibrations in alcohols, phenols, amines, and such acidic carbon compounds as chloroform are shifted by association with anions [25, 26]. Such evidence as this shows that the intensity of the anion-donor interaction increases from iodide through bromide and chloride to fluoride, i.e., with decreasing ionic radius. The interaction is relatively weak with picrate or with perchlorate ion. In a series of phenols the intensity increases generally with increasing acid strength [24, 25], but diortho-substituted phenols may be considerably off line. The frequency shifts in cm^{-1} for tetraethylammonium, tetrabutylammonium, *N*-hexadecylpyridinium, and tetraphenylarsonium chlorides are 334, 355, 324, and 305 [26], but they are nearly independent of the cation for the bromides and iodides. This indicates a specific interaction of the relatively small chloride ion with the cation which is much smaller with the larger halide ions.

8.9 INTERACTION OF HYDROGEN-BOND ACCEPTORS WITH CATIONS

The evidence for this kind of interaction is of the same nature as that for the donor-anion interaction.[1] The conductance of the salt $(CH_3)_3NOH^+$ $C_6H_2(NO_2)_3O^-$ in nitrobenzene is materially increased by water, pyridine, triethylamine, or piperidine [10]. The conductance of tributylammonium picrate or bromide in *o*-dichlorobenzene or in chlorobenzene is increased by pyridine derivatives [27] and the conductance change increases with increasing basicity in the order 4-cyanopyridine, pyridine, and 4-methylpyridine. Glass-electrode pH measurements in acetonitrile [28] show that a wide variety of primary, secondary, and tertiary amines form homoconjugate cations BH^+---B.

8.10 OTHER ION–NEUTRAL-MOLECULE INTERACTIONS

Strong specific interaction between an ion and a neutral molecule can exist without hydrogen bonding. Lichtin [29] points out that the conversion of triphenylmethyl chloride to an ion pair, as measured by the striking change in the spectrum, is 10^8 times more extensive in sulfur dioxide, whose dielectric constant is 15.4 and whose dipole moment is 1.62, than in nitrobenzene, for which the corresponding values are 34.5 and 4.24. There is spectroscopic evidence for an association of sulfur dioxide with chloride ion, none for an

[1] Reviewed in [15], pp. 79–88.

association with triphenylcarbonium ion. The association of sulfur dioxide with halide ions appears to be of the charge-transfer type [29, 30].

The ion-pair association constant of tetrabutylammonium bromide is too small, i.e., less than 10, for measurement in methanol or in nitromethane, but it is 56 in nitrobenzene [31]. The difference between the methanol and the nitrobenzene solutions may be attributed to hydrogen bonding of methanol to bromide ion, but it is not obvious that there should be significant association of nitromethane with either ion. Hyne [32] suggests a specific interaction of nitrobenzene with the ion pair. The three solvents have nearly the same dielectric constant.

Even bulky quaternary ammonium ions can be specifically associated with certain kinds of neutral molecule. Gilkerson and Ezell [33] find that the conductance of methyltri-*n*-butylammonium perchlorate and that of the iodide in *o*-dichlorobenzene is increased by triphenylphosphine oxide in a way which is quantitatively accounted for by the formation of a 1:1 compound of the phosphine oxide with the cation, a compound whose ionic mobility is less than that of the uncomplexed ion, presumably because of the increased bulk. The association can hardly be with the anion because the association constant 39.0 is the same for the perchlorate and the iodide, and because the structure of the triphenylphosphine oxide is one which would be expected to associate with cations and not with anions. The molecule has an exposed negative charge localized on the oxygen atom, in the neighborhood of which there should be a high gradient of electric potential, whereas the balancing positive charge is well buried. There is the same kind of evidence for the formation of a compound of the methyltributylammonium cation with triphenylphosphine oxide in the solvent ethylene dichloride, but the association constant is only 6.8. This indicates a competition between the phosphine oxide and the solvent molecule, and therefore a specific association of the solvent with the quaternary ammonium ion.

8.11 A SURVEY OF ION-SOLVENT INTERACTIONS

Alexander and Parker [34] have determined the solubility of a variety of difficultly soluble electrolytes in a number of solvents, all of whose dielectric constants are over 30. From these data the values of the logarithm of the standard activity a° listed in Table 8.1 were obtained. The values are relative to the solvent dimethylformamide, which is the poorest anion solvator for which the data are complete. They are assigned (Sec. 2.18) on the basis of a value of zero for the least solvated ion tetraphenylboride. The standard activity a°_{ij} of ion i in solvent j is therefore given by

$$\mathbf{R}T \log a^\circ_{ij} = (\mu^\circ_{ij} - \mu^\circ_{0j}) - (\mu^\circ_{i0} - \mu^\circ_{00}) \qquad (5)$$

where μ°_{0j} = standard potential of $B(C_6H_5)_4^-$ in solvent j

μ°_{i0} = standard potential of anion i in dimethylformamide

μ°_{00} = standard potential of $B(C_6H_5)_4^-$ in dimethylformamide

Table 8.1 Logarithms of assigned standard activities of anions relative to dimethylformamide at 25°C[a]

	H_2O	CH_3OH	$HCONH_2$	DMSO	CH_3CN	HMPT	DMAC	A
OAc^-	−18.4	−11.9		−3.0	−2.4		+1.0	−11.2
Cl^-	−15.3	−9.2	−8.8	−1.3	−1.2	+0.2	+1.3	−9.2
Br^-	−13.3	−7.6	−7.3	−1.6	−1.7	+0.1	+1.0	−7.7
N_3^-	−13.0	−7.6		−1.7	−1.2	+0.2	+1.3	−7.5
OTs^-	−10.6	−5.9	−5.0					−5.8
I^-	−10.4	−5.3		−1.6	−1.2	−1.3	+0.4	−5.6
SCN^-	−10.2	−5.4		−1.6	−1.1		+0.5	−5.6
Pic^-	−5.0	−2.0			−0.3			−2.4
ClO_4^-	−6.7	−2.0		+0.3				−2.9
I_3^-	−0.7	−0.7			−0.6		−1.0	−0.9
BPh_4^-	0	0	0	0	0	0	0	0
S	+1.76	+1.0	+0.92	+0.24	+0.19	−0.08	−0.11	

[a] Based on data of Alexander and Parker [34]. Values for picrate and perchlorate are relatively uncertain. The dielectric constants of these solvents are water, 78.5; methanol, 32.6; formamide, 109; dimethylsulfoxide (DMSO), 46.7; acetonitrile, 37.5; dimethylformamide (DMF), 36.7; dimethylacetamide (DMAC), 37.8. HMPT is hexamethylphosphorotriamide. OAc^- is acetate ion, OTs^- is toluenesulfonate ion, Pic^- is picrate ion. S and all $\log a^\circ$ values are by definition zero in dimethylformamide.

Operationally the values are obtained as similar fourfold differences between solubility-product values.

Considering that the $\log a^\circ$ values are fourfold differences, that they are values of the quantity $\mu - \mathbf{R}T\ln c$ at finite although small concentrations and not the limiting value μ°, and that the variety of ions and of solvents is large, the regularity exhibited in Table 8.1 is remarkable. Except for a few minor inversions the sequence of the values for the ions is the same for all the solvents, and the sequence of the values for the solvents is the same for all the ions. The symmetrical bromide and the unsymmetrical azide ions have nearly the same value no matter what the solvent, and the same is true of the symmetrical iodide and the unsymmetrical thiocyanate. The values in acetonitrile are nearly the same as those in dimethylsulfoxide, no matter what the ion.

For symmetrical ions the sequence is that of the crystallographic radii, solvation being greater the smaller the radius of the bare ion, but with respect to the interaction with a series of solvents the unsymmetrical ions behave just like the symmetrical ones. It is reasonable therefore to suppose that a single parameter characterizes the solvating potential of the solvent and another the tendency to be solvated of the anion. The solvent parameters S, which are included in Table 8.1, are averaged values of the quantity $\log a_{ij}^\circ/(\log a_{i0}^\circ)$, where solvent 0 is methanol. The anion parameters A are averaged values of the quantity $(\log a_{ij}^\circ)/S$. The $\log a^\circ$ values in the table can be reproduced with an rms deviation of 0.5 as values of the product SA.

Table 8.2 lists log a° values for a series of cations relative to the solvent acetonitrile and with the assignment of zero for tetraphenylarsonium ion. The data are scantier than for the anions, but the indications are that here also there are large differences in cation solvating potential between the solvents and that the effect of a change in solvent is greater the smaller the ion.

The solvents listed in Tables 8.1 and 8.2 are classifiable into three groups. Water, methanol, and formamide are strong solvators, both for cations and for anions. Acetonitrile is a weak solvator for either kind of ion. Dimethylformamide, dimethylacetamide, dimethylsulfoxide, and hexamethylphosphorotriamide are strong cation solvators but weak anion solvators. On the basis of a variety of observations Parker [35] lists the cation-solvating potentials of some solvents in the order Me_2SO, $Me_2NAc > Me_2NCHO$, SO_2, $H_2O >$ $COMe_2$, sulfolane $>$ MeOH $\gg$ MeCN, $MeNO_2 >$ PhCN, $PhNO_2$. All the solvents in this list but water, methanol, and sulfur dioxide are poor anion solvators.

There is a large amount of qualitative evidence from solubility, from conductance phenomena, and from reaction rates [35] which indicates that lithium ion has a much more negative log a° value in cation-solvating solvents than sodium ion. Similar evidence indicates very negative log a° values for fluoride ion and for hydroxyl ion in anion-solvating solvents. For instance, the ratio of the solubility of potassium fluoride to that of potassium chloride is 0.36 in methanol and 0.029 in the poor anion solvator acetone [36].

With alkali and halide ions intensity of solvation is paralleled by extent of solvation. This is illustrated by the data of Prue and Sherrington [37] in Table 8.3. The Stokes law radii are the ionic radii calculated from the ionic conductances on the basis that ions behave like macroscopic spheres in a structureless viscous medium. They should not be taken too seriously as actual values of the ionic radii in solution, but the relative values for different ions are undoubtedly significant. It appears, therefore, (1) that the average size of the aggregate of cation and associated solvent molecules is greater the smaller the cation in its unsolvated state, both in methanol and in dimethyl-

Table 8.2 Logarithms of assigned standard activities of cations relative to acetonitrile at 25°C[a]

	H_2O	$HCONH_2$	CH_3OH	DMSO	HMPT	DMF
Na^+			−2.4	(−3.9)	−4.4	(−4.6)
K^+	−2.2		+0.1	(−3.3)	+0.1	−1.3
Cs^+	−2.9	−2.5	−0.2			−1.1
NBu_4^+	−0.4		0.0			
Ph_4As^+	0	0	0	0	0	0

[a] Based on data of Alexander and Parker [34]. Values in parentheses are relatively uncertain.

Table 8.3 Stokes law radii and crystallographic radii of ions[a]

	Li^+	Na^+	K^+	Rb^+	Cs^+	Cl^-	Br^-	I^-	ClO_4^-
CH_3OH	3.8	3.3	2.9				2.7	2.4	2.1
$HCON(CH_3)_2$	4.1	3.4	3.3	3.2	3.0	1.9	1.9	2.0	2.0
Crystallographic	0.60	0.95	1.33	1.48	1.69	1.81	1.95	2.16	2.4

[a] Data of Prue and Sherrington [37].

formamide; (2) that anion solvation is large in methanol and more extensive the smaller the unsolvated ion; and (3) that there is relatively little solvation of anions in dimethylformamide.

8.12 THE SIGNIFICANCE OF DIELECTRIC CONSTANT

The dielectric constant of the medium has an influence on the stability of an ion, but it is an important influence only when the constant is small. The electrostatic energy per mole of an ion of 2 Å radius in chlorobenzene, with a dielectric constant of 5.62, is 21.6 kcal less than in benzene, with a dielectric constant of 2.27. But the corresponding difference between the energy in water, with a dielectric constant of 78.5, and methanol, with one of 32.6, is only 1.48 kcal. In media of dielectric constant less than 10 or so the effect of the dielectric constant of the medium should be at least comparable to that of its specific solvating action. In media of dielectric constant greater than 30 or so the effect of the dielectric constant is of minor importance compared with the specific solvating action.

The overwhelming importance of specific solvation effects in solvents of high dielectric constant was emphasized 40 years ago by Fredenhagen [38], who showed that HCN with a dielectric constant of 113 at 22°C is a considerably poorer solvent for electrolytes than water. The solubility in HCN at 0°C of potassium chloride is 0.037 *M*, that of potassium nitrate is 0.050, and that of potassium cyanide is 0.1. Fredenhagen also pointed out that in liquid ammonia, which forms a very stable complex with silver ion, silver iodide is very soluble and the solubility decreases through the bromide and chloride to a difficultly soluble silver fluoride. In water, which strongly solvates small anions but combines less firmly with silver ion than ammonia does, the order is reversed. Silver fluoride is a soluble salt, and the other halides are difficultly soluble, the solubility decreasing in the order chloride, bromide, and iodide.

8.13 ON ALKALI DERIVATIVES OF ORGANIC COMPOUNDS

The familiar alkali salts of inorganic chemistry are what Fuoss calls ionophores; i.e., they are inherently ionic substances. By contrast HCl, which ionizes by proton transfer, is called an ionogen. The salts exist in the crystalline state as ionic lattices in which no simple molecules are detectable. At high temperatures they go into the vapor state as simple or polymeric molecules like KCl or $(KCl)_2$, in which there does not appear to be any considerable measure of covalence. They have considerable solubility in water, and in the aqueous solutions there is little if any association to ion pairs or higher aggregates. With a few exceptions the solubility in organic solvents is very low.

By contrast alkali salts which contain large organic anions may have considerable solubility in organic solvents, but even when the dielectric constant is relatively high the concentration of free ions in the solution is small. In nitrobenzene, whose dielectric constant is 35.7, potassium, sodium, and lithium picrates are present chiefly as ion pairs, with dissociation constants to the free ions of 6.9×10^{-4}, 2.8×10^{-4}, and 6×10^{-8}, respectively [10].

In solvents of low polarity the simple ion pairs associate to polymers, in the extreme case to aggregates of colloidal or near colloidal dimensions. The freezing point of benzene is not measurably depressed by the sodium derivative of butylmalonic ethyl ester in 0.14 *M* solution [39]. The degree of polymerization must therefore be at least 40.

Alkyl lithiums are moderately volatile and are soluble in media of low polarity, but both in the vapor state and in solution they are present as stable and rather definite polymers. Ethyl lithium is hexameric in benzene [40] and appears to be a tetramer or hexamer or a mixture of these in the vapor state [41]. Mixed polymers containing ethyl lithium and *t*-butyl lithium form readily in benzene solution [42]. In ethyl ether or in hexane containing ether, *n*-butyl lithium forms a stable compound consisting of two butyl lithium molecules and one ether molecule [43]. These polymers and compounds have been considered by some to be of electrostatic nature, involving lithium ion and a carbanion; others [43, 44] have considered them to involve a three- or four-center binding involving lithium and carbon.

Alkyl derivatives of sodium and the heavier alkalis are essentially insoluble in solvents with which they do not react. Since a crystal is merely the extreme case of a high-polymer molecule, these compounds may possibly differ only in degree from the lithium alkyls.

Sodium and potassium as well as lithium derivatives of phenylated methanes are soluble in so nonpolar a solvent as benzene. A detailed study by Hogen-Esch and Smid [45, 46] of the alkali derivatives of fluorene in a variety of solvents has shown that these substances exist in two spectroscopically recognizable forms in mobile equilibrium, forms which they refer to as contact ion pairs and solvent-separated ion pairs. As Table 8.4 shows, the latter are favored by lower atomic number of the alkali and by cation-solvating solvents. They are also favored by a decrease in temperature. In tetrahydrofuran the equilibrium constant for the conversion of the contact to the solvent-separated form is 0.064 at 24.2°C and increases to 6.15 at –63°C. The change corresponds to a $\Delta\bar{H}^\circ$ value of –7.6 kcal. All of this is consistent with the

Table 8.4 Fraction f of solvent-separated ion pairs and absorption maxima λ_c and λ_s in millimicrons of contact and of solvent-separated ion pairs in alkali derivatives of fluorene[a]

Cation	*Tetrahydrofuran*			*Dimethoxyethane*		
	λ_c	λ_s	f	λ_c	λ_s	f
Li^+	349	373	0.80		373	1.00
Na^+	356	373	0.05	358	373	0.95
K^+	362	373	0.0	362		~0.1
Cs^+	364		0.0	364		0.0
NBu_4^+	368		0.0			

[a] Data of Hogen-Esch and Smid [45]. No solvent-separated pairs were detected with either Li^+ or Na^+ in dioxane or with Li^+ in toluene. The absorption maxima were 346 to 348 for the Li^+ compound and 353 for the Na^+ compound. No contact pairs were detected with either Li^+ or Na^+ in pyridine or in dimethylsulfoxide. The absorption maxima were all at 373.

assumption that the contact form is indeed less solvated than the solvent-separated form and that the solvation involves interaction of the solvent with an alkali ion or with something not very different from an alkali ion. That the conversion does not involve a polymerization or a dissociation is demonstrated by the facts that a hundredfold dilution does not affect the relative amounts of the two forms and that sodium tetraphenylboride, which is considerably dissociated to free ions in this solvent, does not alter the relative amounts. The conductance of the alkali fluorene solutions is very small. That only two forms are involved is shown by the sharp isobestic point (cf. Sec. 9.20) observed when small amounts of dimethylsulfoxide are added to a solution of fluorenelithium in dioxane.

Further evidence on the nature of these ion pairs is supplied by the wavelengths of the absorption maxima. For the solvent-separated form this is independent of solvent and of the cation, but for the contact form the wavelength is shorter the smaller the cation, indicating increasing intensity of interaction.

8.14 THE EFFECT OF ANION SOLVATORS ON THE RATES OF ANION–NEUTRAL-MOLECULE REACTIONS

The rates of reactions which involve an anion and a neutral molecule are dramatically affected by the solvent in ways which have become appreciated only with the availability of such solvents as dimethylsulfoxide and dimethylformamide. The inertness of aromatic halogen in reactions of the heterolytic type is proverbial, yet bromobenzene reacts rapidly with potassium *t*-butoxide at room temperature when the solvent is dimethylsulfoxide, whereas the same reaction is negligible at temperatures below 180°C when the solvent is *t*-butanol [47].

Such effects as this, which are now recognizable as very general, are accounted for by a hypothesis, due to Miller and Parker [35, 36, 48], which pictures the transition states of reactions of this kind as bulky anions with a broadly distributed charge. Picrate ion is suggested as a comparable structure. As such, the transition-state anion interacts much less strongly with hydrogen-bonding donors than do such compact reactant anions as chloride, bromide, or azide. The standard potential of the reactant ion is therefore decreased much more by the transfer from a weak anion solvator like dimethylformamide to a strong one like methanol than is that of the transition state. The result of the transfer is consequently an increase in the $\Delta\mu^{\ddagger}$ value for the reaction and a decrease in specific rate.

With respect to a change of solvent the rates of anion–neutral-molecule reactions correlate rather well with the solvent parameter S of Table 8.1. This is illustrated in Fig. 8.4 for three reactions:

$$CH_3I + Cl^- \rightarrow CH_3Cl + I^- \qquad \text{(VI)}$$

$$p\text{-}NO_2C_6H_4F + N_3^- \rightarrow p\text{-}NO_2C_6H_4N_3 + F^- \qquad \text{(VII)}$$

$$2,4\text{-di-}NO_2C_6H_3I + SCN^- \rightarrow 2,4\text{-di-}NO_2C_6H_3SCN + I^- \qquad \text{(VIII)}$$

In each case the quantity $\log(k/k_d)$, where k_d is the specific rate in dimethylformamide, is plotted against S. If the effect of the solvent on the rate is indeed determined by the effect on the ratio $a^\circ/a^{\ddagger}$, where a° refers to the reactant ion and $a^{\ddagger}$ to the transition state, the slope of this kind of plot is the difference, $A^\circ - A^{\ddagger}$, between the anion parameters of the reactant ion and of the transition state. From the slopes, which are –6.3, –4.2, and –1.6, and the A° values of Table 8.1 one obtains an $A^{\ddagger}$ of –2.9 for the transition state of reaction (VI), one of –3.3 for that of reaction (VII), and one of –4.0 for that of reaction (VIII). These values are only a little more negative than that of Miller and Parker's suggested model picrate ion.

From the value –4.0 for the $A^{\ddagger}$ value of the transition state of reaction (VIII) and data reported by Miller and Parker the S value for nitromethane is +0.38 and that for sulfolane is +0.09. A value derived in the same way for the solvent acetone would have doubtful validity because of the considerable cation-anion association in this solvent.

The sensitivity of a bulky transition state to a change in solvent should not only be less than that of a compact reactant anion, but it should be less

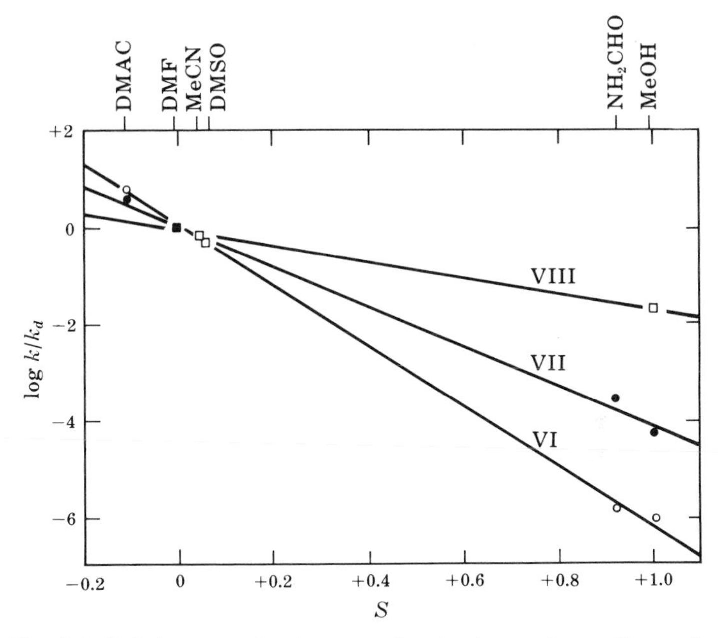

Fig. 8.4 Relative rate of anion–neutral-molecule reactions. (*Data of Miller and Parker* [36] *and Parker* [48].)

dependent on the nature of the anion involved. As Table 8.5 shows, this is the case in the reaction of methyl iodide with a number of anions. The $A^{\ddagger}$ value, which measures the sensitivity of the transition state to change of solvent, varies by only 0.3, while the A° value for the reactant anion varies by 3.8.

The bulkier the transition state and the more evenly its charge is distributed, the less sensitive its standard activity should be to change in solvent. That this is the case is shown by the data of Coniglio et al. [49] in Table 8.6.

Table 8.5 Specific rates of reaction $CH_3I + X^-$ in methanol k_m and in dimethylformamide k_d and $A^{\ddagger}$ values for the transition states[a]

X^-	$10^5 k_m$	k_d	$\log \frac{k_m}{k_d}$	$A^{\ddagger}$
SCN^-	2.0	0.011	−2.74	−2.9
N_3^-	0.30	0.136	−4.66	−2.8
Cl^-	0.010	0.130	−6.11	−3.1

[a] Data of Parker [48].

Table 8.6 Ratio of the specific rate k_m in methanol to that of k_d in dimethylformamide[a]

Reaction	k_m	$\frac{(k_m/k_d)_I}{(k_m/k_d)_X}$
$CH_3Cl + N_3^-$	20×10^{-5}	0.05
$CH_3Br + N_3^-$	5.9×10^{-5}	0.17
$CH_3I + N_3^-$	1.0×10^{-5}	(1)
$CH_3Cl + SCN^-$	0.025	0.17
$CH_3Br + SCN^-$	0.010	0.23
$CH_3I + SCN^-$	0.0043	(1)

[a] Data of Coniglio et al. [49].

The ratio whose values are listed in the right-hand column is equal to the quantity

$$\frac{a_I^\circ}{a_X^\circ}\frac{a_X^{\ddagger}}{a_I^{\ddagger}}$$

where the a's are standard activities in methanol relative to those in dimethylformamide. Since the values of this ratio for the reaction with thiocyanate ion are different from those for the reaction with azide ion, the effect cannot be determined solely by the ratio a_I°/a_X°, which is independent of the anion. There must therefore be differences in the standard activities of the transition state, and the data are consistent with the supposition that solvation of the transition state by methanol is more intense the smaller the leaving ion and that the effect of a change in the leaving ion is greater the smaller the entering ion.

8.15 THE EFFECT OF SPECIFIC CATION SOLVATORS ON THE RATES OF ANION–NEUTRAL-MOLECULE REACTIONS

In the absence of strong solvators and especially in solvents of low dielectric constant cation-anion interaction has a powerful influence on the rates of anion–neutral-molecule reactions. Because this interaction is usually (cf. Sec. 8.14) considerably stronger with the reactant anion than with the transition state, the effect is likely to be a relatively low reaction rate. Transfer to a solvent which is a strong specific cation solvator, i.e., one which does not substitute solvent-anion interaction for cation-anion interaction, can then produce spectacular increases in rate. In the reaction of the sodium derivative of n-butylmalonic ethyl ester with n-butyl bromide the relative rates are in benzene 1, tetrahydrofuran (THF) 14, ethylene glycol dimethyl ether (monoglyme) 80, dimethylformamide (DMF) 970, dimethylsulfoxide (DMSO) 1,420 [39, 50]. Even relatively small proportions of the strong cation solvators have large effects. The relative rates in benzene solution in the presence of 1 M concentrations of the following had the following values: acetone 1.4; pyridine 1.9; THF 1.2; ethanol 6.4; monoglyme 10.6; dimethylisobutyro-amide 20; dimethylbenzamide 34; DMF 36; dimethylacetamide 41; *N*-methyl-2-pyrolidone 57; *N*-methyl-2-pyridone 141. Zaugg finds that high cation-solvating potential correlates with a calculated high electron density in a π orbital such as that on oxygen in the amides. It does not correlate with the dipole moment of the molecule.

The intensity of cation-anion interaction appears to be affected by the nature of the ions in much the same way as that of either kind of ion-solvent interaction, i.e., for symmetrical ions it is greater the smaller the ion. This leads to interesting inversions in the order of the reactivity of a series of ions. In acetone the specific rates of the reaction of tetrabutylammonium halides with isobutyl toluenesulfonate are in the proportion iodide 1, bromide 4.9, chloride 18, but the corresponding values for the reaction of lithium halides are iodide 1, bromide 0.92, chloride 0.16 [51]. The difference can be fully accounted for by assuming that there is no ion pairing with lithium ion in the transition state and calculating from conductance data the extent of the disso-ciation of the lithium halide ion pairs. This dissociation is smaller the smaller the anion. In an anion-solvating solvent the solvation of the anion is stronger the smaller the ion. In a dioxane-water mixture the relative rates of the reaction of ethyl toluenesulfonate with sodium or potassium halides are in the proportion iodide 1, bromide 0.32, chloride 0.14 [52]. In dimethylformamide, which is a much better cation solvator than acetone, the specific rates of the reaction of lithium halides with methyl toluenesulfonate are in the proportion iodide 1, bromide 3.4, chloride 9.1 when extrapolated to zero salt concentration [53]. The addition of 5 moles/liter of water reduces the specific rate of the reaction with chloride by a factor of 24, but reduces that of the reaction with iodide by a factor of only 2.

It appears that the order of reactivity, often called the order of nucleo-philicity, of the unencumbered anions increases from iodide through bromide to chloride but that the intensity of the interaction of the anion, either with solvent or with a cation, increases in the same order, often so rapidly as to reverse the order of nucleophilicities in an anion-solvating solvent or under conditions that favor strong cation-anion interaction.

8.16 CHELATE SOLVATION OF CATIONS

In many cases, including the alkylation of sodio–malonic ester derivatives, anion–neutral-molecule reactions are considerably faster in ethylene glycol dimethyl ether than in tetrahydrofuran or in diethyl ether [54–56]. The effect has been ascribed [56] to a chelate coordination of the two oxygens in the glycol ether with the metal ion. Such a structure has a considerable entropy advantage over the coordination of the ion with two separate oxygen-containing molecules. Conductance phenomena involving tetraphenylborides in the two solvents support the interpretation [57]. Both the Stokes' law radii and the equilibrium constants for ion association are consistent with a combination of one sodium ion with two glycol ether molecules or with four tetrahydrofuran molecules and with a coordination of cesium ion with the glycol ether but not with tetrahydrofuran. Spectroscopic and nmr evidence for the formation of definite compounds of fluorenyllithium and of fluorenylsodium with the polyglycol ethers $CH_3O(CH_2CH_2O)_xCH_3$ with x from 1 to 4 is reported by Chan and Smid [46].

8.17 KINETICS OF REACTIONS INVOLVING ION AGGREGATES

The reaction

$$\text{Fluorene (9-H, H)} + \text{RLi} \longrightarrow \text{9-Fluorenyllithium (9-H, Li)} + \text{RH} \qquad \text{(IX)}$$

in benzene solution is first order in hydrocarbon. With *n*-butyl lithium the order with respect to the lithium alkyl is 0.18, with *t*-butyl lithium it is 0.26. The values are nearly the same for the reaction of the lithium alkyls with 1,1-diphenylethylene [58]. According to the colligative properties of the lithium alkyls in benzene, the *n*-butyl compound is a hexamer [59] and the *t*-butyl compound is a tetramer [60]. The kinetics suggests therefore a mechanism in which the polymeric alkyl lithium is in mobile equilibrium with a monomer and in which the transition state consists of this monomer plus one molecule of hydrocarbon.

This situation is very different in the alkylation of sodio–malonic ester derivatives (Sec. 8.15). These are at least a fortyfold polymer in benzene. The initial rate of the alkylation reaction is proportional to the concentration of the sodium compound, although there are complications in the time course of the reaction, and is also proportional to the concentration of the alkyl halide. These phenomena can be accounted for by supposing a transition state containing one molecule each of monomeric sodium derivative and alkyl halide and a mobile equilibrium

$$n\text{-Polymer} \rightleftharpoons (n-1)\text{-polymer} + \text{monomer} \qquad \text{(X)}$$

The concentration of monomer determined by such an equilibrium is nearly independent of n if n is large. The phenomena can also be accounted for by supposing a reaction on the surface of the polymer aggregate. If the average degree of polymerization is not very sensitive to the concentration, the number of sites available for the reaction (and hence the rate) will be nearly proportional to the total concentration of the sodium compound. Cryoscopic evidence indicates that the addition of dimethylformamide to the solution of the sodium compound leaves it still highly polymerized. With this or other strong cation solvators present, the time course of the alkylation is first order at least to 80 percent completion. The rate of the catalyzed reaction, i.e., that of the additional reaction produced by the addition of the cation solvator, is proportional to from the first to the three-halves power of the catalyst concentration.

Both the alkyl lithium reactions and the sodio–malonic ester reactions are first order in monomeric metal alkyl. The transition states must therefore contain the metal ion as well as the anion and the neutral reactant. It follows that the acceleration by a cation solvator need not depend on the formation of free anions; what is necessary is that the solvator interact more strongly with the metal ion in the transition state than in the reactant, thus lowering the barrier against reaction of the anion with the neutral molecule. An anion solvator would increase the height of the barrier.

8.18 THE INERTNESS OF SOLID REACTANTS

Such reactions as that of bromobenzene with potassium *t*-butoxide (Sec. 8.14) go much faster in a specific cation-solvating solvent than they do when an inert solvent is used, with the alkoxide introduced as the solid material. Comparisons between homogeneous and heterogeneous reactions are dangerous because an otherwise rapid heterogeneous reaction may be suppressed by the formation of an impenetrable layer of reaction product on the surface of the reactant particles. Insofar, however, as this kind of effect can be discounted, the reaction of the solid is essentially identical with that of a high polymeric dissolved aggregate which has a low surface-to-volume ratio. Solution, even as a polymer, is equivalent to a large increase in the number of sites available for reaction per unit quantity of reactant. It is also equivalent to a large increase in the cross section of the diffusion layer which a monomeric reactant must traverse in order to react in the body of the solution.

8.19 THE INFLUENCE OF THE SOLVENT ON THE REACTIONS OF AN AMBIDENT ANION

The β-naphthoxide ion is what Kornblum calls ambident. It can react with an alkylating agent either at oxygen to form an alkyl naphthyl ether or at carbon to form a 1-alkyl-2-naphthol. In the reaction of sodium β-naphthoxide with benzyl bromide no carbon alkylation is found when the solvent is dimethylformamide or dimethylsulfoxide, but there is 22 percent carbon alkylation in ethylene glycol dimethyl ether, 36 percent in tetrahydrofuran, 34 percent in methanol, 28 percent in ethanol, 85 percent in 2,2,2-trifluoethanol, and 84 percent in water [61]. The same kind of effect of solvent on the product distribution is found in the alkylation of sodium β-naphthoxide with methyl or n-propyl bromide and in the reaction of alkali phenoxides with allyl chloride or bromide or with benzyl chloride [62]. When conducted in methanol or ethanol, alkylations of this sort show little variation in product distribution if the cation is varied, but in diethyl ether, tetrahydrofuran, benzene, or toluene the proportion of carbon alkylation decreases as the cation is varied in the sequence lithium, sodium, potassium, and tetraalkylammonium.

These phenomena indicate that a phenoxide ion which is strongly solvated or is strongly paired with a small cation reacts preferentially at carbon. Presumably the solvation or the interaction with the cation involves the oxygen atom in the phenoxide ion and shields it against reaction. On the other hand a free phenoxide ion or one which is paired with a bulky or strongly solvated cation reacts preferentially at oxygen. The difference between the proportion of carbon alkylation in ethylene glycol dimethyl ether and in tetrahydrofuran is significant. The dielectric constants, 6.8 and 7.3, of the two solvents are nearly the same, but the glycol ether is a decidedly better cation solvator.

8.20 THE EFFECT OF SOLVENT ON CATION-ANION REACTIONS

The specific rate k_1 of the reaction

$$(CH_3)_3S^+ + Br^- \underset{k_{-1}}{\overset{k_1}{\rightleftharpoons}} CH_3Br + (CH_3)_2S \qquad \text{(XI)}$$

at low ionic strengths and at 100°C is 11,700 in dimethylformamide and 3.6 in an 88% by weight mixture of methanol with water [63]. The ratio is 3,300. The equilibrium constants in the same solvents are 290 and 0.06. The ratio is 4,800. The effect of the change in solvent on the standard potential of the transition state is not therefore very different from its effect on that of the reaction product. At the same time the entropy of activation of the reaction in dimethylformamide is +31 while the increase in standard entropy from reactants to products is 71. The difference in standard entropy between transition state and products is so great that most if not all of it must be attributed to the liberation of solvent molecules in the process. The phenomena can be accounted for by supposing that anion solvation is largely lost in the formation of the transition state from the reactants but cation solvation is not. The anion is less solvated in dimethylformamide than in the methanol-water solvent; consequently the increase in potential is greater and the rate slower in the hydroxylic solvent. The disappearance of the cation solvation in the progression from transition state to reaction product is then responsible for the 40 cal/deg entropy increase, but since both solvents interact with the cation, the difference in standard potential between transition state and product has much the same value in one solvent as in the other.

The $\Delta\bar{S}^\circ$ value for the formation of ion pairs from $(CH_3)_3S^+$ and Br^- is

+28 in dimethylformamide, nearly the same as the value for the formation of the transition state of reaction (XI). This suggests that the ion pair and the transition state have about the same intensity of interaction with the solvent.

The specific rate of the reaction of *p*-nitro malachite green C with azide ion is 6.1×10^4 in methanol;

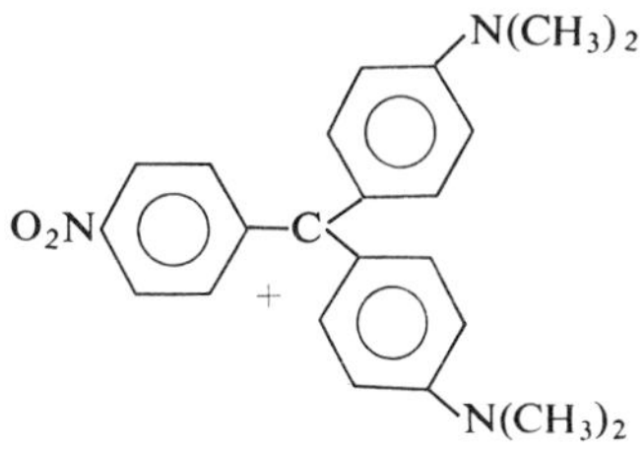

(C)

it can reliably be set at more than 5×10^7 in dimethylsulfoxide [64]. The ratio of the rates in the two solvents is therefore greater than 300. The ratio of the equilibrium constants is only 120. Consequently the change from dimethylsulfoxide to methanol increases the standard potential of the transition state considerably more relative to C than it does that of the *p*-nitro malachite green azide. So far as the immediate environment of the reaction zone is concerned, one would expect the transition state, in which a residue of ionic character presumably persists, to interact more strongly, not less strongly, with methanol than the reaction product does. It must, however, be recognized that the dimethylamino groups in the reaction product probably hydrogen-bond with methanol and that this interaction should be weaker in the transition state in which some positive charge is still delocalized to the amino group from the carbonium carbon.

8.21 DISPERSION FORCES

In the absence of such strong and specific interactions as hydrogen bonding the forces between electrically neutral molecules are solely those which lead to the *a* constant in the van der Waals equation. They decrease in intensity very rapidly with increasing distance, and only a few solvent molecules are therefore appreciably influenced by the solute in dilute solution when these forces alone are present. In the quantum-mechanical interpretation of London [65] they depend on the number and the looseness of binding of the electrons of the molecules involved. Since the number of electrons increases with the volume of the molecule, there is a tendency for the magnitude of the energy required to remove a molecule from a condensed phase to the dilute gas state to increase with its molecular volume. Because the contributions to the partition functions which are involved in such a transfer derive from fully excited motions

(Sec. 3.4), the enthalpy change for the evaporation should closely parallel the change in potential energy. Forces of this kind are sometimes called van der Waals forces, sometimes London forces, and sometimes dispersion forces.

8.22 COHESIVE ENERGY DENSITY

The parallelism between enthalpy of evaporation and molecular volume is not exact. For saturated hydrocarbons the ratio $\Delta \bar{H}^\circ / \Delta \bar{V}$ in calories per cubic centimeter, a quantity called the cohesive energy density, runs from 40 for propane to 65 for hexadecane. It is 57 for *n*-hexane, 73 for cyclohexane, 90 for benzene, and 34 for perfluorohexane. It is 81 for carbon tetrachloride and 100 for dioxane [66, pp. 435–439].

8.23 REGULAR AND IDEAL SOLUTIONS

In binary mixtures whose components are both of the dispersion-force-only type and whose molecular volumes are not very different an equation of the form

$$\mu_a = \mu_a{}^l + \mathbf{R}T \ln x_a + \phi_b{}^2 \bar{V}_a(\delta_a - \delta_b)^2 \tag{6}$$

applies with a good precision for each component over the whole range of compositions.[1] Here x_a is the mole fraction and $\bar{V}_a$ the molal volume of component *a*. The superscript *l* refers to the pure liquid state. ϕ_b is the volume fraction of component *b*, and the solubility parameter δ is approximately the square root of the cohesive energy density. The fit, however, is better if δ is taken as an adjustable parameter characteristic of each component. Hildebrand calls solutions whose behavior is adequately described by Eq. (6) regular solutions.

If δ_a is equal to δ_b, Eq. (6) reduces to

$$\mu_a = \mu_a{}^l + \mathbf{R}T \ln x_a \tag{7}$$

in which case the solution is called ideal. Ideal-solution behavior is found not only with such closely similar pairs as benzene and toluene but in some less obviously similar ones such as benzene and ethylene chloride, and chlorobenzene and naphthalene. To the precision of the perfect-gas law for the vapor, Raoult's law

$$P_a = P_a{}^l x_a \tag{8}$$

where *P* is vapor pressure, is a necessary consequence of Eq. (7). Since $\ln x$ is independent of temperature, the relations

$$\bar{H}_a = H_a{}^l \tag{9}$$

and

$$\bar{S}_a = \bar{S}_a{}^l - \mathbf{R} \ln x_a \tag{10}$$

[1] See [66], especially chap. XIII and XVII.

are also necessary consequences (see Sec. 2.19). The heat of mixing of the components of an ideal solution is therefore zero. Since an ideal solution is presumably one in which the intermolecular forces have the same intensity between unlike as between like molecules, it is not surprising that volume changes on mixing are also zero or very nearly so.

Since each factor in the last term on the right of Eq. (6) is inherently positive, the potential of each component of a regular but nonideal solution must be greater than the value it would have in an ideal solution of the same mole fraction. It follows that for such solutions

$$P_a > P_a^{\,l} x_a \tag{11}$$

i.e., that the vapor pressure of each component is greater than it would be from an ideal solution of the same mole fraction. By differentiation of the quantity μ_a/T with respect to temperature

$$\bar{H}_a = \bar{H}_a^{\,l} + \phi_b^{\,2}\,\bar{V}_a(\delta_a - \delta_b)^2 - T\frac{\partial[\phi_b^{\,2}\,\bar{V}_a(\delta_a - \delta_b)^2]}{\partial T} \tag{12}$$

Unless the last term is large and positive, which seems never to be the case, the molal enthalpy of a component of a regular but nonideal solution is greater than that of the pure liquid component, and the heat of mixing is positive.

Values of δ for different substances may differ by as much as 5 $\text{cal}^{1/2}/(\text{cm}^3)^{1/2}$, and the standard potential of component a in a regular solution, defined as

$$\mu_a^\circ = \lim_{x_a \to 0} (\mu_a - \mathbf{R}T \ln x_a) \tag{13}$$

may therefore be as much as 2.5 kcal greater than that of the pure liquid substance when $\bar{V}$ is 100 cm^3/mole.

Hildebrand supposes that for a regular solution

$$\bar{S}_a^\circ \equiv \lim_{x_a \to 0} (\bar{S}_a + \mathbf{R} \ln x_a) = \bar{S}_a^{\,l} \tag{14}$$

This is equivalent to setting the last term on the right of Eq. (12) at zero. It involves the inconvenient corollary that the force constant which determines the frequency of the vibration or libration of a molecule in a liquid system is unchanged by a change in the molecular environment which changes the energy of the molecule. It is therefore rather more plausible to assume, in agreement with the Barclay-Butler rule (Sec. 3.10), that $\bar{S}^\circ$ varies linearly with $\bar{H}^\circ$ and therefore with μ°.

8.24 ON THE TRANSFER OF A SOLUTE FROM ONE REGULAR SOLUTION TO ANOTHER

If the standard potential of solute a is defined by Eq. (13), the difference $\Delta\mu^\circ$ for the transfer of a from solvent b to solvent c, both solutions being regular, is, from Eq. (6),

$$\Delta\mu_a^\circ = \bar{V}_a^\circ(\delta_c - \delta_b)(\delta_b + \delta_c - 2\delta_a) \tag{15}$$

If the standard potential of a is defined as

$$\mu_a^\circ = \lim_{c_a \to 0} (\mu_a - \mathbf{R}T \ln c_a) \tag{16}$$

there is an additional term $\mathbf{R}T\ln(\bar{V}_c^\circ/\bar{V}_b^\circ)$ on the right. There is no change in the standard potential of a if b and c have identical solubility parameters or if the value for a is the mean of the values for b and c.

According to an equation [66, p. 201] which has the same theoretical plausibility as Eq. (6), the $\Delta\mu^\circ$ value for the transfer of solute a from pure liquid a to a mixture of solvents b and c is the same as that for transfer to a hypothetical liquid whose solubility parameter δ_m is a volume-weighted mean of the parameters of b and c; that is,

$$\delta_m = \phi_b \delta_b + \phi_c \delta_c \tag{17}$$

It follows that for the transfer of a from a solution in b to one in a mixture of b and c

$$\Delta\mu_a^\circ = \bar{V}_a \phi_c(\delta_c - \delta_b)[\phi_c(\delta_c - \delta_b) - 2(\delta_a - \delta_b)] \tag{18}$$

On this basis $\Delta\mu_a^\circ$ is a not very exciting function of ϕ_c. It is zero if $\delta_b = \delta_c$; otherwise it is concave upward over the whole range. There is a physically significant minimum only if δ_a lies between δ_b and δ_c. At the minimum

$$\phi_c = \frac{\delta_a - \delta_b}{\delta_c - \delta_b} \tag{19}$$

and

$$\Delta\mu_a^\circ = \bar{V}_a(\delta_a - \delta_b)^2 \tag{20}$$

8.25 THE EFFECT OF STRONG INTERACTIONS

The theoretical arguments which are presented in support of Eq. (6) indicate that it can be expected to apply only when the interaction energy between two unlike molecules is the geometric mean of that between like pairs. In exceptional cases this requirement may be satisfied when strong specific interactions are present. Even though there are strong hydrogen-bonding interactions both in methanol and in ethanol, the vapor pressures of their mixtures agree with the ideal-solution relation, Eq. (8) [67].

A more typical case is presented by acetone-chloroform mixtures. As shown in Fig. 8.5, vapor pressures are considerably less than the ideal-solution values. The $\Delta\bar{H}$ value for the formation of an equimolar mixture, which equals $\bar{H}_a - \bar{H}_a{}^l + \bar{H}_b - \bar{H}_b{}^l$, is -45 cal, and the corresponding $\Delta\bar{S}$ value is $+0.27$, which is 2.5 cal/deg less than the ideal-solution value [69]. All these phenomena indicate an especially firm binding of acetone to chloroform, a binding which is presumably hydrogen bonding in nature.

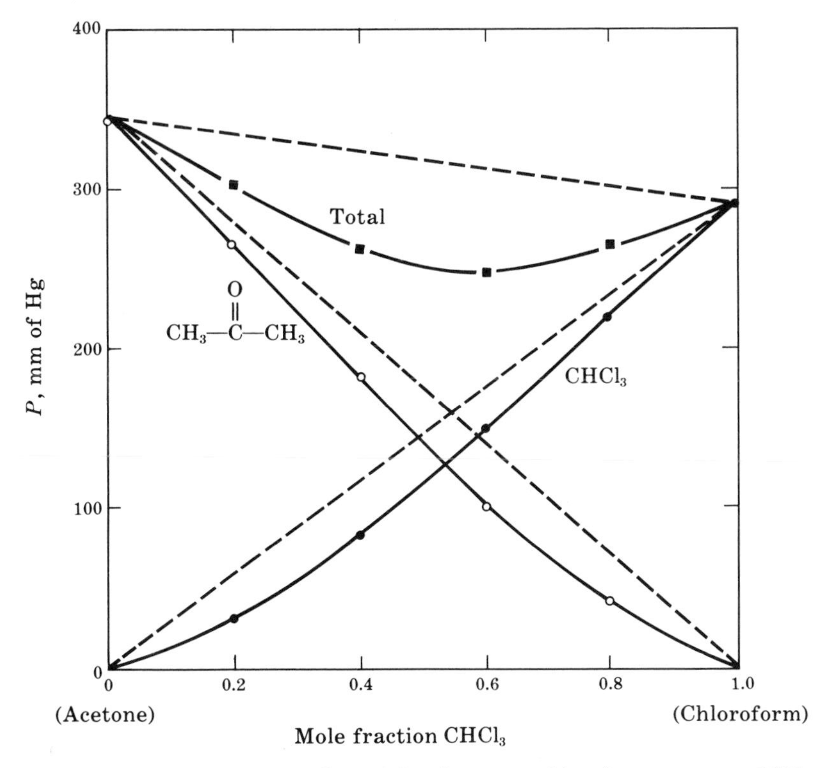

Fig. 8.5 The vapor-pressure diagram for the system chloroform-acetone at 25°C. (*Data of von Zawidski* [68]; *reproduced from G. M. Barrow, "Physical Chemistry." Copyright* 1961. *McGraw-Hill Book Company. Used by permission.*)

When one component of a binary mixture hydrogen-bonds to itself and the other component is neither a donor nor an acceptor, vapor pressures are much greater than the ideal-solution values and $\Delta \bar{H}$ is likely to have a complicated dependence on composition. For mixtures of methanol and carbon tetrachloride it is negative for mixtures high in methanol and positive over the rest of the range [70].

8.26 THE ISOKINETIC RELATIONSHIP FOR VARYING SOLVENT

By the Barclay-Butler rule (Sec. 3.10) the heat of evaporation, $\bar{H}^g - \bar{H}^\circ$, of a solution component is linear in the entropy of evaporation, $\bar{S}^g - \bar{S}^\circ$, both for changes in the composition and structure of the component and for changes in the solvent, the slope being about 800. Consequently when the rule applies, which it probably does only in the absence of strong interactions, the relation

$$\delta_M \bar{H}^\circ = 800 \delta_M \bar{S}^\circ \qquad (21)$$

should hold for a change in solvent. Here δ_M is the Leffler-Grunwald [71] solvent-stabilization operator which describes the effect of a solvent change on the quantity whose symbol follows it. Further, the relation

$$\delta_M \Delta\bar{H}^{+} = 800\delta_M \Delta\bar{S}^{+} \qquad (22)$$

should apply to enthalpy and entropy of activation of a reaction in the solution.

There appear to be no data on reactions in systems in which strong interactions are absent by which to test Eq. (22), but Leffler [72] has pointed out that the relationship, called an isokinetic relationship,

$$\delta_M \Delta\bar{H}^{\circ} = \beta\delta_M \Delta\bar{S}^{\circ} \qquad (23)$$

with β varying from reaction to reaction and more likely to be about 300 to 400 than 800, does hold for many reactions over a considerable variation of solvent. Figure 8.6 [73] illustrates the relationship for a case in which β is 320. Leffler and Grunwald [71, pp. 327ff] report 25 cases in which Eq. (23) applies with a correlation coefficient of 0.95 or better. The list of cases to which the iso-

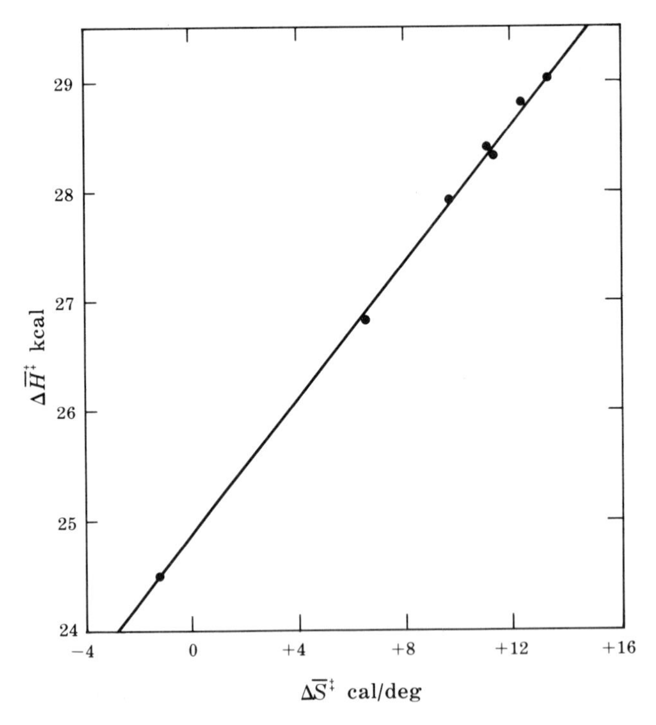

Fig. 8.6 Isokinetic relation for decomposition of $C_6H_5N{=}NC(C_6H_5)_3$. Solvents from left to right are cyclohexane, benzene, malonic ester, nitrobenzene, chlorobenzene, anisole, and benzonitrile. (*Data of Alder and Leffler* [73].)

kinetic relationship applies could be considerably expanded by including those in which either $\delta_M \Delta \bar{H}^{+}$ or $\delta_M \Delta \bar{S}^{+}$ is so small that the scatter always present obscures the enthalpy-entropy relationship but in which the relationships

$$\delta_M \Delta\mu^{+} = \left(1 - \frac{T}{\beta}\right) \delta_M \Delta \bar{H}^{+} \tag{24}$$

or

$$\delta_M \Delta\mu^{+} = (T - \beta)\, \delta_M \Delta \bar{S}^{+} \tag{25}$$

apply. These are necessary corollaries of Eq. (23).

In general terms

$$\delta_M \Delta \bar{H}^{+} = \delta_M \Delta E_0{}^{+} + \delta_M \Delta \left(\mathbf{R}T^2 \frac{\partial \ln Q}{\partial T}\right) \tag{26}$$

and

$$\delta_M \Delta \bar{S}^{+} = \delta_M \Delta \mathbf{R} \ln Q + \delta_M \Delta \left(\mathbf{R}T \frac{\partial \ln Q}{\partial T}\right) \tag{27}$$

It appears (Sec. 3.10) that the Barclay-Butler rule is possible only when the quantity $\delta_M(\partial \ln Q/\partial T)$ is zero and the ratio $\partial_M \ln Q/\partial_M E_0$ is independent both of solvent and of solute and that this occurs only when dispersion forces alone are involved. The isokinetic relationship is possible with more specific solute-solvent interactions if the ratio $\partial_M \ln Q/\partial_M E_0$ has the same value for reactant and transition state in the reaction involved even if it is not generally independent of solute, provided also that $\delta_M \Delta(\partial \ln Q/\partial T) = 0$.

It is not surprising that these rather stringent requirements are not always met and that the isokinetic relationship often fails, especially when mixed solvents are involved. Leffler and Grunwald [71] remark that the plot of $\Delta \bar{H}^{+}$ against $\Delta \bar{S}^{+}$ is sometimes hook-shaped, and sometimes N-shaped, and that if they have to invent a term for the case of the solvolysis of *t*-butyl chloride in ethanol-water mixtures, they can think of no better one than Thurber shaped.

8.27 SOLVOLYSIS IN ALCOHOL–WATER MIXTURES

The solvolysis rate of *t*-butyl chloride at 25°C is more than seven orders of magnitude faster in water than in ethanol [74] and the $\Delta\mu^{+}$ value is an uneventful function of the mole fraction of water (Fig. 8.7). Since the transition state is presumably more polar than the reactant, i.e., is part way along the route toward a carbonium ion and a chloride ion, it would be natural to attribute this effect to a lowering of the standard potential of the transition state when the less polar alcohol is replaced by the more polar water. But Olson and Halford showed that $\Delta\mu^{+}$ rather closely parallels the μ° value of the butyl chloride; i.e., the effect of the variation of solvent depends primarily on those forces which make *t*-butyl chloride less soluble in water than it is in ethanol.

A study by Winstein and Fainberg [75] of the temperature coefficient of

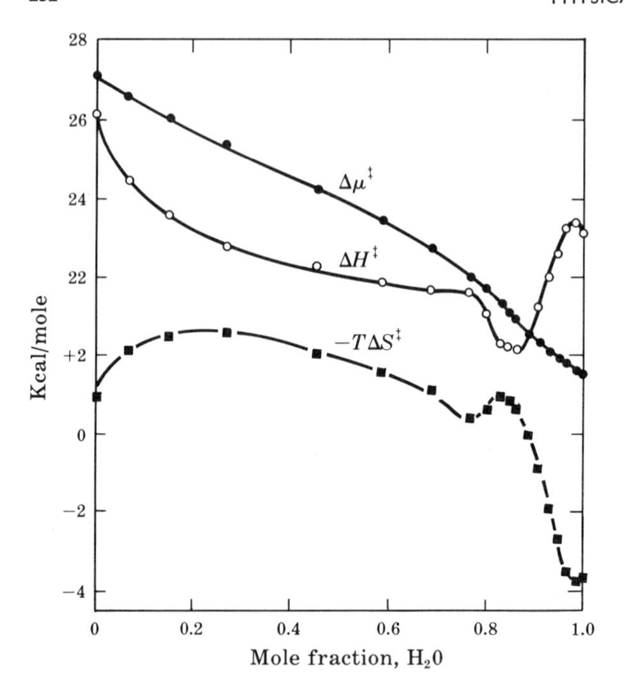

Fig. 8.7 Solvolysis of *t*-butyl chloride in aqueous ethanol. (*By permission of Winstein and Fainberg* [75].)

the reaction rate showed that by contrast to the placid behavior of $\Delta\mu^{\ddagger}$, enthalpy and entropy of activation indulge in complicated antics when the solvent composition is changed (Fig. 8.7). Much the same sort of thing happens with solvents composed of water-dioxane mixtures and with water-acetic acid mixtures.

Arnett and coworkers [76] have recently developed a recording calorimeter which not only makes the direct measurement of the heat of solution of reactive solutes possible but makes it convenient. With this they find that the standard enthalpy $\bar{H}_s$ of *t*-butyl chloride has a maximum at a mole fraction of water of about 0.85, which closely parallels the minimum in the value of $\Delta\bar{H}^{\ddagger}$ for the solvolysis (Fig. 8.8). The standard enthalpy of the transition state $\bar{H}^{\ddagger}$ appears to have a weak minimum in this region of composition. This may, however, be spurious because experimental data on the rate are difficult to obtain in the high water region and other investigators have disagreed with the Winstein and Fainberg value of $\Delta H^{\ddagger}$ in pure water [77].

Arnett and coworkers have further found that the heat of solution in ethanol-water mixtures of a wide variety of nonelectrolytes and of organic electrolytes behaves much like that of *t*-butyl chloride, showing a strong

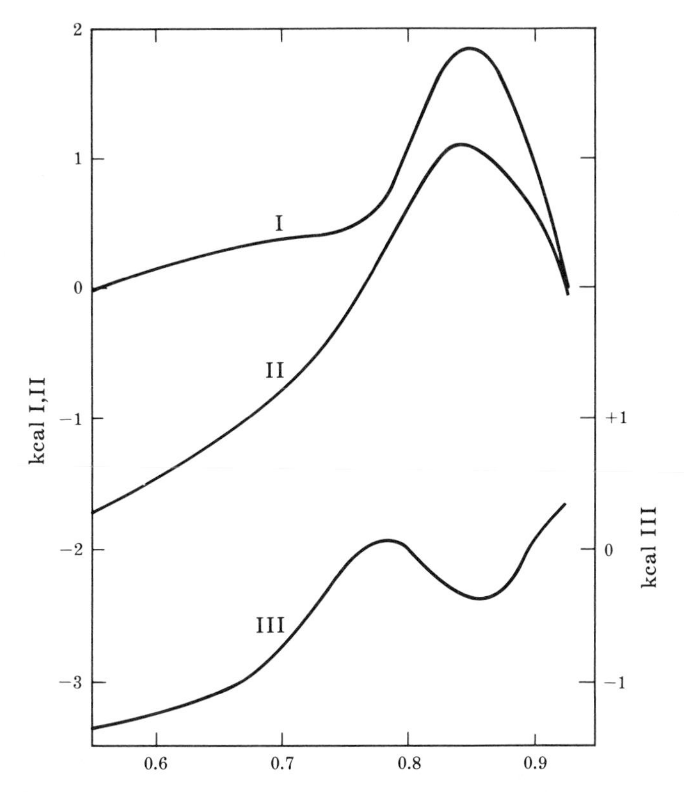

Fig. 8.8 Solvolysis of *t*-butyl chloride in ethanol-water mixtures. Abscissa: mole fraction water. Ordinates: I, $22 - \Delta\bar{H}^{\ddagger}$; II, $\bar{H}^0$ of *t*-butyl chloride relative to 0.765 mole fraction of water; III, $\bar{H}^{\ddagger}$ of transition state relative to 0.765 mole fraction of water. (*Data of Winstein and Fainberg* [75] *and of Arnett, Bentrude, Burke, and Duggleby* [76].)

maximum in the region of a mole fraction of water between 0.8 and 0.9. This is the case with *n*-butyl chloride, with isopropyl bromide, with carbon tetrachloride, with *t*-butanol, and with ethyl acetate. The effect is especially large with sodium tetraphenylboron, with tetra-*n*-butylammonium iodide, with tetraphenylarsonium chloride, and with sodium benzenesulfonate. The maximum is present but weak with potassium chloride, bromide, and iodide, with tetramethylammonium chloride, and with *t*-butyldimethylsulfonium iodide.

The $\Delta C_p^{\ddagger}$ value for the solvolysis of *t*-butyl chloride also is strongly dependent on solvent composition. Martin and Robertson [78] report a value of −83 cal/deg in water, one of −116 at a mole fraction of water of 0.89, one of −49 at a mole fraction of 0.85, and one of −34 at a mole fraction of 0.75.

The large changes in enthalpy and the even more striking changes in heat capacity accompanying small changes in standard potential are what would be expected if there are strong solute-solvent interactions. In particular they are consistent with the Frank and Evans (Sec. 3.11) concept that a solute molecule in dilute water solution builds a structure of a considerable number of water molecules around itself. This decreases the entropy of the system, and if it is to happen, it must also decrease the enthalpy. The structure formation around a solute like *t*-butyl chloride must compete for water molecules with structures composed of water only, and when small amounts of another solvent like alcohol are added, it must compete with structures built around the alcohol molecules. Because many water molecules are involved in these structures, a small decrease in the activity of water leads to a large decrease in the extent of formation of the structure and therefore to a considerable increase in the molal enthalpy and entropy of the solute. When the structures built around solute molecules have essentially disappeared, further addition of alcohol, which decreases the average intensity of attraction between a solvent molecule and its neighbors, decreases the molal enthalpy and entropy of the solute because it becomes easier for a bulky molecule like *t*-butyl chloride to push its way into the system.

8.28 OTHER EFFECTS OF SOLVENT ON SOLVOLYSIS RATE

It is unlikely that the lack of dependence on solvent of the thermodynamic properties of the transition state in the solvolysis reaction which is observed in ethanol-water mixtures is general. In inert solvents hydrogen-bond donors at small concentrations have an effect on reactions closely related to solvolysis which it would be difficult to attribute to anything but hydrogen bonding to the nascent X^- ion. Thus the camphene hydrochloride rearrangement in nitrobenzene is accelerated by hydrogen chloride and by phenols. The effect of a particular phenol is greater the more acidic it is [79].

Linear free-energy relationships of a limited range of applicability appear when the effect of variation in solvent on the solvolysis rate of one reactant is compared with the effect on another. Grunwald and Winstein [80] write

$$\log k - \log k^\circ = mY \tag{28}$$

in which k is the specific rate of the solvolysis of reactant R in solvent S, Y is the difference between $\log k$ for the solvolysis of *t*-butyl chloride in solvent S and $\log k^\circ$ for the solvolysis of *t*-butyl chloride in a standard solvent, a 20:80 by volume mixture of water with ethanol, and m is the slope of a plot of $\log k$ for reactant R against Y. If m were completely determined by the nature of the reactant and Y by the nature of the solvent, a plot of $\log k$ for a given reactant in a variety of solvents against the Y value of the solvent should constitute a single straight line with slope m and with an intercept equal to the specific rate of the solvolysis of reactant R in the standard solvent.

It turns out that the plots are linear for mixtures of a given pair of solvents but that the plot for one pair does not in general coincide with that for another pair [81]. This is illustrated in Fig. 8.9, in which log k for the solvolysis of neophyl chloride, 2,2-dimethyl-2-phenylethyl chloride, is plotted against Y. The term "ionizing power of the medium" has been referred to as descriptive of the parameter Y. However, Smith, Fainberg, and Winstein [82] consider the solvolysis of *p*-methoxyneophyl toluenesulfonate a better measure of "solvent polarity" than that of *t*-butyl chloride. This is because mechanism studies indicate that there is no significant internal return (Sec. 6.12) with this reactant. Consequently the observed specific rate is taken to be that of the ionization process and not the quantity $k_1 k_2/(k_{-1} + k_2)$, which might well have a more complicated kind of dependence on the nature of the solvent.

Swain and coworkers [83] fit solvent effects on a wide variety of reactions of the solvolytic type by a four-parameter equation

$$\log\frac{k}{k^\circ} = c_1 d_1 + c_2 d_2 \tag{29}$$

in which k° is the specific rate of solvolysis of reactant R in 80% aqueous ethanol and k is that in solvent S. c_1 and c_2, set at zero for *t*-butyl chloride, depend only on the reactant, and d_1 and d_2, set at zero in the 80% ethanol, depend only on the solvent. As further normalizing conditions, c_1 was set at $3.00c_2$ for methyl bromide and at $0.33c_2$ for triphenylmethyl fluoride. The reactants range from *p*-nitrobenzoyl derivatives to triphenylmethyl derivatives and from fluorides

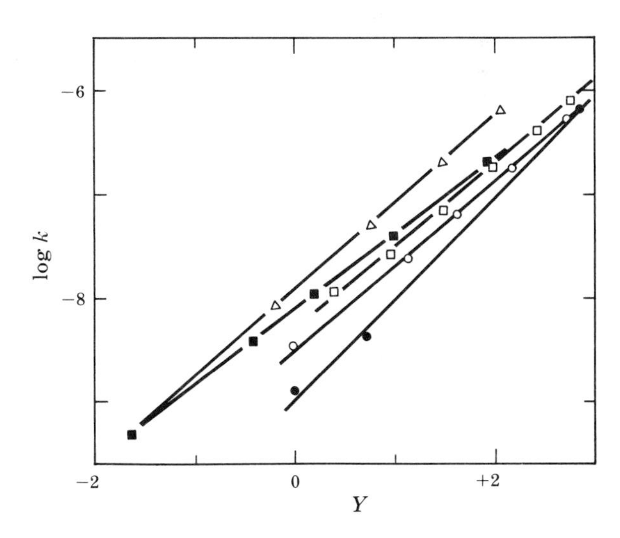

Fig. 8.9 Plot of log k against Y for the solvolysis of neophyl chloride at 50°C; ○ = ethanol–water, □ = methanol–water, ● = dioxane–water, ■ = acetic acid–water, △ = acetic acid–formic acid. (*By permission of Fainberg and Winstein* [81].)

to arylsulfonates. The fit is excellent; the mean error for all compounds corresponds to a factor of 1.33 in k for data for which k/k° varies by nine orders of magnitude.

Swain and coworkers interpret the relationship in the sense that the transition state for solvolysis of an RX compound interacts with the solvent in two distinct ways, involving on the one hand attachment of a solvent molecule to X and on the other hand attachment to the nascent carbonium carbon atom on the side opposite to X. It might perhaps also be interpreted in the sense that each of the terms on the right refers to an independent reaction, in one of which a solvent molecule is in the process of becoming attached to the carbonium carbon in the transition state while in the other this is not happening. Or one term might represent the effect of the medium on the reactant and the other term the effect on the transition state. In any case it must be recognized that a four-parameter equation is a very powerful way of correlating any kind of experimental data.

8.29 CHARGE-TRANSFER COMPLEXES

Compounds of significant stability are frequently formed between two molecules one of which, the acceptor, has a high affinity for electrons while the other, the donor, contains loosely bound electrons. In terms of the theory developed in detail by Mulliken [84] a certain increment of electronic charge is transferred in the compound from donor to acceptor. The compound may therefore be pictured as a resonance hybrid of $A + D$ with a structure $A^- + D^+$ in which there is an electrostatic binding force between A and D. Very characteristically such compounds have a relatively low-lying excited electronic energy level and possess an absorption of low frequency which is unrelated to the absorption of A or of D alone. As a result colorless components often form colored compounds and colored components often form compounds which absorb at a lower frequency. Compounds of this type are called charge-transfer complexes or π complexes, the latter because the loosely held electrons in the donor are usually in π orbitals.

The compounds of silver ion with olefins [85] and the compounds of iodine with benzene derivatives [86] are of the charge-transfer type. So are the multitudinous highly colored compounds formed by polynitro compounds with aromatic derivatives, such as the compound of 1,3,5-trinitrobenzene with naphthalene [87].

Equilibrium constants for the formation of the compounds of iodine with benzene derivatives in carbon tetrachloride run from 0.151 for benzene to 1.52 for hexamethylbenzene [88]. The value for the compound of picric acid and naphthalene in chloroform solution is 1.51 [89], that for the compound of 1,3,5-trinitrobenzene with acenaphthene is 2.43 [90].

Generally, although perhaps not always, the rates of formation and of dissociation of charge-transfer compounds are large. The compounds may have a considerable effect on kinetic behavior (Sec. 4.19).

The possibility that charge-transfer compounds play an important role in aromatic substitution reactions has been much discussed pro and con.[1]

8.30 MULTIPOLAR OR DIPOLAR COMPLEXES

There is evidence from a variety of sources that molecules containing groups which have large localized electric dipoles can form compounds of considerable stability, a stability which depends on the strength of the localized dipole. Thus Ritchie and coworkers [92] find that when dimethylsulfoxide is added to a dilute solution of benzonitrile in carbon tetrachloride solution, the intensity of the infrared absorption in a spectral region characteristic of the CN group decreases in a way which can be accounted for by the formation of a 1:1 compound of nitrile and sulfoxide and which is inconsistent with the formation of a compound in any other proportion. The equilibrium constant for the compound formation is 0.9, and the same value is found with *p*-chlorobenzonitrile and for both the *m*- and the *p*-nitro derivatives. The net dipole moments of the para derivatives are much smaller than the moment of the unsubstituted nitrile, but the near additivity of group dipole moments in benzene derivatives shows that the localized moment of the CN group will be little affected by the substituents. On the other hand, such substituents have a large effect on the rate and the equilibrium of processes which involve primarily either the nitrogen or the carbon of the group. Consequently Ritchie and coworkers argue that the compound formation involves a side-by-side alignment of the CN dipole with the OS dipole of the sulfoxide:

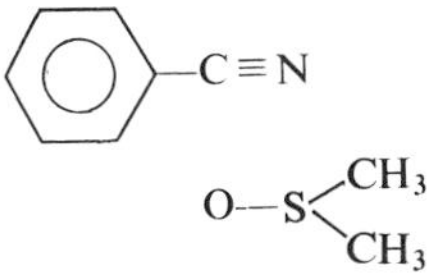

$$C_6H_5\text{—}C\equiv N$$
$$O\text{—}S(CH_3)_2$$

(D)

Taft and coworkers [93] find that in carbon tetrachloride solution the fluorine nmr shielding parameter of *p*-fluoronitrobenzene relative to fluorobenzene, i.e., the difference between the parameter for the nitro compound and that for unsubstituted fluorobenzene, varies significantly with the concentration of the fluoronitrobenzene. For concentrations up to 2 M the change corresponds closely to the formation of a dimer with an association constant of 0.25, and with the shielding parameter for the dimer -1.7 relative to that for the monomer. Similarly an association constant of 0.29 is found for 3,4-difluoronitrobenzene. Since a fluorine substituent in the 3 position relative to a nitro group normally has a larger effect on reaction rates and equilibria

[1] There is an excellent review by Berliner [91].

than one in the 4 position, it seems probable that the association constant for nitrobenzene without the fluorine substituent is also close to 0.25. A dimerization constant of this magnitude plus the assumption that the dimer has zero dipole moment accounts quantitatively for Höjendahl's data[1] on the variation with concentration of the dielectric constant of solutions of nitrobenzene in carbon tetrachloride up to 2 *M*. A dimerization constant of 0.4 at 3°C accounts quantitatively for the data of Bury and Jenkins [95] on the freezing point of solutions of nitrobenzene in benzene. Both the small effect of a fluorine in the 3 position on the shielding parameter and the data on the dielectric constant of nitrobenzene solutions support the hypothesis that the dimer is formed by electrostatic pairing of the nitro groups with the group dipoles of the two molecules opposed.

This picture is strongly supported by the fact [96] that nmr shielding evidence indicates the formation of a 1:1 compound of *p*-fluoronitrobenzene with *p*-fluoronitrosobenzene which has an equilibrium constant for formation of about 1 and in which both fluorine signals are shifted downfield compared with the free componenent. The shifts are about −1.80 ppm for the nitroso compound and −1.06 for the nitro compound. By contrast, in all equilibria involving proton transfer, hydrogen bonding, and Lewis acid-base combination the signal for the fluorine in the acid component is shifted upfield, and that for the basic component is shifted downfield. Thus in the reaction

$$FC_6H_4BCl_2 + N{\equiv}C{-}C_6H_4F \rightleftharpoons FC_6H_4{-}\underset{Cl}{\overset{Cl}{B}}{-}N{\equiv}C{-}C_6H_4F \qquad \text{(XII)}$$

the shift is +12 for the fluorine in the boron derivative and −10.9 for that in the nitrile. In the hydrogen-bonded complex of *p*-fluorophenol with *p*-fluoroacetophenone the shift for the fluorine in the phenol is about +2, and that for the fluorine in the ketone is about −2.

The nmr data demonstrate that the compound formation in cases of this sort is very rapid, the time scale being less than that of the nmr measurement. Ritchie calls complexes of this sort dipolar complexes; Taft prefers the term multipolar complexes.

Taft and coworkers have developed the same kind of evidence for the formation of 1:1 compounds composed on the one hand of substances of the general formula *p*-XC_6H_4F, in which X is NO, NO_2, CN, $COCH_3$, CF_3, $COCF_3$, SO_2F, or SO_2CF_3, and on the other hand of substances whose molecule possesses a strong localized dipole moment, at least one of the components being neither a good hydrogen-bond donor nor acceptor. Substances in the second group include $(CH_3)_2SO$, CH_3CN, $C_6N_5NO_2$, $(CH_3)_2NCHO$,

[1] Cited in [94].

$(CH_3CO)_2O$, pyridine, diethyl ketone, and ethyl acetate. The association constant roughly parallels the localized dipole moment of the single predominant polar center.

As pointed out by Taft, the transition state of a solvolytic reaction or that of such reactions as

$$NH_3 + RX \rightarrow RNH_3^+ + X^-$$

is a structure with a strong localized dipole. It should therefore form compounds of the multipolar type with solvents which also contain strong localized dipoles. And indeed the compound formation revealed by the fluorine nmr shielding does parallel closely the rates of typical solvolytic reactions. Figure 8.10 plots log k for the solvolysis of p-methoxyneophyl toluenesulfonate against

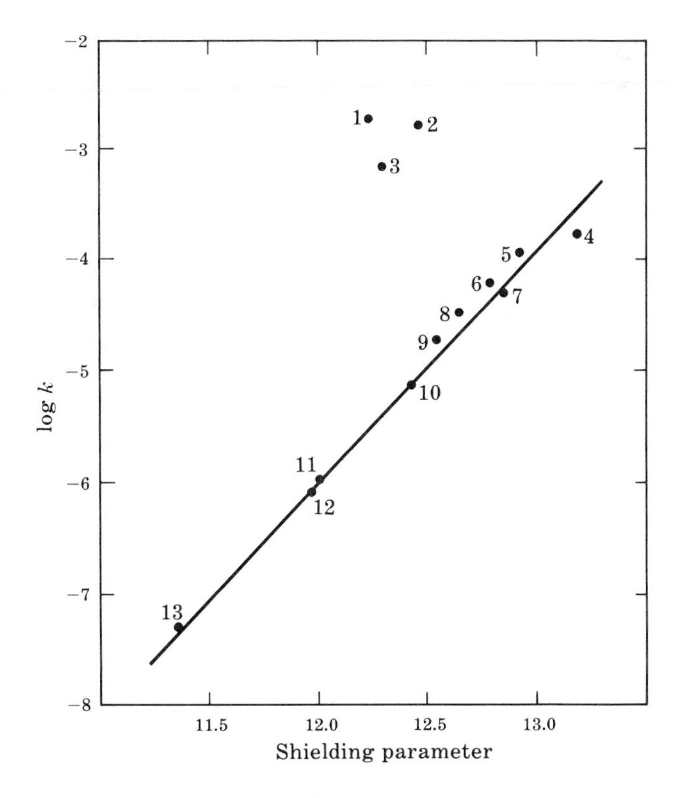

Fig. 8.10 Correlation of log k for solvolysis of p-methoxyneophyl toluenesulfonate with fluorine-nmr shielding parameter of p-fluoronitrosobenzene. 1 = acetic acid, 2 = methanol, 3 = ethanol, 4 = dimethylsulfoxide, 5 = nitromethane, 6 = acetonitrile, 7 = dimethylformamide, 8 = acetic anhydride, 9 = pyridine, 10 = acetone, 11 = ethyl acetate, 12 = tetrahydrofuran, 13 = diethyl ether. (*Data of Taft, Klingensmith, Price, and Fox* [96].)

the shielding parameter of *p*-nitrosofluorobenzene relative to fluorobenzene for a variety of solvents. The correlation is excellent for solvents which are not active hydrogen-bond donors, the range of specific rate involved being well over three orders of magnitude. As expected, the rates in acetic acid, methanol, and ethanol are considerably larger than for non-hydrogen-bonding solvents which form compounds of the same stability with nitrosofluorobenzene. Similar parallelisms are found for such second-order displacements as

$$(CH_3)_3N + p\text{-}NO_2C_6H_4CH_2Cl \rightarrow (CH_3)_3NCH_2C_6H_4NO_2^+ + Cl^-$$

Clearly the formation of multipolar complexes between polar solvents and transition states, reactants, or both is an important factor in the effect of solvent on reactivity. The fluorine nmr shielding is a powerful probe for this kind of molecular interaction [97].

REFERENCES

1. Gurney, R. W.: "Ionic Processes in Solution," McGraw-Hill Book Company, New York, 1953.
2. Kirkwood, J. G.: *J. Chem. Phys.*, **2:** 351 (1934).
3. Geddes, J. A., and C. A. Kraus: *Trans. Faraday Soc.*, **32:** 585 (1936).
4. Denison, J. T., and J. B. Ramsey: *J. Am. Chem. Soc.*, **77:** 2615 (1955).
5. Fuoss, R. M.: *J. Am. Chem. Soc.*, **80:** 5059 (1958).
6. Kraus, C. A.: *J. Chem. Educ.*, **35:** 324 (1958).
7. Fuoss, R. M., and L. Onsager: *J. Phys. Chem.*, **67:** 628 (1963).
8. Nash, G. R., and C. B. Monk: *Trans. Faraday Soc.*, **54:** 1650 (1958); R. L. Kay and D. F. Evans: *J. Am. Chem. Soc.*, **86:** 2748 (1964).
9. Inami, Y. H., H. K. Bodenseh, and J. B. Ramsey: *J. Am. Chem. Soc.*, **83:** 4745 (1961).
10. Witschonke, C. R., and C. A. Kraus: *J. Am. Chem. Soc.*, **69:** 2472 (1947).
11. Copenhafer, D. T., and C. A. Kraus: *J. Am. Chem. Soc.*, **73:** 4557 (1951); H. S. Young and C. A. Kraus: *ibid.*, 4732.
12. Gordy, W. C., and S. C. Stanford: *J. Chem. Phys.*, **8:** 170 (1940); L. P. Hammett: *ibid.*, 644.
13. Arnett, E. M.: *Progr. Phys. Org. Chem.*, **1:** 256 (1963).
14. Tamres, M., S. Searles, E. M. Leighly, and D. W. Mohrman: *J. Am. Chem. Soc.*, **76:** 3983 (1954).
15. Davis, M. M.: Acid-Base Behavior in Aprotic Organic Solvents, *Natl. Bur. Std. U.S. Monograph* 105, 1968.
16. Davis, M. M., and P. J. Schuhman: *J. Res. Natl. Bur. Std.*, **39:** 221 (1947); M. M. Davis and M. Paabo: *J. Am. Chem. Soc.*, **82:** 5081 (1960).
17. Yerger, E. A., and G. M. Barrow: *J. Am. Chem. Soc.*, **77:** 6206 (1955).
18. Barrow, G. M.: *J. Am. Chem. Soc.*, **78:** 5802 (1956).
19. Coetzee, J. F., and G. P. Cunningham: *J. Am. Chem. Soc.*, **87:** 2534 (1965).
20. Kolthoff, I. M., and M. K. Chantooni, Jr.: *J. Am. Chem. Soc.*, **85:** 426 (1963).
21. Kolthoff, I. M., and M. K. Chantooni, Jr.: *J. Am. Chem. Soc.*, **85:** 2195 (1963).
22. Agarwal, B. R., and R. M. Diamond: *J. Phys. Chem.*, **67:** 2785 (1963).
23. Bufalini, J., and K. H. Stern: *J. Am. Chem. Soc.*, **83:** 4362 (1961).
24. Bartlett, P. D., and H. J. Dauben, Jr.: *J. Am. Chem. Soc.*, **62:** 1339 (1940).
25. Lund, H.: *Acta Chem. Scand.*, **12:** 298 (1958).
26. Allerhand, A., and P. von R. Schleyer: *J. Am. Chem. Soc.*, **85:** 1233 (1963).

27. Ralph, E. K., III, and W. R. Gilkerson: *J. Am. Chem. Soc.*, **86:** 4783 (1964).
28. Coetzee, J. F., and G. R. Padmanabhan: *J. Am. Chem. Soc.*, **87:** 5005 (1965).
29. Lichtin, N. N.: *Progr. Phys. Org. Chem.*, **1:** 88 (1963).
30. Lippincott, E. R., and F. E. Welch: *Spectrochim. Acta*, **17:** 47 (1956).
31. Kay, R. L., and D. F. Evans: *J. Am. Chem. Soc.*, **86:** 2748 (1964).
32. Hyne, J. B.: *J. Am. Chem. Soc.*, **85:** 304 (1963).
33. Gilkerson, W. R., and J. B. Ezell: *J. Am. Chem. Soc.*, **87:** 3812 (1965).
34. Alexander, R., and A. J. Parker: *J. Am. Chem. Soc.*, **89:** 5549 (1967).
35. Parker, A. J.: *Quart. Rev. (London)*, **16:** 163 (1962).
36. Miller, J., and A. J. Parker: *J. Am. Chem. Soc.*, **83:** 117 (1961).
37. Prue, J. E., and P. J. Sherrington: *Trans. Faraday Soc.*, **57:** 1795 (1961).
38. Fredenhagen, K., and J. Dahmlos: *Z. Anorg. Allgem. Chem.*, **179:** 77 (1929); K. Fredenhagen: *ibid.*, **186:** 1 (1930).
39. Zaugg, H. E., B. E. Horrom, and S. Borgwardt: *J. Am. Chem. Soc.*, **82:** 2895 (1960).
40. Brown, T. L., and M. T. Rogers: *J. Am. Chem. Soc.*, **79:** 1859 (1957).
41. Berkowitz, J., D. A. Bafus, and T. L. Brown: *J. Phys. Chem.*, **65:** 1380 (1961).
42. Weiner, M. A., and R. West: *J. Am. Chem. Soc.*, **85:** 485 (1963).
43. Cherma, Z. K., G. W. Gibson, and J. F. Eastham: *J. Am. Chem. Soc.*, **85:** 3517 (1963).
44. Brown, T. L., D. W. Dickerhoof, and D. A. Bafus: *J. Am. Chem. Soc.*, **84:** 1371 (1962).
45. Hogen-Esch, T. E., and J. Smid: *J. Am. Chem. Soc.*, **88:** 307, 318 (1966).
46. Chan, L. L., and J. Smid: *J. Am. Chem. Soc.*, **89:** 4547 (1967).
47. Cram, D. J., B. Rickborn, and G. R. Knox: *J. Am. Chem. Soc.*, **82:** 6412 (1960).
48. Parker, A. J.: *J. Chem. Soc.*, **1961:** 1328.
49. Coniglio, B. O., D. E. Giles, W. R. McDonald, and A. J. Parker: *J. Chem. Soc.*, **B1966:** 152.
50. Zaugg, H. E.: *J. Am. Chem. Soc.*, **82:** 2903 (1960); **83:** 837 (1961).
51. Winstein, S., L. G. Savedoff, S. Smith, I. D. R. Stevens, and J. S. Gall: *Tetrahedron Letters*, **9:** 24 (1960).
52. McCleary, H. R., and L. P. Hammett: *J. Am. Chem. Soc.*, **63:** 2254 (1941).
53. Weaver, W. M., and J. D. Hutchinson: *J. Am. Chem. Soc.*, **86:** 261 (1964).
54. Wittig, G., and E. Stahnecker: *Ann.*, **605:** 69 (1957).
55. Zook, H. D., and T. Russo: *J. Am. Chem. Soc.*, **82:** 1258 (1960).
56. Zook, H. D., and W. L. Gumby: *J. Am. Chem. Soc.*, **82:** 1386 (1960).
57. Carvajal, C., K. J. Tölle, J. Smid, and M. Swarc: *J. Am. Chem. Soc.*, **87:** 5548 (1965).
58. Evans, A. G., and D. B. George: *J. Chem. Soc.*, **1961:** 4653; A. G. Evans and N. H. Rees, *ibid.*, **1963:** 6039; R. A. H. Casling, A. G. Evans, and N. H. Rees, *ibid.*, **B1966:** 519.
59. Margerison, D., and J. P. Newport: *Trans. Faraday Soc.*, **59:** 2058 (1963).
60. Weiner, M., G. Vogel, and R. West: *Inorg. Chem.*, **1:** 654 (1962).
61. Kornblum, N., R. Seltzer, and P. Haberfield: *J. Am. Chem. Soc.*, **85:** 1148 (1963).
62. Kornblum, N., P. J. Berrigan, and W. J. le Noble: *J. Am. Chem. Soc.*, **85:** 1142 (1963).
63. Mac., Y. C., W. A. Millen, A. J. Parker, and D. W. Watts: *J. Chem. Soc.*, **B1967:** 525.
64. Ritchie, C. D., G. A. Skinner, and V. G. Badding: *J. Am. Chem. Soc.*, **89:** 2063 (1967).
65. London, F.: *Z. Physik*, **63:** 245 (1930).
66. Hildebrand, J. H., and R. L. Scott, "The Solubility of Nonelectrolytes," 3rd ed., Reinhold Publishing Corporation, New York, 1950.
67. Schmidt, G. C.: *Z. Physik. Chem.*, **99:** 71 (1921).
68. Zawidski, J. von: *Z. Physik. Chem.*, **35:** 129 (1900).
69. Prigogine, I., and R. Defay, "Thermodynamique chimique," p. 414, Desoer, Liège, 1950.
70. Scatchard, G., S. E. Wood, and J. M. Mochel: *J. Am. Chem. Soc.*, **68:** 1962 (1946).
71. Leffler, J. E., and E. Grunwald: "Rates and Equilibria of Organic Reactions," John Wiley & Sons, Inc., New York, 1963.

72. Leffler, J. E.: *J. Org. Chem.*, **20:** 1201 (1955).
73. Alder, M. G., and J. E. Leffler: *J. Am. Chem. Soc.*, **76:** 1425 (1954).
74. Olson, A. R., and R. S. Halford: *J. Am. Chem. Soc.*, **59:** 2644 (1937).
75. Winstein, S., and A. H. Fainberg: *J. Am. Chem. Soc.*, **79:** 5937 (1957).
76. Arnett, E. N., P. M. Duggleby, and J. J. Burke: *J. Am. Chem. Soc.*, **85:** 1351 (1963); E. M. Arnett, W. G. Bentrude, J. J. Burke, and P. M. Duggleby: *ibid.*, **87:** 1541 (1965).
77. Moelwynn-Hughes, E. A., R. E. Robertson, and S. Sugamori: *J. Chem. Soc.*, **1965:** 1965.
78. Martin, J. G., and R. E. Robertson: *J. Am. Chem. Soc.*, **88:** 5354 (1966).
79. Bartlett, P. D., and I. Pockel: *J. Am. Chem. Soc.*, **60:** 1585 (1938); P. D. Bartlett and H. J. Dauben: *ibid.*, **62:** 1339 (1940). For other examples of this kind of effect see P. D. Bartlett and R. W. Nebel: *ibid.*, **62:** 1345 (1940); E. Gelles, E. D. Hughes, and C. K. Inbold: *J. Chem. Soc.*, **1954:** 2918; M. F. Hawthorne and D. J. Cram: *J. Am. Chem. Soc.*, **76:** 3451 (1954); C. G. Swain and M. W. Kreevoy: *ibid.*, **77:** 1122 (1955).
80. Grunwald, E., and S. Winstein: *J. Am. Chem. Soc.*, **70:** 846 (1948).
81. Fainberg, A. H., and S. Winstein: *J. Am. Chem. Soc.*, **79:** 1608 (1957).
82. Smith, S. G., A. H. Fainberg, and S. Winstein: *J. Am. Chem. Soc.*, **83:** 618 (1961).
83. Swain, C. G., R. B. Mosely, and D. E. Bown: *J. Am. Chem. Soc.*, **77:** 3731 (1955).
84. Mulliken, R. S.: *J. Am. Chem. Soc.*, **72:** 600 (1950); **74:** 811 (1952).
85. Eberz, W. F., H. J. Wedge, D. M. Yost, and H. J. Lucas: *J. Am. Chem. Soc.*, **59:** 54 (1937).
86. Benesi, H. A., and J. H. Hildebrand: *J. Am. Chem. Soc.*, **70:** 2832 (1948); **71:** 2703 (1949).
87. Briegleb, G.: "Elektronen-Donator Komplexe," Springer-Verlag, 1961.
88. Keefer, R. M., and L. J. Andrews: *J. Am. Chem. Soc.*, **77:** 2164 (1955).
89. Ross, S. D., and I. Kuntz: *J. Am. Chem. Soc.*, **76:** 74 (1954).
90. von Halban, H., and E. Zempelmann: *Z. Physik. Chem.*, **A117:** 461 (1925).
91. Berliner, E.: *Progr. Phys. Org. Chem.*, **2:** 253 (1964).
92. Ritchie, C. D., B. A. Bierl, and R. J. Honour: *J. Am. Chem. Soc.*, **84:** 4687 (1962); C. D. Ritchie and A. L. Pratt: *ibid.*, **86:** 1571 (1964).
93. Taft, R. W., G. B. Klingensmith, and S. Ehrenson: *J. Am. Chem. Soc.*, **87:** 3620 (1965).
94. Smyth, C. P.: "Dielectric Constant and Molecular Structure," p. 173, The Chemical Catalog Co., 1931.
95. Bury, C. R., and H. O. Jenkins: *J. Chem. Soc.*, **1934:** 688.
96. Taft, R. W., G. B. Klingensmith, E. Price, and I. R. Fox: *U.S. Army Res. Off. Symp. Linear Free Energy Correlations*, Durham, N.C., Oct. 21, 1964, preprints of papers, p. 265.
97. Taft, R. W., E. Price, I. R. Fox, I. C. Lewis, K. K. Andersen, and G. T. Davis: *J. Am. Chem. Soc.*, **85:** 709, 3146 (1963); M. Karplus and T. P. Das: *J. Chem. Phys.*, **34:** 1683 (1961); F. Prosser and L. Goodman: *ibid.*, **38:** 374 (1963); R. W. Taft, F. Prosser, L. Goodman, and G. T. Davis: *ibid.*, **38:** 380 (1963).

9

The Quantitative Study of Acids and Bases

9.1. THE ELECTROMETRIC pH IN AQUEOUS SOLUTION

In the common parlance of the chemist the phrases more or less acid, more or less basic occur frequently. Unfortunately it is impossible to attach any meaning which is both general and precise to this terminology.

Within the limits of dilute aqueous solutions, however, the electrometric pH, a quantity which is easily determined with commercially available instruments, is precise and has great utility, notably in the investigation of biological systems and in the control of industrial processes. The value in an aqueous solution X is operationally defined as

$$\mathrm{pH}_{\mathrm{X}} = -\frac{\mathbf{F}}{2.303\mathbf{R}T}(\mathscr{E}_{\mathrm{X}} - \mathscr{E}_0) \qquad (1)$$

in which $\mathscr{E}_{\mathrm{X}}$ is the electromotive force of the galvanic cell

Reference electrode | reference solution | KCl satd | solution X | measuring electrode

$\mathscr{E}_0$ is defined as

$$\mathscr{E}_0 = \mathscr{E}_{st} + \frac{2.303\mathbf{R}T}{\mathbf{F}}\text{pH}_{st} \tag{2}$$

in which $\mathscr{E}_{st}$ is the electromotive force of the cell

Reference electrode | reference solution | KCl satd | standard solution | measuring electrode

Reference electrode, reference solution, and measuring electrode are the same in the second cell as in the first.

The electrometric pH is interpreted as $-\log a_{H^+}$, that is, as the negative logarithm of the activity of hydrogen ion. Two difficulties are involved in this interpretation. First, there are inevitably liquid junction potentials at the boundary between the saturated KCl solution on the one hand and solution X or the standard solution on the other. These contribute to the observed potentials of the cells. There is no present theory nor any theory which may reasonably be expected to appear in the future which predicts in unambiguous fashion the value of these junction potentials.

Second, individual ionic activities are meaningless except in terms of an arbitrary assignment of values to some one ion (Sec. 2.18). The accepted assignment for use in pH measurements in aqueous solution sets the activity coefficient for chloride ion γ_{Cl^-} at

$$\log \gamma_{Cl^-} = -\frac{AI^{1/2}}{1 + 1.5I^{1/2}} \tag{3}$$

The working out of the consequences of this assignment by Bates [1] involves measurements on cells which contain both hydrogen and chloride ions and in which there are no significant junction potentials. From these measurements unambiguous values of the product $a_{H^+}a_{Cl^-}$ can be obtained and defined so that

$$\lim_{c \to 0} \frac{a_{H^+}a_{Cl^-}}{c_{H^+}c_{Cl^-}} = 1 \tag{4}$$

by way of similar measurements on cells which contain only dilute aqueous HCl. The assigned activity of hydrogen ion is then $a_{H^+}a_{Cl^-}/c_{Cl^-}\gamma_{Cl^-}$, with γ_{Cl^-} given by Eq. (3).

In this way Bates has established a self-consistent sequence of standard solutions. King [2] estimates that pH values measured in essentially aqueous solutions of ionic strength not over 0.1 and in the pH range between 2 and 12 are independent of the standard solution employed in the measurement to +0.02 units. That the electrometric pH measurement works as well as this in dilute aqueous solutions can only be considered a lucky break. Any extension of the interpretation of the operational measurement beyond the limits cited is clearly hazardous.

9.2 ELECTROMETRIC ESTIMATES OF ACIDITY IN NONAQUEOUS SOLUTIONS

Electrometric estimates of acidity within the limits of a single nonaqueous solvent do, however, have valuable applications. The process which occurs at an electrode suitable for such purposes is

$$HA + e \rightleftharpoons A^- + H \tag{I}$$

H is gaseous hydrogen in the case of the hydrogen electrode and some form of hydrogen ion dissolved in the glass in the case of the glass electrode. The contribution which this process makes to the cell potential is therefore $(1/\mathbf{F})(\mu_{HA} - \mu_{A^-} - \mu_H)$. This applies to each acid present, including SH^+, the conjugate acid of the solvent S, provided the various acid-base pairs are in mobile equilibrium. Consequently $\mu_{SH^+} - \mu_S$ may be substituted for $\mu_{HA} - \mu_{A^-}$. With identical electrodes μ_H has the same value in solution X as in the standard solution, and if the solutions are dilute, the value of μ_S will be nearly the same in the two solutions. If the difference in the effects of the two liquid junctions may be neglected, the pH of solution X relative to a standard in the same solvent can be defined as

$$\text{pH}_X = \text{pH}_{st} - \frac{(\mu_{SH^+})_X - (\mu_{SH^+})_{st}}{\mathbf{R}T} \tag{5}$$

Some assignment is necessary if the μ_{SH^+} values are to be meaningful. In default of a better one the value of γ_{SH^+} can be set at unity for all solutions as a hopefully useful approximation.

Potassium chloride is used in the salt bridge in aqueous solutions, ostensibly because the cation and the anion have the same mobility as well as because its solubility is large. It is not at all certain that the equal mobility is an important factor, but it does seem probable that the junction should not involve different solvents on the two sides and that a high electrolyte concentration in the bridge is desirable. A salt bridge is unnecessary if it is permissible for the purpose in hand to have the same relatively high concentration of the same electrolyte in solution X and in the standard solution. In this case γ_{SH^+} will have nearly the same value in the two solutions, and the double measurement with a reference electrode is unnecessary. The same conclusions probably apply also when the electrolyte in the one solution is similar to, although not identical with, that in the other. This might well be the case if each solution is a buffer mixture of a moderately bulky organic acid and its salt with the same cation.

Even in solvents so different from water as acetonitrile [3, 4] and dimethylsulfoxide [5, 6] the pH determination with the glass electrode appears to yield useful measures of acidity. In both solvents a salt bridge of 0.1 *M* tetraethylammonium perchlorate in the solvent under investigation and a reference electrode consisting of silver metal in a silver salt solution in the same solvent are recommended.

It is difficult to see how any significance whatsoever can be attached to measurements in which the solvent is not the same in solution X as in the standard solution.

9.3 ACIDITY MEASUREMENTS WITH INDICATORS

An acid-base indicator may be defined as a conjugate acid-base pair for which in some accessible region of the spectrum the light absorption of the acid differs considerably from that of the base. Originally the term indicator was used only for pairs for which there was a visual difference in color intensity or in color quality between acid and base, but with modern equipment there is no reason to restrict the term in this way or even to limit it to absorption spectrophotometry. For an effective indicator measurement the intensity of the absorption or other measured property must be so large that measurements can be made with indicator concentrations so small that the addition of the indicator has a negligible effect on the acidity of the solution.

The measured quantity is an intensity of absorption which may be translated into a value of the ratio I of the concentration of the acid form of the indicator to that of the base form. The equilibrium relation involved may be written as

$$\frac{a_{H^+} a_B}{a_A} = K^{\circ\circ} \tag{6}$$

in which the a's are the activities of hydrogen ion, of the base form B of the indicator, and of the acid form A. $K^{\circ\circ}$, the reference value of the indicator constant, is given by

$$K^{\circ\circ} = \lim_{c\to 0} \frac{[SH^+][B]}{[A]} \tag{7}$$

in a reference solvent S in which by definition $\lim a/c = 1$ for all substances involved. Since the concentrations of A and B are small, γ_A and γ_B may be taken to be unity in any solvent, and Eq. (6) then leads to

$$I = \frac{a_{H^+} a_B^\circ}{K^{\circ\circ} a_A^\circ} \tag{8}$$

a_A° and a_B° are standard activities (Sec. 2.10)[1] with the two forms of the indicator considered the only solutes.

If small concentrations of two indicators X and Y are added to separate portions of a well-buffered solution,

$$\frac{I_X}{I_Y} = \frac{K_Y^\circ}{K_X^\circ} \tag{9}$$

where K°, the indicator constant in the particular medium involved, is given by

$$K^\circ = K^{\circ\circ}\frac{a_A^\circ}{a_B^\circ} \tag{10}$$

It is therefore possible to determine the ratio of the K° values for any two indicators in any medium in which I is measurable for both. In general the ratio is a function of the medium because the ratio a_A°/a_B° depends on the medium. To take an extreme case; if one chooses water as a reference solvent and picks two indicators which have the same $K^{\circ\circ}$ value but in which the base form of X is an electrically neutral derivative of aniline and the base form of Y is a negatively charged derivative of phenolate ion, K_Y°/K_X° is unity in a dilute solution of HCl in water and about 10^5 for a dilute solution of HCl in ethanol.

For measurements limited to a single solvent a_A° and a_B° are constant, and

$$a_{H^+} = [SH^+]\gamma_{SH^+} \tag{11}$$

with SH^+ the lyonium ion, i.e., the conjugate acid of the solvent. Within this limitation, but only within this limitation, determination of I and knowledge of K° yields an estimate of the acidity of the solution which is independent of the indicator employed.

9.4 THE ACIDITY FUNCTION H_0

It is, however, possible to obtain from indicator measurements, if not a unique measure of the acidity of a solution without the limitation to a single solvent, at least an intelligible spectrum of measures. To do this one must select a group of indicators which resemble each other as closely as possible with respect to the molecular structure in the region in which the proton transfer occurs. Such a group is constituted for instance by the primary nitroanilines.

With water as a reference solvent p-nitroaniline is a strong enough base to permit the determination of I in aqueous solutions so dilute that $K^{\circ\circ}$ can be estimated from Eq. (7) with satisfactory precision. From consideration of the closely agreeing results in a variety of aqueous solutions of strong acids

[1] In previous publications I have used the symbol f where I now use a°. Others have used γ. The distinction between a°, γ, and the product $a^\circ\gamma = a$, as I have defined them in Secs. 2.7 and 2.10, is important in the present connection.

Paul and Long [7] obtained the value +0.99 for the quantity $pK^{\circ\circ} = -\log K^{\circ\circ}$ for this substance.

The value of I for p-nitroaniline is measurable with adequate precision in sulfuric acid–water systems only up to about 24% acid. Within this range one may define an operational measure H_0 of the acidity of the solution by the relation

$$H_0 = pK^{\circ\circ} - \log I \tag{12}$$

By virtue of Eq. (8)

$$H_0 = -\log a_{H^+} \frac{a_B^\circ}{a_A^\circ} \tag{13}$$

H_0 is therefore a measure of the potential of the solution for transfer of a proton to a base for which the ratio a_B°/a_A° responds to changing medium in the same way that p-nitroaniline does.

In order to extend this measure of acidity to higher acid concentrations one makes use of the following facts: (1) over the range of sulfuric acid concentration from 9 to 24% I is measurable for the weaker base o-nitroaniline as well as for p-nitroaniline; (2) over this range the difference between the log I values for the two bases does not change measurably; (3) the difference has nearly the same value in a variety of strong-acid–water mixtures, being 1.24 in sulfuric acid, 1.28 in hydrochloric acid, 1.31 in nitric acid, and 1.30 in perchloric acid. By virtue of Eqs. (9) and (10)

$$\log I_o - \log I_p = pK_o^{\circ\circ} - pK_p^{\circ\circ} + \log \frac{a_{Bo}^\circ a_{Ap}^\circ}{a_{Bp}^\circ a_{Ao}^\circ} \tag{14}$$

the subscript p referring to p-nitroaniline and the subscript o to o-nitroaniline. The essential constancy of the difference $\log I_o - \log I_p$ within the region of measurable overlap of the two indicators means that within this region the last term in Eq. (14) is essentially independent of the medium for all these strong-acid–water mixtures. It is not unreasonable to assume that the constancy extends beyond the overlap region to very dilute solutions in water and that the value of the term is therefore zero. To the extent that this assumption is justified Eq. (14) becomes

$$\log I_o - \log I_p = pK_o^{\circ\circ} - pK_p^{\circ\circ} \tag{15}$$

and the limiting value of the indicator constant of o-nitroaniline referred to the solvent water is thereby determined. Paul and Long [7] arrive at a best value of −0.29 for this quantity. This method of obtaining $K^{\circ\circ}$ values for bases for which the value is not directly measurable is frequently called the overlap method, and the assumption on which it is based is called the overlap assumption. With the $pK^{\circ\circ}$ value of *o*-nitroaniline known, H_0 values can be obtained for the region of aqueous sulfuric acid from 24 to 35%. This is the region in which I is measurable for *o*-nitroaniline but too small for measurement for *p*-nitroaniline.

The value of I for *p*-chloro-*o*-nitroaniline is measurable from 19 to 51% aqueous sulfuric acid. In the region from 19 to 35% in which I is also measurable for *o*-nitroaniline the difference in the log I values for the two bases is essentially constant at 0.72. It ranges from 0.71 to 0.77 for other strong-acid–water mixtures. Accepting the overlap assumption, Paul and Long [7] arrived at a best value for the $pK^{\circ\circ}$ value of *p*-chloro-*o*-nitroaniline of −1.03, while Bascombe and Bell [8], using modern spectrophotometric methods, find −1.02.

This overlap procedure may be repeated so long as suitable indicators can be found. From the early work of Hammett and Deyrup [9] and the recent work of Jorgenson and Hartter [10] a series of primary nitroaniline derivatives is available from which measurable values of I can be obtained for at

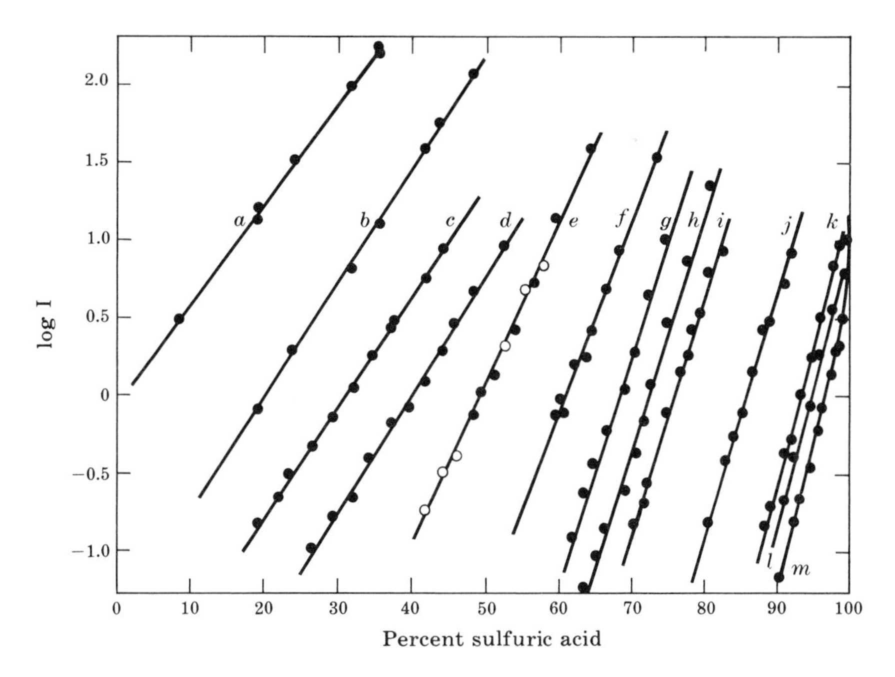

Fig. 9.1 Values of log I for indicators of the H_0 type in sulfuric acid-water mixtures. For letter symbols see Table 9.1. [*By permission of M. J. Jorgenson and D. R. Harrter, J. Am. Chem. Soc.*, **85:** 878 (1963).]

Table 9.1 **pK^{oo} values of indicators of the H_0 type in sulfuric acid–water and in perchloric acid–water systems**

	H_2SO_4[a]	$HClO_4$[b]
m-Nitroaniline	+2.50	
p-Nitroaniline	+0.99	
o-Nitroaniline (*a*)[c]	−0.29	−0.29
4-Chloro-2-nitroaniline (*b*)	−1.03	−1.07
2,5-Dichloro-4-nitroaniline (*c*)	−1.78	−1.79
2-Chloro-6-nitroaniline (*d*)	−2.43	−2.41
2,6-Dichloro-4-nitroaniline (*e*)	−3.27	−3.20
2,4-Dichloro-6-nitroaniline (*e*)	−3.27	
2,4-Dinitroaniline (*f*)	−4.53	−4.26
2,6-Dinitroaniline (*g*)	−5.54	−5.25
4-Chloro-2,6-dinitroaniline (*h*)	−6.14	−6.12
2-Bromo-4,6-dinitroaniline (*i*)	−6.68	−6.69
3-Methyl-2,4,6-trinitroaniline (*j*)	−8.22	−8.56
3-Bromo-2,4,6-trinitroaniline (*k*)	−9.46	−9.77
3-Chloro-2,4,6-trinitroaniline (*l*)	−9.71	
2,4,6-Trinitroaniline (*m*)	−10.10	

[a] Data from Hammett and Deyrup [9], revised by Paul and Long [7], and from Jorgenson and Hartter [10].
[b] Data from Yates and Wai [11].
[c] Letters refer to Fig. 9.1.

least two indicators in all sulfuric acid–water mixtures up to 98% acid. Plots of log I against percent acid are shown in Fig. 9.1. The difference between the log I values for any two indicators in each region of overlap is closely constant, the apparent exception in the case of indicators *d* and *e* being more apparent than real. Table 9.1 lists the pK^{oo} values of these indicators, and Table 9.2 shows how the H_0 values vary with sulfuric acid concentration. A plot of H_0 against acid concentration is included in Fig. 9.2.

Yates and Wai [11] have carefully redetermined the pK^{oo} values of a number of primary nitroanilines from measurements on perchloric acid–water mixtures and derived H_0 values for these solutions up to 78.6% acid. The pK^{oo} values are included in Table 9.1. For the most part they are much the same as those obtained in sulfuric acid–water mixtures. It should be noted that the value for 2,4-dinitroaniline in sulfuric acid–water mixtures is based only on the older data obtained by visual colorimetry and is probably one of the least reliable of the values thus obtained. H_0 values in the perchloric acid mixtures are remarkably close to those for sulfuric acid mixtures of the same percentage composition up to 50%. Above this the value in perchloric acid solutions becomes negative considerably more rapidly than that in sulfuric

Table 9.2 Acidity functions and related data for sulfuric acid–water systems[a]

% acid	H_0	H'''	H_I	H'_R	H_A	$\log a_w$	$\log c_A$	$H_0 + \log c_A$
5	+0.11	+0.01	+0.05	−0.06			−0.28	−0.17
10	−0.31	−0.53	−0.55	−0.69	−0.29	−0.026	+0.03	−0.28
15	−0.66	−0.99	−0.97	−1.28	−0.70		+0.228	−0.43
20	−1.01	−1.47	−1.42	−1.86	−1.00	−0.059	+0.367	−0.64
25	−1.37	−1.96	−1.85	−2.46	−1.25	−0.086	+0.479	−0.89
30	−1.72	−2.44	−2.35	−3.10	−1.50	−0.124	+0.572	−1.15
35	−2.06	−2.93	−2.88	−3.82	−1.74	−0.175	+0.653	−1.41
40	−2.41	−3.46	−3.42	−4.55	−2.00	−0.246	+0.726	−1.68
45	−2.85	−4.01	−4.02	−5.31	−2.24	−0.341	+0.782	−2.07
50	−3.38	−4.54	−4.65	−6.15	−2.51	−0.454	+0.853	−2.53
55	−3.91	−5.11	−5.32	−7.07	−2.77	−0.604	+0.910	−3.00
60	−4.46	−5.91	−6.06	−8.13	−3.10	−0.793	+0.962	−3.50
65	−5.08	−6.73	−6.87	−9.13	−3.38	−1.040	+1.014	−4.07
70	−5.80	−7.65	−7.79	−10.16	−3.74	−1.363	+1.061	−4.74
75	−6.56	−8.53			−4.15	−1.765	+1.106	−5.45
80	−7.34	−9.44		−11.84	−4.62	−2.282	+1.148	−6.19
85	−8.14	−10.30			−5.02	−2.79	+1.187	−6.95
90	−8.92	−11.14		−13.23	−5.57	−3.51	+1.221	−7.70
95	−9.85	−11.89		−13.61		−4.47	+1.249	−8.60
100	−12.2							

[a] H_0 values up to 55% sulfuric acid inclusive are those listed by Paul and Long [7]. Except for a critical examination of the extrapolation to water as a reference solvent they are based on the colorimetric data of Hammett and Deyrup [9]. H_0 values for acid concentrations above 60% are those of Jorgenson and Hartter [10]. H''' values are taken, some by interpolation, from those listed by Arnett and Mach [18]. H_I values are taken by interpolation from those listed by Hinman and Lang [19]. H'_R values were obtained from the H_R values of Deno, Jaruzelski, and Schriesheim [22], using the values of $\log a_w$ included in the table. H_A values are interpolated from the data of Yates, Stevens, and Katritzky [20], supplemented by data of Johnson, Katritzky, and Shakir [21]. Values of $\log a_w$ are those of Shankman and Gordon [12] up to 65% acid. At higher concentrations they are taken from "International Critical Tables" vol. III, p. 302.

acid solutions. At 80% H_0 is −10.75 for perchloric acid and −7.34 for sulfuric acid.

H_0 values derived solely from measurements on primary nitroanilines are available for aqueous hydrochloric acid up to 38% acid, for aqueous phosphoric acid up to 85%, and for aqueous *p*-toluenesulfonic acid up to 55% [13]. Values (not all of which were obtained solely with primary nitroaniline indicators) are available for hydrofluoric acid–water mixtures from 0 to 100% acid [14, 15], for $DCl–D_2O$ and $D_2SO_4–D_2O$ mixtures [16], and for a number of other acid-water mixtures [7]. The values for the deuterium systems are close to those for the corresponding protium systems.

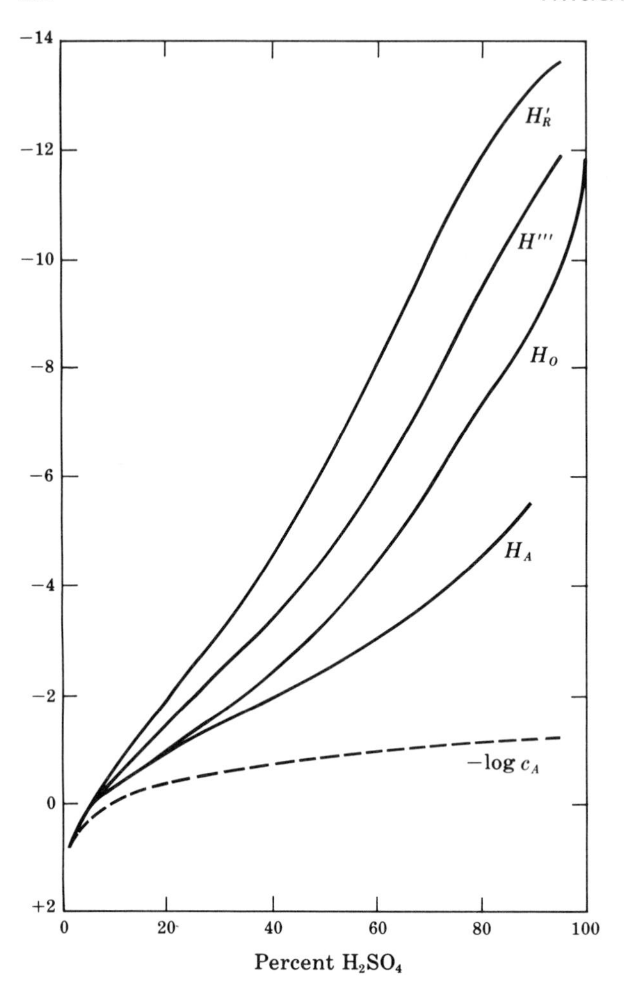

Fig. 9.2 Acidity functions in sulfuric acid–water mixtures.

9.5 HISTORICAL NOTE[1]

In 1923, perhaps even a bit later, I was contentedly telling students in the course in qualitative analysis that HCl is less acid in benzene than it is in water because it is less ionized and that the failure of the benzene solution to react with calcium carbonate demonstrates this. By 1927 I was satisfied in my own mind, that (1) water is a base in the same sense that ammonia is a base; (2) the so-called hydrogen ion in water solution is OH_3^+ in the same way that it is NH_4^+ in liquid ammonia; (3) measured by any homogeneous equilibrium or rate

[1] This is essentially an excerpt from *J. Chem. Educ.*, **43**: 464 (1966) (cf. Sec. 4.25).

phenomena HCl is more acid in benzene than it is in water; (4) since water is a base, it masks or levels the differences in strength of strong acids and prevents any determination in aqueous solution of the relative strengths of weak bases. This revolution of opinion derived more than anything else from the ideas of Hantzsch [17], although I was also strongly influenced by P[illegible]nsted and by Franklin's work on solutions in liquid ammonia.

On the basis of these ideas, Deyrup and I developed a series of basic indicators of overlapping range which measured the changing acidity of systems extending from water to 100% sulfuric acid [9], we defined the acidity function H_0, and we showed that this measure of acidity helped materially in understanding the effect of strong acids as condensing and dehydrating agents. The only tools we had were a visual colorimeter and a Beckmann freezing-point apparatus. It was the limitations of these tools, not any deliberate choice, that led us to the selection of indicators most of which were primary nitroanilines. We now know that this was fortunate, that if we had had a wider choice we might well have been completely bewildered. In spite of the limitations the quality of Deyrup's experimental work was such that, except for the region above 60% sulfuric acid, it has not been significantly revised by later work with modern spectrophotometers.

9.6 THE ACIDITY FUNCTIONS H''', H_I, AND H_A

There is, as time has shown, nothing unique about H_0 as a measure of acidity. Thus Arnett and Mach [18] have selected a group of 15 *N,N*-dialkylnitro-anilines and *N*-alkylnitrodiphenylamines which define an acidity function H''' which changes considerably more rapidly with increasing acid concentration than H_0 does. With this group the value of I is measurable for at least two indicators in all mixtures of water and sulfuric acid up to 96% acid. The ranges of successive indicators overlap well, and the difference in the log I values is independent of the acid concentration to a good precision. The $pK^{\circ\circ}$ values obtained by the overlap method range from +0.66 for *N,N*-dimethyl-4-nitroaniline to −10.56 for *N*-methyl-2,4,2′,4′-tetranitrodiphenyl-amine. Values of H''', defined as $H''' = pK^{\circ\circ} + \log I$ using these $pK^{\circ\circ}$ values are listed for sulfuric acid–water mixtures in Table 9.2 and are plotted against acid concentration in Fig. 9.2.

Similarly Hinman and Lang [19] have based an acidity function H_I on the behavior of a group of alkylated indoles whose $pK^{\circ\circ}$ values range from +0.30 for 1,2-dimethylindole to −6.31 for tryptamine. There is good overlap between successive indicators and the difference in the log I values for over-lapping indicators is satisfactorily independent of acid concentration. Values of H_I for sulfuric acid–water mixtures are included in Table 9.2. They are close to the H''' values.

Yates, Stevens, and Katritzky [20] have based an acidity function H_A, which changes less rapidly with increasing acid concentration than H_0 does, on the behavior of a group of amides. The p$K^{\circ\circ}$ values range from -1.23 for 2-pyrrolecarboxamide to -4.08 for 2,4,6-trinitrobenzamide. The conditions for the overlap method are well satisfied. Plots of log I against sulfuric acid concentration for a number of pyridine N-oxides have also been found to parallel those of the amides [21]. The more basic of them have been used to fix the H_A scale more firmly at low acidities. By the same criterion phenazine-5,10-dioxide has been used to extend it to somewhat higher acidities. H_A values for sulfuric acid–water mixtures are included in Table 9.2 and are plotted against acid concentration in Fig. 9.2.

There is no reason except the large accumulation of data which accompanies its seniority in time for preferring H_0 as a measure of acidity over any of the other acidity functions.

9.7 THE ACIDITY FUNCTIONS H_R AND H_R'

In terms of seniority the second place among acidity functions belongs to the H_R function of Deno, Jaruzelski, and Schriesheim [22]. This is based on an overlapping series of arylcarbinols which range from 4,4′,4″-trimethoxytriphenylmethanol, with a p$K^{\circ\circ}$ value of $+0.82$, through 4,4′,4″-trinitrotriphenylmethanol, with a value of -16.27, to 2,4,6-trimethylbenzyl alcohol, with one of -17.38. It differs from those previously discussed in that the reaction whose progress is observed by the change in light absorption is not merely the addition of a proton to a neutral base. Rather it is typically

$$(C_6H_5)_3COH + H^+ \rightleftharpoons (C_6H_5)_3C^+ + H_2O \qquad \text{(II)}$$

the water formed being converted to oxonium ion to a degree which depends on the acid concentration. If therefore one defines the function H_R by the relation

$$H_R = \mathrm{p}K^{\circ\circ} - \log I \qquad (16)$$

it must be interpreted as

$$H_R = -\log a_{H^+}\frac{a^{\circ}_{ROH}}{a^{\circ}_{R^+}} + \log a_w \qquad (17)$$

where a_w is the activity of water. If however one defines an acidity function H_R' by the relation

$$H_R' = \mathrm{p}K^{\circ\circ} - \log I - \log a_w \qquad (18)$$

then

$$H_R' = -\log a_{H^+}\frac{a^{\circ}_{ROH}}{a^{\circ}_{R^+}} \qquad (19)$$

One would therefore expect H_R' to be more nearly comparable with H° and the other previously discussed acidity functions than H_R is. And indeed Deno, Groves, and Saines [23] find that for the addition of a proton to such diaryl-olefins as 1,1-diphenylethylene the plot of log I against H_R' has a slope of unity within experimental error. Values of H_R' for sulfuric acid–water mixtures are included in Table 9.2, and the function is plotted against acid concentration in Fig. 9.2. H_R' changes considerably more rapidly with increasing acid concentration than any of the previously discussed acidity functions, and H_R increases almost exactly twice as fast as H_0 does.

9.8 OTHER ACIDITY-FUNCTION DATA

Values of H''' are available for aqueous hydrochloric, phosphoric, and toluenesulfonic acids [24]; of H_I for perchloric acid [19]; of H_A for hydrochloric acid [25]; and of H_R and H_R' for perchloric and nitric acids [26], and for hydrochloric, phosphoric, and toluenesulfonic acids [24].

9.9 THE THREE-VARIABLE HYPOTHESIS

The way in which the acidity-function plots of Fig. 9.2 fan out without intersections suggests that the extent of conversion of a base to its conjugate acid in strong-acid–water mixtures is determined by three variables and by three only. One of these can reasonably be the degree to which the base is converted to conjugate acid under some specified reference condition. One may call it the strength of the base and represent it by the p$K^{\circ\circ}$ values. It must, however, be kept in mind that these values represent the relative strengths of a group of bases only in an arbitrarily defined reference medium. A second variable, which may be called the acidity of the solution, would represent the tendency of the solution to transfer a proton to bases in general, a tendency which increases with increasing acid concentration. The third variable, which may suitably be called the solvation variable, must measure the difference in the response which different bases of the same strength exhibit to the same medium. The hypothesis that only three variables are involved is strongly supported by the near identity of the H''' and H_I functions and by the agreement with the H_A function of the behavior of the pyridine N-oxides.

9.10 THE SOLVATION VARIABLE ϕ

A possible choice for the second variable would be one of the acidity functions, presumably H_0 because of its seniority. But as Bunnett and Olsen [27] have pointed out, substantial advantage can be derived from the use of the quantity $H_0 + \log c_A$, where c_A is the molarity of the acid. As shown in Figs. 9.3 and 9.4 the plot of $H_X + \log c_A$, where H_X is an acidity function other than H_0, against $H_0 + \log c_A$ runs smoothly to the origin of coordinates, whereas the

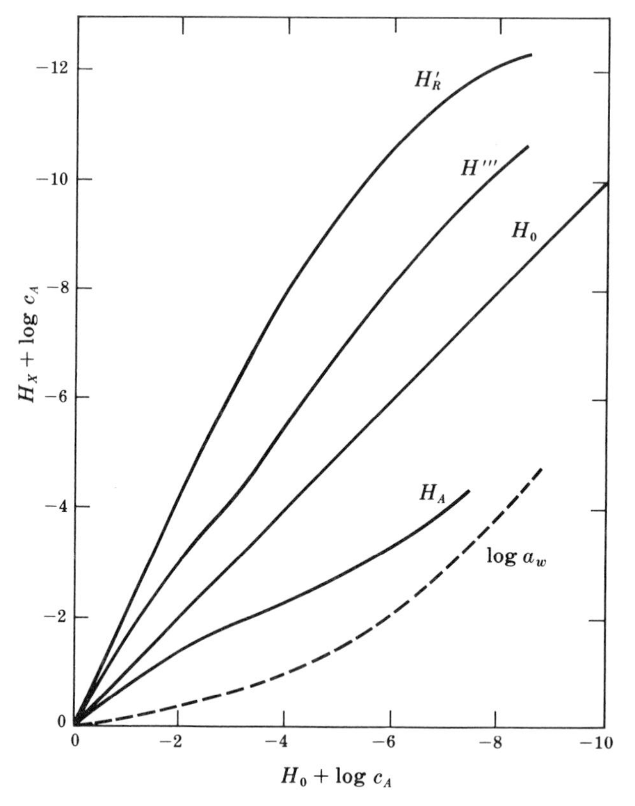

Fig. 9.3 Plots of $H_X + \log c_A$ against $H_0 + \log c_A$ for various acidity functions in sulfuric acid–water mixtures.

plot of H_X against H_0 has a sharp curvature in the region. And in general the plots of Figs. 9.3 and 9.4 are more nearly linear than plots of H_X against H_0.

Bunnett and Olsen define the quantity $\phi_i - 1$ for a base i as the slope of a plot of $\log I_i - \log c_A$ against $H_0 + \log c_A$. If the base is of the class to which H_X applies,

$$\log I_i - \log c_A = pK_i^{\circ\circ} - (H_X + \log c_A) \tag{20}$$

The definition is therefore equivalent to

$$1 - \phi = \frac{\delta(H_X + \log c_A)}{\delta(H_0 + \log c_A)} \tag{21}$$

i.e., the quantity $1 - \phi$ for bases of class X is the slope of the $H_X + \log c_A$ plot.

If the slope were constant (and Bunnett and Olsen suggest that the curvature, especially in the case of the H_A function, arises from errors in the estimation of H_X by the overlap procedure), Eq. (21) would become

$$\log I_i - \log c_A = pK_i^{\circ\circ} + (\phi - 1)(H_0 + \log c_A) \tag{22}$$

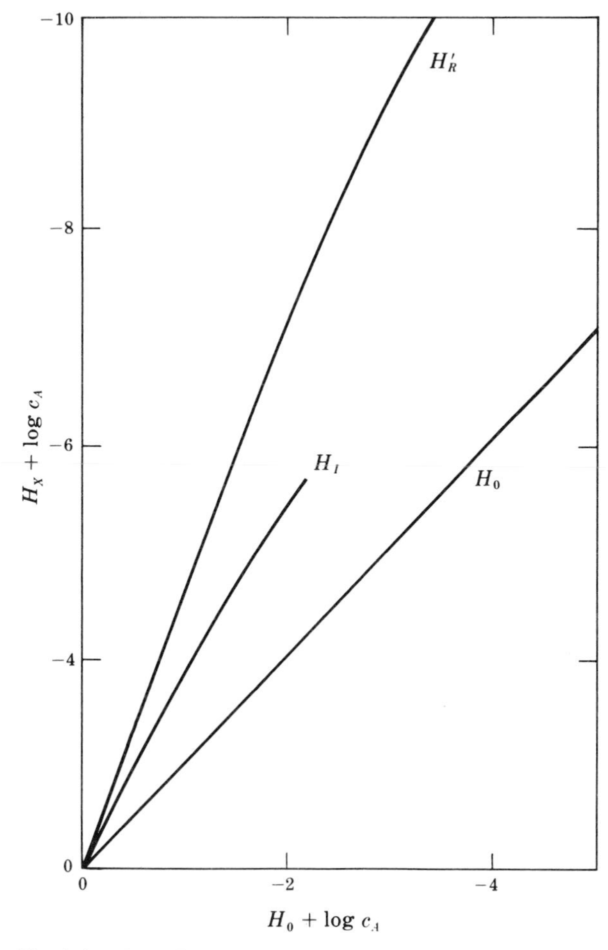

Fig. 9.4 Plots of $H_X + \log c_A$ against $H_0 + \log c_A$ for various acidity functions in perchloric acid–water mixtures.

From this the intercept on the axis of ordinates of a plot of the quantity $\log I_i - \log c_A$ for base i against $H_0 + \log c_A$ would be the value of $pK_i^{\circ\circ}$. Within the modest precision to which Eq. (22) would appear to apply the equation offers a means of estimating $pK^{\circ\circ}$ values for bases of unknown class and of predicting I values for bases of known class. The procedure could perhaps be refined by taking account of the curvature.

The value of ϕ in some arbitrarily chosen medium, say one for which $H_0 + \log c_A = -4$, is a suitable choice of a numerical value of the solvation variable.

A considerable amount of information on the log I values of individual bases or of small groups of related bases is available. Values of ϕ for many of these are included in the Bunnett and Olsen article. It is rather clear that ϕ or any other choice of a solvation variable is a continuous variable and that the lines plotted in Figs. 9.2 to 9.4 are merely samples of an infinite number of nonintersecting lines of the same general character, any of which could be interpolated with considerable certainty.

That bases of very different structure may have the same value of the solvation variable is demonstrated by the near coincidence of the H''' and H_I functions. That bases of apparently similar structure may have different values is demonstrated by the ability of Hinman and Lang [19] to base the H_I function, which has a ϕ value of about 0.5, on the consistent behavior of a selected group of alkylated indoles, although indole itself has a value near zero and several other substituted indoles have values very different from 0.5.

9.11 THE AMBIGUITY OF THE CONCEPT OF ACIDITY

It is now abundantly evident that a unique operational definition of the acidity of a system is a will-o'-the-wisp. Qualitatively one conveys some significant information by saying for instance that 80% aqueous sulfuric acid is more acid than 5% acid. This represents a semantic change, for 50 years ago one would have said that the 80% acid is less acid because it is less ionized. But by one standard, that of reaction with bases of the H_R' type, the 80% acid is 11.8 logarithmic units more acid than the 5% acid, and by another standard, that of reaction with bases of the H_A type, it is only 4.3 units more acid. The concept of the acidity of a solution blurs even more seriously when one compares different acids; 80% phosphoric acid is less acid than 55% sulfuric acid by 0.86 units in terms of the reaction of a base of the H_0 type but more acid by 0.37 units in terms of a base of the H_R' type [24].

9.12 STANDARD ACTIVITIES IN STRONG-ACID–WATER MIXTURES

In order for a single variety of acidity function to apply to two bases it is necessary that the quantity $\delta_M \log(a^\circ_{BH^+}/a^\circ_B)$ have the same value for the two, the operator δ_M denoting the effect of changing acid concentration. The linearity of the plots of Figs. 9.3 and 9.4 over a limited range requires not only that over this range the value of the quantity $\delta_M \log(a^\circ_{BH^+}/a^\circ_B)$ for a base of one class be proportional to the value for a base of another class but also that both quantities be proportional to the quantity $\delta_M \log(a_{H^+}/c_A)$.

In view of these requirements the individuality exhibited by the behavior of the quantities $\delta_M \log a^\circ_B$ and $\delta_M \log a^\circ_{BH^+}$ is surprising. These quantities can be determined, the first in solutions in which the conversion of B to BH^+ is negligible, the second in solutions in which the conversion is essentially complete, by solubility or distribution methods. For a difficultly soluble solute B the product sa°, where s is solubility, is nearly independent of medium if there is no conversion to BH^+. Consequently the standard activity a°_X in a medium X is given by

$$a^\circ_X = \frac{s^\circ}{s_X} \tag{23}$$

where s_X is solubility in medium X and s° that in the reference medium. Figure 9.5 plots against percent of sulfuric acid values of $\log a^\circ$ obtained in this

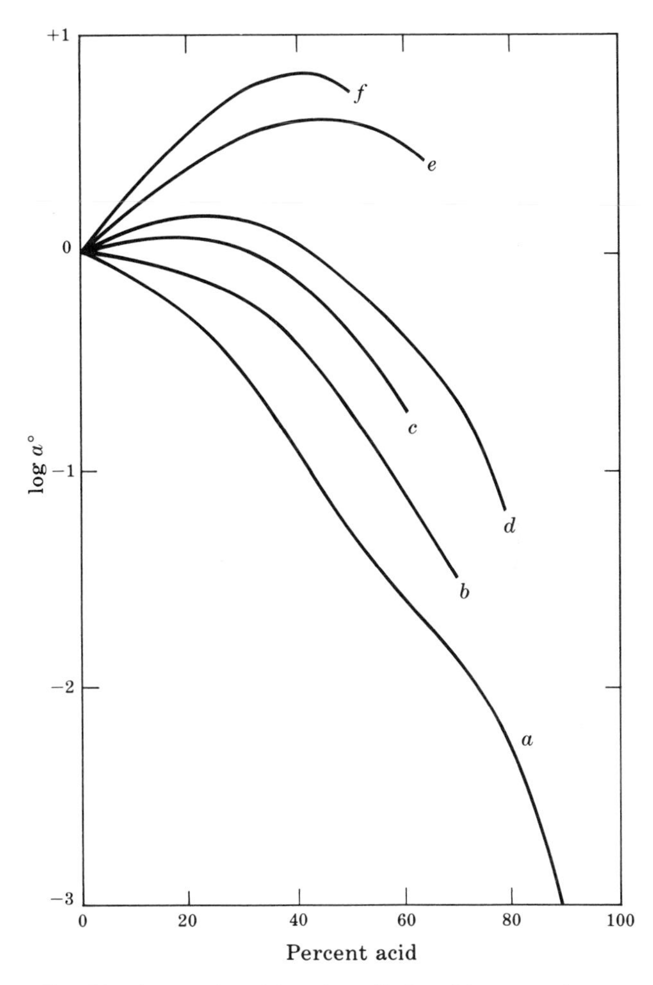

Fig. 9.5 Standard activities in sulfuric acid–water mixtures. (*a*) 2,4,6-trinitroaniline; (*b*) 2,4-dinitroaniline; (*c*) 2,6-dichloro-4-nitroaniline (*data of Boyd* [29]); (*d*) nitrobenzene; (*e*) benzoic acid (*data of Hammett and Chapman* [28]; (*f*) triphenylcarbinol [29].

way by Hammett and Chapman [28] and by Boyd [29]. None of the substances involved is significantly converted to the conjugate acid within the range plotted. Sweeting and Yates [30] have reported solubility data on a number of benzamides in sulfuric acid–water mixtures. The variation in standard activity with acid concentration resembles that of the nitroanilines of Fig. 9.5. The value of log a° for 2,4-dinitrobenzamide is a linear function of that for 2,4-dinitroaniline.

Boyd [29] has found that the pentacyanopropene salts of many organic bases are difficultly soluble in sulfuric acid–water mixtures. From the relation

$$\left(\frac{s_{XP}}{s^\circ_{XP}}\right)^2 = \frac{1}{a^\circ_{X^+} a^\circ_{P^-}} \tag{24}$$

where X^+ is a cation and P^- is the pentacyanopropenide anion, it follows that

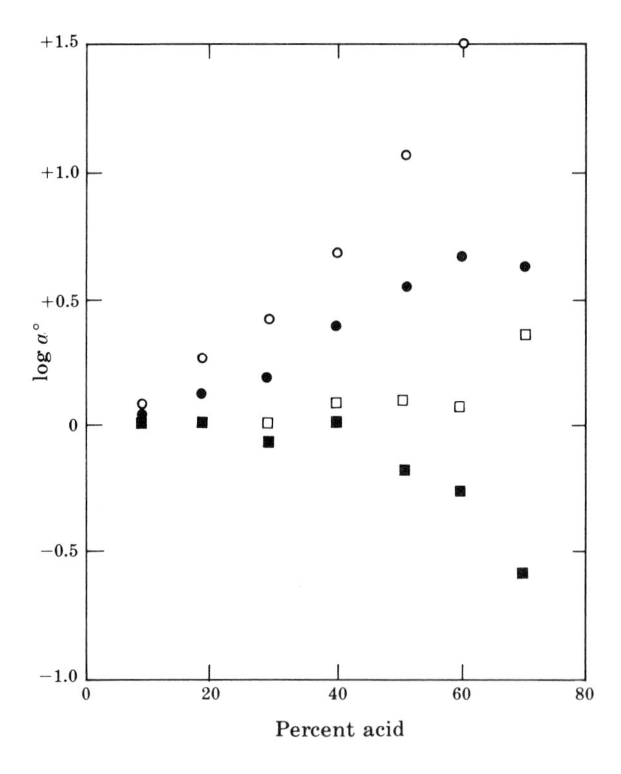

Fig. 9.6 Standard activities relative to that of tetraethylammonium ion in sulfuric acid–water mixtures. ○ anilinium ion; ● dimethylanilinium ion; □ phenyltrimethylammonium ion; ■ tris(*p*-methoxyphenyl)carbonium ion. (*By permission of Boyd* [29].)

for the salts of two cations X^+ and Y^+

$$\left(\frac{s_{XP}\, s^\circ_{YP}}{s^\circ_{XP}\, s_{YP}}\right)^2 = \frac{a^\circ_{Y^+}}{a^\circ_{X^+}} \tag{25}$$

Some of Boyd's value of log $a^\circ_{Y^+}/a^\circ_{X^+}$, where Y^+ is tetraethylammonium ion, are plotted against sulfuric acid concentration in Fig. 9.6. Values for *p*-nitro- and *p*-chloroanilinium ions are close to those for anilinium ion; the values for *m*-nitroanilinium ion are about half of those for anilinium ion.

These results are consistent with a suggestion of Deno [22, 23] and of Taft [31] that there is strong hydrogen bonding between water and the NH_3^+ group of an anilinium ion. As the acid concentration increases and the activity of water decreases, the intensity of this bonding diminishes and the standard activity of anilinium ion and its derivatives increases. The effect is smaller with dimethylanilinium ion, and the difference accounts almost quantitatively for the difference between the H''' and the H_0 functions. There should be no such bonding in a carbonium ion or in a quaternary ammonium ion.

It is evident, however, that differences in the effect of changing medium on the standard activity of a collection of bases are as important for their acid-base behavior as differences in the standard activity of the conjugate acids. The individuality of the effects of changing medium on standard activities gives some reason for concern about the validity of the overlap assumption, but there is no necessary inconsistency between the data and the assumption.

9.13 CONSIDERATIONS RELATED TO THE ACTIVITY OF WATER

If one were to assume (1) that the cation XH^+ binds a constant number m of water molecules, (2) that the value of m is the same for all bases of the class to which a single type of acidity function applies but differs from class to class, and (3) that there are no other differences between bases of different classes, the indicator reaction would be

$$XH^+(H_2O)_m + nH_2O \rightleftharpoons X + H^+(H_2O)_{m+n} \tag{III}$$

n might be either positive or negative. The acidity function H_X would be given by

$$H_X = -\log \frac{a_{H^+}\, a^\circ_X}{a^\circ_{XH^+}} + n_X \log a_w \tag{26}$$

The acidity function H_0 would be given by

$$H_0 = -\log \frac{a_{H^+}\, a^\circ_B}{a^\circ_{BH^+}} + n_0 \log a_w \tag{27}$$

where B is a base of the H_0 class. In accordance with assumption 3, the first terms on the right of Eqs. (26) and (27) would be identical. Consequently it would be necessary that

$$H_X + \log c_A = H_0 + \log c_A + (n_X - n_0) \log a_w \tag{28}$$

The near proportionality of the quantities $H_X + \log c_A$ and $H_0 + \log c_A$ would therefore be possible only if the quantity $(n_X - n_0) \log a_w$ were proportional to $H_0 + \log c_A$. As the plot of $\log a_w$ included in Fig. 9.3 shows, $\log a_w$ is not so proportional. The assumption that the difference between indicators of different classes depends only on differences in the number of water molecules bound to the cation can be accommodated to the facts only by making the quantity $n_X - n_0$ a function of the acid concentration. This is not unreasonable, but it is not very helpful.

H_0 is closely the same function of $\log a_w$ in mixtures with water of sulfuric, perchloric, hydrochloric, and nitric acids [32], and the agreement in the case of sulfuric and perchloric acids is remarkable in its exactness throughout the range of acid concentrations to which it applies [11]. However, a different functional relationship applies to H_0 in water–phosphoric acid and in water–hydrofluoric acid mixtures. Furthermore the H_R' function does not have the same value in mixtures of water with perchloric and with sulfuric acid at the same value of a_w, and neither does H_I. The quantity $H''' - H_0$ is differently related to a_w in different acid-water mixtures [24].

Instead of putting the whole responsibility for solvation on water, it would seem more reasonable to suppose that the XH^+ ions bond to any of the basic constituents of the acid-water mixture. The gradual replacement of water by HSO_4^- as the acid concentration increases may well lead to a value for the solvation energy which is not so sharply dependent on that concentration as the quantity $\mathbf{R}T \log a_w$ is. At the same time, increasing bonding of the solute base to the acidic constituents of the solution would lead to a decrease in the standard activity of the base.

9.14 ACIDITY FUNCTIONS AT HIGH ACID CONCENTRATIONS

At sulfuric acid concentrations above 70% the differences $H_R' - H_0$ and $H''' - H_0$ become nearly independent of acid concentration. It would seem therefore that if one were to choose sulfuric acid instead of water as the reference solvent, differences between the various acidity functions would begin to appear only at water concentrations over something like 30% and that the quantity $a_X^\circ a_{BH^+}^\circ / a_{XH^+}^\circ a_B^\circ$ would be unity for all bases at water concentrations less than this. The conclusion is consistent with other evidence that sulfuric acid–water mixtures in this range constitute a system of remarkably simple behavior.

Brand [33] showed that the relation

$$H_0 = -8.36 + \log \frac{x_{HSO_4^-}}{x_{H_2SO_4}} \tag{29}$$

where the x's are mole fractions, applies in the region from 90 to 99.5% sulfuric acid if it is assumed that the reaction

$$H_2O + H_2SO_4 \rightleftharpoons OH_3^+ + HSO_4^- \qquad (IV)$$

is essentially complete. By assuming that the ratio $x/a = 1$ for each entity involved in reaction (IV), Deno and Taft [34] were able to account for the values of H_0 and of $\log a_w$ for water concentrations up to 17%, the value of the equilibrium constant

$$K = \frac{x_{OH_3^+} x_{HSO_4^-}}{x_{H_2O} x_{H_4SO}} \qquad (30)$$

being 50. By supposing that both OH_3^+ and HSO_4^- are largely but not completely converted to monohydrates and that the activities of all molecular species are equal to their mole fractions, Wyatt [32] accounts for H_0 and $\log a_w$ over the range from 0 to 19.5% water.

One must not, however, assume that all a° values are independent of water concentration in this region. It has long been known that the solubilities of dinitrobenzene and of trinitrotoluene decrease sharply with increasing water concentration in this region [35] even though no conversion of these substances to the conjugate acid can be detected cryoscopically in essentially anhydrous sulfuric acid [36]. It is probably pertinent that nearly anhydrous sulfuric acid is a complex material which contains appreciable concentrations of SO_3, of $H_2S_2O_7$, and of $HS_2O_7^-$. A specific reaction of one of these with the nitro compound would account for the variation in solubility.

9.15 ACIDITY FUNCTIONS AND THE RATES OF ACID-CATALYZED REACTIONS

When the composition of the transition state differs from the sum of the compositions of the reactants by one hydrogen ion, the limiting value k° of the specific rate is given by

$$k^\circ = k^{\circ\circ} a_{H^+} \frac{a_S^\circ}{a^\ddagger} \qquad (31)$$

$k^{\circ\circ}$ is the limiting value of the specific rate in a reference solvent, while a_S° is the standard activity of the reactant s, and $a^\ddagger$ that of the transition state in the medium in which reaction takes place. It is to be expected that the ratio $a_S^\circ/a^\ddagger$ will have the same dependence on the medium as the ratio for the proton-transfer equilibrium of one or another class of base because in both cases the ratio involves the same kind of interactions with the medium. If so, the quantity $\log(a_{H^+} a_S^\circ/a^\ddagger)$ should equal the negative of the appropriate acidity function H_X and the relation

$$\log k^\circ = \log k^{\circ\circ} - H_X \qquad (32)$$

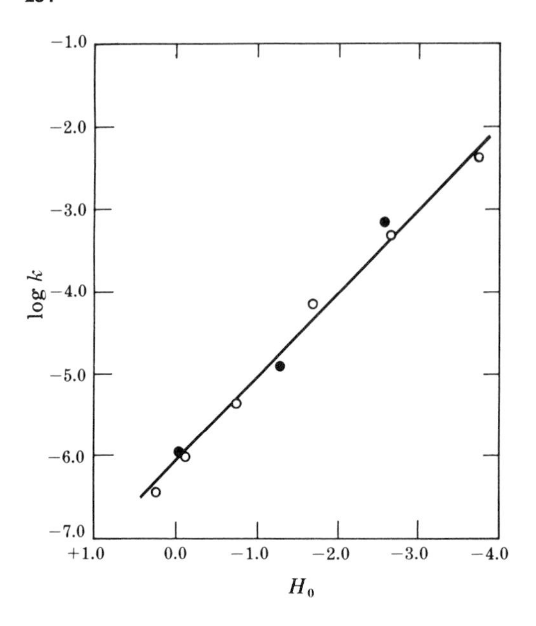

Fig. 9.7 Log k against H_0 for the acid-catalyzed decomposition of trioxane: ○ = H_2SO_4 in water; ● = HCl in water. (*By permission of Paul* [38].)

should apply. Over the range of H_0 values from −1 to −6 in strong-acid–water mixtures the various acidity functions are not far from linear functions of H_0. It is therefore not surprising that for a large variety of acid-catalyzed reaction in such media log k° is linear in H_0 but with a slope which often differs from unity. Many examples are included in the critical review by Long and Paul [37].

A striking case (Fig. 9.7) because the range of acidity involved is so wide is the depolymerization of trioxane. As shown by Paul [38], log k at 40°C is linear in H_0 with unit slope for a variety of strong-acid–water mixtures. Later work by Bell, Bascombe, and McCoubray [15] at 25°, which extended only to an H_0 value of −2, led to a best value of 1.2 for the slope using the combined data for sulfuric, hydrochloric, and perchloric acids.

Figure 9.8 from the work of Long and Bakule [39] shows both how close is the linearity of the plots of log k against H_0 and how widely the slopes vary. The k_f of the figure is the specific rate of the conversion of the enol form of 1,1-cyclohexanedione to the hydrated keto form, and the k_r is the specific rate of the reverse process. The slopes of the lines are −0.5 for k_f and −0.8 for k_r in perchloric acid, and the corresponding values are −0.7 and −0.9 for sulfuric acid. Values of −0.7 and −1.0 were found in hydrochloric acid.

Many of the available kinetic data traverse the region near a zero value of H_0 in which the slopes of plots of H_X against H_0 may vary rather rapidly but in which plots of $H_X + \log c_A$ against $H_0 + \log c_A$ are close to linear (Sec. 9.10). A comprehensive survey by Bunnett and Olsen [27], which involves 160 sets of kinetic data in moderately concentrated aqueous solutions of strong acids,

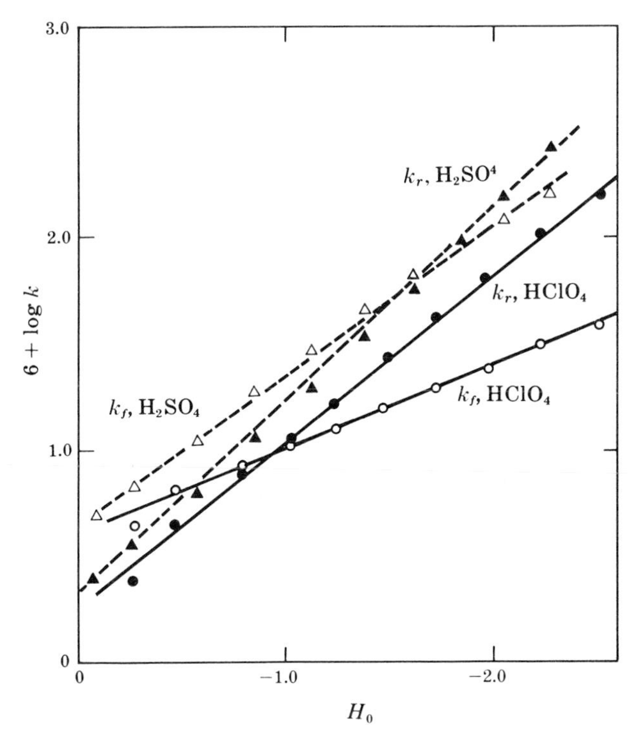

Fig. 9.8 Specific rate of keto-enol interconversion of 1,1-cyclohexanedione. [*By permission of F. A. Long and R. Bakule, J. Am. Chem. Soc.*, **85**: 2313 (1963).]

shows that the equation

$$\log k^\circ - \log c_A = -(1 - \phi)(H_0 + \log c_A) + C \tag{33}$$

or its equivalent

$$\log k^\circ + H_0 = \phi(H_0 + \log c_A) + C \tag{34}$$

is widely applicable. If Eq. (22) were exact, the constant C would be the value of $\log k^{\circ\circ}$. For the whole 160 sets of data the median standard deviation of points from the linear regression lines is 0.03 logarithmic units, which is not much worse than the probable experimental error. Visual inspection of the plots did not suggest any systematic deviation from linearity. Figure 9.9 shows a typical example of a reaction for which ϕ has a large positive value, +0.90 in this case, the hydrolysis of isonicotinamide. The standard deviation from the best straight line of the points in the figure is 0.027. As is typical for reactions which have large positive values of ϕ and for which the data involve

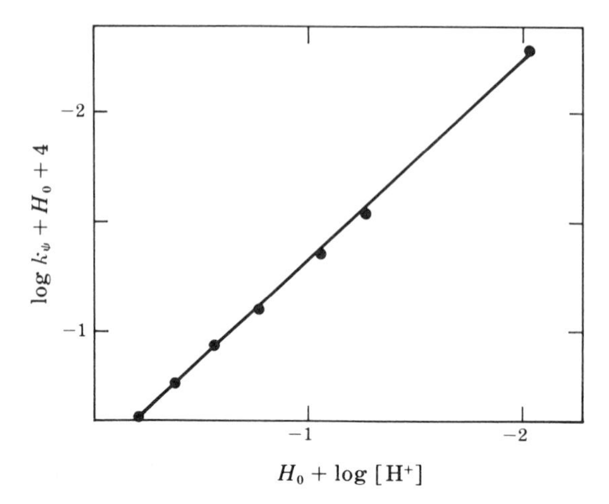

Fig. 9.9 Bunnett and Olsen correlation for isonicotinamide hydrolysis in hydrochloric acid solution. [*By permission of J. F. Bunnett and F. P. Olsen, Can. J. Chem.*, **44**: 1917 (1966).]

the critical region around $H_0 = 0$, the correlation is considerably poorer for a plot of log k against H_0, the standard deviation being 0.113.

The Bunnett and Olsen ϕ values run from −1 to +1.34 with no obvious segregation into groups or significant gaps in the progression. For a ϕ value of +1 Eq. (33) reduces to

$$\log k^\circ = \log c_A + C \tag{35}$$

i.e., the specific rate becomes proportional to c_A. Zucker and Hammett [40] noted that the specific rate of the iodination of acetophenone in moderately concentrated aqueous acids is more nearly linear in log c_A than in H_0 and suggested that there might be a qualitative difference between reactions linear in log c_A and those linear in H_0. The Bunnett and Olsen analysis makes it clear, however, that linearity in log c_A is not an isolated phenomenon but rather one which grades imperceptibly into linearity in H_0. Indeed Bunnett and Olsen find that the Zucker and Hammett data fit Eq. (34) excellently, the ϕ values being +0.62 for sulfuric acid and +0.80 for perchloric acid.

9.16 AROMATIC NITRATION IN SULFURIC ACID–WATER MIXTURES

log k for the nitration of nitrobenzene in sulfuric acid–water mixtures has unit slope against $-H_R$, the acidity function defined by the arylcarbinol–carbonium ion reaction (Sec. 9.7) [41]. This is consistent with the hypothesis that the process by which the transition state is formed is

$$X + HNO_3 + H^+ \rightleftharpoons XNO_2^+ + H_2O \tag{V}$$

a hypothesis which is commonly expressed in the statement that the active nitrating agent is NO_2^+.

9.17 SYSTEMS INVOLVING TWO ACIDITY FUNCTIONS

When a reactant S contains two different atoms each capable of adding a proton, it is possible for it to be rapidly and reversibly converted to a conjugate acid SH^+ and also to be converted relatively slowly to a product P by way of a transition state which is isomeric with SH^+. In such a case the primitive concentration of S, that is, the sum $[S] + [SH^+]$, is given by

$$c_S = [S]\left(1 + \frac{a_{H^+} a_S^\circ}{K^{\circ\circ} a_{SH^+}^\circ}\right) \tag{36}$$

and the primitive value $k^{(p)}$ of the specific rate by

$$k^{(p)} = k^{\circ\circ} \frac{a_{H^+} a_B^\circ}{a^{\ddagger}} \frac{1}{1 + (a_{H^+} a_S^\circ / K^{\circ\circ} a_{SH^+}^\circ)} \tag{37}$$

This becomes

$$\log k^{(p)} = \log k^{\circ\circ} - H_{\ddagger} - \log\left(1 + \frac{h_S}{K^{\circ\circ}}\right) \tag{38}$$

by virtue of the substitutions

$$H_{\ddagger} = -\log \frac{a_{H^+} a_S^\circ}{a^{\ddagger}} \tag{39}$$

and

$$\log h_S = -H_S = \log \frac{a_{H^+} a_S^\circ}{a_{SH^+}^\circ} \tag{40}$$

$H_{\ddagger}$ is the acidity function appropriate to the conversion of S to the transition state, and H_S is the one appropriate to the conversion to SH^+.

When $h_S \ll K^{\circ\circ}$, that is, at low acidity, Eq. (38) reduces to

$$\log k^{(p)} = \log k^{\circ\circ} - H_{\ddagger} \tag{41}$$

and $\log k^{(p)}$ is linear in $-H_{\ddagger}$ with unit slope. As h_S approaches $K^{\circ\circ}$ the slope decreases, and at higher acidities the relation becomes

$$\log k^{(p)} = \log k^{\circ\circ} K^{\circ\circ} - (H_{\ddagger} - H_S) \tag{42}$$

If $H_{\ddagger} = H_S$, $\log k^{(p)}$ becomes constant at the higher acidities; if $H_{\ddagger}$ increases more rapidly than H_S, the specific rate goes through a maximum and decreases at higher acidities.

The specific rates of the hydrolysis of many carboxylic amides and thioamides show maxima in the region of 4 to 6 *M* concentrations of aqueous solutions of strong acids [7]. Rosenthal and Taylor [42] found that the data for the hydrolysis of thioacetamide in perchloric acid solutions from 0.3 to

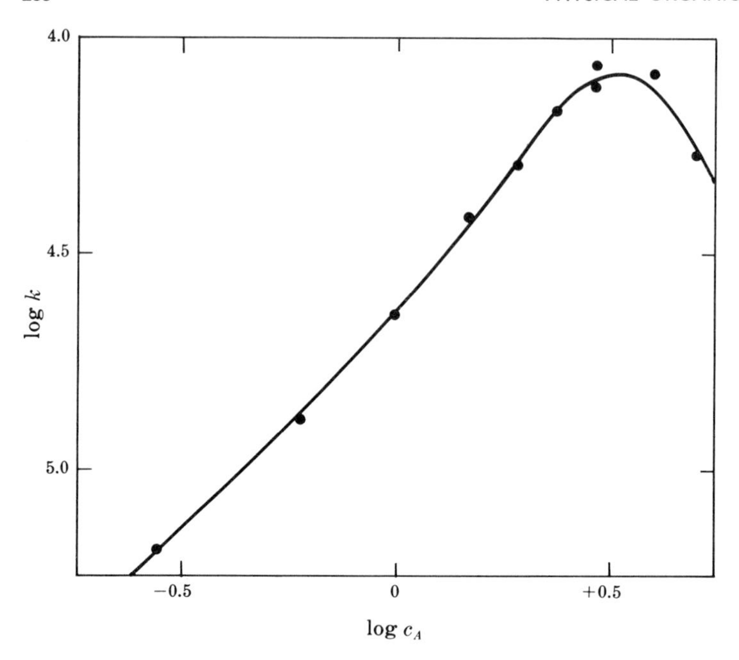

Fig. 9.10 Hydrolysis rate of thioacetamide in perchloric acid solution. (*Data of Rosenthal and Taylor* [42].)

5 *M* are consistent with Eq. (38) if H_S is H_0 and $H_{\ddagger}$ is $\log c_A$. A better fit can be obtained by setting $\phi_{\ddagger} = 0.8$, that is,

$$H_{\ddagger} + \log c_A = 0.2(H_0 + \log c_A) \tag{43}$$

and $\phi_S = -0.8$. The curve plotted in Fig. 9.10 represents the equation

$$\log k^{(p)} = -4.7 + 0.8 \log c_A - 0.2H_0 - \log\left[1 + 0.00159 c_A \left(\frac{h_0}{c_A}\right)^{1.8}\right] \tag{44}$$

which was derived on this basis. Yates and Riordan [25] find that the hydrolysis of a variety of amides in hydrochloric acid solution can be accounted for by an essentially equivalent relationship.

Schubert and Quacchia find that the $pK^{\circ\circ}$ value of 1-methoxy-3,5-dihydroxybenzene is −3.60 and that the substance is a base of the H_0 class in perchloric acid–water solutions [43, p. 1278]. They find further [43, p. 1284] that the specific rate of the hydrolysis of the substance at 50°C continues to increase with increasing acid concentration beyond the point at which protonation of the reactant is essentially complete. This behavior is quantitatively accounted for by assuming that $H_{\ddagger} = 1.30H_0$. The curve in Fig. 9.11

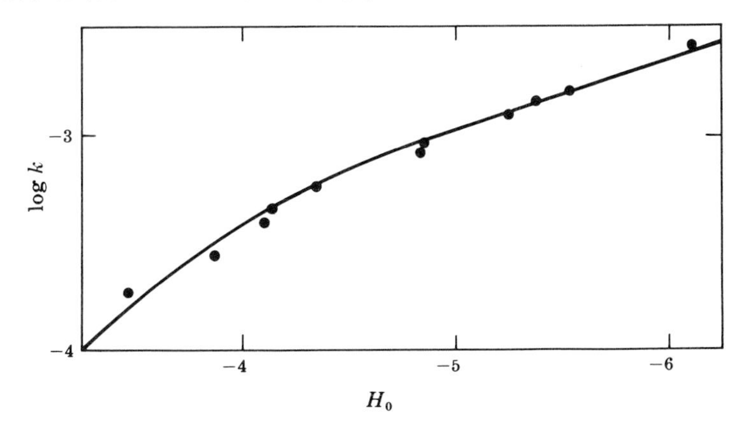

Fig. 9.11 Hydrolysis rate of 1-methoxy-3,5-dihydroxybenzene in perchloric acid–water mixtures. (*Data of Schubert and Quacchia* [43].)

represents the equation

$$\log k^{(p)} = -8.06 - 1.3H_0 - \log\left(1 + \frac{h_0}{3.98 \times 10^3}\right) \tag{45}$$

and the points represent the Schubert and Quacchia data.

9.18 THE AMBIGUITY OF THE CONCEPT OF BASE STRENGTH

The strength of a base in a particular medium A may suitably be defined in terms of the p$K°$ value, where

$$pK° = -\log K° = -\log \frac{a_{H^+}}{I°} \tag{46}$$

and $I°$ is the limiting value of the ratio $[BH^+]/[B]$. The difference in strength of bases X and Y in medium A is therefore given by $\log I_X^\circ - \log I_Y^\circ$. For any other medium in which the quantity $a_X^\circ a_{YH^+}^\circ / a_{XH^+}^\circ a_Y^\circ$ has the same value as it has in medium A the difference in strength of X and Y will be the same as it is in A. But if X and Y belong to classes to which different acidity functions apply, the activity ratio changes with changing medium and consequently the relative strength of X and Y changes. If for instance a base of the H_R' type and one of the H_A type have the same strength in 40% aqueous sulfuric acid, the H_R' base will be 2.54 logarithmic units weaker in dilute aqueous solution than the H_A base, but it will be 4.78 units stronger in 80% sulfuric acid.

The concept of an inherent measure of the strength of a base or of an acid is therefore as meaningless as the concept of an absolute measure of the acidity of a solution. But to quote Arnett [44], "There is the saving grace that the study of weak bases can serve as a splendid proving ground for the development of the structural theory of solvation which organic chemistry so sorely needs."

9.19 THE ESTIMATION OF $pK^{\circ\circ}$ VALUES

If the conversion ratio I° of base to conjugate acid can be measured with sufficient precision and over a sufficient range to establish the slope of the plot of $\log I^\circ$ against any convenient measure of acidity, the appropriate acidity function H_X can be recognized either in terms of those listed in Table 9.2 or by interpolation between them. To the precision to which the overlap procedure may be trusted $pK^{\circ\circ}$ is then given as an average value of the sum $H_X + \log I^\circ$. The only uncertainty is the reliability of the overlap procedure for the H_X function.

Bunnett and Olsen [27] use Eq. (22) or the equivalent

$$\log I^\circ + H_0 = \phi(H_0 + \log c_A) + pK^{\circ\circ} \tag{47}$$

as a means of estimating $pK^{\circ\circ}$ values. The procedure bases on the approximation that ϕ is independent of acid concentration, which is not far from the fact for sulfuric acid–water mixtures up to 85% acid. They find that the median difference between the $pK^{\circ\circ}$ value obtained in this way and that obtained by the overlap method is only 0.25 for all of the bases of the H_A, H''', H_I, and H_R types for which I° values are measurable in the range from 10 to 85% sulfuric acid. The values tend to be somewhat less negative than those obtained by the overlap method because ϕ values become more positive with increasing acid concentration. Equation (22) or (47) is a considerably poorer approximation for perchloric acid solutions than it is for sulfuric acid solutions.

9.20 INTERFERENCE FROM MEDIUM EFFECTS IN THE SPECTROPHOTOMETRIC ESTIMATION OF BASE STRENGTH

The task of characterizing the strength of a base is complicated by the fact that the absorption spectrum of a solute often changes with changing medium even in the absence of a recognizable chemical reaction. The nature of the phenomenon is illustrated by Fig. 9.12, in which the logarithm of the extinction coefficient ϵ is plotted against wavelength for acetophenone in various concentrations of sulfuric acid. There is a rapid change, qualitative as well as quantitative, in the absorption as the acid concentration increases from 55 to 86%. This is presumably the region of acid concentration in which the base is being converted to the conjugate acid. But outside this region there is a relatively minor change in the spectrum. That this change continues throughout the region of base-acid conversion is demonstrated by the failure of the isobestic requirement. This requirement applies [45, n. 11] to any series of solutions which contain two and only two absorbing substances each of which has an unvarying spectrum. In such a series a point at which the absorption curves of any two solutions intersect must be common to the curves of all of the solutions. Because of the shift one cannot take the extinction coefficient in water or in dilute acid to be an exact measure of the value which the

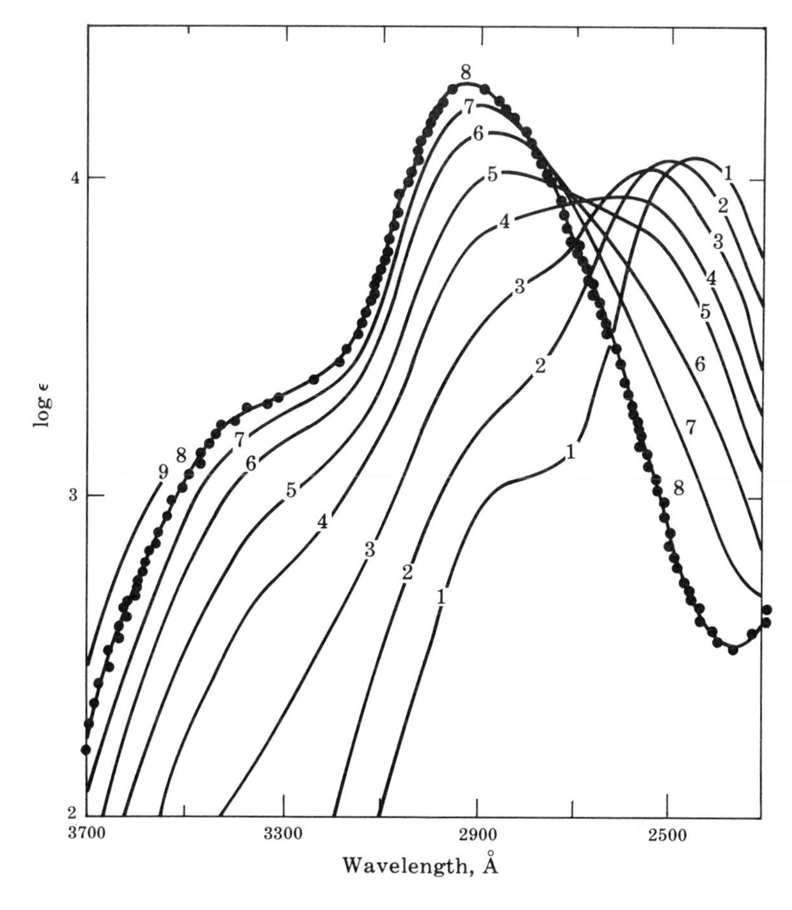

Fig. 9.12 Ionization of acetophenone as a base: Curve 1, solvent is water; other curves sulfuric acid: 2 = 55%; 3 = 65.15%; 4 = 70.45%; 5 = 73.65%; 6 = 77.66%; 7 = 80.40%; 8 = 85.96%; 9 = 95.99%. (*By permission of Flexser, Hammett, and Dingwall* [45].)

coefficient ϵ_B of the basic form of acetophenone will have at the wavelength involved within the region of conversion. Similarly one cannot take the extinction coefficient in 95 or 100% acid to be an exact measure of the coefficient of the conjugate acid in the conversion region.

If, however, ϵ_B and ϵ_{BH^+} do not change rapidly in the relatively narrow region within which most of the protonation occurs, it should be possible to select average values of these quantities which will make the equation

$$\log \frac{\epsilon_B - \epsilon}{\epsilon - \epsilon_{BH^+}} = pK^{\circ\circ} - H_X \tag{48}$$

a close approximation. The early discussions of this problem assumed that H_X is H_0 for all bases, an assumption which is now known to be invalid. But over the range of useful measurements of the left side of Eq. (48) for a single base the relations between the various acidity functions are so nearly linear that the equation can be replaced by

$$\log \frac{\epsilon_B - \epsilon}{\epsilon - \epsilon_{BH^+}} = C - xH_0 \tag{49}$$

with C and x independent of acid concentration. If the region of protonation occurs at low enough acid concentrations to make the difference significant, this should be replaced by

$$\log \frac{\epsilon_B - \epsilon}{\epsilon - \epsilon_{BH^+}} + H_0 = \phi(H_0 + \log c_A) + C \tag{50}$$

(Sec. 9.10). Either of the equations involves four adjustable parameters, and, even though the range of permissible variation of ϵ_B and ϵ_{BH^+} is limited, the constancy of these two quantities is not entirely trustworthy. The problem of obtaining values of x and C or of ϕ and C from experimental data is therefore a formidable one. Much can be gained, however, from a wise choice of wavelength.

As Fig. 9.12 suggests and as the data in Table 9.3 clearly show, 2500 Å is a particularly favorable frequency in the acetophenone case. This is close to the peak frequency in the absorption band of the base both in water and in 50% sulfuric acid, and the lateral shift of the band from one medium to the other has therefore little effect on the extinction coefficient at this frequency. At the same time the absorption of the conjugate acid is so weak that an exact value

Table 9.3 Extinction coefficient in the neighborhood of 2500 Å for acetophenone at various sulfuric acid concentrations[a]

% H_2SO_4	ϵ_{2400}	ϵ_{2500}	ϵ_{2600}	H_0
0	11,000	11,000	4,300	
50.0	9,000	11,500	7,700	−3.38
55.0	8,600	11,700	8,400	−3.91
65.2	6,200	10,100	10,000	−5.10
70.5	4,300	7,500	9,000	−5.87
73.7	3,000	5,800	7,700	−6.36
77.7	1,650	3,350	5,800	−6.98
80.4	830	2,000	4,200	−7.40
86.0	375	900	2,600	−8.29
96.0	200	400	1,500	−10.04

[a] Data of Flexser, Hammett, and Dingwall [45].

of the coefficient is unimportant except at high I values. In view of these considerations one can arrive reasonably at ϵ_B and ϵ_{BH^+} values of 12,100 and 220, respectively, and at the equation

$$\log \frac{\epsilon_B - \epsilon}{\epsilon - \epsilon_{BH^+}} = -3.62 + 0.582 H_0 \tag{51}$$

which is represented by the straight line in Fig. 9.13. The closed circles represent the experimental values of ϵ. The rms deviation of the log I values is 0.037.

The data are completely inconsistent with unit slope in this plot, i.e., with H_0 as the appropriate acidity function for acetophenone. If one pushes the estimated ϵ_B value down to the unreasonable figure of 10,500, the slope in the midconversion region rises only to 0.7 and the plot is decidedly nonlinear. The open circles in Fig. 9.13 represent this choice of an ϵ_B value.

With the 12,100 value for ϵ_B and the H_A values listed in Table 9.2 the equation

$$\log I = -4.41 + 1.11 H_A \tag{52}$$

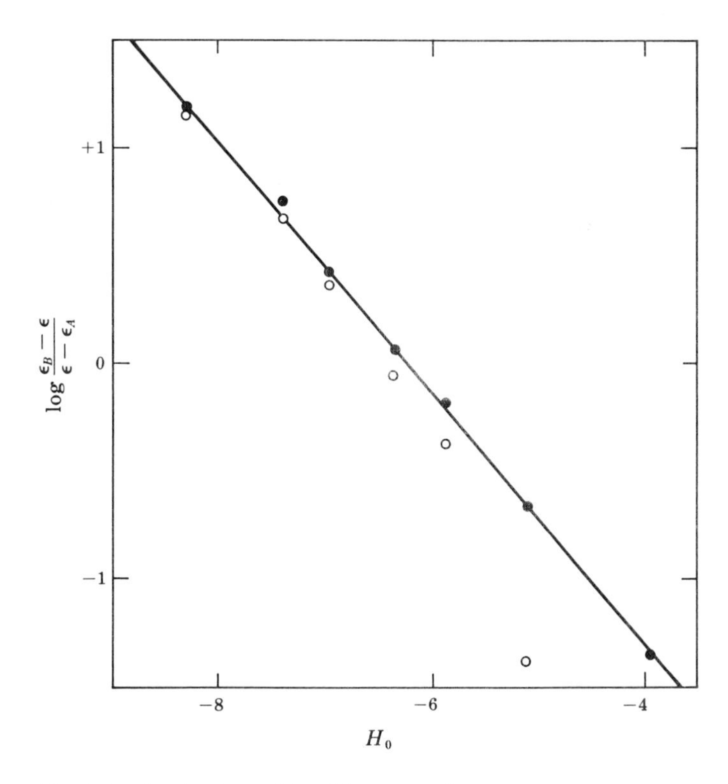

Fig. 9.13 Application of Eq. (51) to acetophenone.

fits the data with an rms deviation of 0.021. The indicated value of $pK^{\circ\circ}$ for acetophenone is therefore in the neighborhood of -4.

Yet Flexser, Hammett, and Dingwall, using the same data, found no inconsistency with H_0 as the applicable acidity function (they knew of no other) and concluded that the $pK^{\circ\circ}$ value of acetophenone is somewhat more negative than -6. Stewart and Yates [46], using new experimental data, obtained a $pK^{\circ\circ}$ value identical with the Flexser one. In the Flexser work Eq. (49) was put in the form

$$\frac{\epsilon}{h_0(\epsilon - \epsilon_{BH^+})} = -\frac{1}{K^{\circ\circ}} + \frac{1}{h_0(\epsilon - \epsilon_{BH^+})}\epsilon_B \tag{53}$$

The value of ϵ_{BH^+} was estimated from the spectrum at high acid concentration, and the value of $1/K^{\circ\circ}$ was obtained from the intercept of a plot of the left side of this equation against the reciprocal of the quantity $h_0(\epsilon - \epsilon_{BH^+})$. A satisfactorily linear plot can be obtained, the position of which is only slightly affected by the choice of a value of ϵ_{BH^+}. Corrected for the difference between the zero point of the H_0 scale employed and that of Paul and Long [7], the $pK^{\circ\circ}$ value obtained from the data at 2500 Å is -6.08. while the average of the values obtained in a similar fashion over all wavelengths is -6.15. These figures, which are based on the Paul and Long values of H_0, cannot be directly compared with those derived from Eq. (51), which are based on the Jorgenson and Hartter values. With the Paul and Long values Eq. (51) is replaced by

$$\log I = 4.08 + 0.68\ H_0 \tag{54}$$

which fits the data with an rms deviation of 0.037 and leads to an H_0 value at half protonation of -6.00.

The Flexser, Hammett, and Dingwall method is in fact a surprisingly effective way of estimating the value at half protonation of a particular base of any acidity function one chooses to apply. If one substitutes the h_A function for the h_0 function in Eq. (53), one gets just as good a linear plot but the $pK^{\circ\circ}$ value comes out -4.1, which is in reasonable agreement with the value given by Eq. (52). At the same time the method is a convenient one to employ if one is ignorant of (or chooses to overlook) the possibility that the acidity function used is not really the applicable one.

Stewart and Yates also obtained a $pK^{\circ\circ}$ value of -6.15 for acetophenone in terms of the Paul and Long H_0 values. They used a method of treating the data which had been proposed by Davis and Geissman [47]. In this it is assumed that the quantities $\epsilon_{B2} - \epsilon_{B1}$ and $\epsilon_{BH^+2} - \epsilon_{BH^+1}$ are unaffected by a medium-induced wavelength shift. ϵ_{B2} and ϵ_{B1} are the extinction coefficients of base form at wavelengths 2 and 1, and ϵ_{BH^+2} and ϵ_{BH^+1} are the corresponding coefficients of the conjugate acid. The assumption is justified only if ϵ_B and ϵ_{BH^+} are both linear in the wavelength, a requirement which is of doubtful generality. Nevertheless this method frequently leads to estimates of the H_0 value at half protonation which agree with those obtained in other ways.

It therefore appears that there is no great difficulty in locating the H_0 value at half protonation even when there is a medium-induced wavelength shift. But the determination of the applicable acidity function and thereby the value of $pK^{\circ\circ}$ presents a considerably more difficult problem. It should, however, be recognized that all the members of such a closely related group of substances as the substituted acetophenones investigated by Stewart and Yates are likely to have the same applicable acidity function and that this function will be approximately linear in H_0. If this is the case, the $pK^{\circ\circ}$ values for the series will be linearly related to the H_0 values at half protonation. The conclusions which Stewart and Yates draw from linear relations between these $(H_0)_{1/2}$ values and substituent constants are therefore unaffected.

Fortunately the estimates of the ratio I upon which the acidity function values of Table 9.2 depend derive from, or have been verified by, measurements under conditions for which medium effects should be negligible. The data were taken at wavelengths at which one form absorbs strongly and the other weakly and at which the absorption of the strongly absorbing form is near a maximum. Further, the medium effects outside the region of protonation amount only to small lateral shifts. The results of the early work using visual colorimetry [9] have either been verified by spectrophotometric methods [8] or replaced by newer data [10], and the reason for the validity of the colorimetric method is understood [45, p. 2111].

When the data in the midconversion range of a base can be fitted to a particular acidity function H_X, the variation of the a_B/a_{BH^+} ratio within that range must be that characteristic of the H_X function. The consistency of the plots of Figs. 9.2 to 9.4 argues strongly for the conclusion that this relationship persists outside the midconversion range. Apparent inconsistency at high or at low conversion should not be weighted heavily against the conclusion because the uncertainty in the estimation of I values which arises from uncertainty in the ϵ_B or in the ϵ_{BH^+} value then becomes large.

9.21 METHODS OF CORRECTING FOR THE MEDIUM EFFECT

Katritzky, Waring, and Yates [48] suppose that the medium effect is linear in H_0. This leads to

$$\epsilon = \frac{1}{1+I}(\epsilon_B + G_B H_0) + \frac{I}{1+I}(\epsilon_{BH^+} + G_{BH^+} H_0) \tag{55}$$

If the values of ϵ_B, ϵ_{BH}, G_B, and G_{BH^+} are evaluated from the absorption outside the protonation range, the value $\epsilon_{1/2}$ of the absorption at half protonation can be obtained from the equation

$$\epsilon_{1/2} = \epsilon_B + \epsilon_{BH^+} + H_0(G_B + G_{BH^+}) \tag{56}$$

and the value $(H_0)_{1/2}$ of H_0 at half protonation can then be obtained from the empirical relation between ϵ and H_0. The slope $d\epsilon/dH_0$ is given by

$$\frac{d\epsilon}{dH_0} = \frac{\epsilon_{BH^+} - \epsilon_B + (G_{BH^+} - G_B)\,H_0}{(1+I)^2}\frac{dI}{dH_0} + \frac{G_B + G_{BH^+}I}{1+I} \tag{57}$$

If log I is linear in H_0 with slope x then

$$\frac{dI}{dH_0} = -\frac{xI}{0.434} \tag{58}$$

and

$$x = \frac{0.87[2(d\epsilon/dH_0)_{1/2} + G_B + G_{BH^+}]}{\epsilon_B - \epsilon_{BH^+} + (G_B - G_{BH^+})(H_0)_{1/2}} \tag{59}$$

The slope $d\epsilon/dH_0$ is not changing rapidly at the half protonation point and can be estimated with relatively good precision. The other quantities in Eq. (59) are known, and the value of x is therefore indicated with considerable reliability.

Reeves [49] has used a mathematically sophisticated technique for deciding whether a significant medium effect exists within the protonation range and of correcting for it if necessary.

9.22 OTHER METHODS OF ESTIMATING THE STRENGTH OF WEAK BASES

Arnett and coworkers [50] determined the equilibrium ratio $D = c_0/c_a$ of a base between an acid-water mixture and an inert solvent such as isooctane. c_0 is the concentration of base in the inert solvent, and c_a is the primitive value of the concentration in the acid mixture. The value of c_0 is determined by gas chromatographic analysis, and c_a is calculated from the concentration in the acid layer before the inert solvent was added and the relative volumes of the layers. If B represents the base,

$$c_a = [\mathrm{B}]\left(1 + \frac{h_X}{K^{\circ\circ}}\right) \tag{60}$$

with

$$\log h_X = -H_X \tag{61}$$

H_X being the applicable acidity function. The sophisticated concentration [B] of the base in the acid layer is given by

$$[\mathrm{B}] = \frac{c_0}{D^{\circ\circ}\,a_B^{\circ}} \tag{62}$$

where $D^{\circ\circ}$ is the distribution constant for the reference solvent. From these relations

$$\log \frac{D^{\circ\circ} a_B^\circ - D}{D} = pK^{\circ\circ} - H_X \tag{63}$$

The problem of selecting the appropriate acidity function and of estimating the value of $pK^{\circ\circ}$ is essentially the same as it is in the spectrophotometric method of investigating weak bases. The quantity $(D^{\circ\circ} a_B^\circ - D)/D$ in the one method corresponds to the quantity $(\epsilon_B - \epsilon)/(\epsilon - \epsilon_{BH^+})$ in the other. There is one less adjustable parameter in the distribution method, but the likelihood that a_B° will vary rapidly within the protonation range is greater than the corresponding likelihood for ϵ_B or ϵ_{BH^+}.

Assuming that a_B° does not change significantly within the protonation range and that H_0 is the applicable acidity function, the distribution method led to a $pK^{\circ\circ}$ value of −6.51 for anisole. This agrees well with the value of −6.54 obtained by the spectrophotometric method [51]. There is considerable evidence that the distribution method leads generally to useful estimates of the basicity of ethers [52]. On the other hand it is clearly inapplicable to benzoic acid or to nitrobenzene (Sec. 9.12). Arnett and Wu cite a number of other cases where it is inapplicable.

Other techniques for the estimation of the strength of weak bases have had more or less isolated application. The relation between hydrogen bonding and base strength (Sec. 8.6) leads to useful estimates for a number of bases which would be difficult to approach in other ways. Many of these methods are discussed along with the resulting estimates of base strength in the review by Arnett [53]. More recently Deno and Wisotsky [54] have applied Raman spectroscopy to the problem and have also discussed critically the applicability of nuclear magnetic resonance.

9.23 TEMPERATURE COEFFICIENTS

The temperature coefficient of the quantity $pK^{\circ\circ}$ is given (Sec. 2.20) by

$$\frac{d(pK^{\circ\circ})}{dT} = -\frac{\Delta \bar{H}^{\circ\circ}}{2.303\mathbf{R}T^2} + \frac{d\rho^{\circ\circ}}{dT} \tag{64}$$

If water is the reference solvent, the term involving the density $\rho^{\circ\circ}$ contributes only 36 cal/mole to the value of $\Delta \bar{H}^{\circ\circ}$ at 300°K. This is well within the experimental error of any available experimental data. The effect is several times larger for the typical organic solvent. $\Delta \bar{H}^{\circ\circ}$ is the standard-enthalpy change of the process

$$BH^+ + S \rightleftharpoons B + SH^+ \tag{VI}$$

in the reference solvent S.

In any medium other than the reference medium $\Delta\bar{H}^\circ$, the limiting value of the molal enthalpy change for the conversion of BH^+ to B, the limit being for zero concentrations in that medium of B and BH^+, is given by

$$\Delta\bar{H}^\circ = \Delta\bar{H}^{\circ\circ} - 2.303RT^2\frac{d\log(a_B^\circ/a_{BH^+}^\circ)}{dT} + \bar{H}_{H^+} - \bar{H}_{SH^+}^{\circ\circ} \tag{65}$$

$\bar{H}_{H^+}$ is the molal enthalpy of all of the forms of solvated hydrogen ion present in the medium of measurement, and $\bar{H}_{SH^+}^{\circ\circ}$ is the molal enthalpy of the solvated hydrogen ion in the reference medium. The equation is a direct consequence of the relation

$$\bar{H}_i^\circ - \bar{H}_i^{\circ\circ} = -2.303RT^2\frac{d\log a_i^\circ}{dT} \tag{66}$$

Because $a_B^\circ/a_{BH^+}^\circ$ has the same value for two bases a and b to which the same acidity function applies, the relation

$$\Delta\bar{H}_a^\circ - \Delta\bar{H}_b^\circ = \Delta\bar{H}_a^{\circ\circ} - \Delta\bar{H}_b^{\circ\circ} \tag{67}$$

applies to such a pair of bases. It cannot be expected to apply to bases which are not so related.

The temperature coefficient of the acidity function H_X is given by

$$\frac{dH_X}{dT} = \frac{\bar{H}_{H^+} - \bar{H}_{SH^+}^{\circ\circ} + \bar{H}_B^\circ - \bar{H}_B^{\circ\circ} - \bar{H}_{BH^+}^\circ + \bar{H}_{BH^+}^{\circ\circ}}{2.303RT^2} \tag{68}$$

The numerator on the right is the difference between the molal enthalpy change for the conversion of BH^+ to B in the medium of measurement and the value of the same quantity in the reference medium. It is also the standard-enthalpy change per mole of the process in which equivalent infinitesimal amounts of B and of hydrogen ion are transferred from the reference medium to the medium of measurement and an equivalent amount of BH^+ is transferred in the opposite direction.

Gelbstein, Shscheglova, and Temkin [55] have determined the temperature coefficient of the indicator ratio I in sulfuric acid–water mixtures for the H_0 indicators listed in Table 9.4. The p$K^{\circ\circ}$ value for p-nitroaniline was estimated by extrapolation in dilute hydrochloric acid solution at each of the temperatures involved, namely, 20, 40, 60, and 80°C. The values for the other indicators were obtained by the overlap procedure at each temperature. There was no actual overlap between 2,4-dinitroaniline and the bromodinitroaniline and between the latter and trinitroaniline, and the data for the last two are less reliable than those for the other bases because some extrapolation was required. Within experimental error p$K^{\circ\circ}$ is linear in $1/T$ in every case. Values of p$K^{\circ\circ}$, $\Delta\mu^{\circ\circ}$, $\Delta\bar{H}^{\circ\circ}$, and $\Delta\bar{S}^{\circ\circ}$, all for a temperature of 50°C, are listed in the table.

$\Delta\mu^{\circ\circ}$ and $\Delta\bar{H}^{\circ\circ}$ vary in parallel fashion, and the relation

$$\Delta\bar{H}^{\circ\circ} = 3{,}940 + 0.49\Delta\mu^{\circ\circ} \tag{69}$$

Table 9.4 Thermodynamic data at 50°C for H_0 indicators[a]

	$pK^{\circ\circ}$	$\Delta\mu^{\circ\circ}$	$\Delta\bar{H}^{\circ\circ}$	$\Delta\bar{S}^{\circ\circ}$
p-Nitroaniline	+0.81	+1,190	+4,600	+10.5
o-Nitroaniline	−0.36	−1,240	+3,360	+12.1
4-Chloro-2-nitroaniline	−1.09	−1,610	+3,075	+14.45
2,4-Dichloro-6-nitroaniline	−3.07	−4,530	+1,680	+19.21
2,4-Dinitroaniline	−4.42	−6,530	+420	+21.5
6-Bromo-2,4-dinitroaniline	−6.59	−9,710	0	+30.14
2,4,6-Trinitroaniline	−9.08	−13,400	−3,100	+31.7

[a] Data of Gelbstein, Shscheglova, and Temkin [55].

applies with a rms deviation in $\Delta\bar{H}^{\circ\circ}$ of 400 for all the bases and of 160 if the two least basic ones are omitted. There must of course be similarly linear relations between $\Delta\bar{S}^{\circ\circ}$ and $\Delta\mu^{\circ\circ}$ and between $\Delta\bar{S}^{\circ\circ}$ and $\Delta\bar{H}^{\circ\circ}$.

To the extent that the same acidity function applies to all these bases Eq. (69) should hold in all acid-water mixtures. Specifically it should hold in the 96.48% sulfuric acid in which Arnett and Burke [56] have determined by calorimetry the quantity $\Delta\bar{H}_t^\circ$ for the transfer of a number of primary anilines from tetrachlorethane solution to the acid solution. Their measurements show an excellent linear relation between $\Delta^\circ H_t$ and the $\Delta\mu^{\circ\circ}$ value calculated for the conversion of the conjugate acid to the base in water solution. From the figure in the Arnett and Burke communication one may estimate that

$$\delta_M \Delta\bar{H}_t^\circ = -1.18\delta_M \Delta\mu^{\circ\circ} \tag{70}$$

where δ_M is the Leffler-Grunwald solvent-stabilization operator. Since

$$\delta_M \Delta\bar{H}^\circ = \delta_M \bar{H}_B^\circ - \delta_M H_{BH^+}^\circ \tag{71}$$

and

$$\delta_M \Delta\bar{H}_t^\circ = \delta_M \bar{H}_{BH^+}^\circ - \delta_M \bar{H}_{B(i)}^\circ \tag{72}$$

where $\bar{H}_B^\circ$ and $\bar{H}_{BH^+}^\circ$ are molal enthalpies in the acid solution and $\bar{H}_{B(i)}^\circ$ is the molal enthalpy of the base in the inert solvent, Eqs. (69) and (70) lead to

$$\delta_M \bar{H}_B^\circ - \delta_M \bar{H}_{B(i)} = \delta_M \Delta\bar{H}^\circ + \delta_M \Delta\bar{H}_t^\circ = -0.69\delta_M \Delta\mu^{\circ\circ} \tag{73}$$

The heat of transfer of uncharged base from the inert solvent to the acid solution without accompanying protonation is therefore linear in $\Delta\mu^{\circ\circ}$ and consequently also in the heat of the acid-base conversion. This is not unreasonable in terms of hydrogen bonding between the base and the strongly acidic constituents of the concentrated sulfuric acid.

As Arnett and Burke point out, the simplicity of these relationships argues strongly for the validity of the $pK^{\circ\circ}$ values involved and hence for the validity of the overlap assumption.

The values of dH_0/dT reported by Gelbstein and coworkers show no sharp change with acid concentration. The quantity has a minimum of -0.0025 at 8% sulfuric acid, it is steady at -0.0020 between 12 and 18% and at 0 between 32 and 50%, and it then rises gradually to $+0.013$ at 100%. The enthalpy difference of Eq. (68) ranges therefore from -1200 cal/mole to $+6000$.

Arnett and Bushick [57] have determined the temperature coefficient of the indicator ratio for a series of H_R type indicators in sulfuric acid–water mixtures. Here both $\Delta\bar{H}^{\circ\circ}$ and $\Delta\bar{S}^{\circ\circ}$ increase with decreasing $\Delta\mu^{\circ\circ}$, but the plots appear to be nonlinear. $\Delta\bar{S}^{\circ\circ}$ reaches the notable value of $+139$ cal/deg for 4,4′,4″-trinitrotriphenylcarbinol and is already $+82$ for the dinitro derivative. By contrast it is -15 for 4,4′-dimethoxytriphenylcarbinol. Entropy changes of this magnitude must not only involve the interaction of a solute molecule with a large number of solvent molecules but also an interaction whose extent varies rapidly with temperature, with medium, and with structure. Experimentally the quantity $dpK^{\circ\circ}/d(1/T)$ appears to be independent of temperature over the 45° range involved, but such appearances can be illusory.

The quantity $\Delta H_R/\Delta(1/T)$ varies both with temperature and with acid concentration in a way in which it is difficult to see much pattern. It does become steadily more positive as the acid concentration increases above 65%. In 80% acid one can assign a value of -0.034, which corresponds to a value of -13.5 kcal for the enthalpy difference of Eq. (68).

9.24 ACID-BASE REACTIONS IN POORLY DISSOCIATING SOLVENTS

With respect to the interpretation of acid-base reactions the simplest systems are those in which ionic dissociation is small. Long-range interactions have a negligible effect, and ideal-solution laws account well for the predominant reactions which are of the type

$$a\mathrm{HA} + b\mathrm{B} \rightleftharpoons (\mathrm{HA})_a(\mathrm{B})_b \qquad \text{(VII)}$$

Because of homoconjugation (Sec. 8.8) the coefficients a and b are frequently not both unity, although one is in most, if not all, cases. The literature on reactions of this kind in such essentially inert solvents as benzene, chlorobenzene, anisole, and carbon tetrachloride has been thoroughly and critically reviewed by a leading investigator in this field [58]. Extensive studies on acid-base reactions in the solvent acetic acid have been reported by Kolthoff and Bruckenstein [59].

The most familiar systems are those in aqueous solution. Ionic dissociation is large, and the effect of long-range interactions is considerable but is to some extent predictable from Debye-Hückel theory. The most difficult systems are the intermediate ones, those in which ion concentrations are considerable and the effect of long-range forces is larger and less definitely predictable than in aqueous solution. There are valuable studies by Guss and

Kolthoff [60] on acid-base reactions in methanol, in which homo- and hetero-conjugation have not been observed. Very extensive studies on solutions in acetonitrile, in which the conjugation is an important factor, have been carried out by Kolthoff and by Coetzee. These are reviewed by Coetzee [61].

9.25 INDICATOR STUDIES IN NITROMETHANE AND IN SULFOLANE

Because they can be used as solvents for the study of very strong acids and of very weak bases as solutes in dilute solution, nitromethane and sulfolane (A)

$CH_2—CH_2$

CH_2 CH_2

S

O O

(A)

are interesting media. The dielectric constants, 36 and 38, are not small, but they are poor ion solvators. Ionic dissociation of quaternary ammonium salts is considerable [62, 63], but it is small for salts in which there is strong cation-anion hydrogen bonding. Nitromethane is a difficult solvent to purify to the extent that it has reproducible properties; sulfolane is not.

Measurements with H_0 type indicators in solutions of sulfuric acid in nitromethane [62, 64] and in sulfolane [65] are consistent with the following assumptions: (1) the indicator base B reacts with the acid HA to form two kinds of ion pairs, BH^+---A^- and BH^+---$A(HA)_2^-$, neither of which is dissociated to free ions to an important extent; (2) the equilibrium constants K_1 and K_3 for the formation of these ion pairs are effectively independent of acid concentration up to at least 1 M; that is, activity coefficients are close to unity over this range; (3) the ratio $\varkappa = K_1/K_3$ is the same for different indicators of the H_0 class; (4) the conversion ratio I determined by spectrophotometry is the ratio

$$\frac{[BH^+\text{---}A^-]+[BH^+\text{---}A(HA)_2^-]}{[B]}$$

It follows from these assumptions that

$$-\log(c_A + \varkappa c_A{}^3) = pK_1 - \log I \qquad (74)$$

provided the concentration c_A of the acid is large compared with that of the indicator.

For the indicators listed in Table 9.5 for nitromethane solution and for those listed in Table 9.7 for sulfolane solution there is for the most part considerable overlap between successive indicators, and the difference in the log I values is satisfactorily constant within the overlap region. There are some gaps in the high acid region in sulfolane, but here log I changes so slowly

Table 9.5 **pK° values of indicators in nitromethane**[a]

	pK°_{VIII}	$pK^{\circ\circ}_w$	$pK^\circ_{VIII} - 4.09$
4-Chloro-2-nitroaniline	+3.06	−1.03	−1.03
2,4-Dichloro-6-nitroaniline	+0.75	−3.27	−3.34
2,4-Dinitroaniline	−0.08	−4.53	−4.17
6-Bromo-2,4-dinitroaniline	−2.37	−6.68	−6.46

[a] Data of Van Looy and Hammett [62].

Table 9.6 **Observed and calculated values of H_0 in nitromethane**[a]

$\log c_A$	0	−0.5	−1.0	−1.5	−2.0	−2.5
H_0 (obs)	−3.15	−1.66	−0.23	+1.03	+1.95	+2.64
H_0 (calc)	−3.16	−1.66	−0.19	+1.11	+1.97	+2.49

[a] Data of Van Looy and Hammett [62].

with acid concentration that the matter is not very serious. The value of pK_{VIII}, the negative logarithm of the equilibrium constant of the reaction

$$BH^+\text{---}HSO_4^- \rightleftharpoons B + H_2SO_4 \qquad \text{(VIII)}$$

in nitromethane can be determined directly for 4-chloro-2-nitroaniline from its behavior in solutions of such low acid concentration that the quantity $\varkappa c_A{}^3$ can be neglected, and the values for the other indicators follow by the overlap method. These values parallel more closely than might be expected the $pK^{\circ\circ}_w$ values for the same indicators referred to dilute aqueous solution.

Table 9.7 **pK° values of indicators in sulfolane**[a]

	pK°_{rel}	$pK^{\circ\circ}_w$
4-Chloro-2-nitroaniline	−1.03	−1.03
2,5-Dichloro-4-nitroaniline	−2.12	−1.78
2,4-Dichloro-6-nitroaniline	−3.37	−3.32
2,4-Dinitroaniline	−4.36	−4.53
Benzalacetophenone	−5.55	−5.73
6-Bromo-2,4-Dinitroaniline	−6.55	−6.71
Anthraquinone	−8.64	−8.27
2,4,6-Trinitroaniline	−8.82	−9.41

[a] Data of Arnett and Douty [65].

This can be appreciated by comparing the values of the quantity $pK_{VIII} - 4.09$ in Table 9.5 with the $pK_w^{\circ\circ}$ values also listed there.

If one defines an acidity function for solutions of sulfuric acid in nitromethane as

$$H_0 = pK_{VIII} - 4.09 - \log I \tag{75}$$

then one can say that an equal value of H_0 for a solution in nitromethane and for one in water corresponds to an equal degree of protonation of the base 4-chloro-2-nitroaniline in the two solutions. To a modest degree of approximation it corresponds to an equal degree of protonation in the two solutions of another base of the H_0 type.

The quantity H_0 thus defined is plotted against $\log c_A$ in Fig. 9.14 both for sulfuric acid alone and for sulfuric acid to which various quantities of pyridinium bisulfate have been added. The validity of Eq. (74) for the sulfuric acid solutions is illustrated in Table 9.6 by comparing H_0 values taken from a smoothed plot of the data with the quantity $-4.09 - \log(c_A + 1450\, c_A{}^3)$. As predicted by the equation, the slope of the plot is close to -3 at higher acid

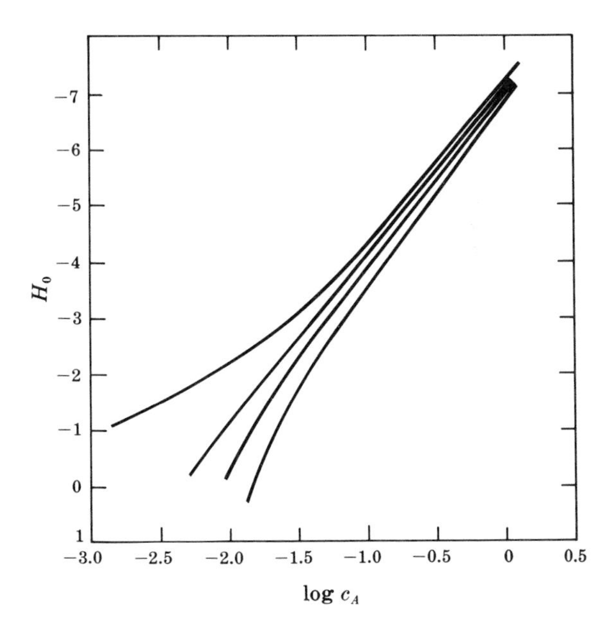

Fig. 9.14 Plots of the acidity function H_0 against the logarithm of c_A, the molar concentration of sulfuric acid in nitromethane at 25°: (*top curve*) acid and indicator alone; (*second from top*) 0.0048 *M* pyridinium bisulfate added; (*third from top*) 0.0096 *M* pyridinium bisulfate added; (*bottom curve*) 0.0192 *M* pyridinium bisulfate added. (*By permission of Van Looy and Hammett* [62].)

concentrations and approaches −1 at lower concentrations. Agreement is as good but no better with a three-term equation based on the additional presence of BH^+---AHA^-.

Values of the quantity pK_{rel} obtained by Arnett and Douty for solutions of sulfuric acid in sulfolane are listed in Table 9.7. pK_{rel} is defined as

$$pK_{rel} = pK_{VIII} - pK_{ref} - 1.03$$

where pK_{ref} is the pK_{VIII} value of 4-chloro-2-nitroaniline. Over the range from 0.1 to 1 M the slope of a plot of $pK_{rel} - \log I$ against $\log c_A$ is close to −3, the best value being reported as −2.8. Again the pK_{rel} values closely parallel the pK_w values, the relation

$$pK_{rel} = -0.20 + 0.955\, pK_w$$

fitting the data with an rms deviation of 0.25.

Aside from the validity of the equation the assumptions on which Eq. (74) is based are supported by the following considerations. Although nitromethane has a dielectric constant of 38, which is higher than the 33 of methanol, it does not have the strong anion-solvating quality of a hydroxylic solvent. The conductance of pyridinium bisulfate indicates an association constant of 600 [62]. With this constant an ion pair would be only 15 percent dissociated in 0.1 M solution. This is not surprising because in the similar solvent nitrobenzene, whose dielectric constant is only 3 units less than that of nitromethane, salts of tertiary amines are considerably associated to ion pairs (Sec. 8.7). Because the conjugate acids of the indicators of Table 9.5 are many orders of magnitude less acidic than pyridinium ion, they should hydrogen-bond to an anion considerably more firmly.

If there were significant dissociation of the BH^+---HSO_4^- pairs of the indicators, the value of I at a particular acid concentration would decrease with increasing concentration of indicator. A careful study in which the indicator concentration was varied ten- to twentyfold showed no such effect at acid concentration of 0.05 or more with two of the indicators and a possible small effect with 4-chloro-2-nitroaniline at acid concentrations of 0.005 or less. If there were significant dissociation, the addition of the partly dissociated salt pyridinium bisulfate would produce a large decrease in I. As Fig. 9.14, shows there is a decrease, but it can be adequately accounted for in terms of the reaction

$$PyH^+\text{---}HSO_4^- + 2H_2SO_4 \rightleftharpoons PyH^+\text{---}HSO_4^-(H_2SO_4)_2 \qquad \text{(IX)}$$

With respect to assumption 4 the situation is a particularly favorable one, since a region of the spectrum can be employed in which neither BH^+ nor the ion pairs have an appreciable absorption. In general, however, hydrogen bonding and ion pairing appear to have no large effect on the ultraviolet absorption of organic cations.

Assumption 3 is justified by the constancy of the difference in log I values for successive indicators over the region in which the relative amounts of BH^+---HSO_4^- and BH^+---$HSO_4^-(H_2SO_4)_2$ are changing rapidly.

In terms of the extent of protonation of the base 4-chloro-2-nitroaniline, dilute solutions of sulfuric acid in nitromethane are about 2 logarithmic units more acid than solutions of the same concentration in sulfolane, the latter are more acid than solutions in acetic acid by about the same amount, and the acetic acid solutions are more acid than aqueous ones by a somewhat larger amount [62, 65]. Some of these differences are readily intelligible. Both water and acetic acid are effectively completely converted to their conjugate acids in 100% sulfuric acid, while nitromethane and sulfolane are converted only to a small extent. Sulfuric acid in water is converted to the less potent hydrogen-ion donor OH_3^+; in acetic acid it is presumably converted to an ion pair which contains the conjugate acid of the solvent and which is a less potent donor than H_2SO_4 but a more potent one than OH_3^+. The difference between the nitromethane and the sulfolane solutions indicates that nitromethane solvates such substances as BH^+---HSO_4^- more firmly than sulfolane does, or that nitromethane solvates B or H_2SO_4 less firmly than sulfolane does, or that some combination of these effects is involved.

Alder, Chalkley, and Whiting [66] have reported briefly on some very strong acids in sulfolane. In terms of reaction with indicators of the H_0 type the acid strengths in 0.1 M solution relative to HCl are H_2SO_4, 1.3; HBr, 3.6; HSO_3F, HBF_4, and $HClO_4$, about 6; HPF_6, 7.

When there is homoconjugation, the extent of conversion of a base to its conjugate acid varies as a power of the acid concentration higher than the first. It is to be expected therefore that the rates of reactions involving acids under conditions favorable to homoconjugation will vary more rapidly with acid concentration than with the first power. Such has been found to be the case in the addition of HCl to isobutane in nitromethane, which is second order in HCl [67].

9.26 ACID-BASE REACTIONS IN DIMETHYLSULFOXIDE

One of the many interesting properties of dimethylsulfoxide is the extraordinarily wide range, some 30 logarithmic units, of acidity which can be accommodated within the limits of dilute solutions in this single solvent. This makes possible the quantitative investigation of very weak acids. Because the solvent is a powerful cation solvator (Sec. 8.11) and has the relatively high dielectric constant of 47, a wide variety of alkali compounds and of quaternary ammonium salts are strong electrolytes. Because it is an active hydrogen-bond acceptor, homoconjugation is not observable with certainty [68] except with the alkoxides, where it is strong and where there may also be incomplete dissociation of ion pairs. Much of the behavior of acid-base systems in the solvent is therefore closely analogous to that familiar from aqueous solutions. Even the convenient glass electrode can be employed (Sec. 9.2).

Ritchie and Uschold [6] referred an electrometric pH scale in dimethylsulfoxide to dilute solutions of the monohydrate of toluenesulfonic acid for which over the concentration range from 10^{-4} to 10^{-2} plots of $\mathscr{E}$ against the logarithm of the acid concentration are linear, with the slope 0.059 characteristic of a strong acid. It was assumed that water is enough less basic than the solvent so that what was observed was the behavior of a strong acid and not that of its oxonium salt. In titrations of a variety of weak acids at 0.001 M concentration with the cesium salt of dimethylsulfoxide plots of $\mathscr{E}$ against $\log x/(1 - x)$, where x is the fraction titrated, are linear with the slope of 0.059. This indicates that the electrode is functioning correctly and that complications

Table 9.8 pK° values of acids in dimethylsulfoxide (DMSO)[a, b] and in cyclohexylamine (CHA)[c]

	DMSO	CHA
Hydrazoic acid[a]	7.9	
9-Carbomethoxyfluorene[a]	10.3	
p-Nitrophenol[a]	10.4	
Acetic acid[a]	11.6	
Malononitrile[a]	11.0	
Benzoylacetone[a]	12.1	
Tris(*p*-nitrophenyl)methane[a]	12.2	
Hydrocyanic acid[a]	12.9	
Acetylacetone[a]	13.4	
2,4-Dinitroaniline[a]	14.8	
Nitromethane[a]	15.9	
9-Phenylfluorene[a]	16.4	(16.4)
4-Nitroaniline[b]	18.4	
Indene[a]	18.5	17.8
9-Methylfluorene[a]	19.7	
4,5-Methylenephenanthrene[a]	20.0	20.5
Fluorene[a]	20.5	20.6
9-Phenylxanthene[b]	24.1	26.4
t-Butanol[a]	26.8	
n-Propanol[a]	26.2	
Triphenylmethane[b]	27.1	29.4
Diphenylmethane[b]	28.5	31.0
Dimethylsulfoxide[b]	31.2	

[a] Data of Ritchie and Uschold [6, 71].
[b] Data of Steiner et al. [69, 70].
[c] Data of Streitwieser, Ciuffarin, and Hammons [74].

due to incomplete dissociation of the cesium salts or to homoconjugation are not important. These electrometric pK values are listed in Table 9.8.

The applicability of the electrometric pH determination and the validity of the pH scale are confirmed by comparison with data based on spectrophotometric determinations of the extent of ionization of 2,6-dinitro-4-chlorophenol [6] and of 4-nitrophenol and 2,4-dinitrophenol [68]. Both of these lead by the use of overlapping indicators to a pK value of 11.4 for acetic acid, whereas the Ritchie and Uschold electrometric value is 11.6.

The spectrophotometric values relative to 2,4-dinitroaniline of Steiner et al. [69, 70] are 1.9 for 9-phenylfluorene and 5.8 for fluorene. The agreement with the corresponding values of 1.6 and 5.7 from the electrometric measurements adds further confirmation of the validity of the latter. It also supplies a firm basis for assigning absolute values to the Steiner results.

The values for the two alcohols are based on measurements [71] of the equilibrium in the reaction of triphenylmethane with the cesium alcoholates. The same investigation leads to a value of 31.3 for the pK of dimethylsulfoxide, in good agreement with Steiner's value.

The pH referred to a dilute solution of a strong acid in dimethylsulfoxide of a 0.01 M solution of the cesium derivative of dimethylsulfoxide in this solvent can therefore be put with considerable certainty at something close to 29. In water the physical significance of $-\log[OH_3^+]$ can be assigned to the pH of any dilute solution, subject to minor effects arising from deviations from ideal-solution laws. In dimethylsulfoxide the pH can be identified in the same way with the quantity $-\log[(CH_3)_2SOH^+]$ so long as the system is not too basic. But a concentration of 10^{-29} mole/liter clearly has no physical significance. What the quantity 29 means here is that a reasonable assigned value of the change in standard potential involved in the transfer of a proton from a 0.01 M solution of a strong acid to a solution of pH 29 is 27 times the quantity 2.303 $\mathbf{R}T$ cal, i.e., it is 36,800 cal at 25°C.

9.27 ACIDITY FUNCTION AND BASE STRENGTH IN OTHER HIGHLY BASIC MEDIA[1]

Relative pK values in the solvent cyclohexylamine using cesium derivatives have been determined [74] for some of the hydrocarbons listed in Table 9.8 and for a considerable number of other relatively acidic hydrocarbons. The values included in the table are based on the arbitrary identification of the pK for 9-phenylfluorene in cyclohexylamine with the value in dimethylsulfoxide. They show considerable differences from the values in dimethylsulfoxide with what seems to be a systematic increase in the difference as the pK value increases. In the same connection Steiner and Starkey [70] note a considerable dependence of the relative strength of the hydrocarbon acid 9-phenylfluorene and the nitrogen acid *p*-nitroaniline on the solvent. Here as elsewhere

[1] There are recent reviews by Rochester [72] and Bowden [73].

an absolute measure of the strength of an acid independent of the medium is unattainable.

Stewart and coworkers [75, 76] have developed an H_- scale[1] from spectrophotometric studies of an overlapping sequence of nitroanilines and nitrodiphenylamines. This extends from 2,4,6-trinitroaniline, whose p$K^{\circ\circ}$ value referred to dilute aqueous solution is determined directly as 12.20, to 4-nitroaniline, whose p$K^{\circ\circ}$ referred to the same standard by the overlap method is 18.37. The p$K^{\circ\circ}$ values of the indicators in the sequence are closely spaced, and the difference in the log I values of successive indicators in varying mixtures of water and dimethylsulfoxide containing 0.011 M tetramethylammonium hydroxide is independent of the composition of the solvent. However p$K^{\circ\circ}$ values differing by as much as 0.3 units from those obtained in the dimethylsulfoxide mixtures are observed in water-sulfolane mixtures.

9.28 REACTION RATES IN STRONGLY BASIC SYSTEMS

The H_- value in 0.025 M solutions of sodium methoxide in mixtures of dimethylsulfoxide with methanol increases steeply with increasing content of dimethylsulfoxide, as shown in Fig. 9.15. The rate of increase is not far from linear in the mole fraction. As shown in Fig. 9.16, the logarithm of the specific rate of the racemization of (+)-2-methyl-3-phenylpropionitrile is close to being linear in H_- over the same range. The best value of the slope is 0.87. Since the specific rate of deuterium exchange is approximately the same as that of the racemization, the observed rate of reaction is presumably that of the removal of a proton to form a symmetric or rapidly racemizing carbanion. The situation is notable not only for the large total change in the rate of the racemization and in the equilibrium of the indicator reaction but also for the large change produced by rather small proportions of dimethylsulfoxide.

The large total effect is not difficult to understand. It is reasonable to suppose that the negative charge on methoxide ion is highly concentrated whereas the charge on the anion of the indicators used or on a transition state of the structure B

$$C_6H_5CH_2-\underset{\displaystyle CH_3}{\overset{\displaystyle CN}{\overset{|}{\underset{|}{C}}}}\cdots H\cdots \overset{-}{O}CH_3$$

(B)

[1] Deyrup and I [9] used the symbol H_0 for an acidity function based on the indicator reaction $BH^+ \rightleftharpoons B + H^+$ and suggested the symbol H_- for one based on the reaction $HA \rightleftharpoons A^- + H^+$, H having the same meaning as in pH. An H_- scale for strong-acid–water systems has been based on cyanocarbon acids by Boyd [77] and an H_+ scale for the same systems has been established by Isaks and Jaffé [78]. Neither differs very much from the H_0 scale in the strong-acid–water systems.

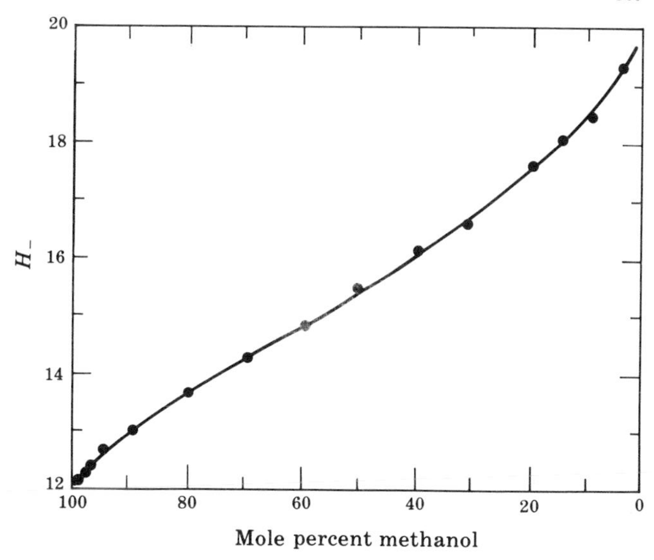

Fig. 9.15 H_- as a function of solvent composition for dimethyl sulfoxide–methanol mixtures containing added sodium methoxide (0.025 M), 25°. [*By permission of R. Stewart, J. P. O'Donnell, D. J. Cram, and B. Rickborn, Tetrahedron*, **18**: 917 (1962).]

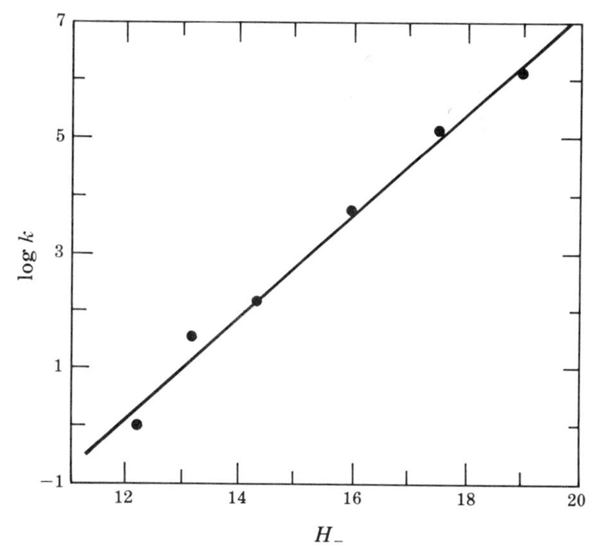

Fig. 9.16 The racemization rate of (+)-2-methyl-3-phenylpropionitrile as a function of the basicity of the medium (H_-) for mixtures of dimethyl sulfoxide–methanol containing added sodium methoxide (0.025 M), 25°. [*By permission of R. Stewart, J. P. O'Donnell, D. J. Cram, and B. Rickborn, Tetrahedron*, **18**: 917 (1962).]

should be broadly distributed. The $\Delta\mu^\circ$ value for the formation of the indicator anion or of the transition state from methoxide ion should therefore be much more positive in an anion-solvating solvent like methanol than in dimethylsulfoxide (Sec. 8.14).

The near linearity of $\Delta\mu^\circ$ or of $\Delta\mu^\ddagger$ in the mole fraction presents a more complex problem. Dimethylsulfoxide is a powerful hydrogen-bond acceptor. Much heat is evolved on mixing it with water, 600 cal/mole at a mole fraction of the sulfoxide of 0.35 [80]. The kind of strong interaction which this indicates presumably exists in mixtures with methanol and decreases the availability of methanol for solvation of methoxide ion. But to account for the phenomena in terms of the process

$$RNH_2 + {}^{-}OCH_3(CH_3OH)_n \rightleftharpoons RNH^- + (n+1)CH_3OH \qquad \text{(X)}$$

would seem to require a surprisingly large value of n.

The rate of reaction of methyl iodide with hydroxyl ion in water-dimethylsulfoxide mixtures, with methoxide ion in methanol-dimethylsulfoxide mixtures, and with ethoxide ion in ethanol-dimethylsulfoxide mixtures increases rapidly and approximately linearly with the mole fraction of the sulfoxide [81]. So also do the rates of a number of other reactions of methoxide ion in methanol-dimethylsulfoxide mixtures [82].

The H_- value of dilute (0.011 M) solutions of tetramethylammonium hydroxide rises nearly linearly with mole fraction of dimethylsulfoxide from 12 in water to 21.2 at a mole fraction of 0.85 [76]. Beyond this the plot turns sharply upward and reaches a value of 26.2 at a mole fraction of 0.996. The value of $\log k$ for the reaction of methyl iodide with hydroxyl ion also increases steeply and nearly linearly with the mole fraction of dimethylsulfoxide [81]. The rate of reaction of ethyl acetate with sodium hydroxide increases considerably less rapidly, the increase being only by a factor of 9 at a mole fraction of 0.7 [83].

If one assumes that the activity of water in mixtures with dimethylsulfoxide at 25°C is the same as it is at 70°, at which it has been measured [80], an explanation of the increase in H_- in terms of the analog of reaction (X) would require an n value of 11. But because the heat of mixing is large and negative, the activity of water must decrease more rapidly with increasing addition of dimethylsulfoxide at 25° than at 70°. The predicted value of n may therefore be considerably less than 11. Data on the effect of moderate proportions of dimethylsulfoxide on the standard potential of alkali hydroxides and of the alkali salts of bulky anions in water solution should contribute considerably toward the understanding of these phenomena.

The effect of dimethylsulfoxide and of sulfolane on the H_- value measured with nitroaniline indicators and on the rate of a number of reactions involving *t*-butoxides in *t*-butanol has been investigated [84]. The situation is complicated by strong ion association in *t*-butanol. Presumably for this reason solutions of tetramethylammonium hydroxide have H_- values more than 3 units more positive than those of potassium butoxide solutions even at 0.001 M concentration.

9.29 THE BASICITY OF THE ALKALI ALKOXIDES

In dimethylsulfoxide the alkali salts of carboxylic acids and of phenols and the alkali derivatives of the phenylated methanes appear to be strong electrolytes, and complications due to homoconjugation are not apparent. The situation, however, is different with the alkali alkoxides. Steiner and Gilbert [69] find, using hydrocarbon indicators with the bases in the form of potassium salts, that normal and tertiary butanol conform to the acid-base reaction

$$\mathrm{ROH} \rightleftharpoons \mathrm{RO^-} + \mathrm{H^+} \qquad \text{(XI)}$$

with a pK value 3.8 units less than that of the solvent, provided the ratio [ROH]/[RO$^-$] is less than ½, but that the pH decreases much more rapidly with increasing concentration of alcohol when the ratio exceeds ½. This indicates that reaction (XI) is replaced by

$$n\mathrm{ROH} \rightleftharpoons {}^-\mathrm{OR(ROH)}_{n-1} + \mathrm{H^+} \qquad \text{(XII)}$$

as the ratio increases. The decrease in pH is more rapid with n-butanol than with t-butanol. Perhaps because of steric effects the tertiary alcohol does not combine as firmly with the tertiary alkoxide ion as the primary alcohol does with the primary alkoxide ion.

The specific rate of the racemization of the methylphenylpropionitrile is 4×10^6 times faster with potassium t-butoxide in t-butanol than it is with potassium methoxide in methanol [85]. The effect is consistent with the Steiner and Gilbert evidence that homoconjugation is stronger with primary than with tertiary alkoxide ions.

There is kinetic evidence for incomplete dissociation of at least some alkoxides in dimethylsulfoxide solution [86]. The specific rate of the racemization of 1-phenylmethoxymethane in dimethylsulfoxide solution by potassium t-butoxide containing 0.9 equivalent of t-butanol is approximately half order in base over the concentration range from 0.05 to 0.23, and the rate is considerably decreased by the addition of potassium iodide, which is a strong electrolyte in the solvent. With sodium t-butoxide containing only 0.32 equivalent of t-butanol the specific rate is about one one-hundredth of the rate with the potassium compound.

REFERENCES

1. Bates, R. G.: "Determinations of pH," John Wiley & Sons, Inc., New York, 1964.
2. King, E. J.: "Acid-Base Equilibria," The Macmillan Company, New York, 1965.
3. Romberg, E., and K. Cruse: *Z. Elecktrochem.*, **63:** 404 (1959).
4. Coetzee, J. F.: *Progr. Phys. Org. Chem.*, **4:** 64 (1967) and earlier papers referred to therein.

5. Kolthoff, I. M., and T. B. Reddy: *Inorg. Chem.*, **1:** 189 (1962).
6. Ritchie, C. D., and R. E. Uschold: *J. Am. Chem. Soc.*, **89:** 1721, 2752 (1967).
7. Paul, M. A., and F. A. Long: *Chem. Rev.*, **57:** 1 (1957).
8. Bascombe, K. N., and R. P. Bell: *J. Chem. Soc.*, **1959:** 1096.
9. Hammett, L. P., and A. J. Deyrup: *J. Am. Chem. Soc.*, **54:** 2721 (1932).
10. Jorgenson, M. J., and D. R. Hartter: *J. Am. Chem. Soc.*, **85:** 878 (1963).
11. Yates, K., and H. Wai: *J. Am. Chem. Soc.*, **86:** 5408 (1964).
12. Shankman, S., and A. R. Gordon: *J. Am. Chem. Soc.*, **61:** 2370 (1939).
13. Arnett, E. M., and G. W. Mach: *J. Am. Chem. Soc.*, **88:** 1177 (1966).
14. Hyman, H. H., M. Kilpatrick, and J. J. Katz: *J. Am. Chem. Soc.*, **79:** 3668 (1957).
15. Bell, R. P., K. N. Bascombe, and J. C. McCoubrey: *J. Chem. Soc.*, **1956:** 1286.
16. Högfeldt, E., and J. Bigeleisen: *J. Am. Chem. Soc.*, **82:** 15 (1960).
17. Hantzsch, A.: *Z. Elektrochem.*, **29:** 221 (1923); **30:** 194 (1924); **31:** 167 (1925).
18. Arnett, E. M., and G. W. Mach: *J. Am. Chem. Soc.*, **86:** 2671 (1964).
19. Hinman, R. L., and J. Lang: *J. Am. Chem. Soc.*, **86:** 3796 (1964).
20. Yates, K., J. B. Stevens, and A. R. Katritzky: *Can. J. Chem.*, **42:** 1957 (1964).
21. Johnson, C. D., A. R. Katritzky, and N. Shakir: *J. Chem. Soc.*, **B1967:** 1235.
22. Deno, N. C., J. J. Jaruzelski, and A. Schriesheim: *J. Am. Chem. Soc.*, **77:** 3044 (1955).
23. Deno, N. C., P. T. Groves, and G. Saines: *J. Am. Chem. Soc.*, **81:** 5790 (1959).
24. Arnett, E. M., and G. W. Mach: *J. Am. Chem. Soc.*, **88:** 1177 (1966).
25. Yates, K., and J. C. Riordan: *Can. J. Chem.*, **43:** 2328 (1965).
26. Deno, N. C., H. E. Berkheimer, W. L. Evans, and H. J. Peterson: *J. Am. Chem. Soc.*, **81:** 2344 (1959).
27. Bunnett, J. F., and F. P. Olsen: *Chem. Commun.*, **1956:** 601; *Can. J. Chem.*, **44:** 1899, 1917 (1966).
28. Hammett, L. P., and R. P. Chapman: *J. Am. Chem. Soc.*, **56:** 1282 (1934).
29. Boyd, R. H.: *J. Am. Chem. Soc.*, **85:** 1555 (1963).
30. Sweeting, L. M., and K. Yates: *Can. J. Chem.*, **44:** 2395 (1966).
31. Taft, R. W., Jr.: *J. Am. Chem. Soc.*, **82:** 1965 (1960).
32. Wyatt, P. A. H.: *Discussions Faraday Soc.*, **24:** 162 (1957).
33. Brand, J. C. D.: *J. Chem. Soc.*, **1950:** 997.
34. Deno, N. C., and R. W. Taft: *J. Am. Chem. Soc.*, **76:** 244 (1954).
35. Hough, A., W. Savage, and D. J. van Marle: *Chem. Met. Eng.*, **23:** 666 (1920).
36. Hantzsch, A.: *Z. Physik. Chem.*, **61:** 257 (1907); **65:** 41 (1908).
37. Long, F. A., and M. A. Paul: *Chem. Rev.*, **57:** 935 (1957).
38. Paul, M. A.: *J. Am. Chem. Soc.*, **72:** 3813 (1950); **74:** 141 (1952).
39. Long, F. A., and R. Bakule: *J. Am. Chem. Soc.*, **85:** 2313 (1963).
40. Zucker, L., and L. P. Hammett: *J. Am. Chem. Soc.*, **61:** 2791 (1939).
41. Westheimer, F. H., and M. S. Kharasch: *J. Am. Chem. Soc.*, **68:** 1871 (1946).
42. Rosenthal, D., and T. I. Taylor: *J. Am. Chem. Soc.*, **79:** 2684 (1957).
43. Schubert, W. M., and R. H. Quacchia: *J. Am. Chem. Soc.*, **85:** 1278, 1284 (1963).
44. Arnett, E. M.: *Progr. Phys. Org. Chem.*, **1:** 243 (1963).
45. Flexser, L. A., L. P. Hammett, and A. Dingwall: *J. Am. Chem. Soc.*, **57:** 2103 (1935).
46. Stewart, R., and K. Yates: *J. Am. Chem. Soc.*, **80:** 6355 (1958).
47. Davis, C. T., and T. A. Geissman: *J. Am. Chem. Soc.*, **76:** 3507 (1954).
48. Katritzky, A. R., A. J. Waring, and K. Yates: *Tetrahedron*, **19:** 4651 (1963).
49. Reeves, R. L.: *J. Am. Chem. Soc.*, **88:** 2240 (1966).
50. Arnett, E. M., C. Y. Wu, J. N. Anderson, and R. D. Bushick: *J. Am. Chem. Soc.*, **84:** 1674 (1962).
51. Arnett, E. M., and C. Y. Wu: *J. Am. Chem. Soc.*, **82:** 5660 (1960).
52. Arnett, E. M., and C. Y. Wu: *J. Am. Chem. Soc.*, **84:** 1680, 1684 (1962).
53. Arnett, E. M.: *Progr. Phys. Org. Chem.*, **1:** 223 (1963).

54. Deno, N. C., and M. J. Wisotsky: *J. Am. Chem. Soc.*, **85:** 1735 (1963).
55. Gelbstein, A. I., G. Shscheglova, and M. I. Temkin: *Zh. Neorgan. Khim.*, **1:** 506 (1956).
56. Arnett, E. M., and J. J. Burke: *J. Am. Chem. Soc.*, **88:** 4308 (1966).
57. Arnett, E. M., and R. D. Bushick: *J. Am. Chem. Soc.*, **86:** 1564 (1964).
58. Davis, M. M.: Acid-Base Behavior in Aprotic Organic Solvents, *Natl. Bur. Std. Monograph* 105, 1968.
59. Kolthoff, I. M., and S. Bruckenstein: *J. Am. Chem. Soc.*, **78:** 1 (1956); **79:** 1 (1957); S. Bruckenstein and I. M. Kolthoff: *ibid.*, **78:** 10, 2974 (1956); **79:** 5915 (1957).
60. Guss, L. S., and I. M. Kolthoff: *J. Am. Chem. Soc.*, **62:** 1494 (1940).
61. Coetzee, J. F.: *Progr. Phys. Org. Chem.*, **4:** 45 (1967).
62. Van Looy, H., and L. P. Hammett: *J. Am. Chem. Soc.*, **81:** 3872 (1959).
63. Burwell, R. L., and C. H. Langford: *J. Am. Chem. Soc.*, **81:** 3799 (1959).
64. Smith, L. C., and L. P. Hammett: *J. Am. Chem. Soc.*, **72:** 301 (1950); R. Natoli: Ph.D. dissertation, Columbia University, 1955, *Univ. Microfilms Publ.* 21809.
65. Arnett, E. M., and C. F. Douty: *J. Am. Chem. Soc.*, **86:** 409 (1964).
66. Alder, R. W., G. R. Chalkley, and M. C. Whiting: *Chem. Commun.*, **1966:** 405.
67. Pocker, Y.: *J. Chem. Soc.*, **1960:** 1292.
68. Clare, B. W., D. Cook, E. C. F. Ko, Y. C. Mac, and A. J. Parker: *J. Am. Chem. Soc.*, **88:** 1911 (1966).
69. Steiner, E. C., and J. M. Gilbert: *J. Am. Chem. Soc.*, **87:** 382 (1965).
70. Steiner, E. C., and J. D. Starkey: *J. Am. Chem. Soc.*, **89:** 2751 (1967).
71. Ritchie, C. D., and R. E. Uschold: *J. Am. Chem. Soc.*, **89:** 2960 (1967).
72. Rochester, C. H.: *Quart. Rev. (London)*, **20:** 511 (1966).
73. Bowden, K.: *Chem. Rev.*, **66:** 119 (1966).
74. Streitwieser, A., Jr., E. Ciuffarin, and J. H. Hammons: *J. Am. Chem. Soc.*, **89:** 63 (1967).
75. Stewart, R., and J. P. O'Donnell: *J. Am. Chem. Soc.*, **84:** 493 (1962); *Can. J. Chem.*, **42:** 1681 (1964).
76. Dolman, D., and R. Stewart: *Can. J. Chem.*, **45:** 911 (1967).
77. Boyd, R. H.: *J. Am. Chem. Soc.*, **83:** 4288 (1961).
78. Isaks, M., and H. H. Jaffé: *J. Am. Chem. Soc.*, **86:** 2209 (1964).
79. Stewart, R., J. P. O'Donnell, D. J. Cram, and B. Rickborn: *Tetrahedron*, **18:** 917 (1962).
80. Kentämaa, J., and J. J. Lindberg: *Suomen Kemistilehti*, **B33:** 32, 98 (1960).
81. Murto, J.: *Suomen Kemistilehti*, **B34:** 92 (1961).
82. Kingsbury, C. A.: *J. Org. Chem.*, **29:** 3262 (1964).
83. Tommila, E., and M-L. Murto: *Acta Chim. Scan.*, **17:** 1947 (1963).
84. Bethell, D., and A. F. Cockerill: *J. Chem. Soc.*, **B1966:** 913, 917, 920; A. F. Cockerill, S. Rottschaefer, and W. H. Saunders, Jr.: *J. Am. Chem. Soc.*, **89:** 901 (1967).
85. Cram, D. J., B. Rickborn, C. A. Kingsbury, and P. Haberfield: *J. Am. Chem. Soc.*, **83:** 3678 (1961).
86. Cram, D. J., C. A. Kingsbury, and B. Rickborn: *J. Am. Chem. Soc.*, **83:** 3688 (1961).

10

Rates of Reactions Involving Acids and Bases

10.1 GENERAL ACID AND BASE CATALYSIS

In the first flush of enthusiasm for the theory of ionization it became dogma that the rate of an acid-catalyzed reaction is proportional to the concentration of hydrogen ion and that the rate of a base-catalyzed reaction is proportional to the concentration of hydroxyl ion. In 1924, however, Brønsted and Pedersen [1] discovered the phenomenon of general base catalysis. The characteristic symptom of this kind of catalysis is illustrated by the data of Table 10.1 on the specific rate of the decomposition of nitramide in benzoate buffers. The reaction is

$$H_2N_2O_2 \rightarrow H_2O + N_2O \tag{I}$$

The buffers used have a nearly constant (0.50 to 0.56) value of the ratio $[HA]/[A^-]$. By the equilibrium relation

$$\frac{[A^-][OH_3^+]}{[HA]} = K_a \tag{1}$$

Table 10.1 Nitramide catalysis in benzoate buffers

Experiment	$C_6H_5CO_2Na$	$C_6H_5CO_2H$	10^5k	10^3k_i
1	0.0225	0.0125	7.76	3.16
2	0.0167	0.00830	5.92	3.17
3	0.01125	0.00625	4.30	3.26
4	0.00750	0.00375	2.90	3.01

the concentration of oxonium ion must be constant except for a very small salt effect. By the relation

$$[OH_3^+][OH^-] = K_w \tag{2}$$

the concentration of hydroxyl ion must be similarly constant. Yet the rate goes up and, indeed, goes up linearly with increasing buffer concentration. The catalytic effect is therefore due neither to "hydrogen" nor to hydroxyl ion; other experiments show that the rate is independent of the concentration of benzoic acid and that the equation

$$k = 1.45 \times 10^{-5} + 7.25 \times 10^{-3}\,[A^-] \tag{3}$$

where k is the first-order specific rate and A^- is benzoate ion, closely represents the data. The catalyst is therefore benzoate ion.

Further investigation showed that the anions of a great variety of carboxylic acids are catalysts for this reaction, the catalytic effect being smaller the stronger the acid, i.e., the weaker the affinity of the anion for protons. Thus in acetic acid buffers the specific rate is given by

$$k = 1.45 \times 10^{-5} + 1.94 \times 10^{-2}[A^-] \tag{4}$$

where A^- is acetate ion. A similar situation appears when buffers of the nature of aniline–aniline hydrochloride are used; aniline is the catalyst, and the rate is independent of the concentration of anilinium ion [2]. There is also catalysis by cations of the nature of $Co(NH_3)_5OH^{++}$ [3]. Hydroxyl ion is so effective a catalyst that the reaction is too fast for measurement in alkaline solutions.

All these catalysts for this reaction have in common an affinity for protons, and they appear to have no other property in common. It is therefore reasonable to attribute the catalysis to the proton affinity, to recognize the term 1.45×10^{-5}, which appears in Eqs. (3) and (4) as evidence of a similar participation by the solvent water, and to write for the specific rate k of the nitramide decomposition

$$k = \sum_i k_i B_i \tag{5}$$

where B is any molecular entity, be it electrically neutral or positively or negatively charged, which has a proton affinity. The coefficient k_i is called the catalytic coefficient of the base B_i, the term base being generalized to include all such molecular entities [4]. Similar discoveries with respect to catalysis by acids justify the proposal that the term acid be generalized to include all entities, such as OH_3^+, NH_4^+, H_2O, and acetic acid, which can lose a proton to form a base.

The nitramide catalysis is a particularly favorable case for the discovery of this kind of effect. There is little if any catalysis by acids [5], and catalysis by carboxylate anions and by aniline bases is pronounced in solutions so acid that catalysis by hydroxyl ion is negligible. More complex situations require more complicated rate expressions and are more difficult to untangle experimentally. Bell and Jones [6] find that the specific rate of the iodination of acetone in acetate buffers at a constant ionic strength of 0.2 is closely represented by the expression

$$k = 4.7 \times 10^{-10} + 2.7 \times 10^{-5}[OH_3^+] + 0.25[OH^-] + 8.3 \times 10^{-8}[HA] + 2.5 \times 10^{-7}[A^-] + 3.3 \times 10^{-7}[HA][A^-] \quad (6)$$

Similar expressions apply to the reaction in trimethylacetate and in glycolate buffers.

The phenomenon of general acid or base catalysis is not observed with all acid- or base-catalyzed reactions. In the inversion of sucrose, the decomposition of diazoacetic ester, and the hydrolysis of ethyl orthoformate the specific rate in dilute aqueous solution is proportional, within the precision of measurement, to the concentration of oxonium ion. A catalysis of this sort is called a specific lyonium-ion catalysis; when the rate in aqueous solution is proportional to the concentration of hydroxyl ion or the rate in ethanol to the concentration of ethoxide ion, the effect is called specific lyate-ion catalysis.

10.2 The BRØNSTED CATALYSIS RELATION

The Brønsted catalysis relation can be put in the form

$$\delta_R \log k_c = \beta \delta_R \log K_b \quad (7)$$

for catalysis by bases and in the form

$$\delta_R \log k_c = \alpha \delta_R \log K_a \quad (8)$$

for catalysis by acids. It involves the catalytic constants k_c exhibited by a series of acids or bases in a particular catalyzed reaction and the equilibrium constants K_a or K_b which measure the acid or base strength of the catalyst. δ_R is the Leffler-Grunwald [7] operator that describes the effect of a change in structure, in this case the structure of the catalyst, on whatever quantity follows it. The parameters β and α are characteristic of a particular catalyzed reaction and are independent of the catalyst.

In the catalysis of nitramide by the ions of carboxylic acids the basicity constants K_b are the equilibrium constants of the reactions

$$RCOO^- + OH_3^+ \rightleftharpoons RCOOH + H_2O \tag{II}$$

and are consequently the reciprocals of the acidity constants of the acids RCOOH. In Fig. 10.1 the logarithms of the catalytic constants for the nitramide reaction are plotted against these basicity constants. For six anions derived from monobasic carboxylic acids the data fit the relation

$$\log k_c = -5.964 + 0.822 \log K_b \tag{9}$$

with an rms deviation of 0.024. For seven ring-substituted anilines the data fit the relation

$$\log k_c = -5.418 + 0.718 \log K_b \tag{10}$$

with a deviation of 0.037.

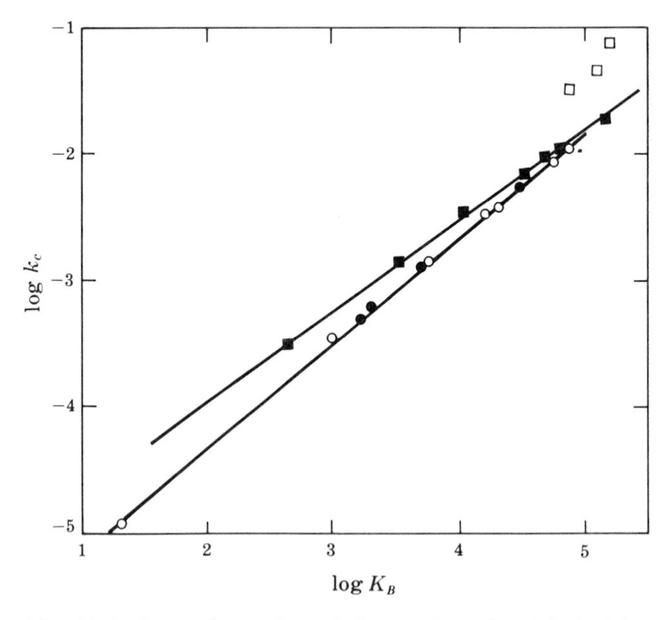

Fig. 10.1 Comparison of catalytic constants k_c with basicity constants K_b in the nitramide catalysis. ○ = carboxylate ions derived from monobasic acids; ● = singly charged carboxylate ions derived from dibasic acids; ■ = nuclear substituted anilines; □ = other amine bases. (*Data of Brønsted et al.* [1].)

10.3 THE STATISTICAL CORRECTION

Singly charged carboxylate ions derived from dibasic acids would deviate from the line determined by the ions derived from monobasic acids considerably if a statistical correction were not made. This correction can be derived from the principle that K_b is not the proper measure of the basicity of an ion such as $HOOC(CH_2)_xCOO^-$ because the ion may be formed from the acid $HOOC(CH_2)_xCOOH$ in two equivalent ways, namely, by the ionization of the proton from the one or from the other carboxyl group. The ion has therefore twice as good a chance of being formed as corresponds to the work needed to remove the proton, and the correct measure of the work is not K_a but $\frac{1}{2}K_a$. By the same token the proper measure of the basicity of the ion is not K_b but $2K_b$. The solid circles in Fig. 10.1 refer to bases of this type and are plotted with the quantity $2K_b$ as the abscissa. The deviation from the line of these points is only 0.018; if the correction had not been made, they would average 0.3 unit to the left of the line.[1]

10.4 STERIC EFFECTS

The three open squares in Fig. 10.1 refer to the Brønsted and Pedersen data for the tertiary amines, pyridine, quinoline, and dimethylaniline. With or without a statistical correction these cannot be persuaded to conform to the line established by the primary aniline derivatives. More recent work [10] has confirmed the effect; very generally tertiary amines are about twice as effective as catalysts for the nitramide decomposition as primary amines of the same K_b value. The phenomenon is one aspect of a general limitation (Sec. 11.10) on linear free-energy relationships; these often fail seriously when the change in structure involves the close neighborhood of the region of the reacting molecule in which the reaction occurs. Effects of the same nature have been observed in a number of other reactions which involve a proton transfer [11].

By the same token the failure of the points for carboxylate ions and for aniline derivatives to lie on the same line cannot be attributed solely to the fact that one group of bases is negatively charged while the other is electrically neutral. Indeed, the bases

$$CH_3COO^-,\ {}^+H_3NCH_2COO^-,\ {}^-OOCCH(NH_3^+)COO^-$$

and

$${}^+H_3N(CH_2)_4CH(NH_3^+)COO^-$$

in which the charge varies from -1 to $+1$ but in which the reacting group, the COO^-, is constant, show no systematic effect of charge in the nitramide decomposition [12].

[1] For a general discussion of symmetry corrections, of which this statistical correction is an example, see Benson [8]. Westheimer [9] has discussed the case of polybasic acids in which the protons are not structurally equivalent.

10.5 THE BRØNSTED CATALYSIS RELATION IN TRANSITION-STATE THEORY

The quantity $-\mathbf{R}T\ln k_i$, where k_i is the catalytic coefficient of the acid HA_i, measures the difference between the sum of the standard potentials of the reactant and of HA_i and the standard potential of the transition state of the catalyzed reaction, a state in which a proton is attached both to the reactant and to the base A_i^-. The quantity $-\mathbf{R}T\ln K_i$, where K_i is the acidity constant of HA_i, measures the $\Delta\mu^\circ$ values for the complete transfer of a proton from attachment to A^- to attachment to a standard base. The catalysis law amounts therefore to a linear relation between the $\Delta\mu^\ddagger$ and the $\Delta\mu^\circ$ values; it is a special case of the linear free-energy relationship.

It follows from these considerations that the law can be put in the form [13]

$$\delta_R(\mu^\ddagger - \mu^\circ_{HA}) = \alpha\delta_R(\mu^\circ_{A^-} - \mu^\circ_{HA}) \tag{11}$$

from which

$$\delta_R\,\mu^\ddagger = \alpha\delta_R\,\mu^\circ_{A^-} + (1-\alpha)\,\delta_R\,\mu^\circ_{HA} \tag{12}$$

The effect of a change in the structure of the acid on the standard potential of the transition state of a reaction subject to general acid catalysis is therefore the weighted mean of the effects on the standard potentials of the catalyst acid and of its conjugate base. The weighting factor is the Brønsted parameter α. When α is large, the change in $\mu^\ddagger$ is nearly the same as the change in $\mu^\circ_{A^-}$; when α is small, the change in $\mu^\ddagger$ approaches the change in μ°_{HA}.

By the same kind of argument the effect of a change in the structure of the base in a reaction subject to general base catalysis on the standard potential of the transition state is the weighted mean of the effects on the standard potential of the base and of its conjugate acid, the weighting factor being the Brønsted parameter β, that is,

$$\delta_R\,\mu^\ddagger = \beta\delta_R\,\mu^\circ_{BH^+} + (1-\beta)\,\delta_R\,\mu^\circ_B \tag{13}$$

Qualitatively these conclusions are reasonable ones. If in the transition state the transfer of a proton between catalyst and reactant is only incipient, a change in the structure of the catalyst should affect the properties of the transition state in much the same way that it affects the properties of the catalyst. If the transfer is nearly complete, a change in the structure of the catalyst should have much the same effect on the properties of the transition state as it has on those of the conjugate base of the catalyst in an acid-catalyzed reaction or on those of the conjugate acid of the catalyst in a base-catalyzed reaction. The quantitative relationships, however, do not follow so obviously from theory.[1]

[1] There is an excellent discussion of the theoretical background in Bell [14], pp. 166–177.

10.6 CATALYSIS BY THE SOLVENT AND BY LYONIUM AND BY LYATE IONS

Assuming that the term 1.45×10^{-5} in Eqs. (3) and (4) represents a process in which the solvent water has the same function as the solute bases, Brønsted and Pedersen [1] argued that the catalytic constant k_c for the solvent—if it is to be compared with the constants for solute bases—should be given by

$$k_c = \frac{v_0}{c_w[\mathrm{R}]} \tag{14}$$

v_0 is the observed rate in the absence of solute catalysts, R is the reactant, and c_w is the number of moles of solvent in 1 liter of solute-free solvent; for water at 25°C, $c_w = 55.5$. For the purpose of comparisons of this sort Brønsted and Pedersen take the value of the acidity constant for the lyonium ion to be c_w and the value of the acidity constant of the solvent to be K_w/c_w, that is 1.79×10^{-16} for water at 25°C, K_w being the ion product constant of the solvent.

These rules can be justified by the following considerations. In a solution which contains a small proportion of a labeled water $H_2{}^*O$ which forms ideal solutions with ordinary water and has the same proton affinity the quantity

$$^*k = \frac{^*v}{[\mathrm{H_2{}^*O}][\mathrm{R}]} \tag{15}$$

is a suitable measure of the catalytic effectiveness of the base water for comparison with the effectiveness of solute bases. Here $^*v$ is that part of the total rate which is due to the labeled water. Because the labeled water is an ideal solute, $^*v = {}^*Nv_0$, where $^*N$ is the mole fraction of labeled water, and since $^*N \ll 1$, $[\mathrm{H_2{}^*O}] = c_w{}^*N$. Consequently

$$^*k = \frac{v_0}{c_w[\mathrm{R}]} \tag{16}$$

The acidity constant K of an acid-base pair in dilute aqueous solution is given by

$$K = \frac{[\mathrm{B}][\mathrm{OH_3}^+]}{[\mathrm{BH}^+]} \tag{17}$$

The acidity constant of the labeled OH_3^+ is therefore

$$^*K = \frac{[\mathrm{H_2{}^*O}][\mathrm{OH_3}^+]}{[\mathrm{{}^*OH_3}^+]} \tag{18}$$

Again all solutes may be taken to be ideal, and $^*N_{\mathrm{OH_3^+}}/N_{\mathrm{OH_3^+}} = {}^*N_{\mathrm{H_2O}}$. Consequently

$$^*K = c_w \tag{19}$$

An analogous argument leads to the relation

$$*K = \frac{K_w}{c_w} \tag{20}$$

for the acidity constant of water.

The structure of such bases as amines and carboxylate ions in the region of the proton addition differs so much from that of water and of hydroxyl ion that no great confidence can be placed in the prediction of the catalytic constants for the bases water and hydroxyl ion by the extrapolation of relationships which apply to the catalytic effectiveness of the solute bases. For the same reason predicted values of the catalytic effectiveness of the acids oxonium ion and water are in principle unreliable. In addition to the structural problem the situation is further complicated, as Bell [15] points out, by the fact that the extrapolations involve at least six orders of magnitude. Bell concludes from a survey of the available data that for catalysis by the base water in the solvent water the catalytic constant given by Eq. (14) and the value predicted by the extrapolation agree nevertheless to within an order of magnitude. But for catalysis by the base hydroxyl ion the observed values are usually smaller than the predicted values, often by as much as three orders of magnitude.

10.7 THE RECOGNIZABILITY OF GENERAL ACID AND BASE CATALYSIS

A general acid catalysis is recognizable only if for some acid HA the rate of the catalyzed reaction can be made significant compared both with the rate due to catalysis by the lyonium ion and with that due to the solvent. For aqueous solutions these conditions can be put in the form that the quantities $k_a[\mathrm{HA}]/(k_\mathrm{H}[\mathrm{OH_3}^+])$ and $k_a[\mathrm{HA}]/k_w$ must both be significant compared with unity. Because of complications arising from medium effects, significant may be defined as not less than 0.1. The first condition is then equivalent to

$$\frac{k_a}{K_a k_\mathrm{H}}[\mathrm{A}^-] \geqslant 0.1 \tag{21}$$

It is more easily met the greater the concentration of A^-, but again a value of this concentration greater than about 0.1 would introduce serious uncertainty because of medium effects. The condition is therefore that

$$\frac{k_a}{K_a k_\mathrm{H}} \geqslant 1 \tag{22}$$

From similar considerations the second condition becomes

$$\frac{k_a}{k_w} \geqslant 1 \tag{23}$$

By virtue of the catalytic law $k_a = GK_a^\alpha$ the conditions become

$$\left(\frac{G}{k_H}\right)^{1/(1-\alpha)} \geqslant K_a \geqslant \left(\frac{k_w}{G}\right)^{1/\alpha} \tag{24}$$

To the crude approximation within which the catalysis law for solute acids applies to catalysis by OH_3^+ and by H_2O, $k_H = G(55.5)^\alpha$ and $k_w = 55.5\,G(1.8 \times 10^{-16})^\alpha$, and the condition for recognizability becomes

$$1.8 \times 10^{-16}\,55.5^{1/\alpha} \leqslant K_a \leqslant 0.018^{\alpha(1-\alpha)} \tag{25}$$

or

$$1.75\frac{\alpha}{1-\alpha} \leqslant pK_a \leqslant 15.75 - \frac{1.75}{\alpha} \tag{26}$$

For $\alpha = 0.8$ these limits are still rather wide, namely,

$$7 \leqslant pK_a \leqslant 13.6 \tag{27}$$

But for $\alpha = 0.9$ they are already impossible, namely,

$$15.7 \leqslant pK_a \leqslant 13.8 \tag{28}$$

A similar argument leads to the conclusion that general base catalysis is recognizable only if the parameter β is significantly less than unity. Values of α and of β which have been reported range from 0.27 to 0.83.

10.8 THE RATES OF PROTON-TRANSFER REACTIONS

The development of methods for studying very fast reactions[1] has shown that when the $\Delta\mu°$ value for the transfer of a proton from an oxygen or nitrogen atom in one molecule to an oxygen or nitrogen atom in another molecule is zero or negative, the specific rate is, with a few exceptions, that of the diffusion together of the molecules involved. The exceptions involve cases in which the proton being transferred is internally hydrogen-bonded in the reactant. For water solutions at room temperature the specific rates of such proton transfers are of the order of 10^{10} to 10^{11} liters/mole-sec. But when $\Delta\mu°$ is positive, a diffusion-controlled process in one direction requires a less-than-diffusion-controlled specific rate in the opposite direction.

Eigen and Schön [18] find a specific rate of 5×10^{10} for the reaction of oxonium and acetate ions to form acetic acid and water. Since the equilibrium constant is 1.8×10^{-5}, the specific rate of the ionization of acetic acid must be 9×10^5. The corresponding values for boric acid are 1.2×10^{10} and 10 [19], and those for trimethylammonium ion are 6×10^{10} and 10 [20]. For the reaction $NH_4^+ + NH_3 \rightleftharpoons NH_3 + NH_4^+$ the specific rate is 1.1×10^9 [21].

[1] For reviews see [14], [16], and [17].

The situation is very different when the proton is transferred from, or becomes attached to, carbon. The specific rate of the reaction $CH_3CHNO_2^- + OH_3^+ \rightarrow CH_3CH_2NO_2 + H_2O$ is only 16 [22] even though the $\Delta\mu^\circ$ value of -11.7 kcal is not very different from the value of -12.6 for the diffusion-controlled reaction of borate ion with oxonium ion. There is, however, evidence [23] that proton transfer to or from carbon may be much faster in dimethylsulfoxide solution than in hydroxylic solvents.

The specific rate of a diffusion-controlled proton transfer is determined by the bulk of the diffusing molecules, by the viscosity of the medium, and sometimes by the electric charges on the reacting molecules. It is independent of the structure and of the internal electron distribution of the reactants. The rate of a chemically controlled proton transfer, i.e., one whose rate is less than the diffusion rate, is determined by the same kind of factors of the electron availability in the region of a reacting molecule in which the transfer takes place and of the molecular shape in this region that determine the equilibrium of the transfer. This difference in behavior is an important diagnostic aid in the interpretation of reaction mechanisms.

10.9 THE ELECTRON-SHIFT HYPOTHESIS

The assumption that any change in the structure of a molecule which shifts a bonding pair toward the part of the molecule which it accompanies in a heterolytic bond-breaking reaction will increase the specific rate and the equilibrium constant of the reaction is implicit in all current thinking about reaction mechanisms and about the relation of structure to reactivity. Equally implicit is the assumption that in a heterolytic bond-making reaction any change in structure increasing the electron density on the atom which supplies the bonding pair or decreasing the density on the atom which receives the pair will increase the rate. These principles had their origin in the "electronic theory of valency," which was developed by Lapworth, by Robinson, and by Ingold in the 1920s [24]. Their validity has been established by the wide applicability of their corollaries in specific cases, not by any detailed quantum-mechanical proof. The qualitative argument in their favor is persuasively presented by Ingold [25].

The addition of a proton to, or the removal of a proton from, a molecule is an especially effective way of producing a shift in the electron distribution in the molecule, and such shifts are no doubt responsible for the powerful catalytic effects of acids and of bases.

10.10 THE HYDRATION OF ACETALDEHYDE

The hydration of acetaldehyde has been thoroughly investigated by Bell and coworkers [26] (see also [14, pp. 151 ff]). It constitutes an uncomplicated case of a broad classification of reactions, most of them more complicated, in which a proton and a nucleophile are added to a C=O or C=N double bond. The reaction is reversible with an equilibrium constant at 25°C of 1.6. There is both general acid and general base catalysis. The Brønsted catalytic relation applies with good precision to a heterogeneous group of acid catalysts, four carboxylic acids, seven pyridines, and one phenol. The parameter α is 0.54. The catalytic coefficients of the conjugate bases of these acids correlate poorly with the basicity constants, although the two quantities show a general trend in the same direction. By extrapolation to zero buffer concentration of the rates in buffer solutions it is found that the equation

$$k = 930[OH_3^+] + 7.9 \times 10^{-3} + 8 \times 10^4[OH^-] \tag{29}$$

would apply at 25°C in the absence of any other catalysts than OH_3^+, H_2O, and OH^-. What is commonly called the pH profile shows therefore a broad minimum, centered at pH 6, and rising steeply both in acid and in alkaline solutions. The half time at the minimum is about 1½ min, and reliable data can therefore be obtained only by considerable skill and forethought.

10.11 MECHANISM OF THE BASE-CATALYZED HYDRATION

An adequate mechanism for the base-catalyzed reaction is

$$\begin{matrix} H_3C \\ H \end{matrix}\!\!>\!C{=}O + OH^- + HA \rightleftharpoons \left[\begin{matrix} CH_3 \\ H \end{matrix}\!\!>\!C\begin{matrix} \cdots O\cdots H\cdots A \\ \cdots O{-}H \end{matrix}\right] \rightleftharpoons \begin{matrix} CH_3 \\ H \end{matrix}\!\!>\!C\!<\!\begin{matrix} O{-}H \\ O{-}H \end{matrix} + A^-$$

(IIIa)

$$A^- + H_2O \underset{k_{-2}}{\overset{k_2}{\rightleftharpoons}} HA + OH^-$$

(IIIb)

in which A^- is the basic catalyst, the brackets enclose the structure of the transition state, and dotted lines represent bonds in the process of being formed or being broken. The partial formation of the bond from the carbonyl oxygen to the proton of HA in the transition state shifts the electron system away from the carbonyl carbon and lowers the barrier against formation of the bond from that carbon to the hydroxyl oxygen. Process (III*b*) is surely fast compared with process (III*a*) in every case in which base catalysis has been observed. For the weakest base investigated, formate ion, the equilibrium constant K_2 is 5.6×10^{-11}. The specific rate k_{-2} is of a kind which has consistently been found to be diffusion-controlled and must therefore be not less than 10^{10}. The specific rate k_2 cannot therefore be less than 0.6. The observed specific rate of the formate-ion–catalyzed hydration is 0.065, and even with an aldehyde concentration as high as 0.1 the rate of the first step of the mechanism is about 1 percent of that of the second step. The situation is therefore that of a mobile equilibrium (III*b*) perturbed by the relatively slow reaction (III*a*). In such a system the net rate is to a close approximation (Sec. 4.18) that of the slow step, and the product [HA][OH^-] is close to the equilibrium value $K_2[A^-]$. Consequently

$$k = k_0[OH^-][HA] = k_0 K_2[A^-] \tag{30}$$

where k is the first-order specific rate. The mechanism accounts therefore for the observed proportionality of rate to concentration of base catalyst.

It follows from Eq. (30) that

$$\delta_R \log k = \delta_R \log k_0 + \delta_R \log K_2 = \delta_R \log k_0 - \delta_R \log K_a \tag{31}$$

where the operator δ_R refers to a change in the catalyst and K_a is the acidity constant of HA. By virtue of the Brønsted catalytic relationship

$$\delta_R \log k_0 = \alpha \delta_R \log K_a \tag{32}$$

where $\alpha < 1$. Consequently

$$\delta_R \log k = -(1 - \alpha)\, \delta_R \log K_a \tag{33}$$

which is the observed relationship.

It is possible, but not particularly important, that a mobile reversible hydrogen bonding between the carbonyl oxygen and HA is involved in the formation of the transition state in this mechanism.

The kinetics also permits the mechanism

$$\mathrm{CH_3(H)C{=}O + H_2O + A^-} \rightleftharpoons \left[\mathrm{CH_3(H)C(O)\cdots O(H)\cdots H\cdots A}\right] \rightleftharpoons \mathrm{CH_3(H)C(O^-)(O{-}H) + HA} \qquad \text{(IVa)}$$

$$\mathrm{CH_3(H)C(O^-)(O{-}H) + HA} \underset{k_{-2}}{\overset{k_2}{\rightleftharpoons}} \mathrm{CH_3(H)C(O{-}H)(O{-}H) + A^-} \qquad \text{(IVb)}$$

The acidity constant of acetaldehyde hydrate is 2.7×10^{-14} [27]. The specific rate k_2 is surely diffusion-controlled, and this sets the value of k_{-2} at not less than 1.6. The observed specific rate of the formate-ion–catalyzed dehydration of the aldehyde hydrate is 0.04. Again the proportions of HA, A^-, and OH^- should be close to the equilibrium values and the rate of the dehydration close to proportionality to [A^-]. However, both the oxygen atoms in the transition state of process (III*a*) carry a full bond and a partial one, whereas in the isomeric transition state of process (IV*a*) one oxygen carries only one bond, a full one, and the other carries one full and two partial bonds. The conversion of the rate-determining transition state of mechanism (III) to that of mechanism (IV) rather certainly therefore involves a considerable increase in energy and presumably also in standard potential. Since by virtue of the effective equilibrium in process (III*b*) the sum of the potentials on the left side of (III*a*) is the same as the corresponding sum for (IV*a*), the reaction rate by way of mechanism (IV) should be negligible compared with that by way of mechanism (III).

It is inconceivable that process (IV*a*) should be mobile and reversible and process (IV*b*) rate-determining. The latter, being the reaction of a moderately strong acid with a very strong base, is surely diffusion-controlled, and its rate would not correlate with the acid strength of HA. And certainly (IV*a*) cannot be fast compared with a diffusion-controlled process.

It has been argued against a one-step mechanism in which the transition state structure is A that structure B

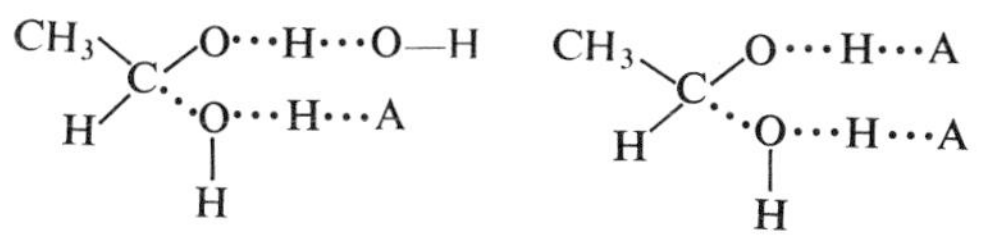

$$\begin{matrix} CH_3\diagdown & \diagup O\cdots H\cdots O{-}H \\ C\vdots & \\ H\diagup & \cdot O\cdots H\cdots A \\ & | \\ & H \end{matrix} \qquad \begin{matrix} CH_3\diagdown & \diagup O\cdots H\cdots A \\ C\vdots & \\ H\diagup & \cdot O\cdots H\cdots A \\ & | \\ & H \end{matrix}$$

(A) (B)

should have less energy and that consequently a term involving the product $[HA][A^-]$ should appear in the rate equation. No such effect has been revealed by a careful search [28]. It must be recognized, however, that the problem involves the relative rates of attachment of the acids H_2O and HA to a very basic atom, namely, a carbonyl oxygen which is on the way to being an alkoxide ion oxygen. There is evidence, both theoretical and experimental,[1] that the value of α is small in such circumstances. With a sufficiently small value catalysis by any other acid than water would be undetectable. On this basis the one-step mechanism cannot safely be rejected. Eigen [16] proposes a cyclic one-step mechanism involving a chain of water molecules. The details are not clear, especially with respect to an explanation of the existence of both acid and base catalysis.

10.12 MECHANISM OF THE ACID-CATALYZED HYDRATION

The specific rate of the process (V*a*)

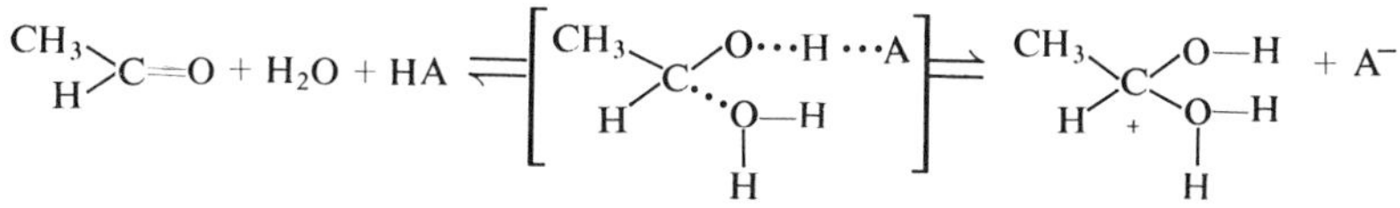

$$\begin{matrix} CH_3 \\ H \end{matrix}\!\!>\!C{=}O + H_2O + HA \rightleftharpoons \left[\begin{matrix} CH_3\diagdown & \diagup O\cdots H\cdots A \\ C\vdots & \\ H\diagup & \cdot O{-}H \\ & | \\ & H \end{matrix}\right] \rightleftharpoons \begin{matrix} CH_3\diagdown & \diagup O{-}H \\ C & \\ H\diagup\;+ & \diagdown O{-}H \\ & | \\ & H \end{matrix} + A^- \qquad \text{(Va)}$$

$$\begin{matrix} CH_3\diagdown & \diagup O{-}H \\ C & \\ H\diagup\;+ & \diagdown O{-}H \\ & | \\ & H \end{matrix} + A^- \underset{k_{-2}}{\overset{k_2}{\rightleftharpoons}} \begin{matrix} CH_3\diagdown & \diagup O{-}H \\ C & \\ H\diagup & \diagdown O{-}H \end{matrix} + HA \qquad \text{(Vb)}$$

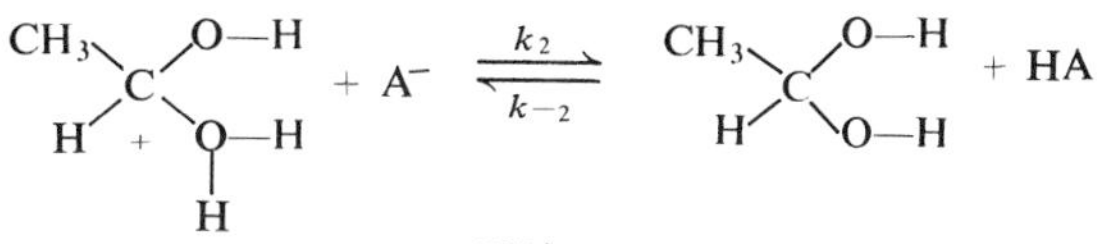

[1] See [14], especially p. 172.

is surely less than that of process (III*a*). The specific rates of both processes increase with an increase in the acid strength of HA, but the rate of (III*a*), in contrast to the specific rate, decreases at a given buffer ratio because the concentration of hydroxyl ion decreases faster than the specific rate increases. It is therefore possible for process (V) to be faster than process (III) and to have a specific rate which increases with acid strength. In the acetaldehyde hydration the acid catalysis is recognizable with all but the weakest acid investigated, 2,4-dichlorophenol, for which $K_a = 1.8 \times 10^{-8}$. With acids of K_a values greater than 10^{-6} the rate of the acid-catalyzed reaction in approximately equimolar buffers is found to be greater than that of the base-catalyzed reaction.

It is not, however, certain that (V) is an acceptable mechanism. The value of k_2 is surely that of a diffusion-controlled process, namely, about 10^{10}. Because of the kinetically simple behavior the value of k_{-2} must be at least 10 times the specific rate of the dehydration of the aldehyde hydrate. With the weakest acid which gives detectable acid catalysis, 2,6-lutidinium ion, whose K_a value is 1.9×10^{-7}, this specific rate is 0.018. The mechanism is therefore acceptable only if $K_2 \leqslant 6 \times 10^{10}$, that is, if the K_a value of the conjugate acid of acetaldehyde hydrate is not over 10^4. There is no direct evidence for the value of this constant; but it must be considerably larger than the value for the conjugate acid of a monohydric alcohol, which appears to be in the neighborhood of 10^2 [29] but how much larger is hard to say.

A one-step mechanism involving a transition state either of structure C or of structure D

CH₃ and H on C; C⋯O⋯H⋯A; C⋯O(H)⋯H⋯OH₂

(C)

CH₃ and H on C; C⋯O⋯H⋯OH₂; C⋯O(H)⋯H⋯A

(D)

is acceptable if the doubts connected with the absence of a term in [HA][A⁻] are discounted.

10.13 CATALYSIS IN THE ENOLIZATION REACTION

There is abundant evidence (Secs. 4.18 and 4.27) that the halogenation of acetone involves the rate-determining conversion of the ketone to an intermediate, followed by a rapid reaction with halogen or with some such halogen derivative as hypohalous acid or hypohalite ion. The intermediate might be either the enol E or the anion F.

$CH_3C(=CH_2)—O—H$ (E)

$CH_3C(—O)(H_2C)^-$ (F)

$CH_3C(—O\cdots H\cdots A)(H_2C\cdots H\cdots A)^-$ (G)

The reaction is so much slower than the acetaldehyde hydration that the acceptance of a two-step mechanism involving mobile proton transfers to or from oxygen is not troubled by doubt that the transfer is fast enough. Unlike the aldehyde hydration, however, there is an unmistakable term in the product $[HA][A^-]$. There appears therefore to be what is called a concerted reaction, i.e., a simultaneous attack by the acid HA and the base A^-, leading to a transition state of structure G.

Against the hypothesis that the reaction is in all cases concerted, Pedersen [30] argued that transition states of the structure H for the term in [HA], of the structure I

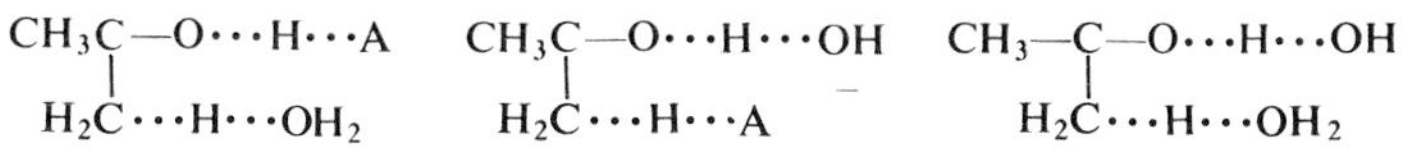

$$\begin{array}{ccc} CH_3C{-}O\cdots H\cdots A & CH_3C{-}O\cdots H\cdots OH^- & CH_3{-}C{-}O\cdots H\cdots OH \\ | & | & | \\ H_2C\cdots H\cdots OH_2 & H_2C\cdots H\cdots A & H_2C\cdots H\cdots OH_2 \\ (H) & (I) & (J) \end{array}$$

for the term in A^-, and of the structure J for the constant term, do not reasonably account for the observed catalytic constants. If these structures represented the sole pathways for reaction, the process in which the attacking base is water would be 180 times faster when the acid is acetic acid than when it is water. But when the attacking base is acetate ion, the rate would be only 1.3 times faster when the acid is acetic acid than when it is water.

This argument was accepted until Swain [31] pointed out that the transition state K, in which the attacking acid is OH_3^+ and the attacking base is A^-, also leads to a term in the rate equation proportional to [HA].

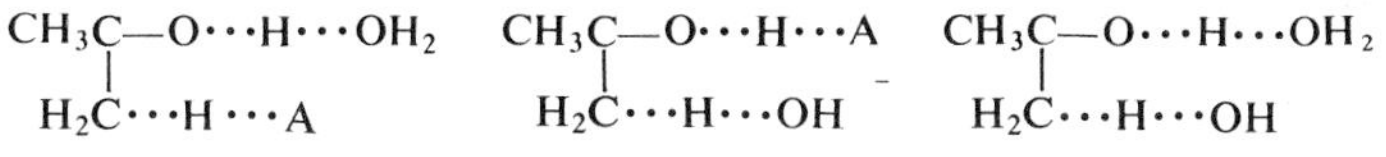

$$\begin{array}{ccc} CH_3C{-}O\cdots H\cdots OH_2 & CH_3C{-}O\cdots H\cdots A & CH_3C{-}O\cdots H\cdots OH_2 \\ | & | & | \\ H_2C\cdots H\cdots A & H_2C\cdots H\cdots OH^- & H_2C\cdots H\cdots OH \\ (K) & (L) & (M) \end{array}$$

Similarly a transition state of structure L leads to an additional term proportional to $[A^-]$, and one of structure M to an additional constant term. On this basis the rate equation contains nine, not six, adjustable parameters, and there is no difficulty in fitting values to almost any desired relation between them.

In this reaction the catalytic coefficients of seven carboxylic acids fit a Brønsted catalytic relationship with normal precision. This would hardly be the case if the observed coefficients were sums of the type $k'[HA] + k''[A^-][OH_3^+]$ with the two terms of comparable magnitude. The result, however, is consistent with either term being predominant.

Swain and coworkers [32] have approached this problem by way of isotope effects. The bromination of nitromethane is zero order in bromine and presumably has the simple proton transfer

$$CH_3NO_2 + B \rightleftharpoons CH_2NO_2^- + BH^+ \qquad (VI)$$

as the rate-determining process. The ratio k_H/k_D, defined as the ratio of the rate of reaction of CH_3NO_2 to that of CD_3NO_2, was found by Reitz [33] to be 3.78 when the base B is water, 4.28 when it is chloracetate ion, and 6.53 when it is acetate ion. The implication is that in some way (Sec. 5.22) the proton being transferred has less zero-point energy the stronger the attacking base. In the enolization of $C_6H_5 \cdot CO \cdot CT(C_6H_5) \cdot CH_2 \cdot CH(CH_3)_2$ and its untritiated analog the ratio k_H/k_T was found to be 9.7 for the term proportional to $[OH_3^+]$, 11.4 for the term proportional to $[CH_3COOH]$, 10.2 for the term proportional to $[CH_3COO^-]$, and 12.9 for the term proportional to $[OH^-]$. If the attacking acid in both of the first two cases is oxonium ion, the increase in the isotope ratio from the first to the second is consistent with the Reitz rule since acetate ion is a stronger base than water. Similarly the increase from the third to the fourth case indicates that the attacking acid is water in both cases. It would appear therefore that the predominant transition-state structure in the catalysis by acetic acid is K not H and that the predominant structure in the catalysis by acetate ion is I not L.

10.14 CYCLIC TRANSITION STATES

The mutarotation of such substances as tetramethylglucose consists in the conversion of a cyclic hemiacetal N to a diastereoisomer, presumably by way of the open-chain aldehyde O. In very dilute solution in benzene in the presence both of a phenol and of an amine the rate of mutarotation is proportional to the production of the concentrations of the amine and the phenol [34]. This can be interpreted as a concerted, or push-pull, process in which the phenol donates a proton to the oxygen starred in structure N while the amine removes the proton starred in the structure. Swain and Brown found that 2-hydroxypyridine at 0.001 *M* concentration is 7,000 times as effective a catalyst as a mixture of 0.001 *M* phenol and 0.001 *M* pyridine, even though the hydroxypyridine is only 0.0001 times as strong a base as pyridine and 0.01 times as strong an acid as phenol. The kinetics is complicated by dimerization of the catalyst and by the rapid reversible formation of a 1:1 compound of tetramethylglucose and hydroxypyridine, but in very dilute solution the rate is first order in catalyst. Both 3- and 4-hydroxypyridine are at least 1,000 times less effective than the 2 derivative, and the reaction is second order in the catalyst, indicating that one molecule acts as a proton donor and the other as a proton acceptor. 2-Hydroxy-4-methylquinoline behaves like 2-hydroxypyridine, and 3-hydroxyquinoline like 3-hydroxypyridine, while 4-hydroxyquinoline has no observable catalytic effect. *N*-Methyl-α-pyridone is a poor catalyst but one much more effective in the presence of phenol.

These striking results suggest strongly that the standard potential of the cyclic transition state P is some 4 kcal lower than that of one in which phenol is in the process of transferring a proton to oxygen while a separate pyridine

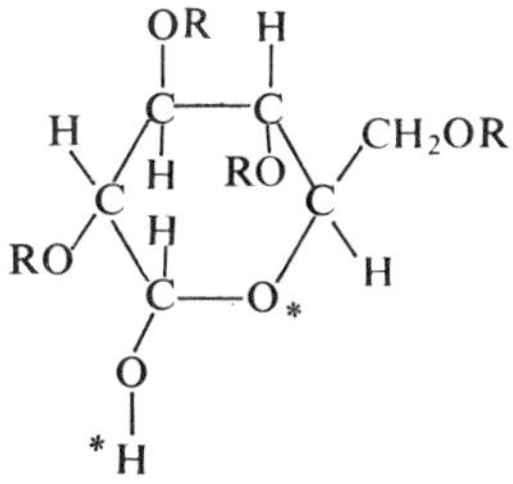

(N)

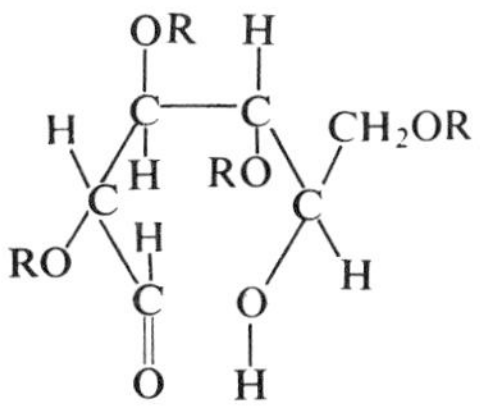

(O)

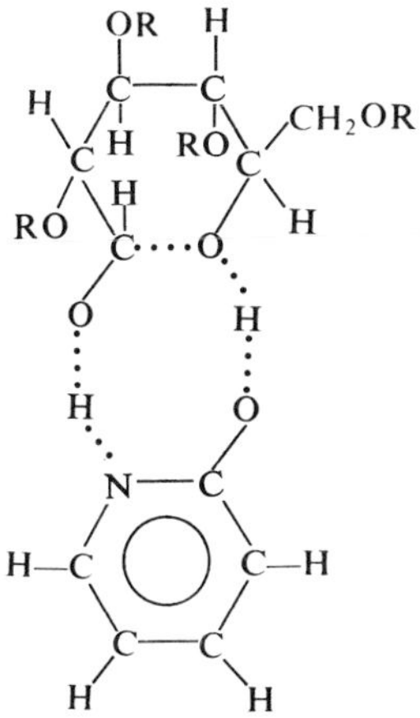

(P)

molecule removes a proton from the hydroxyl group. The cyclic transition state probably has a significant entropy advantage, but one suspects that the easy mobility of the electrons in the hydroxypyridine structure is also important.

The critical configuration in transition state P has much the same geometry as the stable dimer of a carboxylic acid. The similarity suggests that carboxylic acids may form transition states of relatively low standard potential in reactions similar to the mutarotation. In these the carbonyl oxygen of the acid is in the process of removing a proton from one position in the substrate molecule while the hydroxyl group of the acid is donating a proton to another position. In fact carboxylic acids are much more effective catalysts for the mutarotation of glucose in benzene solution [34] or in nitromethane solution [35] than are phenols of the same acid strength. Such structures as this are no doubt less important in aqueous solution because water is so potent both as a proton donor and as a proton acceptor. 2-Hydroxypyridine is only 4 to 5 times as effective a catalyst for the mutarotation of glucose in aqueous solution, as would be expected from its acidic and basic properties.

10.15 ESTER HYDROLYSIS

Using ^{18}O labeling, Bender [36] found in a number of cases that hydrolysis of an ester is accompanied by oxygen exchange between the carbonyl oxygen of the ester and the solvent. Values of the ratio k_h/k_{ex} of hydrolysis rate to exchange rate are listed in Table 10.2. It is particularly notable that the ratio is so nearly the same for acid as for alkaline hydrolysis even though the specific rate of the alkaline hydrolysis at a given temperature is about 10^4 times that of the acid hydrolysis. An adequate interpretation, apparently the only adequate interpretation, of this result involves the mechanism

$$R'-C\begin{matrix}{=O}\\{-O-R}\end{matrix} + H_2O \underset{k_{-1}}{\overset{k_1}{\rightleftharpoons}} R'-\underset{HO}{\overset{OH}{C}}-O-R \xrightarrow{k_2} R'C\begin{matrix}{=O}\\{-O-H}\end{matrix} + ROH \quad \text{(VII)}$$

with k_2 greater but not much greater than k_{-1}.

The typical ester hydrolysis involves acyl-oxygen fission, i.e., the ether oxygen remains attached to the alkyl group [37]. There is pronounced acceleration by oxonium and by hydroxyl ion in aqueous solution or in solutions containing much water but no general acid or general base catalysis. Even though the first step consists in the hydration of a carbonyl group, the ester hydrolysis rates are of the order of 10^6 to 10^7 times slower than that of the hydration of acetaldehyde.

There are atypical esters which hydrolyze by alkyl-oxygen fission. This occurs when a relatively stable carbonium ion may be formed by separation of the alkyl group (Sec. 6.14). It also occurs in the hydrolysis of β-lactones in neutral or acid solution [38].

There are other atypical esters, the ethyl esters of chloracetic, dichloracetic, trichloracetic, and difluoacetic acids and glycine ethyl ester hydrochloride, which show general base catalysis with the Brønsted catalytic relation reasonably well satisfied [39]. A shift from specific lyonium, or lyate-ion

Table 10.2 Ratio k_h/k_{ex} of specific rate of hydrolysis to that of oxygen exchange[a]

	Alkaline hydrolysis		*Acid hydrolysis*
	Water	*33% dioxane-water*	*water*
Ethyl benzoate	4.8	10.6	5.2
Isopropyl benzoate	2.7	3.7	
t-Butyl benzoate		7.6	

[a] Temperature 25°C for alkaline hydrolysis in water and for ethyl benzoate in dioxane-water; 62.5° for isopropyl benzoate and *t*-butyl benzoate in dioxane-water; 99° for acid hydrolysis. Data of Bender [36].

catalysis to general acid or base catalysis with rather small change in the reactant has been noted in other cases. The hydrolysis in water of ethyl orthoacetate is general acid catalyzed; the hydrolysis of ethylorthoformate is specifically catalyzed by oxonium ion [40].

In the hydrolysis of *p*-nitrophenyl acetate but not in the hydrolysis of ethyl acetate imidazole is some 4,000 times more effective as a catalyst than HPO_4^{--}, which has the same basicity constant [41]. There is direct evidence that acetylimidazole is an intermediate in the reaction (Sec. 5.26). A mechanism of this sort is referred to as a nucleophilic catalysis, the mechanism being clearly different from that of the general base catalysis in such reactions as the aldehyde hydration.

10.16 BELLS AND INVERTED BELLS

Despite the complications of detail, the essence of an acid catalysis is the possibility of adding a proton to the reacting system on one side of the bond being made or broken, and the essence of a base catalysis is the possibility of removing a proton from the opposite side of that bond. When both possibilities exist and the reactant or the reactants are simultaneously less acidic and less basic than the solvent, the pH-rate profile has a minimum; it is an inverted bell. This is the case with the aldehyde hydration, the ketone enolization, and the typical ester hydrolysis.

When there are no readily removable protons but sites for proton addition exist, there may be acid catalysis but no base catalysis. The rate at low pH values decreases with increasing pH but levels off to a constant small value at high pH values. This is the case in the hydrolysis of acetals and of orthoesters.

When, however, the acidity or basicity of a reactant is comparable to that of the solvent, the pH profile may level off at a high value of rate or there may be a sharp maximum. The diazo-coupling reaction (Figs. 6.6 and 6.7) is an example. A simpler case, because it is symmetrical, is presented by the chloramine reaction (Sec. 5.18). The acidity constants K_N of ammonium ion and K_C of hypochlorous acid are known, independently of the chloramine reaction, to be 6.1×10^{-10} and 3.7×10^{-8}. Since the reaction $NH_3 + ClOH \rightleftharpoons NH_4^+ + ClO^-$ is reversible and fast compared with the chloramine formation, the primitive concentrations c_N and c_C of ammonia and of hypochlorous acid are given by

$$c_N = [NH_3] + [NH_4^+] = [NH_3]\left(1 + \frac{[H^+]}{K_N}\right) \tag{34}$$

$$c_C = [ClOH] + [ClO^-] = [HOCl]\left(1 + \frac{K_C}{[H^+]}\right) \tag{35}$$

If the only significant pathway from reactants to products is by way of a transition state of the composition $H_3N{\cdot}ClOH$ or of $H_3N{\cdot}ClOH{\cdot}(H_2O)_x$, then

$$k^{(p)} = \frac{kK_N[H^+]}{(K_N + [H^+])(K_C + [H^+])} \tag{36}$$

where k is defined as $v/([NH_3][ClOH])$ and $k^{(p)}$ as $v/c_N c_C$. This equation with $k = 5.3$ liters/mole-min is plotted in Fig. 10.2.

It follows from differentiation of Eq. (36) that the rate is a maximum when

$$[H^+] = \sqrt{K_N K_C} \tag{37}$$

and that the specific rate at the maximum is given by

$$k^{(p)}_{\max} = \frac{k}{\{1 + (K_C/K_N)^{1/2}\}^2} \tag{38}$$

A peak in the pH-rate profile is possible only if the concentration of systems at the summit of the barrier between reactants and products is larger at pH values near the peak than that of systems on the summit which contain one more or one less proton. If K_+ is the equilibrium constant for the conversion of a transition state of the composition $H_4N{\cdot}ClOH{\cdot}(H_2O)_x^{\ +}$ to one of composition $H_3N{\cdot}ClOH{\cdot}(H_2O)_x$ and K_- that for the conversion of the latter to one of composition $H_3N{\cdot}ClO{\cdot}(H_2O)_x^{\ -}$, the complete relation for the primitive value of the specific rate of chloramine formation is

$$k^{(p)} = kK_N \frac{[H^+]^2/K_+ + [H^+] + K_-}{(K_N + [H^+])(K_C + [H^+])} \tag{39}$$

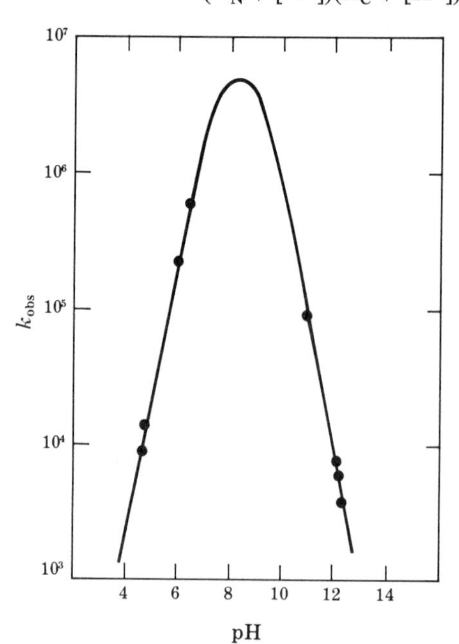

Fig. 10.2 The dependence on pH of the specific rate of the chloramine reaction. (*By permission of Weill and Morris* [42].)

The general condition for the existence of a maximum does not seem to be illuminating. It is, however, clear that the rate at a hydrogen-ion concentration equal to $(K_N K_C)^{1/2}$ cannot be less than the rate given by Eq. (38), i.e., not less than k if K_N/K_C is large and not less than kK_N/K_C if K_N/K_C is small. The value of $k^{(p)}$ at high acidity is given from Eq. (39) as kK_N/K_+. If therefore K_+ is greater than either K_N or K_C, the rate at high acidity will be less than the rate at hydrogen-ion concentrations near $(K_N K_C)^{1/2}$. Similarly the value of $k^{(p)}$ at low acidity reduces to kK_-/K_C. If K_- is smaller than either K_N or K_C, the rate in basic solution will be less than that in the $(K_N K_C)^{1/2}$ region. What this amounts to is that if the rate is to peak at or near a hydrogen-ion concentration of $(K_N K_C)^{1/2}$ and be less both in more acid and in more basic solution, the transition state of composition $H_3N{\cdot}ClOH{\cdot}(H_2O)_x$ must be less basic than either NH_3 or ClO^- and less acidic than either NH_4^+ or ClOH.

It is easy to see that these conditions are met in the case of the chloramine formation. A transition state of the structure Q or R

```
    H                       H
    |                       |       ·Cl·
H—N···Cl···O—H          H—N··           ··O—H
    |                       :               :
    H                       H               H
                              ··         ··
                                 ··O··
                                   |
                                   H

   (Q)                           (R)
```

must be less acidic than ClOH because the partially formed N—Cl bond shifts the electron system in such a way as to make it more difficult to remove the proton from oxygen. It must be less acidic than NH_4^+ because the partially formed N—Cl bond does not facilitate the removal of a proton from nitrogen as effectively as the fully formed fourth N—H bond. In the same way it can be seen that it must be more difficult to add a proton to Q or R than to add it either to NH_3 or to ClO^-.

The decreased rate on the basic side of the peak cannot be attributed to any deficiency in the value of the quantity $[NH_3][ClO^-]$. At the pH of the peak this quantity is 8 times the quantity $[NH_3][ClOH]$, and the proton transfer required to maintain the value should have an ample rate. Similarly, the decreased rate on the acid side cannot be attributed to a deficiency in the value of the quantity $[NH_4^+][ClOH]$.

One may however safely reject the possibility of a transition state of the structure S

```
H               H
 \             /
  N···Cl···O
 /             \
H               H

       (S)
```

on the basis that the proton transfer

$$H_3N + ClOH \rightarrow H_2N^- + ClOH_2^+ \qquad \text{(VIII)}$$

would not be fast enough.

These conclusions may reasonably be generalized to the rule that when an acid HA can react with a base B other than by proton transfer and at a specific rate low compared with that of the proton transfer, the slow reaction will peak at a hydrogen-ion concentration equal to the geometric mean of the acidity constants of HA and BH^+. The specific rate at the peak will be greater the greater the value of the ratio K_{BH^+}/K_{HA}. This will be true no matter what the charges on HA and B. In the chloramine reaction the ratio is 0.0165, the specific rate at the maximum is only $0.013k$, and the peak is sharp. With larger values of the ratio the peak is broader and the specific rate at the peak is a larger fraction of k. When K_{BH^+} is considerably larger than K_{SH^+}, the acidity constant of the pertinent lyonium ion, Eq. (36) reduces for the dilute-solution range to

$$k^{(p)} = \frac{k[SH^+]}{K_{HA} + [SH^+]} \qquad (40)$$

The specific rate increases therefore in proportion to $[SH^+]$ when this is considerably less than K_{HA} but levels off at the constant value k when $[SH^+]$ is considerably larger than K_{HA}. Even here, however, there must be a decrease in rate at a sufficiently high acidity in a less basic solvent because any site on B to which HA can become attached in the slow reaction is necessarily a site to which a proton can be attached.

Because of the existence of bell-shaped profiles the natural idea that if a little acid is good for a reaction, a lot of acid must be better may be misleading. Indeed a useful synthetic procedure might easily be overlooked through this misconception. This is particularly so because a bell-shaped profile is not limited to dilute aqueous solutions. It might for instance appear in strong-acid–water mixtures or in highly basic solutions in dimethylsulfoxide.

10.17 OXIME FORMATION AND SIMILAR REACTIONS

A maximum in the limiting pH-rate profile, i.e., the relation between specific rate and pH for systems in which the only catalysts are solvent, lyonium ion, and lyate ion, may appear for other reasons than those just discussed. If either step of the two-step process

$$R \underset{k_{-1}}{\overset{k_1}{\rightleftharpoons}} X \xrightarrow{k_2} P \qquad \text{(IX)}$$

is acid-catalyzed while the other is pH-independent, if the Bodenstein approximation applies, and if R is in mobile equilibrium with its conjugate acid, whose acidity constant is K_R, the primitive value of the specific rate is given by

$$k^{(p)} = \frac{k_1 k_2[H^+]K_R}{(K_R + [H^+])(k_2 + k_{-1}[H^+])} \tag{41}$$

if step 1 is the acid-catalyzed one, and by

$$k^{(p)} = \frac{k_1 k_2[H^+]K_R}{(K_R + [H^+])(k_{-1} + k_2[H^+])} \tag{42}$$

if step 2 is the acid-catalyzed one. In either case the plot of $k^{(p)}$ against pH has a maximum; in the former case when

$$[H^+] = \sqrt{\frac{K_R k_2}{k_{-1}}} \tag{43}$$

in the latter when

$$[H^+] = \sqrt{\frac{K_R k_{-1}}{k_2}} \tag{44}$$

Jencks [43] has shown that this is essentially the situation in the reaction of carbonyl compounds with hydroxylamine, semicarbazide, and the like. This is illustrated in Fig. 10.3 for the reaction of acetone with hydroxylamine. The acidity constant of the conjugate acid of hydroxylamine is 1.0×10^{-6}. When the pH is in the region of 2 to 3, it was shown spectroscopically that the rate-determining process is

$$(CH_3)_2CO + H_2NOH \rightleftharpoons (CH_3)_2C(OH)NHOH \tag{X}$$

There is a feeble acid catalysis of this reaction, but the rate nevertheless increases rapidly with increasing pH because the concentration of unprotonated hydroxylamine is increasing rapidly. Before a pH of 6 is reached, the reaction has become so fast that the process

$$(CH_3)_2C(OH)NHOH \xrightarrow{k_2} (CH_3)_2C{=}NOH + H_2O \tag{XI}$$

cannot keep up, and because this is an acid-catalyzed reaction the net rate goes through a maximum and then decreases. The concentration of the carbinolamine intermediate is under all conditions so small that the Bodenstein steady-state approximation is applicable, and setting the specific rates in the forward and reverse direction of reaction (X) at $k_1 + k_1'[H^+]$ and $k_{-1}' + k_{-1}[H^+]$, this leads to the equation

$$k^{(p)} = \frac{k_2(k_1 + k_1'[H^+])}{(1 + [H^+]/K_R)(k_2 + k_{-1}' + k_{-1}/[H^+])} \tag{45}$$

This is plotted as the solid line in Fig. 10.3.

If the presence of a maximum is to be taken as diagnostic for a two-step mechanism, it is important that it be a maximum in the limiting pH-rate profile

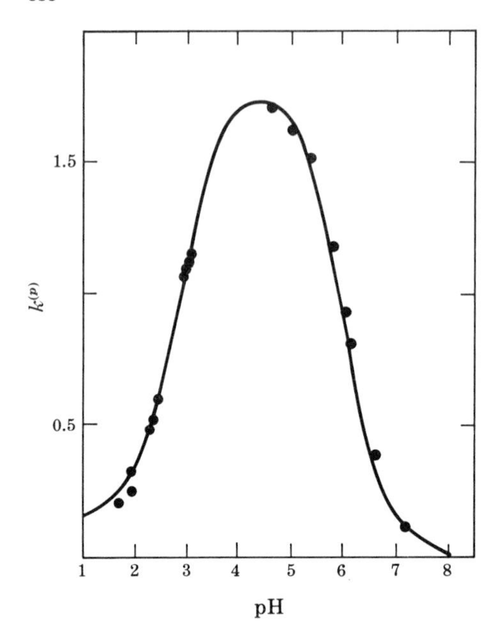

Fig. 10.3 The dependence on pH of the specific rate of the reaction of 0.0005 *M* acetone with 0.0167 *M* hydroxylamine. [*By permission of W. P. Jencks, Progr. Phys. Org. Chem.*, **2**: 63 (1964).]

when there is general acid or general base catalysis. The specific rate of the general acid-catalyzed reaction in buffer mixtures of acid HA and its conjugate base A^- is given, if R is in mobile equilibrium with a conjugate acid, by

$$k^{(p)} = \frac{K_R}{K_R + [OH_3{}^+]}(k_a[HA] + k_H[OH_3{}^+]) \tag{46}$$

where K_R is the acidity constant of RH^+. This can be written

$$k^{(p)} = \frac{k_a K_R c_b[OH_3{}^+]}{(K_R + [OH_3{}^+])(K_a + [OH_3{}^+])} + \frac{k_H K_R[OH_3{}^+]}{K_R + [OH_3{}^+]} \tag{47}$$

where $c_b = [HA] + [A^-]$ and K_a is the acidity constant of HA. If, as is usual in studies of this kind of system, c_b is maintained constant, this relation predicts a maximum in the plot of $k^{(p)}$ against pH. If the catalysis by HA is pronounced so that $k_H[OH_3{}^+] \ll k_a[HA]$, the maximum appears when $[OH_3{}^+] = \sqrt{K_R K_a}$.

10.18 THE PHENYLIMINOLACTONE HYDROLYSIS

The reactions of substances that contain the C═O or C═N group can be rather complicated [44].[1] The study by Schmir and Cunningham [46, 47] of the hydrolysis of the iminolactone 2-phenyliminotetrahydrofuran T

[1] For surveys see [44] and [45].

$$\underset{\text{(T)}}{\begin{array}{l}H_2C{-}CH_2\\ \quad\;\; \diagdown C{=}N\phi \\ H_2C{-}O\diagup\end{array}} \qquad \underset{\text{(U)}}{\begin{array}{l}H_2C{-}CH_2\\ \quad\;\; \diagdown C{=}O\\ H_2C{-}O\diagup\end{array}} + H_2N\phi$$

illustrates very well the way in which the problems presented by a reaction system of this sort can be attacked. The reaction was carried out at 30°C with the ionic strength held to 0.5 *M* by the addition of suitable amounts of potassium chloride. The solvent was 90% water–10% acetonitrile except in very alkaline solutions, where ethanol replaced the acetonitrile. pH and the p*K* values of buffer systems were based on glass-electrode measurements, which appear to have been referred to the dilute aqueous solution standard. This does not affect the validity of conclusions based on the relative values of these quantities.

At pH values below 6 the only recognizable reaction product is aniline plus butyrolactone U; at pH values above 9 the only recognizable product is γ-hydroxybutyranilide V.

$$\underset{\text{(V)}}{\begin{array}{l}CH_2{-}CH_2{-}C({=}O)NH\phi\\ |\\ CH_2{-}O{-}H\end{array}} \qquad \underset{\text{(W)}}{\begin{array}{l}CH_2{-}CH_2\diagdown \quad \cdot\cdot N(\phi)(H)\cdots H\cdots O\diagdown\\ |\qquad\qquad\quad C \qquad\qquad\qquad\qquad C{-}CH_3\\ CH_2{-}O\diagup \quad \diagdown O\cdots H\cdots O\diagup\end{array}}$$

At pH values between 6 and 9 measurable amounts of both reaction products are formed. When the pH is controlled by imidazole or "tris" (trishydroxymethylaminomethane), buffers of low concentration, the relative amounts of the two reaction products are uniquely determined by the pH in accordance with the relation

$$\frac{[U]}{[V]} = 1.2 \times 10^7[H^+] \tag{48}$$

But the addition of an amount of phosphate so small that it produces no appreciable change in pH or in the rate of disappearance of iminolactone increases the proportion of aniline considerably. In a tris buffer at 0.03 *M* concentration at a pH of 7.25 the addition of 0.0005 *M* phosphate increases the proportion of reactant converted to aniline from 40 to 65 percent. Similar effects are produced by arsenate, and in somewhat less degree by bicarbonate, by acetate, by 1,1-cyclopentanediacetic acid, and by monophenylphosphate, but not by *p*-nitrophenol.

This variation of product distribution without change in rate of reaction is absolutely diagnostic (Sec. 5.17) for the presence of an intermediate which, at least in the pH region of variable product composition, is formed irreversibly from the reactants and can react with different reagents to form different products. The substances which have this large specific effect on the product distribution are all of a structure suitable for the formation of a cyclic transition state such as W, the intermediate which controls the product distribution being the carbinolamine X.

(X)

On this basis the distribution in the absence of the specific catalysts might be determined by an acid-catalyzed formation of aniline plus butyrolactone and an uncatalyzed formation of hydroxybutyroanilide or by an uncatalyzed formation of the former and a base-catalyzed formation of the latter.

Operationally speaking, the rate of disappearance of the iminolactone is subject to general acid catalysis. As shown in Fig. 10.4, the specific rate $k^{(p)}$, defined as rate divided by the concentration of iminolactone, increases with increasing buffer concentration at constant pH. The intercept on the vertical axis of each plot represents the limiting value at the pH involved of the limiting specific rate for zero buffer concentration; i.e., it represents the contribution to the specific rate of OH_3^+, of H_2O, and of OH^-, and of these alone. The catalytic coefficient of buffer component HA can be determined from the

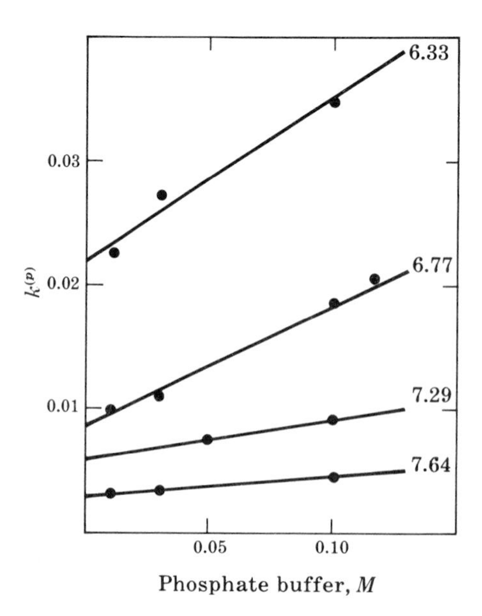

Fig. 10.4 Effect of phosphate buffer concentration on specific rate of iminolactone hydrolysis. Numbers indicate pH for each plot. [*By permission of G. L. Schmir and B. A. Cunningham, J. Am. Chem. Soc.*, **87**: 5692 (1965).]

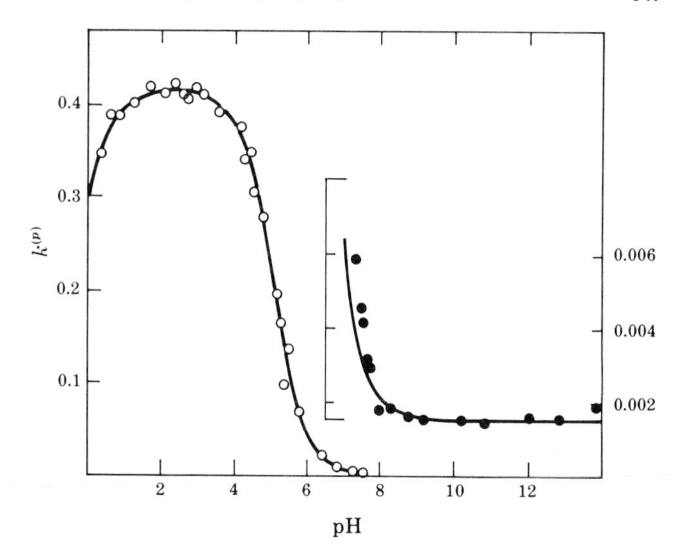

Fig. 10.5 Limiting pH-rate profile for hydrolysis of iminolactone; pH 0 to 7, left ordinate; pH 7 to 14, right ordinate. [*By permission of G. L. Schmir and B. A. Cunningham, J. Am. Chem. Soc.*, **87**: 5692 (1965).]

slope of these plots, the increase in slope with decreasing pH showing that this is acid not base catalysis.

When the limiting specific rate is plotted against pH, the limiting pH-rate profile shown in Fig. 10.5 is obtained. If the carbinolamine is formed by the process

$$\begin{matrix} CH_2-CH_2 \\ | \\ CH_2-O \end{matrix}\!\!>C=\overset{+}{N}<\begin{matrix}\phi \\ H\end{matrix} + H_2O + A^- \rightleftharpoons \left[\begin{matrix} CH_2-CH_2 \\ | \\ CH_2-O \end{matrix}\!\!>C\begin{matrix} -N<\begin{matrix}\phi \\ H\end{matrix} \\ \cdots \underset{\substack{| \\ H}}{O}\cdots H \cdots A \end{matrix}\right] \rightleftharpoons$$

$$\begin{matrix} CH_2-CH_2 \\ | \\ CH_2-O \end{matrix}\!\!>C<\begin{matrix} N<\begin{matrix}\phi \\ H\end{matrix} \\ O-H \end{matrix} + HA$$

(XII)

the iminolactone being in mobile equilibrium with its conjugate acid, the limiting specific rate will be given by

$$k^{(p)} = \frac{k_1 + k_2[OH^-]}{1 + K_I/[H^+]} = \frac{k_1[H^+] + k_2 K_w}{[H^+] + K_I} \tag{49}$$

Here K_I and K_w are the acidity constant of the conjugate acid of the imino-lactone and the water constant and k_1 and k_2 are the specific rates when A^- is water and hydroxyl ion respectively. This is an S-shaped function with an upper limit of k_1 for high hydrogen-ion concentration and a lower limit of k_2K_w/K_I for low hydrogen-ion concentrations. Except for high acidities it corresponds to the curve plotted in Fig. 10.5 if $k_1 = 0.415$, $k_2K_w/K_I = 1.55 \times 10^{-3}$, and $K_I = 8.75 \times 10^{-6}$, time being in minutes.

The dip at high acidities presents a problem. It is possible that this results from a failure of the dilute-solution approximation (cf. [46], n. 24*b*), especially since the pH values refer to a standard of uncertain meaning in the reaction medium. Otherwise one must assume a two-step process, one step acid-catalyzed, the other not, for the formation of the intermediate whose further reaction determines the product distribution. It is not obvious what the mechanism of such a process might be, since the proton transfers involved should all have high specific rates.

10.19 CATALYSIS BY LEWIS ACIDS

From the earliest days of the development of his valence theories Lewis recognized that electron-deficient molecules like BF_3, $AlCl_3$, $SnCl_4$, which are now generally called Lewis acids, can add to a molecule which has an unshared electron pair in the same way that a proton can. In the Franklin Institute paper [48] of 1938 he pointed out that in very dry solvents colored molecules of the nature of dimethylaminoazobenzene, cyanine, and crystal violet show the same change in color with $SnCl_4$ that they do with proton donors like HCl. In 1943 Lewis and Bigeleisen [49] showed in a very careful study that in aceto-nitrile or benzonitrile $SnCl_4$ combines with methylene blue to form a product whose whole absorption spectrum in the visible and the ultraviolet is identical with that of the product formed by the addition of a proton to the dye molecule. The same effect was observed with BCl_3 in acetone solution. The systems were thoroughly dried, and in any case complete hydrolysis of the $SnCl_4$ would not have yielded enough HCl to account for the change in absorption in terms of proton addition.

In this case therefore the addition of the $SnCl_4$ molecule and the addition of a proton have identical effects on the energy absorbed in the electronic transition responsible for the light absorption. By inference the addition of $SnCl_4$ and the addition of a proton produce identical changes in the spatial distribution of electrons in this complex molecule. It is therefore to be expected that Lewis acids should act as catalysts in reactions that are catalyzed by proton donors, and they do act this way in some cases. Bell and Skinner [50] find, for instance, that Lewis acids are such effective catalysts for the depolymerization of paraldehyde, a cyclic trimer of acetaldehyde, in chloro-benzene or in anisole that rate measurements by conventional methods are not possible. As the data presented in Fig. 10.6 show, rates are, however, easily measurable in ether. The reactions are first order in paraldehyde and second order in catalyst, both with Lewis acids and with hydrochloric and hydrobromic acids. Small amounts of water retard, and the catalysis cannot therefore be attributed to the formation of a strong proton donor by such a reaction as

$$AlCl_3 + H_2O + (C_2H_5)_2O \rightleftharpoons AlCl_3OH^- + (C_2H_5)_2OH^+ \qquad \text{(XIII)}$$

On the other hand, there are many reactions in which Lewis acids are effective catalysts only if small amounts of substances are present which together with the Lewis acid act as powerful proton donors. This, for instance, is the case in the polymerization of isobutene [51]. Water can act as what is called a cocatalyst or promoter by virtue of reactions like (XIII), and HCl can do so by reactions like

$$AlCl_3 + HCl + B \rightleftharpoons AlCl_4^- + BH^+ \qquad \text{(XIV)}$$

in which B is any basic substance, including the reactant in the catalyzed process. Why a cocatalyst should be needed in these polymerizations does not seem to be understood. It has been suggested [52] that the effect is steric in

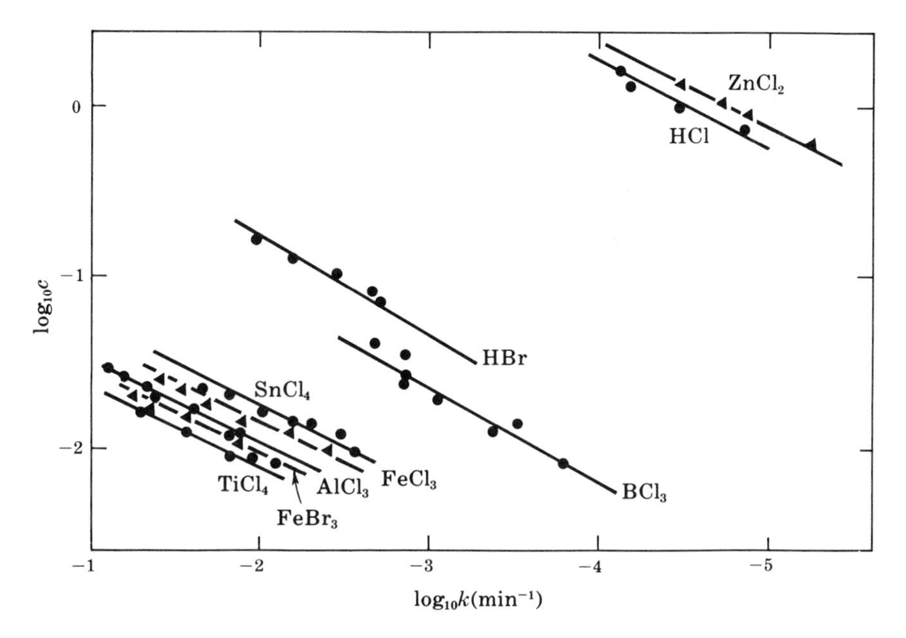

Fig. 10.6 Specific rate of depolymerization of paraldehyde with various catalysts at concentration c. (*By permission of R. P. Bell and B. G. Skinner, J. Chem. Soc.,* **1952**: 2955.)

nature. The addition of an entity like Y to an isobutene molecule might in this sense be considerably more difficult than the addition of the carbonium ion Z.

```
   H           H   Cl              H               H
   |     +     |   |               |       +       |
H—C————C————C—Al—Cl         H—C————C————C—H
   |     |     |   |               |       |       |
   H  H—C—H  H   Cl              H    H—C—H   H
         |                                 |
         H                                 H

        (Y)                               (Z)
```

REFERENCES

1. Brønsted, J. N., and K. Pedersen: *Z. Physik. Chem.*, **108:** 185 (1924).
2. Brønsted, J. N., and H. C. Duus: *Z. Physik. Chem.*, **117:** 299 (1925).
3. Brønsted, J. N., and K. Volqvartz: *Z. Phys. Chem.*, **A155:** 211 (1931).
4. Brønsted, J. N.: *Rec. Trav. Chim.*, **42:** 718 (1923).
5. Marlies, C. A., and V. K. LaMer: *J. Am. Chem. Soc.*, **57:** 1812 (1935).
6. Bell, R. P., and P. Jones: *J. Chem. Soc.*, **1953:** 88.
7. Leffler, J. E., and E. Grunwald: "Rates and Equilibria of Organic Reactions," p. 26, John Wiley & Sons, Inc., New York, 1963.
8. Benson, S. W.: *J. Am. Chem. Soc.*, **80:** 5151 (1958).
9. Westheimer, F. H.: *J. Org. Chem.*, **2:** 431 (1937).
10. Bell, R. P., and G. L. Wilson: *Trans. Faraday Soc.*, **46:** 407 (1950).
11. Pearson, R. G., and F. V. Williams: *J. Am. Chem. Soc.*, **75:** 3073 (1953); **76:** 258 (1954); E. S. Lewis and J. D. Allen: *ibid.*, **86:** 2022 (1964); J. Hine, J. G. Houston, J. H. Jensen, and J. Mulders: *ibid.*, **87:** 5050 (1965); J. A. Feather and V. Gold: *J. Chem. Soc.*, **1965:** 1752.
12. Westheimer, F. H.: *J. Org. Chem.*, **2:** 431 (1937).
13. Leffler, J. E.: *Science*, **117:** 340 (1953).
14. Bell, R. P.: "The Proton in Chemistry," Cornell University Press, Ithaca, N.Y., 1959.
15. Bell, R. P.: "Acid-Base Catalysis," Oxford University Press, New York, 1941.
16. Eigen, M.: *Angew. Chem.*, **75:** 489 (1963).
17. Hammes, G. G.: *Ann. Rev. Phys. Chem.*, **15:** 13 (1964).
18. Eigen, M., and J. Schön: *Z. Elektrochem.*, **59:** 483 (1955).
19. Gilkerson, W. R.: *J. Chem. Phys.*, **27:** 914 (1957).
20. Grunwald, E., A. Loewenstein, and S. Meiboom: *J. Chem. Phys.*, **27:** 630 (1957).
21. Meiboom, S., A. Loewenstein, and S. Alexander: *J. Chem. Phys.*, **29:** 969 (1958).
22. Pearson, R. G., and R. L. Dillon: *J. Am. Chem. Soc.*, **75:** 2439 (1953).
23. Ritchie, C. D., and R. Uschold: *J. Am. Chem. Soc.*, **86:** 4488 (1964); **89:** 1730 (1967).
24. Lapworth, A.: *Nature*, **115:** 625 (1925); J. Allen, A. E. Oxford, R. Robinson, and J. C. Smith: *J. Chem. Soc.*, **1926:** 401; C. K. Ingold and E. H. Ingold: *ibid.*, 1310; C. K. Ingold: *Ann. Rept. Chem. Soc.*, **1926:** 129.
25. Ingold, C. K.: "Structure and Mechanism in Organic Chemistry," pp. 49–52, Cornell University Press, Ithaca, N.Y., 1953.
26. Bell, R. P., M. H. Rand, and K. M. A. Wynne-Jones: *Trans. Faraday Soc.*, **52:** 1093 (1956).
27. Bell, R. P., and D. P. Onwood: *Trans. Faraday Soc.*, **58:** 1557 (1962).
28. Bell, R. P., and J. C. Clunie: *Nature*, **167:** 363 (1951); *Proc. Roy. Soc.* (*London*), **A212:** 33 (1952).

29. Arnett, E. M., and J. N. Anderson: *J. Am. Chem. Soc.*, **85:** 1542 (1963).
30. Pedersen, K. J.: *J. Phys. Chem.*, **38:** 581 (1934).
31. Swain, C. G.: *J. Am. Chem. Soc.*, **72:** 4578 (1950).
32. Swain, C. G., E. C. Stivers, J. F. Reuwer, Jr., and L. J. Schaad: *J. Am. Chem. Soc.*, **80:** 5885 (1958).
33. Reitz, O.: *Z. Physik. Chem.*, **A176:** 363 (1936).
34. Swain, C. G., and J. F. Brown: *J. Am. Chem. Soc.*, **74:** 2534, 2538 (1952).
35. Blackall, E. L., and A. M. Eastham: *J. Am. Chem. Soc.*, **77:** 2184 (1955).
36. Bender, M. L.: *J. Am. Chem. Soc.*, **73:** 1626 (1951).
37. Kursanov, D. N., and R. V. Kudryavtsev: *J. Gen. Chem. USSR (Eng. Transl.)*, **26:** 1183 (1956); S. C. Datta, J. N. E. Day, and C. K. Ingold: *J. Chem. Soc.*, **1939:** 838: F. A. Long and L. Friedman: *J. Am. Chem. Soc.*, **72:** 3692 (1950).
38. Cowdrey, W. A., E. D. Hughes, C. K. Ingold, S. Masterman, and A. D. Scott: *J. Chem. Soc.*, **1937:** 1264; A. R. Olson and R. J. Miller: *J. Am. Chem Soc.*, **60:** 2687 (1938).
39. Jencks, W. P., and J. Carriuolo: *J. Am. Chem. Soc.*, **83:** 1743 (1961).
40. Brønsted, J. N., and W. F. K. Wynne-Jones: *Trans. Faraday Soc.*, **25:** 59 (1929).
41. Bruice, T. C., and R. Lapinski: *J. Am. Chem. Soc.*, **80:** 2265 (1958); W. P. Jencks and J. Carriuolo: *ibid.*, **82:** 1778 (1960).
42. Weill, I., and J. C. Morris: *J. Am. Chem. Soc.*, **71:** 1664 (1949).
43. Jencks, W. P.: *J. Am. Chem. Soc.*, **81:** 475 (1959).
44. Jencks, W. P.: *Progr. Phys. Org. Chem.*, **2:** 63 (1964).
45. Bender, M. L.: *Chem. Rev.*, **60:** 53 (1960).
46. Schmir, G. L., and B. A. Cunningham: *J. Am. Chem. Soc.*, **87:** 5692 (1965).
47. Cunningham, B. A., and G. L. Schmir: *J. Am. Chem. Soc.*, **88:** 551 (1966).
48. Lewis, G. N.: *J. Franklin Inst.*, **226:** 293 (1938).
49. Lewis, G. N., and J. Bigeleisen: *J. Am. Chem. Soc.*, **65:** 1144 (1943).
50. Bell, R. P., and B. G. Skinner: *J. Chem. Soc.*, **1952:** 2955.
51. Evans, A., D. Holden, P. Plesch, M. Polanyi, H. Skinner, and M. Weinberger: *Nature*, **157:** 102 (1946).
52. Norrish, R. G. W., and K. E. Russell: *Trans. Faraday Soc.*, **48:** 91 (1952).

11

Quantitative Relationships Involving Structure and Reactivity

11.1 THE THEORETICAL PROBLEM

From the point of view of abstract theory the straightforward approach to the problem of the relation of structure to reactivity is the following:

1. One learns to calculate the potential energy E_p of the static arrangement of atoms which corresponds to each reactant, reaction product, and transition state. This is the negative of the work required to separate all the atoms in the structure from their positions of lowest potential energy to an infinite distance from each other.
2. One predicts the normal modes of motion of the atoms in each structure. This amounts to setting up a mathematical description of the vibrational and rotational motions of the structure.
3. For many of these motions the lowest kinetic energy is not zero but a half-quantum of the motion. One adds this zero-point energy E_z to the

potential energy to get the energy E_0 characteristic of the structure in its state of lowest possible total energy.

4. From the knowledge of the normal modes of motion one computes the partition function Q as a function of temperature, and from this one gets the standard potential and the standard enthalpy for the dilute gas state by the relations

$$\mu^\circ = E_0 - \mathbf{R}T \ln \frac{Q}{N_0 V} \tag{1}$$

and

$$\bar{H}^\circ = E_0 + \mathbf{R}T^2 \frac{d \ln (Q/N_0 V)}{dT} \tag{2}$$

5. Standard potential and standard enthalpy in solution are then computed from the values in the gas state by adding to the values for the gas state theoretically based values of the changes in standard potential and in standard enthalpy which accompany the transfer from the gas state to the solution.
6. If necessary, activity coefficients and their temperature coefficients are computed in order to make the values of potential and of enthalpy applicable to solutions of finite concentration.
7. Finally $\Delta\mu^\circ$ and $\Delta\bar{H}^\circ$ values are obtained as the difference between the μ° and the $\bar{H}^\circ$ values for reactants and products and $\Delta\mu^\ddagger$ and $\Delta\bar{H}^\ddagger$ values are obtained as the difference between the values for reactants and transition state.

It must be admitted that only a meager fraction of this program has been accomplished. The chemist who, here as elsewhere, feels the necessity of getting on with his job of learning how to predict and control the course of chemical reactions has therefore searched for empirical and semiempirical rules.

11.2 THE LINEAR FREE-ENERGY PRINCIPLE

From its beginnings the science of organic chemistry has depended on the empirical and qualitative rule that like substances react similarly and that similar changes in structure produce similar changes in reactivity. Yet the application of the rule requires so great an exercise of judgment, offers so wide an opportunity for the wisdom that comes only with experience and for the genius that seems almost intuition that there is some justice in the compliment or gibe, whichever it may be, that organic chemistry is not a science but an art.

Within limits, however, the rule can be given quantitative expression in the form of the linear free-energy principle. The name is an abbreviation, probably not a dangerously misleading one, for the quantities involved are differences in standard potential, i.e., in the standard value of the partial molal free energy. The principle is concerned with the reactivity of molecules whose structure can be divided into a reacting group X and a nonreacting residue R. It asserts that in the absence of strong specialized interactions between R and X:

1. The changes in the value of $\Delta\mu^{\ddagger}$ for any reaction involving X which are produced by a series of changes in R are linearly related to the changes in $\Delta\mu^{\circ}$ for the same reaction.
2. The changes in the value of $\Delta\mu^{\ddagger}$ or of $\Delta\mu^{\circ}$ for one reaction involving a reacting group X_1 produced by a series of changes in R are linearly related to the changes in the corresponding values for another reaction involving X_1 and also to those for a reaction involving a different group X_2.

In terms of the Leffler-Grunwald operator δ_R (Sec. 10.2) the linear free-energy principle is represented by the two equations

$$\delta_R \Delta\mu_1^{\ddagger} = a_1 \delta_R \Delta\mu_1^{\circ} \tag{3}$$

and

$$\delta_R \Delta\mu_1^{\ddagger} = b_{12}\,\delta_R \Delta\mu_2^{\ddagger} = a_2 b_{12}\,\delta_R \Delta\mu_2^{\circ} \tag{4}$$

Here $\Delta\mu_1^{\ddagger}$ and $\Delta\mu_1^{\circ}$ refer to a particular reaction 1 and $\Delta\mu_2^{\ddagger}$ and $\Delta\mu_2^{\circ}$ refer to another reaction 2. The quantities a_1, a_2, and b_{12} are independent of R but depend on the reactions involved.

Since δ_R represents a change in structure at constant temperature, Eqs. (3) and (4) can also be written as

$$\delta_R \log k_1 = a_1 \delta_R \log K_1 \tag{5}$$

and

$$\delta_R \log k_1 = b_{12} \delta_R \log k_2 = a_2 b_{12} \log K_2 \tag{6}$$

Here k_1 and k_2 are the specific rates of reactions 1 and 2 and K_1 and K_2 are the equilibrium constants of the same reactions.[1]

11.3 THE RATE-EQUILIBRIUM RELATIONSHIP

The Brønsted catalysis relationship (Sec. 10.2) is the most thoroughly studied case of the application of Eq. (5). The K of the Brønsted relationship is not the equilibrium constant of the rate-determining proton transfer involved in the reaction being observed, but it is a quantity which is of thermodynamic necessity proportional to it. This was recognized by Pedersen [2] in 1924. Historically the catalysis relationship is of key importance because it showed in

[1] For a recent review of linear free-energy relationships see [1].

1924 that a continuous mathematical function can be used to describe the essentially discontinuous effect of a change in structure of reactant, and thus pioneered a multitude of quantitative correlations.

Within a group of catalysts of closely related structure, e.g., a group of carboxylic acids, the standard deviation in log k ranges from 0.024 to 0.1. This corresponds to a random variation of from 6 to 26 percent in the specific rate. The larger deviations exceed any probable experimental uncertainty.

Linear logarithmic relationships involving the effect of a change in structure on the specific rate and the equilibrium constant of the same reaction are not limited to proton-transfer reactions. They have been observed in the air oxidation of a group of leuco dyes [3], in the reduction by a single reducing agent of a group of quinones and in the oxidation by a single oxidizing agent of a group of hydroquinones [4], in the isomerization of a group of substituted 5-aminotriazoles [5], and in the formation of carbinolamines from semicarbazide and a group of meta- and para-substituted benzaldehydes (cf. Sec. 5.19) [6].

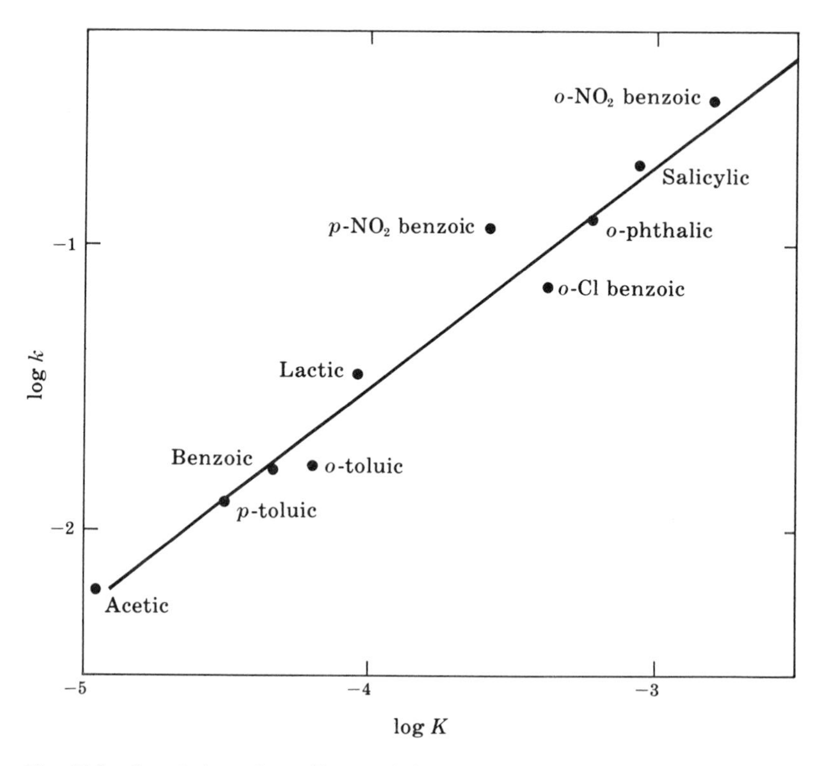

Fig. 11.1 Correlation of specific rate k in the trimethylamine-ester reaction with acidity constant K. Time unit hours. (*Data of Hammett and Pfluger* [8, 9].)

11.4 LINEAR RELATIONSHIPS INVOLVING DIFFERENT REACTIONS

Kindler [7] noted in 1926 that the alkaline hydrolysis rates of a group of meta- and para-substituted cinnamic esters vary as the square root of the rates of the correspondingly substituted benzoic esters. This is a linear logarithmic relationship with a slope of 0.5. Hammett and Pfluger [8, 9] reported in 1933 the relationship shown in Fig. 11.1 between the specific rates at 100°C of the reaction

$$RCOOCH_3 + N(CH_3)_3 \rightarrow RCOO^- + N(CH_3)_4^+ \qquad (I)$$

in methanol and the equilibrium constants at the same temperature of the reaction

$$RCOOH + H_2O \rightleftharpoons RCOO^- + OH_3^+ \qquad (II)$$

in water. The standard deviation of the points from the best line is 0.1. In 1935 both Burkhardt [10] and Hammett [9] recognized a considerable number of linear free-energy relationships in the reactions of substituted benzene derivatives.

11.5 THE GETTLER CORRELATIONS

The abscissas in Fig. 11.2 are the second-order log k values of Fitzpatrick and Gettler [11] for the formation of the oximes of a variety of carbonyl compounds. For plot S the ordinates are the values of Price and Hammett [12] for the formation of the corresponding semicarbazones. For plot T they are the values for the formation of thiosemicarbazones [13], and for plot G they are the values for the formation of guanylhydrazones [14]. The pH was 7 and the temperature 25°C in all cases. As Gettler and coworkers showed, there is an unmistakable tendency toward linear relationships. The deviations appear random and are small compared with the 1,000-fold range of the specific rates. They are, however, considerably larger than would correspond to any reasonable estimate of the experimental uncertainty.

The structure of the nonreacting part of the carbonyl compound varies widely in these experiments; some of the compounds are cyclic, some are not, some have bulky groups near the carbonyl group, some do not, some have aromatic structures in a position to resonate with the carbonyl group, some do not. But the oxime formation and the formation of the various semicarbazone derivatives are very closely related reactions. At the pH involved the rate-determining transition state is of the nature of A or B (Sec. 10.12).

```
         H                        
         |                        
R1\   ..O···H···A         R1\   ..O—H
    C:                        C:
R2/   \N—O—H              R2/   \N···H···A
         |                        |
         H                     H—O

       (A)                       (B)
```

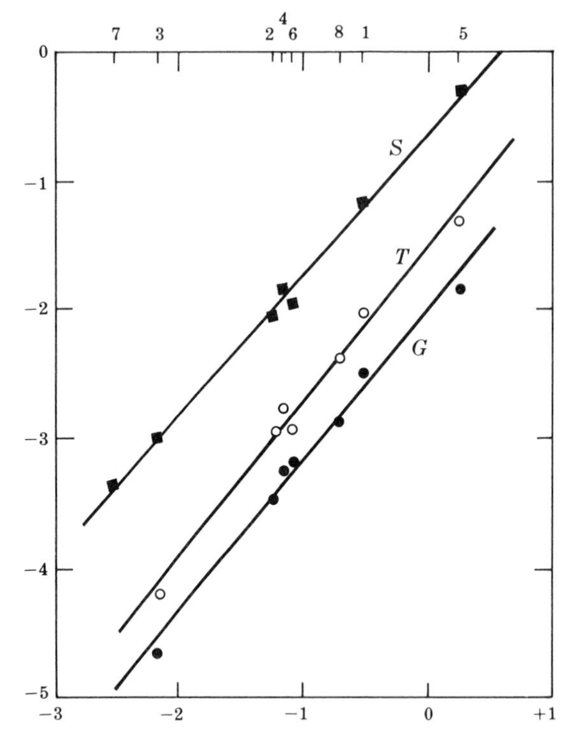

Fig. 11.2 Gettler correlations. Carbonyl compounds: 1 = acetone; 2 = diethyl ketone; 3 = pinacolone; 4 = cyclopentanone; 5 = cyclohexanone; 6 = furfural; 7 = acetophenone; 8 = methyl ethyl ketone.

Evidently the dependence on the R's of the $\Delta\mu^{\ddagger}$ value for the formation of this state from $R_1R_2C{=}O + H_2N{-}OH$ is little affected by the substitution of $-NHCONH_2$, $-NHCSNH_2$, or $-NHC(NH)NH_2$ for the $-OH$ in hydroxylamine.

11.6 ESTER HYDROLYSIS AND ACID STRENGTH

Linear free-energy relationships also hold for reactions of decidedly different nature, provided the range of structural variation in R is strictly limited. Thus Fig. 11.3 plots the log k values for the alkaline hydrolysis of ethyl esters in 87.8% aqueous ethanol [7] against log K/K_0 values for the ionization in water of the corresponding acids, K_0 being the acidity constant of benzoic acid. For the meta- and para-substituted benzoic esters there is an excellent linear correlation, even though the standard deviation of 0.1, which corresponds to a 26 percent random deviation in k, is well outside the probable experimental uncertainty.

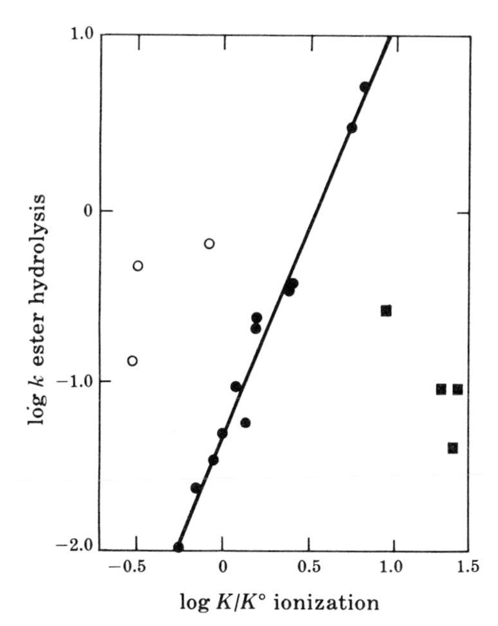

Fig. 11.3 Comparison of hydrolysis rates of esters with ionization constants of acids.

Ortho-substituted benzoic esters, on the other hand, react a couple of orders of magnitude more slowly than would be predicted from this relationship, and aliphatic esters react one or two orders of magnitude faster. The difference in the nature of the reactions being compared is greater in this case than in the one involved in Fig. 11.2, and the range of structural variation compatible with the linear relation is considerably narrower.

11.7 PHENOLS AND CARBOXYLIC ACIDS

Figure 11.4 presents a case in which the range of permissible structural variation is even more restricted. Here log K/K_0 values for the ionization of a group of phenols are plotted against the corresponding values for the ionization of the similarly substituted benzoic acids. For the meta derivatives there is a moderately satisfactory linear correlation, but with a few exceptions the para derivatives deviate, and at the extremes of the diagram they deviate widely [15].

11.8 THE ELECTRONIC INTERPRETATION

The breadth of applicability of the linear free-energy principle reinforces the indication of the Brønsted catalytic relationship that the effect of a change in

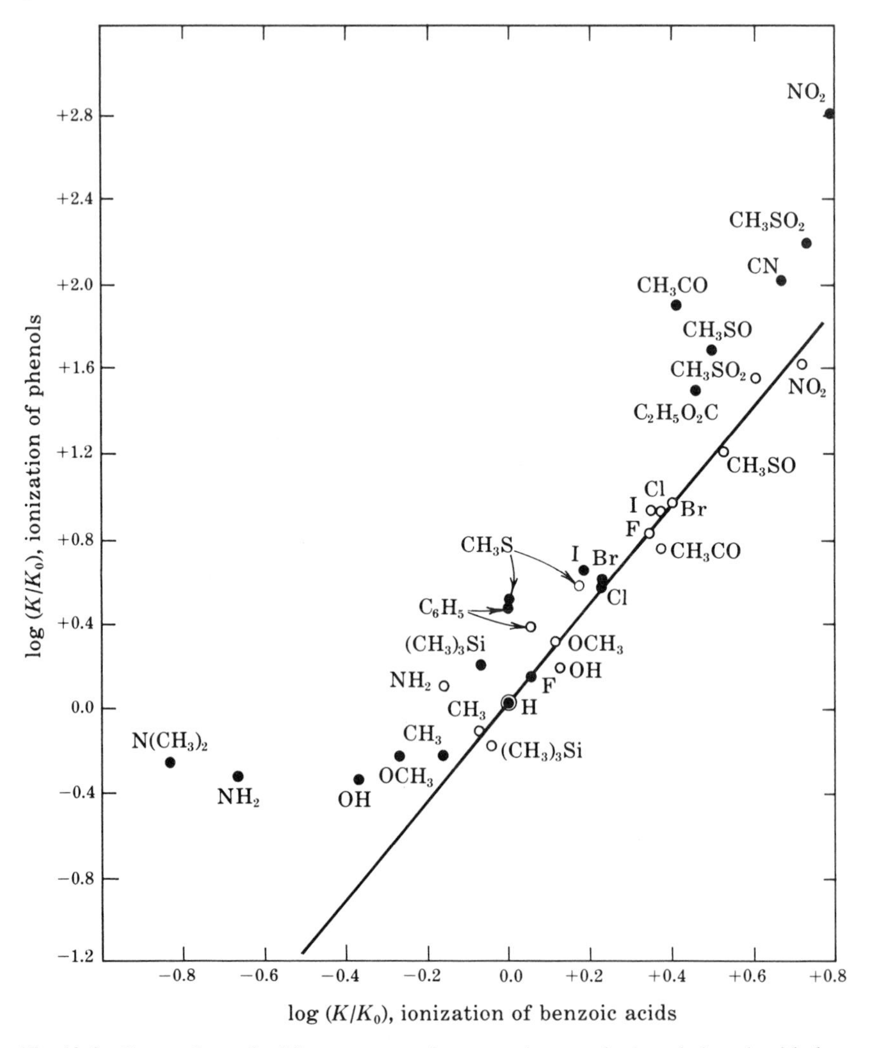

Fig. 11.4 Comparison of acidity constants of meta- and para-substituted phenols with those of correspondingly substituted benzoic acids in water at 25°C. ● = para substituents; ○ = meta substituents. [*By permission of R. W. Taft, Jr., and I. C. Lewis, J. Am. Chem. Soc.*, **80**: 2436 (1958).]

the structure of a reactant depends on a structural variable which changes continuously and not just by the jumps represented by finite changes in structure. It seems reasonable to suppose in accordance with the electron-shift hypothesis (Sec. 10.9) that this variable measures the availability in the reaction zone of electrons from the nonreacting residue. The argument can be illustrated as follows. The conversion of benzoate ion to benzoic acid necessarily involves a shift of electrons from the rest of the molècule into the carboxyl group because the added proton strongly attracts electrons. The replacement of a hydrogen atom attached to the benzene ring by a more electronegative atom like chlorine exerts a tension on the electron system of the molecule which makes a shift toward the carboxyl group more difficult. Consequently more work will be necessary when a proton is added to chlorobenzoate ion than when it is added to benzoate ion. Insofar as standard potentials parallel potential energies, the $\Delta\mu^\circ$ value for the conversion of acid to anion will then be more negative and the acidity constant larger than for unsubstituted benzoic acid.

It has been proposed [16] that two kinds of electron-shift effects must be considered, one called a polarization, which determines reaction equilibrium, another called a polarizability, which exerts an additional effect on reaction rates. In terms of transition-state theory there is no basis in principle for the distinction, and the equal applicability of linear free-energy relationships to rates and equilibria shows that it is not needed to account for the facts.

11.9 THE HAMMETT EQUATION[1]

Linear free-energy relationships involving meta- and para-substituted benzene derivatives of the kind illustrated by Fig. 11.3 are widely applicable. In spite of the kind of deviation shown in Fig. 11.4, they frequently have a degree of precision which lends them a useful predictive value, the magnitude and sign of the slope are important characteristics of a reaction, and even the deviations are significant in connection with the problem of the relation of structure to reactivity.

It is almost obvious and easily demonstrated that two series of rate or equilibrium constants which are both linearly related to a third series are linearly related to each other. Consequently it is possible to relate the various series to a single series of reference. As such, the ionization constants of substituted benzoic acids in water at 25°C are convenient because so many accurate values are available, particularly through the work of Dippy and coworkers [17]. There are recent critical compilations [18, 19].

If then one defines a substituent constant σ_i characteristic of a substituent i by the relation

$$\sigma_i = \log K_i - \log K_0 \qquad (7)$$

[1] It would be what Wright called hypocritical humility for me to pretend that I do not know that Eq. (8) is commonly called the Hammett equation or that I am not grateful to those who have honored me in this way. I can honestly say that I did not initiate the usage and that I have hitherto done nothing to promote it.

where K_0 is the acidity constant of benzoic acid and K_i is the constant of the substituted benzoic acid, the linear free-energy relationship takes the form

$$\log k_{ij} - \log k_{0j} = \rho_j \sigma_i \tag{8}$$

where k_{ij} is the rate or equilibrium constant of reaction j when the substituent i

Table 11.1 [a]

	Meta substituents			*Para substituents*					
	σ	σ^n	σ°	σ	σ^n	σ°	σ^+	σ_p^-	σ_a^-
$CH_2Si(CH_3)_3$	−0.19			−0.22					
t-C_4H_9	−0.10			−0.197			−0.256		
CH_3	−0.069	−0.069	−0.07	−0.170	−0.129	−0.15	−0.311		
$N(CH_3)_2$		−0.049	−0.15		−0.172	−0.44			
NH_2		−0.038	−0.14		−0.172	−0.38			
OCH_3	+0.115	+0.076	+0.13	−0.268	−0.111	−0.12	−0.778		
OH	+0.121	+0.095		−0.37	−0.178				
OC_6H_5	+0.252			−0.320					
$COOCH_3$	+0.39	+0.321	+0.36	+0.31	+0.385	+0.46	+0.489		
COOH					+0.406		+0.421		
OCF_3	+0.40			+0.35				+0.26	+0.27
SCF_3	+0.40			+0.50				+0.57	+0.64
F	+0.337	+0.337	+0.35	+0.062	+0.056	+0.17	−0.073	+0.02	
I	+0.352	+0.352	+0.35	+0.18	+0.299	+0.27	+0.135		
Cl	+0.373	+0.373	+0.37	+0.227	+0.238	+0.27	+0.114		
$COCH_3$	+0.376	+0.376	+0.34	+0.502	+0.502	+0.46		+0.85	
Br	+0.391	+0.391	+0.38	+0.232	+0.265	+0.26	+0.150	+0.26	
CF_3	+0.43	+0.467		+0.54	+0.532		+0.612		
CN	+0.56	+0.613	+0.62	+0.660	+0.674	+0.69	+0.659	+0.89	+1.00
SO_2NH_2	+0.55			+0.62					+0.94
SO_2CH_3	+0.56	+0.678		+0.68	+0.686				+1.14
NO_2	+0.710	+0.710	+0.70	+0.778	+0.778	+0.82	+0.790	+1.25	+1.27
SO_2CF_3	+0.79			+0.93				+1.36	+1.65

[a] σ values are for the most part from the tabulation of McDaniel and Brown [18]. Those for SO_2NH_2 and SO_2CH_3 are from Zollinger and Wittwer [22]; those for OCF_3, SCF_3, and SO_2CF_3 from Sheppard [23]; and that for $CH_2Si(CH_3)_3$ from Exner [24]. The McDaniel and Brown and the Zollinger and Wittwer values are derived directly from the acidity constants of substituted benzoic acids in water at 25°C, the others from acidity constants in partly aqueous media. The underlined σ values are those considered by McDaniel and Brown to most reliably represent K_0. σ^n values are from van Bekkum, Verkade, and Wepster [25]. σ° values are from Taft [26]. σ_p^- values are derived from the data of Fischer, Leary, Topson, and Vaughan [27] on the acidity constants of substituted phenols in water. σ_a^- values are derived from data of Zollinger and Wittwer and of Sheppard on the acidity constants of substituted anilinium ions.

is present and k_{0j} is the corresponding constant in the absence of any substituent. The parameter ρ_j is called the reaction constant of reaction j.

Table 11.1 contains under the heading σ a number of substituent constants obtained directly from data on the ionization of substituted benzoic acids in water at 25°C. Values for a number of other substituents have been obtained indirectly. If the effect of a sufficient number of substituents on rate or equilibrium of reaction j have been determined to establish a reliable value of ρ_j, substitution of the log k_{ij} value for a substituent i in Eq. (8) leads to a value of σ_i. Extensive compilations of σ values are available [1, 19–21]. Jaffé [20] surveyed the available ρ values, and the list has been revised and extended by Wells [1].

11.10 STERIC EFFECTS

The consistent failure of the points for aliphatic compounds and for ortho-substituted benzene derivatives to adhere to the line defined by the meta- and para-substituted benzene derivatives in comparisons of this sort may be attributed, at least to a large extent, to specialized short-range interactions of the sort commonly called steric. This is clearly indicated by the fact that the effects disappear when the reaction zone is more widely removed from the region in which the change in structure occurs. Thus, as shown in Fig. 11.1, log k for reaction (I) is linearly related to log K for reaction (II) both for aliphatic and for aromatic esters and for ortho-substituted as well as for meta- and para-substituted benzoic esters. The structure of the transition state is doubtless C,

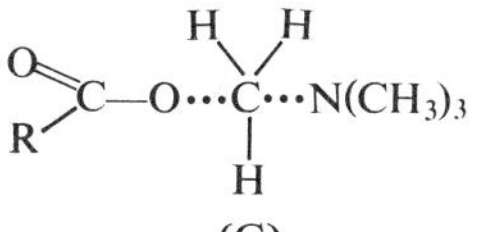

H H
O=C(R)—O···C(H)···N(CH₃)₃
H

(C)

and its formation involves a site further removed from the R group than the carboxyl carbon which is the reaction site in the ester hydrolysis (Sec. 10.15).

11.11 THROUGH-RESONANCE INTERACTIONS

The deviation of the points for the para-substituted compounds in Fig. 11.4 must on the other hand depend on specialized long-range interactions. These can be accounted for qualitatively in terms of a simple picture of resonance interaction between substituent and reacting group [28]. Thus the structure D makes a considerable contribution to the electron distribution in the anion of *p*-nitrophenol, but structure E makes a smaller contribution to that in *p*-nitrophenol itself.

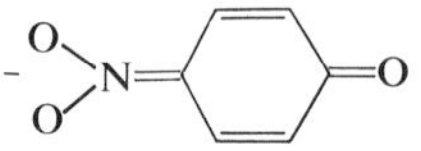

(D) 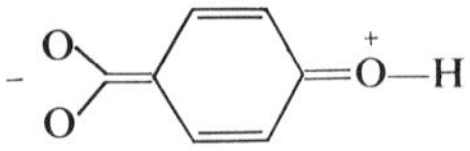 (E)

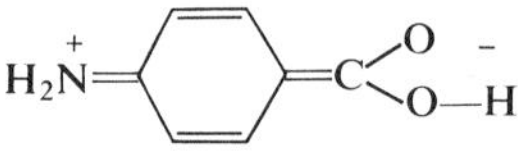

(F) 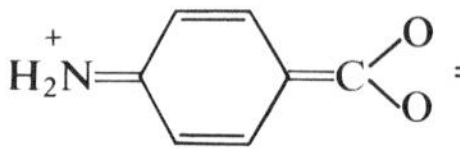 (G)

The anion, being more largely stabilized in this way, is especially favored in the equilibrium with the acid form. No interaction of this sort is to be expected in *p*-nitrobenzoic acid or its anion or in *m*-nitrophenol or its anion. *p*-Nitrophenol is therefore a stronger acid than would be expected from the behavior of *p*-nitrobenzoic acid and of *m*-nitrophenol.

In the same way there should be a larger contribution from structure F to the electron distribution in *p*-aminobenzoic acid than there is from structure G to the distribution in *p*-aminobenzoate ion. This makes *p*-aminobenzoic acid a weaker acid than would be expected from the behavior of *p*-aminophenol and of meta-substituted benzoic acids.

Clark and Perrin [29] call this effect through-resonance.

11.12 NORMAL SUBSTITUENT CONSTANTS

Van Bekkum, Verkade, and Wepster [25] have selected a list of normal substituents, designated σ^n, by a procedure which starts with σ values determined directly from the acidity constants of substituted benzoic acids for substituents, namely, *m*-CH_3, *m*-F, *m*-Cl, *m*-I, *m*-$COCH_3$, *m*-NO_2, *p*-$COCH_3$, and *p*-NO_2, for which in this reaction through-resonance is assumed to be negligible. Using these σ values alone, ρ values were calculated for some 80 reactions for which adequate rate or equilibrium data involving these substituents are available. The remaining values listed in Table 11.1 are average values calculated by way of Eq. (8) using only data for which through-resonance is unlikely. Thus σ^n values were obtained for all substituents for which data on the effect on the ionization constant of $C_6H_5CH_2COOH$ were known, they were obtained for such substituents as *p*-CN and *p*-$COOCH_3$ from the effect on the ionization constant of phenylboric acid or on the specific rate of the solvolysis of benzyl chloride; they were obtained for such substituents as *p*-NH_2 and *p*-OCH_3 from the effect on the ionization constant of phenol.

The σ^n values for substitution in the para position by $+T$ substituents,[1] i.e., those which like NH_2 and OCH_3 can supply electrons by resonance, are applicable only to reactions, such as the ionization of phenol, which are not expected to be affected by through-resonance with substituents of this kind. Similarly, the values for substitution in the para position by $-T$ substituents, those which like NO_2 and CN can withdraw electrons by resonance, are applicable only to reactions, like the ionization of benzoic acid, which are not expected to be affected by through-resonance with substituents of this kind.

With these limitations and with the σ^n values listed, an impressive improvement can be attained in the precision with which rate and equilibrium predictions can be made. This may be expressed in terms of the variability of the quantity $\bar{\sigma}$, which in accordance with a suggestion by Taft [26], is defined as

$$\bar{\sigma} = \frac{\log k/k_0}{\rho} \tag{9}$$

with ρ determined from the relation between log k and normal substituent constants. Without the limitation the difference between the highest and the lowest value of $\bar{\sigma}$ calculated for the p-CN group is 0.54; with the limitation it is 0.11. Without the limitation the difference between the highest and the lowest values for the p-OCH_3 group is 0.74; with the limitation it is 0.04. With the limitation the standard deviation for the 26 cases for which more than one $\bar{\sigma}$ value can be calculated for a given substituent ranges from 0.025 to 0.14, with only one value over 0.1 and seven over 0.05. Even these deviations are in most cases well outside the probable experimental uncertainty, and random as they seem and difficult to interpret, they are not meaningless.

This precision can, however, be attained only by recognizing the presence of systematic deviations which would not be expected from the simple through-resonance picture in the case of the four strong $+T$ substituents p-OH, p-OCH_3, p-NH_2, and p-$N(CH_3)_2$. For these the best values of $\bar{\sigma}$ for equilibria involving substituted anilines are –0.335, –0.223, –0.423, and –0.266, compared with –0.178, –0.111, –0.172, and –0.172 for reactions which do not involve aniline derivatives.

The σ^0 values also listed in Table 11.1 were obtained by Taft [26] by a procedure which differed from that of van Bekkum, Verkade, and Wepster chiefly in that values for para substituents were calculated only from the ionization of substituted $C_6H_5CH_2COOH$ and $C_6H_5CH_2CH_2COOH$ and from the rates of alkaline hydrolysis of substituted $C_6H_5CH_2COOC_2H_5$ and $C_6H_5CH_2OCOCH_3$. For some substituents Taft notes significant differences

[1] $+T$ is Ingold's symbol for this effect. Van Bekkum, Verkade, and Wepster use $+M$ for this classification. $+M$ is Ingold's symbol for an effect which is expected (Sec. 11.8) to account fully only for physical properties and reaction equilibria. Taft uses Wheland's symbol $-R$ for Ingold's $+T$ classification.

between the $\bar{\sigma}$ values calculated from reactions in highly polar media and those calculated from reactions in media of low polarity. For the latter his values for m-OCH_3, p-OCH_3, p-CN, p-$COCH_3$, and p-NO_2 are +0.06, –0.16, +0.63, +0.40, and +0.73, respectively.

11.13 THE σ^- CONSTANT

One can widen the applicability of Eq. (8) by picking two sets of σ values for substituents which are inclined toward through-resonance. This device was suggested [30] in 1937 in terms of the available data on the p-nitro substituent. The value of 0.778 for this substituent obtained from the acidity constant of p-nitrobenzoic acid applied satisfactorily to many reactions (cf. Fig. 11.3), but it failed seriously to predict the effect in reactions of phenols and of anilines. Both the phenol and the aniline reactions were, however, rather well accounted for if a σ value of 1.27 was assigned to the p-nitro group for these reactions but for these alone.

Jaffé's review [20] in 1953 accepted the dual sigma device for $-T$ substituents in the para position and listed dual values for seven such substituents. Jaffé used the symbol σ^* for the values to be used for the reactions of phenols and anilines; it is now more frequently represented by σ^-. A number of values are listed under this heading in Table 11.1.

11.14 THE σ^+ CONSTANT

For $+T$ substituents in the para position a set of σ^+ constants was based by Brown and Okamoto [31] on the effect of substituents on the specific rate of the first-order solvolysis of phenyldimethylcarbinyl chloride in 90% aqueous acetone. In the presence of a $+T$ substituent the transition state of this reaction should be stabilized by the through-resonance indicated in H.

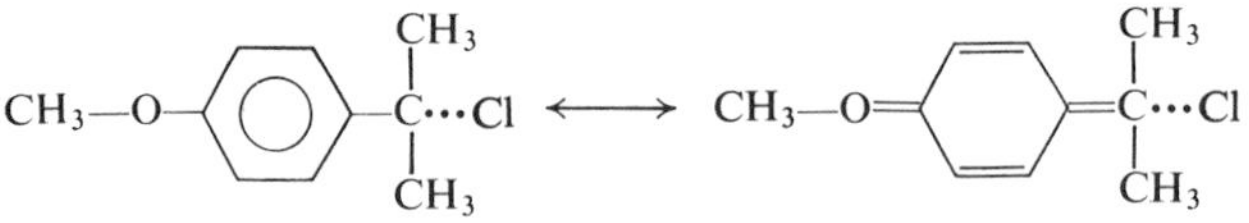

CH_3—O—C_6H_4—$C(CH_3)_2\cdots Cl$ ⟷ CH_3—O=C_6H_4=$C(CH_3)_2\cdots Cl$

(H)

In fact a plot against σ of the $\log k/k_0$ values for this reaction derived from meta substituents is linear to a good precision with a slope of –4.54, and the value for the p-nitro group lies on the same line. On the other hand, values for para substituents of the $+T$ type deviate widely. Substitution of the $\log k/k_0$ values for these substituents in the relation

$$\sigma^+ = \frac{\log k/k_0}{-4.54} \qquad (10)$$

leads to the σ^+ values listed in Table 11.1.

Brown and coworkers have found many reactions of the type in which strong through-resonance between the reaction zone and a $+T$ substituent would be expected for which log k values plot linearly against σ^+ values. This is the case for a number of reactions which involve substitution on the benzene ring rather than a side-chain reaction. For these a statistical factor is

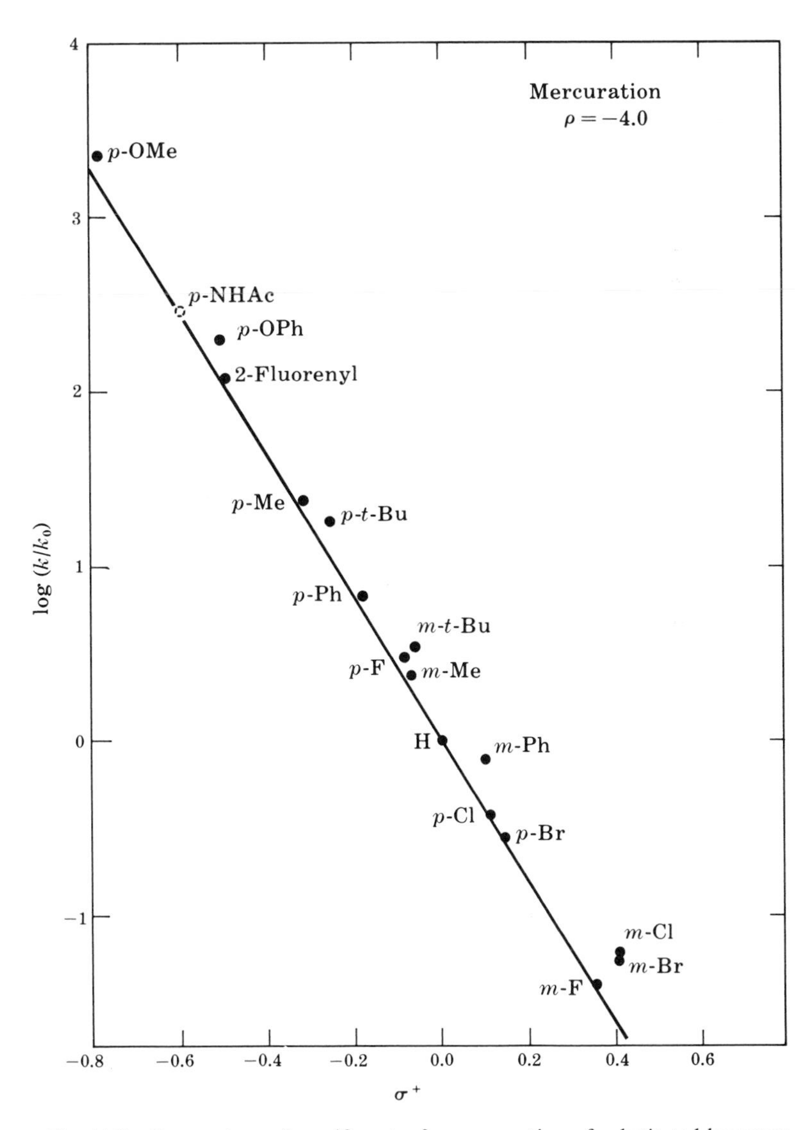

Fig. 11.5 Comparison of specific rates for mercuration of substituted benzenes with σ^+ constants. [*By permission of H. C. Brown and G. Goldman, J. Am. Chem. Soc.*, **84**: 1650 (1962).]

necessary, and $\log(6k/k_0)$ for para substituents and $\log(6k/2k_0)$ for meta substituents is plotted against the σ^+ values. Figure 11.5 shows an example, the mercuration of substituted benzenes by mercuric acetate in acetic acid, in which an especially wide range of substituents is included. Other reactions for which good linearity is found in such plots are nitration, halogenation, and Friedel-Crafts alkylation.[1]

11.15 THE INADEQUACY OF THE DUAL HYPOTHESIS

As a device, the establishment of dual sigma values is useful for systematization and prediction and in the consideration of the nature of transition states. If for instance the log k values for a particular reaction correlate better with σ^+ than with σ^n, it may reasonably be argued that the transition state is such that the reaction zone interlocks strongly with a $+T$ substituent. A number of examples of this kind of reasoning are included in the review by Ritchie and Sager [21].

Nevertheless the hypothesis that the two values for a given substituent indicate a real division of reactions into distinct classes became doubtful with the determination by Bordwell and Andersen [34] that the value of $\bar{\sigma}$ [Eq. (9)] for the *p*-nitro group in the ionization of thiophenols is 1.00, squarely in the middle between the σ and the σ^- values. A definitive decision on the question was established by the analysis of van Bekkum, Verkade, and Wepster [25]. This showed that $\bar{\sigma}$ values for the *p*-nitro group are distributed evenly all the way from 0.6 to 1.4 with no indication of a concentration in the neighborhood of 0.78 or of 1.27. And the values for the *p*-methoxy group are distributed nearly as evenly from –0.8 to 0.

11.16 REGULARITIES IN THE THROUGH-RESONANCE EFFECT

There are groups of reactions, not necessarily of closely similar nature, within which linear free-energy relations apply even though strong through-resonance is present with some substituents. The reactions involved in Fig. 11.5 constitute a case in point. One reaction is a side-chain solvolysis, the other an electrophilic aromatic displacement. Both show strong through-resonance of the $+T$ type. Nevertheless there is an excellent linear free-energy relationship between the two reactions. Figure 11.3, which includes the point for the through-resonating *p*-methoxy substituent, supplies another example, and many others could be cited.

One can usefully define a measure σ^r of the through-resonance effect as

$$\sigma^r = \bar{\sigma} - \sigma^n \qquad (11)$$

[1] Reviewed by Stock and Brown [33].

For a through-resonating substituent x in reaction 1 Eq. (9) then leads to

$$\log \frac{k_{x1}}{k_{01}} = \rho_1(\sigma_x{}^n + \sigma_{x1}{}^r) \tag{12}$$

with ρ_1 determined by the effect of substituents for which through-resonance is negligible. For the same substituent in reaction 2

$$\log \frac{k_{x2}}{k_{02}} = \rho_2(\sigma_x{}^n + \sigma_{x2}{}^r) \tag{13}$$

If the point for this substituent is to lie on the line of slope ρ_1/ρ_2 in a plot of $\log k_1$ against $\log k_2$, it is necessary that

$$\frac{\log k_{x1}/k_{01}}{\log k_{x2}/k_{02}} = \frac{\rho_1}{\rho_2} \tag{14}$$

This is possible only if $\sigma_{x1}{}^r = \sigma_{x2}{}^r$, that is, if the magnitude of the through-resonance effect is the same in the two reactions.

11.17 THE YUKAWA-TSUNO EQUATION

Yukawa and Tsuno [35] propose a more general regularity; namely, they suppose that for a series of through-resonating substituents x, y, z, etc.,

$$\frac{\sigma_{x1}{}^r}{\sigma_{x2}{}^r} = \frac{\sigma_{y1}{}^r}{\sigma_{y2}{}^r} = \frac{\sigma_{z1}{}^r}{\sigma_{z2}{}^r} = \cdots \tag{15}$$

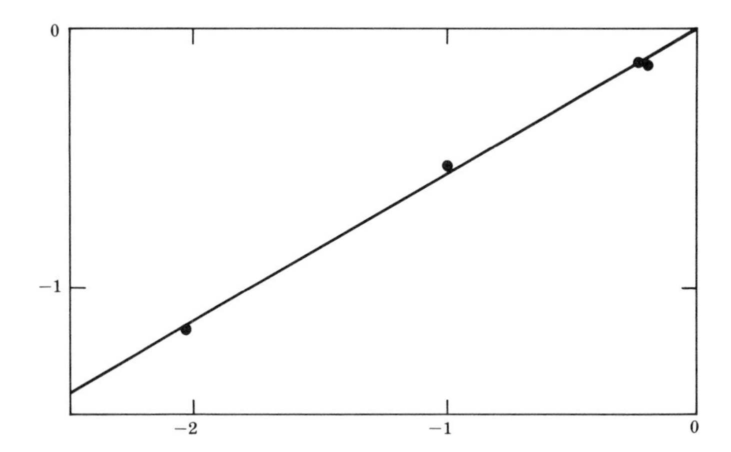

Fig. 11.6 Abscissa = σ^r value for the equilibrium of the ionization of substituted triphenylcarbinols [36]; ordinates = σ^r value for the specific rate of the halogenation of substituted benzenes [37].

with the constant ratio a positive number. In Fig. 11.6 σ^r values derived from the equilibrium constants of the reaction

$$(XC_6H_4)_3COH + 2H_2SO_4 \rightleftharpoons (XC_6H_5)_3C^+ + OH_3^+ + 2HSO_4^-$$

in sulfuric acid solution [36] are plotted against the corresponding values derived from the specific rates of the halogenation of substituted benzenes in acetic acid solution [37].

By defining reaction 2 as the one on which σ^+ values are based, Eq. (15)

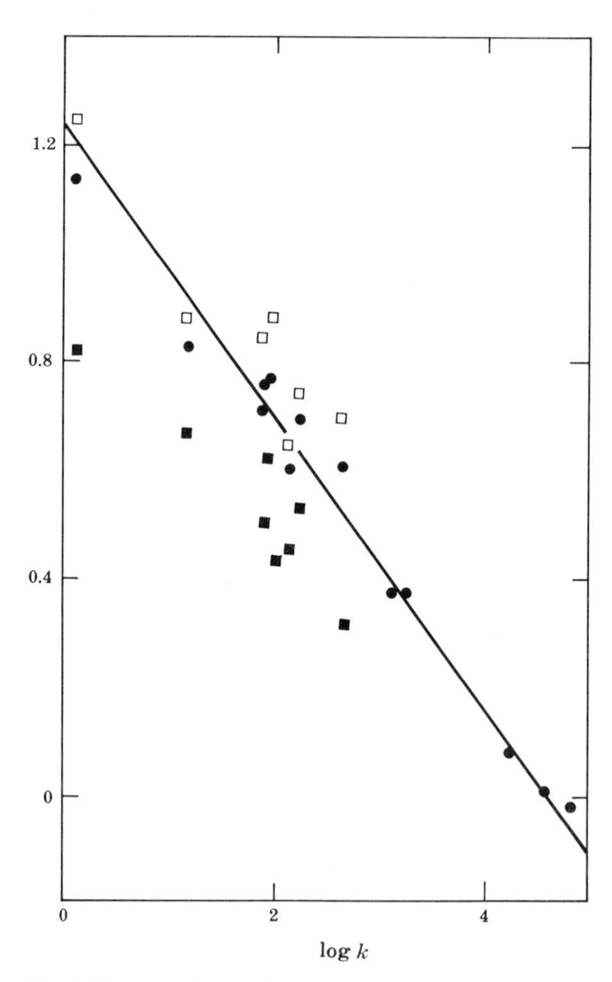

Fig. 11.7 Correlation of log k value for reaction between picryl chloride and meta- and para-substituted anilines with ■ $= \sigma^n$, □ $= \sigma^-$, ● $= 0.76\sigma^- + 0.24\sigma^n$. (*Data of Ryan and Humffray* [38].)

can be written as

$$\log \frac{k}{k_0} = \rho[\sigma^n + r(\sigma^+ - \sigma^n)] \tag{16}$$

This is the form in which Yukawa and Tsuno expressed the hypothesis except for the unimportant difference that they used σ instead of σ^n in the equation. Figure 11.7 presents a test of the equation for a case in which the through-resonance is of the $-T$ variety. The abscissas are the $\log k$ values of Ryan and Humffray [38] for the reaction of picryl chloride with meta- and para-substituted anilines.

It does not always seem to be recognized that effective evidence for the Yukawa-Tsuno hypothesis is obtainable only from correlations which include more than one strong through-resonating substituent and for which the value of r is neither close to unity nor close to zero.

11.18 RANDOM DEVIATIONS OR SYSTEMATIC DEVIATIONS

There are always deviations from linear free-energy relationships, deviations which on the average are well beyond the range of experimental uncertainty. Often they have no discernible pattern; in other cases patterns suggest themselves, but patterns which are often distinguishable from a random scatter only by the exercise of a considerable measure of optimism. The interpretation is especially worrisome when the total range of variation of one of the variables is small.

Figure 11.8 plots against σ the $\log k$ values of Dickinson and Eaborn [39] for the reaction of mono-substituted benzophenones with hydroxylamine in an acetate buffer in a 70% by volume mixture of methanol with water. The specific rate of the fastest reaction is only 3.5 times that of the slowest. One can approach the problem presented by this kind of data as Leffler and Grunwald [40] do by drawing a zigzag line, the dotted line in the figure. The standard deviation of the points from the zigzag is 0.036. Or one can, with Dickinson and Eaborn, fit the data to a standard deviation of 0.034 by an equation which is equivalent to

$$\log k = -2.025 + 0.064[\sigma + 11(\sigma^+ - \sigma)] \tag{17}$$

a relationship which can be interpreted as indicating a small normal substituent effect plus a large through-resonance effect. The standard deviation for the equation

$$\log k = -2.030 + 0.128[\sigma^n + 4.06(\sigma^+ - \sigma^n)] \tag{18}$$

is nearly the same, namely, 0.031. Or one can suppose that the apparently systematic deviations are in fact random and draw the straight line, solid in the figure, whose equation is

$$\log k = -2.150 + 0.337\sigma \tag{19}$$

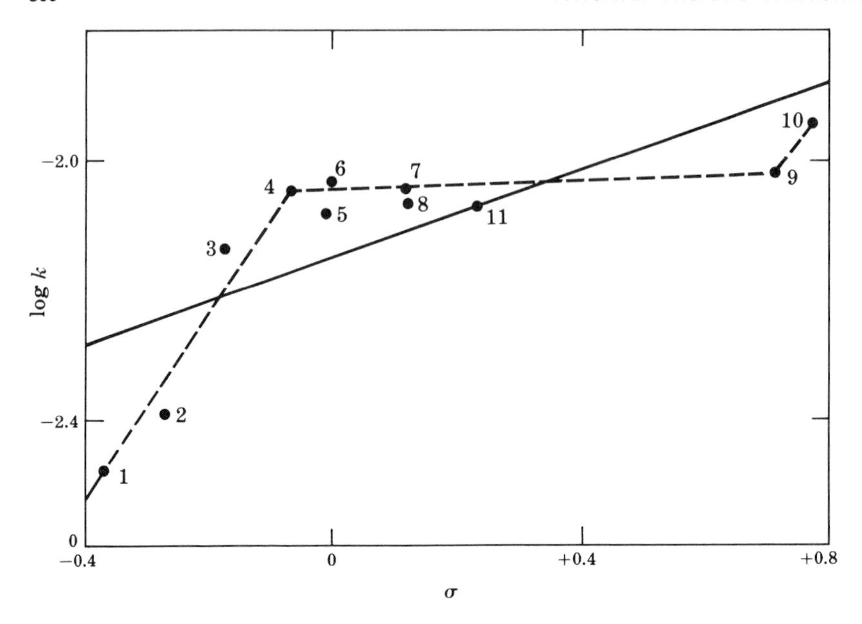

Fig. 11.8 Plot of log k for the reaction of mono-substituted benzophenones with hydroxylamine against σ. Substituents: 1 = p-OH; 2 = p-OCH_3; 3 = p-CH_3; 4 = m-CH_3; 5 = p-C_6H_5; 6 = H; 7 = m-OCH_3; 8 = m-OH; 9 = m-NO_2; 10 = p-NO_2; 11 = p-Br. (*Data of Dickinson and Eaborn* [39].)

and for which the standard deviation is 0.105. Better yet one can fit the data to the equation

$$\log k = -2.106 + 0.284\sigma^+ \tag{20}$$

with a standard deviation of 0.07.

11.19 ATTENUATION DOWN A SIDE CHAIN

The effect of a substituent in the benzene ring on a particular kind of reaction in a side chain decreases with increasing length of the chain [41, 42]. There is a consistency in the effect which is intelligible in terms of the electronic interpretation. Thus the value of ρ for the ionization of substituted *trans*-cinnamic acids in water at 25°C is 0.466. Since the value for substituted benzoic acids is unity, the attenuation ratio ϵ which measures the weakening of the effect of a substituent produced by the interposition of the vinyl group is 0.466. The ρ value for the alkaline hydrolysis of substituted *trans*-cinnamic ethyl esters is 1.31, while that for the hydrolysis of substituted benzoic esters is 2.43. The attenuation ratio is therefore 1.31/2.43 = 0.54. In the same way the attenuation ratio for the reaction of the acids with diphenyldiazomethane is 0.45, and the average value of the attenuation ratio for a vinyl group may therefore be put at 0.48 ± 0.03.

In terms of the electronic interpretation one would say that the tension exerted by a substituent is weakened by the interposition of the vinyl group to a degree which is essentially the same for a reaction which is highly sensitive to a change in the tension as it is for a reaction which is relatively insensitive.

From the effect of substituents on the reactions of phenylacetic acid and phenylacetic esters one gets an ϵ value for the interposition of a methylene group of 0.43 ± 0.06. It is perhaps surprising that the value is so nearly the same as that for a vinyl group, which is considered to be a highly effective transmitter of electronic effects. From the effect of substituents on the reactions of phenylpropionic acid and phenylpropionic ester one gets an ϵ value for the successive interposition of two methylene groups of 0.22 ± 0.02. This does not differ very much from the square of the value for the interposition of a single methylene group. Miller [42] lists average values of ϵ for the interposition: of a *p*-phenylene group, 0.24 ± 0.01; of a trans cyclopropylene group, 0.28 ± 0.06; of the corresponding cis group 0.39 ± 0.04; of a —C≡C— group 0.39 ± 0.04.

11.20 MULTIPLE SUBSTITUTION

Another important property of meta- and para-substituted benzene derivatives is the additivity of the effect of multiple substitution. Jaffé [20] surveyed 33 reactions for which adequate data were available at the time for the effect of 3,4 disubstitution, of 3,5 disubstitution, and for 3,4,5 trisubstitution and found that the relation

$$\log \frac{k}{k_0} = \rho \sum \sigma \tag{21}$$

applies with a median deviation of 0.052 in the value of $\sum \sigma$. The reactions included among others the ionization of substituted benzoic acids, the alkaline hydrolysis of substituted benzoic esters, and the methylation by picryl methyl ether of substituted dimethylanilines.

McCullough and coworkers [43] found that in the reaction

$$(C_6H_5)_2SeBr_2 \rightarrow (C_6H_5)_2Se + Br_2 \tag{III}$$

the effect of simultaneous substitution in the two benzene rings is well accounted for by the relationship

$$\log \frac{k}{k_0} = \rho(\sigma_1 + \sigma_2) \tag{22}$$

where σ_1 is the substituent constant appropriate to the substituent in one ring and σ_2 that appropriate to that in the other ring. Jaffé (20) surveyed 24 reactions for which adequate data for the application of Eq. (22) were available and found agreement as good as it is in general with the Hammett equation. The situation in which substitution occurs in both of two benzene rings which are unsymmetrically placed in a single reactant is not clear because of limited data.

Hancock and Westmoreland [44] find that the relationship

$$\log k = -0.1089 - 1.620 \sum \sigma_D + 2.37 \sum \sigma_B \tag{23}$$

applies with a standard deviation of 0.078 to 46 cases of the reaction of meta- and para-substituted benzoic acids with meta- and para-substituted diphenyldiazomethanes. σ_D is here the substituent constant appropriate to the substituent in the diphenyldiazomethane, and σ_B that appropriate to that in the benzoic acid.

11.21 STERIC INHIBITION OF RESONANCE

Westheimer and Metcalf [45] found the specific rate of the alkaline hydrolysis of the ester I to be an order of magnitude larger than the value predicted by the additivity rule.

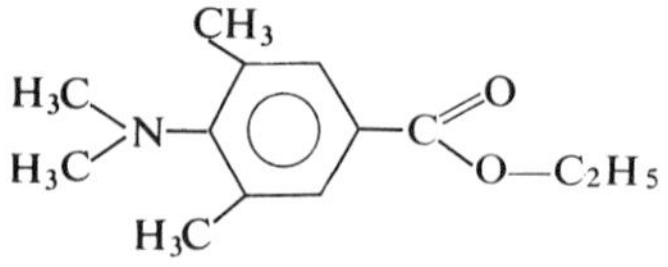

(I)

(J)

They point out that ester J is stabilized by the resonance indicated, whereas the transition state for the hydrolysis is not so stabilized. The effect contributes considerably to the large reduction in hydrolysis rate produced by the dimethylamino substituent, but it can do so only if the dimethylamino structure is coplanar, or nearly so, with the benzene ring. The adjacent methyl groups in I interfere with the coplanarity, inhibit the resonance, and increase the rate over the additivity value.

A particularly convincing example of steric inhibition of resonance involves nitro- and cyanophenols. Wheland, Brownell, and Mayo [46] find the pK of 3,5-dimethyl-4-nitrophenol to be 8.25. The pK of phenol is 9.99, that of 3,5-dimethylphenol is 10.18, and that of 4-nitrophenol is 7.16. Additivity predicts therefore the value $7.16 + 10.18 - 9.99 = 7.35$ for the trisubstituted compound. The considerable difference between this and the observed value may be accounted for on the basis that the resonance K requires the nitro group to be coplanar with the benzene ring.

(K)

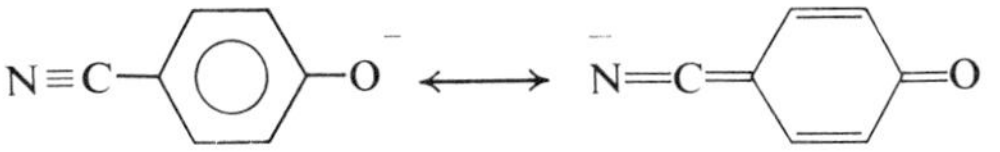

(L)

The resonance contributes considerably toward the acid-strengthening effect of the nitro group; the pK of 3-nitrophenol is 8.35. The adjacent methyl groups in 3,5-dimethyl-4-nitrophenol interfere with the coplanarity, decrease the stability of the anion, and increase the pK. By contrast the pK of 4-cyanophenol is 7.95 and that of 3,5-dimethyl-4-cyanophenol is 8.21, close to the additivity value of 8.14. The resonance shown in structure L is important, but because the CN group is linear, there is no interference from the adjacent methyl groups in the dimethyl derivative.

Schaefer and Miraglia [47] have determined the pK values of a series of 4-substituted 3,5-dimethylbenzoic acids in a 50% by volume ethanol-water mixture, for which the value of ρ for the ionization of substituted benzoic acids is 1.522. They measure the effect of steric inhibition of resonance as the difference between the sum of the σ values of the substituents and the quantity $(\mathrm{p}K_0 - \mathrm{p}K)/1.522$, a negative sign indicating that the resonance involved stabilizes the acid more than it does the anion. Their values are −0.63 for $N(CH_3)_2$; −0.18 for OC_2H_5; −0.16 for $NHCOCH_3$; −0.03 for NH_2; +0.11 for NO_2; +0.13 for CO_2CH_3, and 0 for OH, Cl, Br, and CN.

11.22 THE NATURE OF STERIC EFFECTS

The highly specific effect of a change in structure close to the reacting zone of a molecule (Fig. 11.3) was first recognized and called steric hindrance by Meyer [48] in the acid-catalyzed esterification of carboxylic acids. In benzoic acid the rate is appreciably decreased by a single methyl, halogen, or nitro group in the ortho position, and so largely decreased by substitution in both ortho positions that conditions which otherwise lead to quantitative yields result only in negligible reaction. The characteristic features of this, as of similar cases, are the unexpectedly large effect of the double substitution, the fact that methyl and nitro groups produce effects in the same direction, the positive dependence of the effect on the bulk of the substituent, and the relatively large effect even of a single ortho substitution. The pronounced retardation by double ortho substitution appears very generally in the reactions of carboxylic esters, amides, and acid halides, and of nitriles, ketones, and amines, and is a well-recognized phenomenon in preparative chemistry.

The data listed in Table 11.2 show that the acidity constants in water of benzoic acids and of anilinium ions and the specific rates of the alkaline hydrolysis of benzoic esters and of the reaction of anilines with dinitrochlorobenzene exhibit the characteristic phenomenon that ortho methyl and ortho nitro groups have effects in the same direction and that ortho substituents have effects of very different magnitude than those produced by substituents in the meta and para positions. For reasons which derive from the history of the steric-hindrance concept it is sometimes overlooked that the effects are just as pronounced in equilibrium phenomena like the ionization of benzoic acids as they are in rate phenomena.

The steric-hindrance effects consistently disappear when the reaction zone is transferred to a point further removed from the region of structural change. One example has already been cited (Sec. 11.10). Another is the fact, illustrated in Table 11.2, that ortho- and para-substituted cinnamic

Table 11.2 Effect of ortho substituents on equilibrium and rate[a]

	(1)	(2)	(3)	(4)	(5)	(6)	(7)
p-CH_3	0.68	0.47	0.33	2.47	0.71	0.77	0.59
p-Cl	1.67	4.32	3.8	0.28	2.03	1.21	3.63
p-NO_2	6.00	104	3,100	<0.001	9.8	5.00	34.7
o-OCH_3	1.29		1.2	0.58	0.38	1.49	
o-CH_3	1.96	0.124	1.6	0.103		0.87	0.48
o-F	8.63	5.55			2.34		1.62
o-Cl	18.2	1.91	65	<0.001	1.99	1.46	6.60
o-Br	22.3	1.89	96		3.06		8.13
o-I	21.9	0.84			2.52		9.10
o-NO_2	107	5.71	58,000	<0.001	7.93	4.02	151

[a] The entries are the ratios K/K_0 or k/k_0, where K_0 and k_0 are equilibrium constant and specific rate for the unsubstituted reactant. A few data on para substituents are included for comparison. The values in column 1 derive from the acidity constants of benzoic acids in water at 25°C [17]; in 2 from the specific rates of the alkaline hydrolysis of ethylbenzoates in an ethanol-water mixture at 30° [7, 49]; in 3 from the acidity constants of anilinium ions in water at 25° [50]; in 4 from the specific rates of the reaction of anilines with dinitrochlorobenzene at 100° [51]; in 5 from the alkaline hydrolysis of ethyl cinnamates, conditions same as in 2 [7]; in 6 from the specific rates of the hydrolysis of phenylsulfuric acids in water at 78.6° [52]; in 7 from the equilibrium of the reaction of benzoic acids with diphenylguanidine in benzene at 25° [53].

esters have nearly the same hydrolysis rates. Presumably the near identity of the effects of ortho and para substitution on the rate of the hydrolysis of arylsulfuric acids is another example.

The steric effects are therefore associated with short-range forces which alter the standard potentials of reactant and product or of reactant and transition state by different amounts. A variety—perhaps too great a variety—of detailed interpretations suggest themselves. The formation of the transition state for the hydrolysis of a benzoic ester requires the conversion of the carbethoxy group to a bulkier structure such as M,

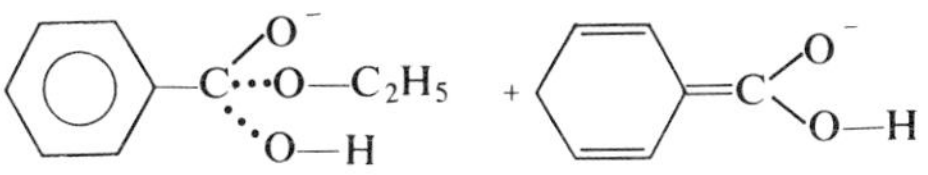

(M) (N)

in which short-range repulsions from ortho substituents may well increase the energy and thus reduce the specific rate. In the ionization of benzoic acid one may suppose that structure N makes a greater contribution to the electron distribution in the acid than in the anion. Interference by ortho substituents with the coplanarity required for this structure would increase the energy of the acid more than it does that of the anion and would thus increase the acidity constant.

There is considerable evidence that changes in structure in the neighborhood of the reaction zone alter the solute-solvent interactions and that this is an important factor in the steric effects. Thus Fig. 11.9 plots the relative acidity constants K/K_0 of Wooten and Hammett [54] for a solvent consisting of *n*-butanol containing 0.05 *M* lithium chloride against the corresponding values for the solvent water, K_0 being the acidity constant of benzoic acid. The points for meta- and para-substituted benzoic acids are in good agreement with a linear free-energy relationship with a slope of 1.5. The points for ortho-substituted benzoic acids, except for the *o*-methoxy derivative, lie to the right of this line, and the points for aliphatic acids not substituted in the α position lie to the left. The qualitative resemblance to Fig. 11.3 is striking.

The data of Davis and Hetzer (column 7 of Table 11.2) supply another example of the importance of the solute-solvent interaction. In the relatively inert solvent benzene, *o*-toluic acid is weaker than *p*-toluic acid instead of stronger, as it is in water. In benzene, *o*-chlorobenzoic acid is only 1.8 times stronger than *p*-chlorobenzoic acid instead of 11 times stronger, and *o*-nitrobenzoic acid is 4.4 times stronger than the para isomer instead of 18 times stronger.

The specialized effect of ortho substitution on entropies or enthalpies of reaction or of activation (Sec. 12.2) is doubtless also related to the solute-solvent interaction.

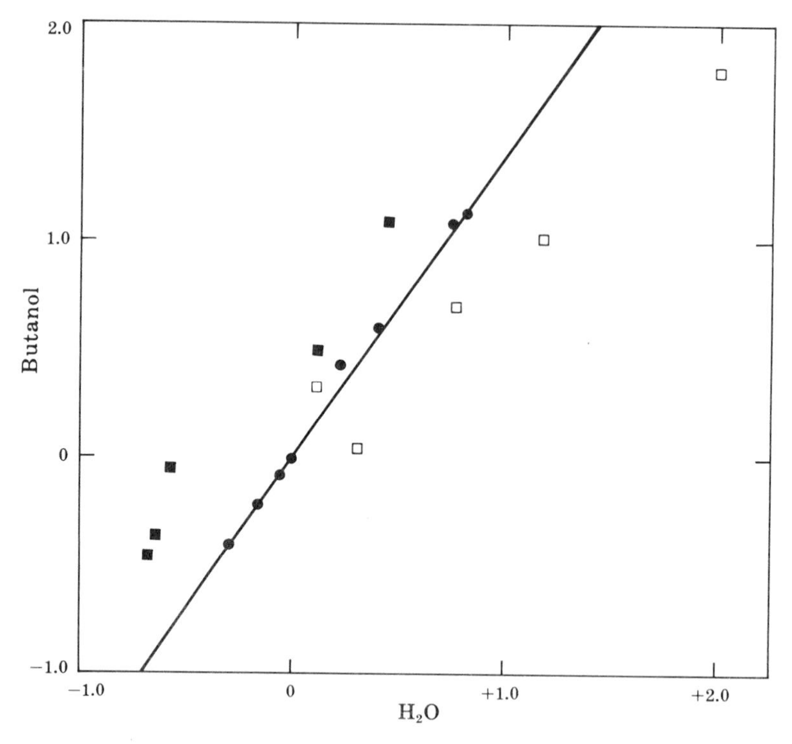

Fig. 11.9 Comparison of log K/K_0 for ionization in *n*-butanol [57] and in water. Reference acid benzoic. ● = meta- and para-substituted benzoic acids from *p*-OCH_3 to *p*-NO_2; □ = *o*-OCH_3, *o*-CH_3, *o*-Cl, and *o*-NO_2 benzoic acids; ■ = butyric, propionic, β-chloropropionic, acetic, and formic acids.

11.23 ADDITIVITY IN STERIC EFFECTS

In some cases the value of ρ in the equation

$$\log\frac{k}{k_0} = \sigma_1\,\rho + \mathrm{X} \tag{24}$$

when the meta or para substituent R_1 is varied in the series of compounds $R_1R_2C_6H_3Y$ is the same as it is in the equation

$$\log\frac{k}{k_0} = \sigma_1\,\rho \tag{25}$$

when R_1 is varied in the series $R_1C_6H_4Y$. Y is here the reacting group, R_2 is ortho to it, and k_0 is the value of k for C_6H_5Y. The equation applies, for instance, when R_2 is methyl and k is the specific rate of reaction of a series of benzoic acids with diphenyldiazomethane [55]. In such cases as this the total effect, including the steric, of the ortho substituent adds a constant increment to the long-range effect of the meta or para substituent.

Considerable deviations from this additivity rule appear, however, when there is severe crowding of the reacting group by ortho substituents. Thus a plot of the p*K* values for 4-substituted di-*t*-butylphenols against the corresponding values for 4-substituted phenols, although satisfactorily linear, has a slope of 1.65 for aqueous solutions and one of 1.73 for 50% ethanol–water solutions [56]. Cohen and Jones interpret the effect in the sense that (1) there is a transfer of charge from the phenolate oxygen to the para substituent; (2) interaction of solvent with the anion is an important factor tending to stabilize the ion; (3) the *t*-butyl groups hamper this solvation process insofar as it occurs on the phenolate oxygen and thereby decrease the acidity constant; (4) the effect is less important the greater the extent of charge transfer to the para substituent.

With less bulky ortho substituents the deviations from additivity become less pronounced. A plot of the p*K* values of 4-substituted 2,6-dimethylphenols against the corresponding values for 4-substituted phenols has a slope of 1.21 for aqueous solutions, and the same kind of plot for 4-substituted 2,6-dichlorophenols has a slope of 1.17 [57]. For 4-substituted 2-nitrophenols the slope is unity within an uncertainty of the order of 2 percent.

A plot of p*K* values for dimethylanilinium ions against the values for anilinium ions has a slope of 1.15 [58]. A plot of p*K* values for *N*-(2,4-dinitrophenyl)benzylammonium ions against the values for benzylammonium ions has a slope of 1.60 [59].

11.24 FURTHER LIMITATIONS ON LINEAR FREE-ENERGY RELATIONSHIPS

One must not expect a linear free-energy relationship to apply to a pair of reactions in which the bond-making or bond-breaking process varies widely. In the catalysis of the hydration of acetaldehyde (Sec. 10.12) acids, such as nitromethane, in which the proton donated in the reaction is initially attached to carbon are poorer catalysts by from one to two orders of magnitude than carboxylic acids or phenols of the same acid strength [60]. On the other hand, a number of ketoximes are more effective catalysts by from one to two orders of magnitude than carboxylic acids or phenols of the same acid strength.

As Table 11.3 shows, the rates of reactions in which a nucleophile becomes attached to carbon present a bewildering pattern when the nucleophilic atom is varied widely. There is at most a mere vestige of a relation to the base strength of the nucleophile as it is measured by the p*K* of its conjugate acid. Attempts at interpretation must of course take into account the strong dependence of the relative rates of reactions of this sort on the solvent in which the reaction takes place (Sec. 8.15). There is an excellent survey of this important, although confusing, field by Bunnett [61].

Table 11.3 Relative reactivities of nucleophiles[a]

Nucleophile	(1) pK	(2)[b] CH_3Br	(3)[c] NPA
I^-	$\ll 0$	5.04	<-5
Cl^-	$\ll 0$	3.04	<-5
$S_2O_3^{--}$	1.9	6.36	−3.0
F^-	3.2	2.0	−3.0
$CH_3CO_2^-$	4.7	2.72	−3.3
C_5H_5N	5.3	3.6	−1.0
NH_2OH	6	6	2.0
SH^-	7.2	5.1	
ClO^-	7.2		3.2
CN^-	9.1	5.1	1.0
HOO^-	11.5		5.3
OH^-	15.7	4.20	3.0

[a] The entries in column 1 are the p*K* values of the conjugate acids in water; in column 2 they are the values of log *k* for the second-order nucleophilic displacement on CH_3Br; in column 3 the values of log *k* for reaction with *p*-nitrophenyl acetate.
[b] Data from [62].
[c] Data from [63].

11.25 INDUCTIVE AND RESONANCE EFFECTS

One can account qualitatively for the reactivity of benzene derivatives in terms of the electron-shift hypothesis as follows. A chlorine atom stripped of its valence electrons has a charge of +7, whereas a hydrogen atom thus stripped has a charge of +1. Consequently the substitution of chlorine for hydrogen replaces a region of relatively low positive charge density by one of much higher density, and this tends to pull the whole electron system of the molecule toward the region of the substitution. The shift makes it easier to remove a proton from an acid group in the molecule or to attach a nucleophilic reagent such as hydroxyl ion in ester hydrolysis. It makes it more difficult to attach an electrophilic reagent such as NO_2^+ in nitration. When the substitution of chlorine or other electronegative atom for hydrogen occurs on a saturated carbon atom and the point of the substitution and the region of reaction are sufficiently separated to eliminate short-range effects due to the bulk of the chlorine, the shift, called an inductive effect, should closely approximate the total effect of the substitution.

When, however, the substitution occurs on an unsaturated carbon, the inductive effect does not sufficiently account for the facts. An adequate picture in the case of chlorobenzene bases on the resonance hybridization O

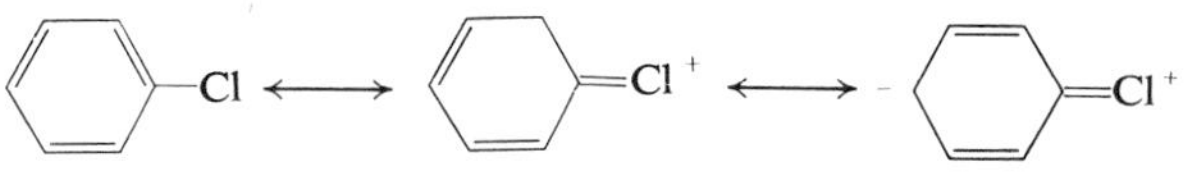

(O)

in which the electrons in the unshared pairs on the chlorine have been partially delocalized to the ortho and para positions of the ring. This delocalization, called a resonance effect, increases the availability of electrons for reactions which occur on the ortho or para carbon atoms or in side chains attached to these atoms.

The resonance effect of the substitution of chlorine for hydrogen is opposite in sign to the inductive effect but is weaker than the inductive effect. The substitution therefore decreases electron availability at all ring positions but not so much at the ortho and para positions as at the meta position. This is consistent with the fact that both *m*- and *p*-chlorobenzoic acids are stronger than benzoic acid and that the para acid is weaker than the meta acid. It is also consistent with the fact that nitration on a ring carbon atom in chlorobenzene is slower than it is on one in benzene but is faster on an ortho or para carbon than on a meta atom.

Similarly one accounts for the fact that *m*-methoxybenzoic acid is stronger but *p*-methoxybenzoic acid weaker than benzoic acid. The inductive effect of the methoxy group decreases the availability of electrons in both positions but it is more than compensated in the para position by a resonance effect in the opposite direction.

A nitro group has an inductive effect which decreases the availability of electrons on the ring carbon atoms of nitrobenzene. The resonance effect predicted by the picture P

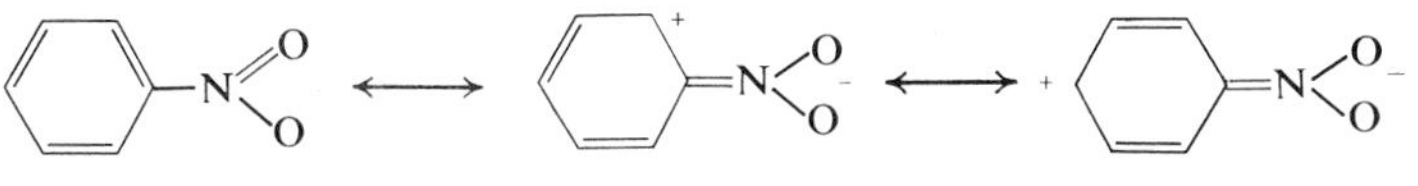

(P)

should further decrease the availability of electrons on the ortho and para positions. This is consistent with the fact that *p*-nitrobenzoic acid is stronger than *m*-nitrobenzoic acid and that both are stronger than benzoic acid. It is also consistent with the fact that a nitro group lowers reactivity in such reactions as nitration and lowers it more in the para position than in the meta position.

There are other ways than the electron-shift hypothesis in which one can approach the problem of structure and reactivity. An electric field theory originally proposed by Bjerrum [64] and highly refined by Kirkwood and Westheimer [65] accounts for the ratio of the first and second ionization constants of dibasic acids in terms of the effect of the negative charge of the COO^- group in the singly charged ion on the work required to remove a proton from the remaining COOH group. It further accounts for the effect of the substitution of chlorine for hydrogen in an acid in terms of the electric field of the C—Cl dipole on the work of proton removal.

Both the inductive effect and the electric field effect should be recognized as methods of mathematical approximation to the overwhelmingly difficult problem of calculating the fourfold difference in energy involving substituted and unsubstituted reactant and substituted and unsubstituted reaction product or transition state. It is entirely possible that one or the other may be a better approximation or that a linear combination of the two may be a still better approximation. The temptation to treat them as distinct physical phenomena should, however, be firmly resisted.

In terms of presently available information there is no operational need for more than two independent structural variables to account for the long-range effects of substitution.[1] Should more become necessary as further data appear, theory is well prepared for the challenge. Dewar and Grisdale [66] remark, "There are at least five distinct processes by which substituents can affect a distant reaction center."

11.26 THE TAFT EQUATION

Taft proposes [67] that, regardless of the presence or absence of steric and resonance effects, the inductive effect (I) may usefully be represented as

$$I = \rho_I \sigma_I \tag{26}$$

where ρ_I depends only on the reaction and σ_I depends only on the composition and structure of the nonreacting part of the molecule. The value of σ_I for a group X is defined by the relation

$$\sigma_I = 0.262 \log \frac{K}{K_0} \tag{27}$$

where K_0 is the acidity constant of acetic acid in aqueous solution at 25°C and K is the corresponding constant for the acid XCH_2COOH. The substitution of X for hydrogen in acetic acid would not be expected to involve either steric or resonance effects, and Taft found a variety of other reactions in which inductive effects alone are to be expected and to which Eq. (27) applies with considerable precision.

[1] An important statistical analysis by Swain and Lupton [83], which appeared too late for detailed discussion in this book, emphasizes this conclusion.

The most notable of these reactions involves the acidity constants of the 4-X-bicyclo[2.2.2]octane-1-carboxylic acids Q,

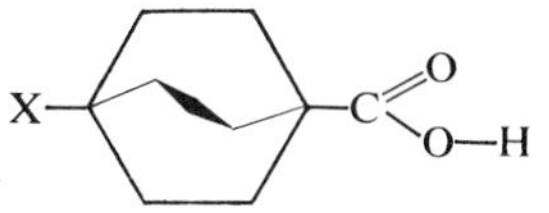

(Q)

and the specific rate of the hydrolysis of the corresponding ethyl esters. The importance in theory of these substances was pointed out by Roberts and Moreland [68], who synthesized a number of them and measured the constants. Figure 11.10, which includes data for a number of substituents not studied by Roberts and Moreland, shows how good the correlation is.

Another correlation demonstrates in an interesting way the fact that steric effects can sometimes be estimated by comparison of different reactions. Taft [67] put in quantitative terms a suggestion of Ingold [70] that steric effects might be identical in the alkaline and the acid hydrolysis of an ester.

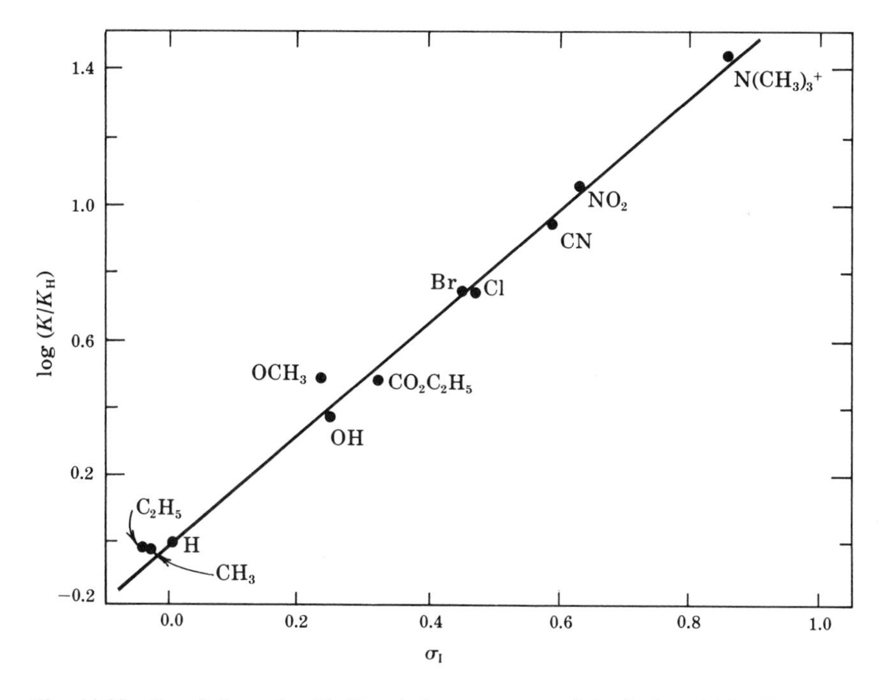

Fig. 11.10 Correlation of acid dissociation constants of 4-substituted bicyclo[2.2.2.]-octane-1-carboxylic acids with σ_I. Carboxylate substituent, not shown, obeys this relationship. [*By permission from H. D. Holtz and L. M. Stock, J. Am. Chem. Soc.*, **86:** 5188 (1964).]

If so, the quantity

$$A = \log\left(\frac{k}{k_0}\right)_B - \log\left(\frac{k_0}{k}\right)_A \tag{28}$$

should be free of steric effects. Here the k's are the specific rates for the hydrolysis of RCOOR′, the k_0's are the corresponding values for the hydrolysis of CH_3COOR', and the subscripts B and A refer to hydrolysis in alkaline and in acid solution respectively. Taft averaged the A values for a variety of R′ groups and of solvents and showed that a plot of this average for XCH_2COOR' against $\log(K/K_0)$ for the ionization of XCH_2COOH is linear with a slope of 0.236 and a standard deviation of 0.35.

11.27 HISTORICAL NOTE

Taft originally wrote

$$I = \rho^* \sigma^* \tag{29}$$

with the value of σ^* for a group R defined by

$$\sigma^* = \frac{1}{2.48}\left[\log\left(\frac{k}{k_0}\right)_B - \log\left(\frac{k}{k_0}\right)_A\right] \tag{30}$$

Finding that σ^* thus defined for $R = XCH_2$ correlates well with the acidity constants of the acids XCH_2COOH, he then defined the value of σ_I for the group X as

$$\sigma_I = 0.45\sigma^* \tag{31}$$

The choice of the coefficient 0.45 was intended to make σ_I equal to $\log(K/K_0)$ for the acidity constants of the Roberts and Moreland acids in water. Since a large proportion of the available σ_I values derive from data on the acidity constants of XCH_2COOH, Eq. (27) is preferable to Eq. (31) as a definition.

11.28 THE CORRELATION OF ALIPHATIC AND AROMATIC REACTIVITIES

A plot (Fig. 11.11) of $\log(K/K_0)$ for the ionization of meta- and para-substituted benzoic acids against σ_I scatters widely [71]. Even for meta substituents alone the scatter is considerable. There is, however, direct evidence that the σ_I parameters derived from aliphatic reactivities apply to the properties of benzene derivatives. Thus, as shown in Fig. 11.12, the fluorine nmr shielding-parameter values relative to fluobenzene in carbon tetrachloride solution of meta-substituted fluobenzenes are linearly related to σ_I. The shielding is presumably a sensitive measure of the electron density in the immediate neighborhood of the fluorine atom, but it appears to respond only to that part

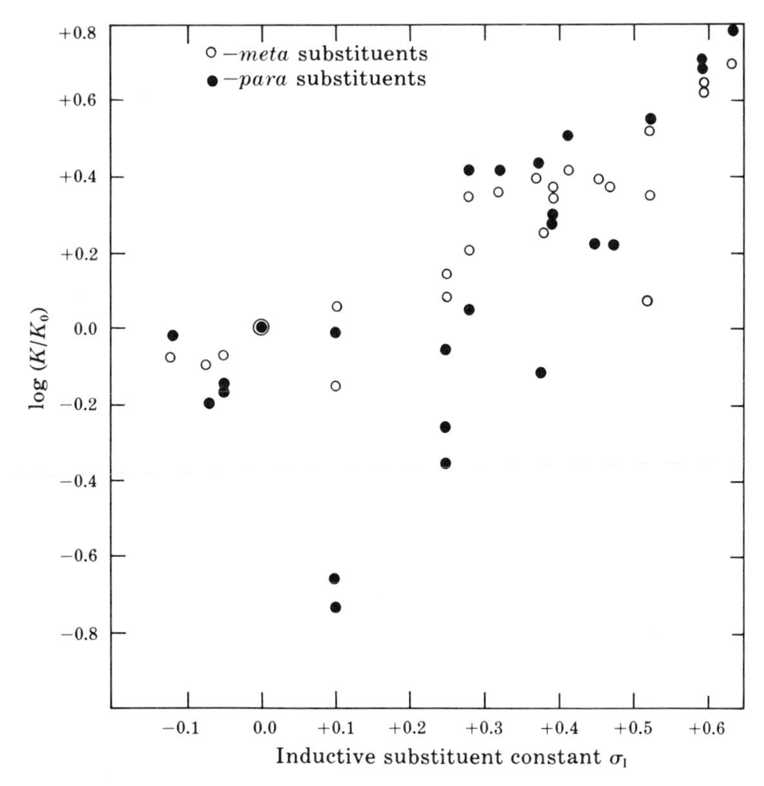

Fig. 11.11 Lack of correlation of acidity constants of meta- and para-substituted benzoic acids in water with σ_I. [*By permission from R. W. Taft, Jr,. and P. C. Lewis, Tetrahedron*, **5**: 210 (1959).]

of the change in density which can be assigned to the inductive effect. It would seem therefore that additional factors are involved in the effect of para substituents on the shielding, an effect much greater than that of meta substituents, and in the effect both of meta and of para substituents on reactivity.[1]

In the light of these phenomena it is reasonable to write as trial equations

$$\log \frac{k_p}{k_0} = \rho_I{}^p \sigma_I + \rho_R{}^p \sigma_R^\circ \tag{32}$$

and

$$\log \frac{k^m}{k_0} = \rho_I{}^m \sigma_I + \rho_R{}^m \sigma_R^\circ \tag{33}$$

the superscript p referring to para substituents and the superscript m to meta substituents. Two equations and two sets of ρ_I and ρ_R values are necessary

[1] For a theoretical discussion of the shielding see [73]. See also [74].

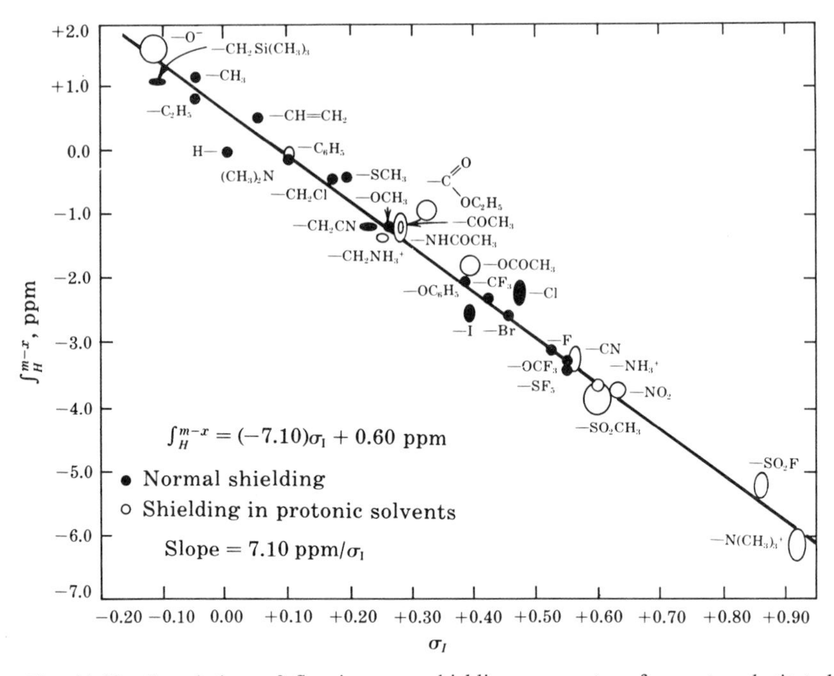

Fig. 11.12 Correlation of fluorine nmr shielding parameters for meta-substituted fluobenzenes with σ_I. [*By permission from R. W. Taft, Jr., E. Price, I. R. Fox, J. C. Lewis, K. K. Andersen, and G. T. Davis, J. Am. Chem. Soc.*, **85:** 709 (1963).]

because the substituent constants σ_I and σ_R° are independent of the position of the substituent.[1] It follows from Eqs. (32) and (33) that

$$\frac{\log(k^p/k_0)}{\log(k^m/k_0)} = \frac{\rho_I{}^p\,\sigma_I + (\rho_R{}^p/\rho_I{}^p)\,\sigma_R^\circ}{\rho_I{}^m\,\sigma_I + (\rho_R{}^m/\rho_I{}^m)\,\sigma_R^\circ} \tag{34}$$

where k^p and k^m refer to the same substituent in the para and in the meta position. In the absence of through-resonance and to the precision of the Hammett equation, the ratio

$$\frac{\log(k^p/k_0)}{\log(k^m/k_0)} = \frac{\sigma^p}{\sigma^m} \tag{35}$$

is independent of the reaction. Within these limitations, therefore, the ratios

$$K_I = \frac{\rho_I{}^p}{\rho_I{}^m} \tag{36}$$

$$K_R = \frac{\rho_R{}^p}{\rho_R{}^m} \tag{37}$$

[1] A relationship of this sort is implicit in the discussion by Taft and Lewis [75]. The equations in the form stated above and with the above stated definitions of the symbols were used by Ehrenson [76].

and

$$K_m = \frac{\rho_R{}^m}{\rho_I{}^m} \tag{38}$$

must be independent both of reaction and of substituent provided the ρ's depend only on the reaction. In terms of these parameters and the definition of σ Eqs. (32) and (33) are equivalent to

$$\sigma^p = \frac{\rho_I{}^m}{\rho}(K_I\,\sigma_I + K_R\,K_m\,\sigma_R^\circ) \tag{39}$$

and

$$\sigma^m = \frac{\rho_I{}^m}{\rho}(\sigma_I + K_m\,\sigma_R^\circ) \tag{40}$$

The parameters $\rho_I{}^m/\rho$ and K_m can be fixed without altering the generality of these relationships; for an increase in the former simply decreases all σ_I and σ_R° values in a fixed ratio, and an increase in the latter decreases all σ_R° values in a fixed ratio. There is no basis for an absolute scale of values either of σ_I or of σ_R°. Setting $\rho_I{}^m/\rho = 1$ and $K_m = 1/K_R$, one gets

$$\sigma^p = K_I\,\sigma_I + \sigma_R^\circ \tag{41}$$

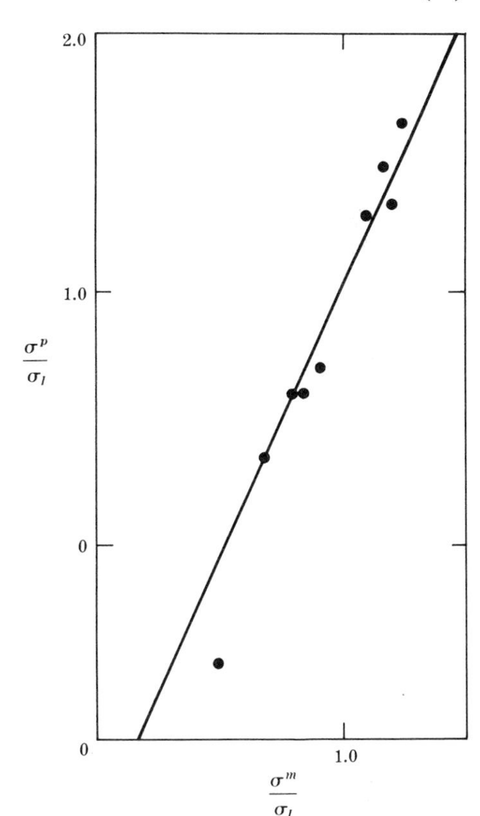

Fig. 11.13 Correlation of σ^p/σ_I with σ^m/σ_I. Substituents in order of σ^p value are OCH_3, F, Cl, Br, I, NO_2, $COOCH_3$, CN, and $COCH_3$.

and

$$\sigma^m = \sigma_I + \frac{1}{K_R}\sigma_R^\circ \tag{42}$$

From these

$$\frac{\sigma^p}{\sigma_I} = (K_I - K_R) + K_R\frac{\sigma^m}{\sigma_I} \tag{43}$$

If the assumptions which underlie Eqs. (41) and (42) are valid, a plot of σ^p/σ_I against σ^m/σ_I using σ_I values derived from aliphatic reactivities must be linear. Such a plot is shown in Fig. 11.13. The standard deviation from the relation

$$\frac{\sigma^p}{\sigma_I} = -1.60 + 2.61\frac{\sigma^m}{\sigma_I} \tag{44}$$

is 0.11. The σ^p values used here are Taft's σ° values for para substituents, and points for CH_3, NH_2, and $N(CH_3)_2$ are omitted because the value of σ_I is small and uncertain. Equation (44) leads to values of 1.01 for K_I and of 2.61 for K_R. Taft and coworkers [77] arrived by somewhat different reasoning at values of unity for K_I and at estimates ranging from 2 to 3 for K_R.

11.29 THE EXNER ANALYSIS

The values of σ_I used in Eq. (44) are based on an intuitively chosen numerical coefficient in the defining equation, Eq. (27). Replacement of this σ_I value by $\sigma_I' = a\sigma_I$ does not alter the form of the equation or the value of the slope K_R, but it changes the value of the intercept to $a(K_I - K_R)$. The replacement entails therefore a new value of K_I and by virtue of Eq. (41) a new set of values of σ_R°. Mathematically an unlimited choice of values for a is allowable, but accepted chemical theory sets rather narrow limits. A value of a greater than 1.12 leads to a negative value for the σ_R° value of the nitro group, a shocking result in terms of the resonance picture. A value less than 0.88 leads to the equally shocking result of a positive σ_R° value for iodine.

An analysis by Exner [24] leads to a definite choice of a value for K_I and consequently to a value of a and a set of σ_R° values. This derives from his determination of the acidity constants in 80% by weight methylcellosolve-water and in 50% by volume ethanol-water solvents of a remarkable variety of substituents for which no resonance interaction with the benzene ring is expected. These range from $CH_2Si(CH_3)_3$, with a σ^p value of -0.22, to SO_2CF_3, with one of $+0.91$. As illustrated by Fig. 11.14, for the methylcellosolve-water solvent there is an excellent linear relation between the effect of these substituents in the para position and the effect in the meta position. A similar correlation and the same slope, 1.14, is found in the ethanol-water solvent.

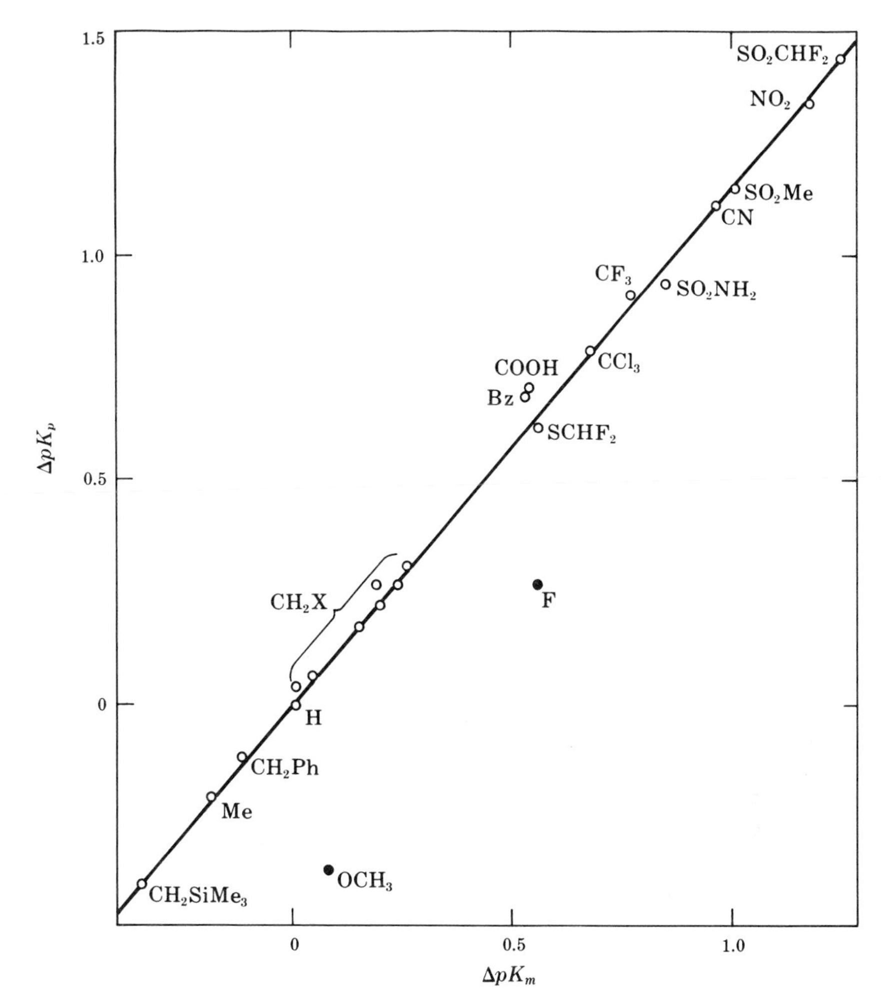

Fig. 11.14 Correlation of acidity constants of meta- and para-substituted benzoic acids. [*By permission from O. Exner, Collection Czech. Chem. Commun.*, **31:** 65 (1966).]

Rather surprisingly, the points for NO_2 and CN lie closely on the line, but those for $+T$ substituents like F, Cl, OCH_3, and OH deviate widely.

The implication is clear that when σ_R° is negligible, $\sigma^p/\sigma^m = 1.14$, and from Eqs. (41) and (42) that $K_I = 1.14$. From the relation $-1.60 = a(1.14 - 2.61)$ the value of a is 1.09. It is therefore desirable, at least in connection with the correlation of aliphatic and aromatic reactivities, to change the definition of σ_I from Eq. (27) to

$$\sigma_I = 0.276 \log \frac{K}{K_0} \tag{45}$$

and to write

$$\sigma^p = 1.14\sigma_I + \sigma_R^\circ \tag{46}$$

and

$$\sigma^m = \sigma_I + 0.38\sigma_R^\circ \tag{47}$$

Table 11.4 lists a number of σ_I and σ_R° values based on this analysis. The values of σ_R are obtained from Eq. (46) using Taft's σ° values for para substituents for σ^p. They differ from those listed by Exner, chiefly because he used σ instead of σ° values.

On a pragmatic basis one must conclude that there is a group of substituents, which includes many $-T$ types as well as those for which no resonance interaction of substituent with ring is expected, for which the σ° value in the para position is 1.14 times that in the meta position and for which the σ° value in either position is proportional to the σ_I value defined by the reactions of aliphatic compounds. For $+T$ substituents there is an added effect, which is 2.6 times larger in the para position than in the meta position.

There are difficulties, largely semantic in nature, in the theoretical interpretation of these conclusions. In terms of the simple kind of resonance theory discussed in Sec. 11.25 one expects no resonance effect for any substituent in the meta position, yet the quantity σ_R° has an important effect on the value of σ^m for $+T$ substituents. In terms of the simple theory one expects the inductive effect to decrease with increasing distance between substituent and reaction zone, yet the term involving σ_I has a greater effect on the value of σ^p than it has on that of σ^m. In terms of the simple theory considerable resonance

Table 11.4 Inductive and resonance parameters

Substituent	σ_I	σ_R°
$CH_2Si(CH_3)_3$	−0.19	0.0
CH_3	−0.05	−0.08
$N(CH_3)_2$	+0.11	−0.57
NH_2	+0.11	−0.51
OCH_3	+0.27	−0.43
$COCH_3$	+0.31	+0.10
$OCOCH_3$	+0.33	+0.08
I	+0.43	−0.22
Br	+0.49	−0.29
Cl	+0.51	−0.31
F	+0.57	−0.48
CN	+0.63	−0.06
NO_2	+0.69	+0.03
SO_2CF_3	+0.80	0.0

interaction involving $-T$ substituents like NO_2 and CN is usually predicted, yet the σ_R values for these substituents are not reliably different from zero. The only possible conclusion is that the simple theory is much too simple and that the words in which it is stated are dangerous.

11.30 ON FLEXIBLE AND RIGID MOLECULES

Siegel and Komarmy [78] find that the $\log(K/K_0)$ values for the acidity constants of the rigid *trans*-4-X-cyclohexane carboxylic acids are proportional to the corresponding values for the Roberts and Moreland bicyclooctane acids Q. In 50% by volume ethanol-water the ratio is 0.78 with a standard deviation of 0.021 for the four substituents studied in both series, it being assumed that Cl and Br have the same effect; $\log(K/K_0)$ values for the cyclohexane acids in water are proportional to those in ethanol-water, the ratio being 0.64 with a standard deviation of 0.017. One may therefore estimate that the $\log(K/K_0)$ value in water for the bromine substituent in the bicyclooctane acid is 0.49. This is identical with the contribution of the inductive effect to the acidity constant in water of *p*- and of *m*-bromobenzoic acids.

While the effect of substituents in the cyclohexane acids is 22 percent less than in the bicyclooctane acids, it averages 7 percent greater in the bicyclooctene acids R [79].

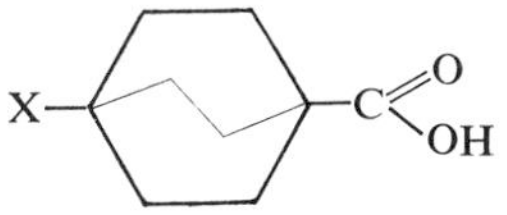

(R)

The correlation with the bicyclooctane acids of the 4-substituted dibenzobicyclo[2.2.2]octa-2,5-diene-1-carboxylic acids is not very good, but the average value of the slope is 0.75 [79].

In striking contrast to the behavior of the rigid cyclic acids, the $\log(K/K_0)$ value for the substitution of bromine for hydrogen on the terminal carbon of valeric acid is only 0.09. In the valeric acid a single flexible chain of four carbon atoms intervenes between the halogen and the carboxyl group instead of the rigid double or triple chain of the same length in the cyclic acids. Comparison of the effects in the bicyclooctane and the cyclohexane cases suggests a value of 0.26 for the effect of bromine substitution at the end of a rigid chain of the length of that in valeric acid. It appears therefore that considerable complications are to be expected when the link between substituent and reacting group is flexible.

The effects of trans-3 substituents on the acidity constant of acrylic acid can be correlated with values for para substituents in benzene derivatives [80]. The slope is 2.23 and the standard deviation 0.12. Correlations of similar precision with slopes not far from 2 are also found for the effect of substituents in the 3 position of acetylenecarboxylic acid and in the trans-3 position in 3-methylacrylic acid and in 3-carboxyacrylic acid. Cis substitution in the acrylic acid derivatives leads to no correlation.

11.31 SOLVENT EFFECTS ON $\delta_R \Delta\mu^{\ddagger}$ AND ON $\delta_R \Delta\mu^{\circ}$

Taft found it necessary to assign significantly different σ° values to some substituents, depending on the kind of solvent in which the reaction occurs (Sec. 11.12). An effect of this sort is not surprising. If a polar substituent interacts with solvent A by hydrogen bonding or by multipolar complexing and does not so interact with solvent B, the nature of the substituent and its effect on the electronic system of the reactant, the reaction product, or the transition state will be to some extent different in the two solvents.

A significant systematic effect of a change in medium appears in the data of Davis and Hetzer [53] on the equilibrium constant K_b of the reaction

$$XC_6H_4COOH + B \rightleftharpoons XC_6H_5COO^- \text{---} BH^+ \qquad \text{(IV)}$$

in benzene solution at 25°C. B is diphenylguanidine, and the structure of the association product is presumably a hydrogen-bonded ion pair (Sec. 8.7). A plot of $\log K_b$ against σ (lower plot in Fig. 11.15) shows considerable deviations for $+T$ substituents. The line drawn in the figure represents the relationship

$$\log K_b = 5.27 + 2.17\sigma \qquad (48)$$

to which Davis and Hetzer found that all meta substituents except NH_2, $N(CH_3)_2$, OCH_3, and OH conform closely. As Taft and coworkers [77] suggest, a plot (upper plot in Fig. 11.15) against σ^n or σ° shows considerably smaller deviations. One could no doubt get an even better fit with a Yukawa-Tsuno kind of relationship.

These phenomena may reasonably be attributed to the effect of the solvent on the magnitude of such contributions as that which the structure F makes to the electron distribution in *p*-aminobenzoic acid. A highly polar, strongly hydrogen-bonding solvent like water must be favorable to a large contribution, an inert solvent of low dielectric constant unfavorable. The result should be a stabilization of acids containing $+T$ substituents in water and a relatively lower acidity constant for such acids in water.

Okamoto, Inukai, and Brown [81] have made a careful study of the solvolysis of meta- and para-substituted phenyldimethylcarbinyl chlorides in four solvents. When the specific rate in methanol k_m is compared with that in 90% aqueous acetone k_a, the relationship

$$\log k_m = 1.93 + 1.063 \log k_a \qquad (49)$$

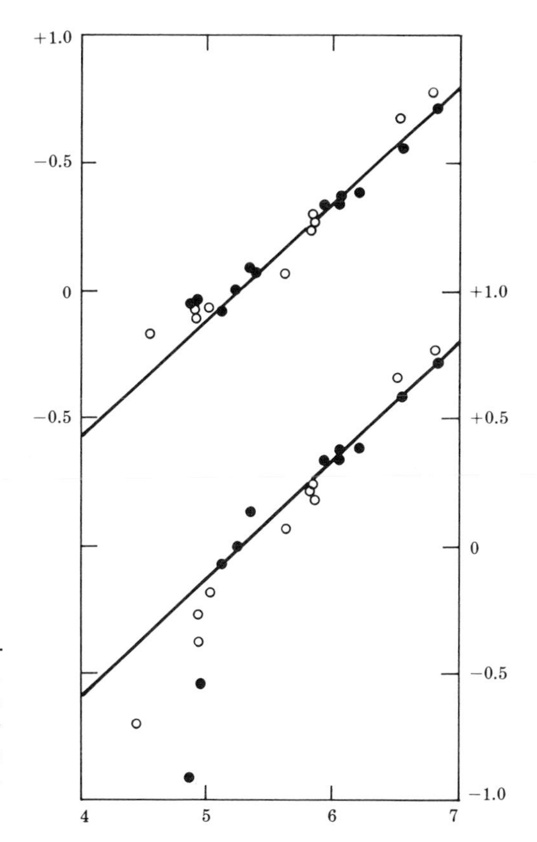

Fig. 11.15 Abscissa: log *K* for reaction of meta- and para-substituted benzoic acids with diphenylguanidine in benzene. Ordinate: (*lower plot*) scale on right, σ constants; (*upper plot*) scale on left, σ^n constants.

applies with a standard deviation of 0.06 for 12 substituents. Much the same quality of correlation is found for the specific rates in ethanol and in isopropanol. The investigators estimate the experimental uncertainty of an individual k value to be 3 percent, which implies an uncertainty of 0.026 in the quantity which measures the effect of changing solvent on the difference between the specific rates of reaction of two differently substituted reactants. There is no obvious pattern or trend in the deviations, but, random as they appear, there is considerable probability that they are not solely the result of experimental error.

Ritchie and Lewis [82] have determined the effect of the substitution of OH, $CO_2C_2H_5$, COOH, Br, and CN for hydrogen in the 4 position of bicyclo-[2.2.2]octane-1-carboxylic acid in 11 solvents or aqueous solvent mixtures. For alcohol and aqueous alcohol solvents the data correlate well with the Roberts and Moreland data for 50% aqueous ethanol (Sec. 11.26). The standard deviation is 0.075 for methanol, 0.089 for 90% by volume aqueous methanol, 0.095 for 75% methanol, 0.036 for ethanol, 0.098 for 90% ethanol, and 0.10 for 75% ethanol. In acetone, however, the standard deviation is 0.14, in dimethylsulfoxide it is 0.29, in 90% aqueous dimethylsulfoxide 0.21, and in 75% dimethylsulfoxide 0.17. The deviations in the latter group of solvents appear to be systematic, with the effect of OH smaller than in the first group and the effect of Br larger. These solvent effects are important for theory because in principle the substituent effects are inductive only.

REFERENCES

1. Wells, P. R.: *Chem. Rev.*, **63:** 171 (1963).
2. Pedersen, K. J.: Dissertation, Copenhagen, 1932.
3. Barron, E. S. G.: *J. Biol. Chem.*, **97:** 287 (1932).
4. Dimroth, O.: *Z. Angew. Chem.*, **46:** 571 (1933).
5. Lieber, E., C. N. Ramachandra Rao, and T. S. Chao: *J. Am. Chem. Soc.*, **79:** 5962 (1957).
6. Anderson, B. M., and W. P. Jencks: *J. Am. Chem. Soc.*, **82:** 1773 (1960).
7. Kindler, K.: *Ann.*, **450:** 1 (1926).
8. Hammett, L. P., and H. L. Pfluger: *J. Am. Chem. Soc.*, **55:** 571 (1933).
9. Hammett, L. P.: *Chem. Rev.*, **17:** 125 (1935).
10. Burkhardt, G. N.: *Nature*, **136:** 684 (1935).
11. Fitzpatrick, F. W., and J. D. Gettler: *J. Am. Chem. Soc.*, **78:** 530 (1956).
12. Price, F. P., and L. P. Hammett: *J. Am. Chem. Soc.*, **63:** 2387 (1941).
13. Fiarman, I. D., and J. D. Gettler: *J. Am. Chem. Soc.*, **84:** 961 (1962).
14. Brooks, D. W., and J. D. Gettler: *J. Org. Chem.*, **27:** 4469 (1962).
15. Taft, R. W., Jr., and I. C. Lewis: *J. Am. Chem. Soc.*, **80:** 2436 (1958).
16. Ingold, C. K., and F. R. Shaw: *J. Chem. Soc.*, **1927**: 2918.
17. Dippy, J. F. J., and F. R. Williams: *J. Chem. Soc.*, **1934:** 161, and subsequent papers through 1937.
18. McDaniel, D. H., and H. C. Brown: *J. Org. Chem.*, **23:** 420 (1958).
19. Barlin, G. B., and D. D. Perrin: *Quart. Rev.* (*London*), **20:** 75 (1966).
20. Jaffé, H. H.: *Chem. Rev.*, **53:** 191 (1953).
21. Ritchie, C. D., and W. F. Sager: *Progr. Phys. Org. Chem.*, **2:** 323 (1964).
22. Zollinger, H., and C. Wittwer: *Helv. Chim. Acta*, **39:** 347 (1955).
23. Sheppard, W. A.: *J. Am. Chem. Soc.*, **85:** 1314 (1963).
24. Exner, O.: *Collection Czech. Chem. Commun.*, **31:** 65 (1966).
25. van Bekkum, H., P. E. Verkade, and B. M. Wepster: *Rec. Trav. Chim.*, **78:** 815 (1959).
26. Taft, R. W., Jr.: *J. Phys. Chem.*, **64:** 1805 (1960).
27. Fischer, A., G. J. Leary, R. D. Topson, and J. Vaughan: *J. Chem. Soc.*, **B1966:** 782.
28. Branch, G. E. K., and M. Calvin: "The Theory of Organic Chemistry," pp. 246–257, 417, Prentice-Hall, Inc., New York, 1941.
29. Clark, J., and D. D. Perrin: *Quart. Rev.* (*London*), **18:** 295 (1964).
30. Hammett, L. P.: *J. Am. Chem. Soc.*, **59:** 96 (1937).
31. Brown, H. C., and Y. Okamoto: *J. Am. Chem. Soc.*, **79:** 1913 (1957); **80:** 4979 (1958).
32. Brown, H. C., and G. Goldman: *J. Am. Chem. Soc.*, **84:** 1650 (1962).
33. Stock, L. M., and H. C. Brown: *Advan. Phys. Org. Chem.*, **1:** 35 (1963).
34. Bordwell, F. G., and H. M. Andersen: *J. Am. Chem. Soc.*, **75:** 6019 (1953).
35. Yukawa, Y., and Y. Tsuno: *Bull. Chem. Soc. Japan*, **32:** 971 (1959).
36. Deno, N. C., and A. Schriesheim: *J. Am. Chem. Soc.*, **77:** 3051 (1955).
37. Robertson, P. W., P. D. B. de la Mare, and E. B. Swedlund: *J. Chem. Soc.*, **1953:** 782; J. Miller: *Australian J. Chem.*, **9:** 61 (1956).
38. Ryan, J. J., and A. A. Humffray: *J. Chem. Soc.*, **B1967:** 1300.
39. Dickinson, J. D., and C. Eaborn: *J. Chem. Soc.*, **1959:** 3036.

40. Leffler, J. E., and E. Grunwald: "Rates and Equilibria of Organic Reactions," p. 383, John Wiley & Sons, Inc., New York, 1963.
41. Jaffé, H. H., *J. Chem. Phys.*, **21:** 415 (1953); E. N. Trachtenberg and G. Odian: *J. Am. Chem. Soc.*, **80:** 4018 (1958); M. Charton: *J. Org. Chem.*, **26:** 735 (1961); R. M. O'Ferrall and S. I. Miller: *J. Am. Chem. Soc.*, **85:** 2440 (1963).
42. Miller, S. I.: *U.S. Army Res. Off. Symp. Linear Free Energy Correlations*, Durham, N.C., 1964, p. 45.
43. McCullough, J. P., and B. A. Eckerson: *J. Am. Chem. Soc.*, **67:** 707 (1945); J. P. McCullough and M. K. Barsh: *ibid.*, **71:** 3029 (1949).
44. Hancock, C. K., and J. S. Westmoreland: *J. Am. Chem. Soc.*, **80:** 545 (1958).
45. Westheimer, F. H., and R. P. Metcalf: *J. Am. Chem. Soc.*, **63:** 1339 (1941).
46. Wheland, G. W., R. M. Brownell, and E. C. Mayo: *J. Am. Chem. Soc.*, **70:** 2492 (1948).
47. Schaefer, J. P., and T. J. Miraglia: *J. Am. Chem. Soc.*, **86:** 64 (1964).
48. Meyer, V.: *Ber.*, **27:** 510 (1894).
49. Evans, D. P., J. J. Gordon, and H. B. Watson: *J. Chem. Soc.*, **1937:** 1430.
50. Hall, N. F.: *J. Am. Chem. Soc.*, **52:** 5115 (1930); N. F. Hall and M. R. Sprinkle: *ibid.*, **54:** 3469 (1932); L. P. Hammett and M. A. Paul: *ibid.*, **56:** 827 (1934); H. C. Farmer and F. J. Warth: *J. Chem. Soc.*, **85:** 1713 (1904).
51. Van Opstall, H. J.: *Rec. Trav. Chim.*, **52:** 901 (1933).
52. Burkhardt, G. N., W. G. Ford, and E. Singleton: *J. Chem. Soc.*, **1936:** 17; G. N. Burkhardt, C. Horrex, and D. I. Jenkins: *ibid.*, **1936:** 1654.
53. Davis, M. M., and H. B. Hetzer: *J. Res. Natl. Bur. Std.*, **60:** 569 (1958).
54. Wooten, L. A., and L. P. Hammett: *J. Am. Chem. Soc.*, **57:** 2289 (1935).
55. Roberts, J. D., and J. A. Yancey: *J. Am. Chem. Soc.*, **73:** 1011 (1951).
56. Cohen, L. A., and W. M. Jones: *J. Am. Chem. Soc.*, **85:** 3397 (1963).
57. Fischer, A., G. J. Leary, R. D. Topsom, and J. Vaughan: *J. Chem. Soc.*, **B1966:** 782; **B1967:** 686.
58. Fickling, N. M., A. Fischer, B. R. Mann, J. Packer, and J. Vaughan: *J. Am. Chem. Soc.*, **81:** 4226 (1959).
59. Fischer, A., M. P. Hartshorn, U. M. Senanayake, and J. Vaughan: *J. Chem. Soc.*, **B1967:** 833.
60. Bell, R. P., and W. C. E. Higginson: *Prov. Roy. Soc. (London)*, **A197:** 141 (1949); R. P. Bell and R. G. Pearson: *J. Chem. Soc.*, **1953:** 3443; R. P. Bell: "The Proton in Chemistry," pp. 164ff, Cornell University Press, Ithaca, N.Y., 1959.
61. Bunnett, J. F.: *Ann. Rev. Phys. Chem.*, **14:** 271 (1963).
62. Swain, C. G., and C. B. Scott: *J. Am. Chem. Soc.*, **75:** 141 (1953).
63. Jencks, W. P., and J. Carriuolo: *J. Am. Chem. Soc.*, **82:** 1778 (1960).
64. Bjerrum, N.: *Z. Physik. Chem.*, **106:** 219 (1923).
65. Kirkwood, J. G., and F. H. Westheimer: *J. Chem. Phys.*, **6:** 506, 513 (1938).
66. Dewar, M. J. S., and P. J. Grisdale: *J. Am. Chem. Soc.*, **84:** 3539 (1962).
67. Taft, R. W., Jr.: *J. Am. Chem. Soc.*, **75:** 4231 (1953); R. W. Taft, Jr., in M. S. Newman: "Steric Effects in Organic Chemistry," chap. 13, John Wiley & Sons, Inc., New York, 1956; R. W. Taft, Jr., and I. C. Lewis: *J. Am. Chem. Soc.*, **80:** 2436 (1958).
68. Roberts, J. D., and W. T. Moreland: *J. Am. Chem. Soc.*, **75:** 2167 (1953).
69. Holtz, H. D., and L. M. Stock: *J. Am. Chem. Soc.*, **86:** 5188 (1964).
70. Ingold, C. K.: *J. Chem. Soc.*, **1930:** 1032.
71. Taft, R. W., Jr., and I. C. Lewis: *Tetrahedron*, **5:** 210 (1959).
72. Taft, R. W., E. Price, I. R. Fox, I. C. Lewis, K. K. Andersen, and G. T. Davis: *J. Am. Chem. Soc.*, **85:** 709 (1963).
73. Taft, R. W., F. Prosser, L. Goodman, and G. T. Davis: *J. Chem. Phys.*, **38:** 380 (1963).
74. Pews, R. G., Y. Tsuno, and R. W. Taft: *J. Am. Chem. Soc.*, **89:** 2391 (1967); C. S. Giam and R. W. Taft: *ibid.*, 2397.

75. Taft, R. W., Jr., and I. C. Lewis: *J. Am. Chem. Soc.*, **80:** 2442 (1958).
76. Ehrenson, S.: *Tetrahedron Letters*, **7:** 351 (1964).
77. Taft, R. W., S. Ehrenson, I. C. Lewis, and R. E. Glick: *J. Am. Chem. Soc.*, **81:** 5352 (1959).
78. Siegel, S., and J. M. Komarmy: *J. Am. Chem. Soc.*, **82:** 2547 (1960).
79. Baker, F. W., R. C. Parish, and L. M. Stock: *J. Am. Chem. Soc.*, **89:** 5677 (1967).
80. Charton, M., and H. Meislich: *J. Am. Chem. Soc.*, **80:** 5940 (1958); M. Charton: *J. Org. Chem.*, **26:** 735 (1961).
81. Okamoto, Y., T. Inukai, and H. C. Brown: *J. Am. Chem. Soc.*, **80:** 4972 (1958).
82. Ritchie, C. D., and E. S. Lewis: *J. Am. Chem. Soc.*, **84:** 591 (1962).
83. Swain, C. G., and E. C. Lupton: *J. Am. Chem. Soc.*, **90:** 4328 (1968).

12

Effect of Structure on Enthalpy and Entropy Changes

12.1 THE ISOKINETIC RELATIONSHIP

Linear relationships involving the effect of changes in structure of reactant on standard potentials, standard enthalpies, and standard entropies of reaction or of activation are not uncommon, especially when the changes do not encroach closely on the reaction zone. Proportionality of any one of the variations $\delta_R \Delta\mu^\circ$, $\delta_R \Delta\bar{H}^\circ$, or $\delta_R T\Delta\bar{S}^\circ$ to one of the others requires mutual proportionality of all three, except that when any two are equal, the third is necessarily zero. The same rules apply to the variations $\delta_R \Delta\mu^+$, $\delta_R \Delta\bar{H}^+$, and $\delta_R T\Delta\bar{S}^+$. They are necessary consequences of the thermodynamic principle that $\mu = H - TS$.

Probably because of the prevalence of the idea that enthalpy and entropy are more fundamental quantities than standard potential, the relationship most often cited is the enthalpy-entropy one. The Barclay-Butler rule (Sec. 3.10) is an example of a linear relation between $\Delta\bar{H}^\circ$ and $\Delta\bar{S}^\circ$. Suggestions equivalent to a linear relation between $\Delta\bar{H}^+$ and $\Delta\bar{S}^+$ for changes in structure of reactants, for changes in solvent, or for both have appeared in the literature with some frequence [1].

Because of the inherent difficulty (Sec. 2.23) of obtaining reliable values of $\Delta \bar{H}^{+}$ and $\Delta \bar{S}^{+}$, the evidence that the relationship is not always a computational artifact remained dim until Leffler [2] reported a number of instances in which the real applicability of the relationship seemed clear. Leffler proposed the name isokinetic relationship for the equation

$$\delta_R \Delta \bar{H}^{+} = \beta \delta_R \Delta \bar{S}^{+} \tag{1}$$

and pointed out some corrollaries of the assumption that β is independent of temperature. The relation

$$\delta_R \Delta \bar{H}^{\circ} = \beta \delta_R \Delta \bar{S}^{\circ} \tag{2}$$

is sometimes called an isoequilibrium relationship. By 1963 Leffler and Grunwald [3] could list 42 reactions in which both $\delta \Delta \bar{H}^{+}$ and $\delta \Delta \bar{S}^{+}$ are decidedly dependent on structure and in which the effect of changing structure on one is proportional to the effect on the other with a correlation coefficient of 0.95 or better.

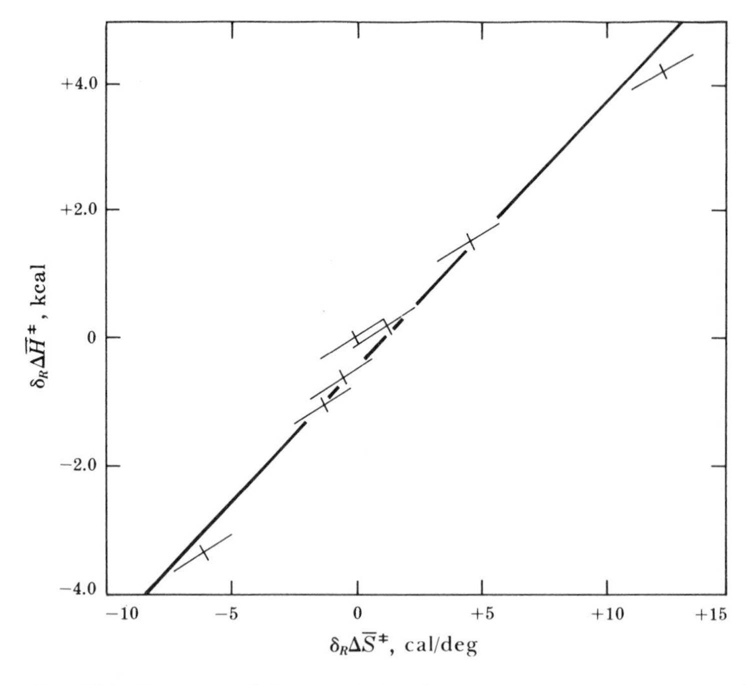

Fig. 12.1 Entropy-enthalpy correlation for solvolysis of para-substituted benzoyl chlorides. (*Data of Branch and Nixon* [4].) Substituents in order of increasing $\delta_R \Delta \bar{S}^{+}$, NO_2, Cl, Br and I, H, F, CH_3, OCH_3.

Figure 12.1 presents a typical example from data [4] on the solvolysis rate of para-substituted benzoyl chlorides in an ether-ethanol mixture at 0 and 25°C. The least-squares line corresponds to a β value of 411.

The equations

$$\delta_R \Delta\mu^{+} = (\beta - T)\, \delta_R \Delta\bar{S}^{+} \tag{3}$$

and

$$\delta_R \Delta\mu^{+} = \left(1 - \frac{T}{\beta}\right) \delta_R \Delta\bar{H}^{+} \tag{4}$$

are necessary corollaries of Eq. (1). To the precision of the isokinetic relation the equations

$$\delta_R \Delta\mu^{+} = 113 \delta_R \Delta\bar{S}^{+} \tag{5}$$

and

$$\delta_R \Delta\mu^{+} = 0.28 \delta_R \Delta\bar{H}^{+} \tag{6}$$

apply to the benzoyl chloride solvolysis at 298°K.

12.2 ISOENTROPIC REACTION SERIES

As β becomes infinite, Eqs. (1) and (4) approach

$$\delta_R \Delta\bar{S}^{+} = 0 \tag{7}$$

and

$$\delta_R \Delta\mu^{+} = \delta_R \Delta\bar{H}^{+} \tag{8}$$

Table 12.1 presents data on a reaction series for which these relations are rather closely applicable. The total variation in $\Delta\bar{S}^{+}$ is 2.0 cal/deg, and the standard deviation from the mean is 0.6. Meanwhile the variation in $\Delta\mu^{+}/T$ at 298°K is 11.8, and the variation in $\Delta\bar{H}^{+}/T$ is 11.3. If the last four items in the table are omitted, the standard deviation drops to 0.2. It is hard to say whether it is more significant that these items involve the most strongly electron-attracting substituents or that they are the most liable to error because of the high reaction rate.

The regularity fails, however, when a wider range of structural variation is involved (Table 12.2). The entropy of activation of ethyl acetate is 10.6 cal/deg more negative than that of ethyl benzoate, and for other aliphatic esters both $\Delta\bar{H}^{+}$ and $\Delta\bar{S}^{+}$ vary in a helter-skelter fashion. Studies on ester hydrolysis in 85 percent by volume ethanol-water [6] lead to a similar picture and add the information that the $\Delta\bar{S}^{+}$ values for the *o*-nitro, *o*-chloro, and *o*-methyl esters are 4.3, 4.5, and 3.1 cal/deg more negative than the mean for the meta- and para-substituted esters but that the value for the *o*-fluo esters is the same as that mean. The standard deviation from the mean of the meta

Table 12.1 Alkaline hydrolysis of ethyl esters of substituted benzoic acids in 56% by weight acetone–water[a]

Substituent	$10^2 k$, *liters/mole-sec* 25°C	$\Delta\bar{S}^{\ddagger}$, *cal/deg*	$\Delta\bar{H}^{\ddagger}$, *kcal*
p-$N(CH_3)_2$	0.00634	−23.0	16.24
p-NH_2	0.00864	−22.9	16.7
p-CH_3	0.114	−22.9	15.16
m-NH_2	0.166	−22.8	14.98
m-CH_3	0.169	−23.2	14.87
H	0.289	−23.1	14.56
m-OCH_3	0.3918	−23.3	14.35
p-F	0.586	−23.1	14.2
p-Cl	1.167	−22.8	13.8
p-Br	1.390	−22.8	13.73
p-I	1.219	−22.8	13.80
m-I	1.495	−22.9	13.67
m-Br	1.785	−22.7	13.60
m-Cl	1.819	−22.9	13.55
m-CN	12.20	−21.3	12.83
m-NO_2	13.65	−21.4	12.8
p-CN	15.70	−22.0	12.6
p-NO_2	24.63	−21.4	12.4

[a] Data of Tommila [5].

and para group is 0.45, and the values for aliphatic ethyl esters run from 5.1 to 8.5 cal/deg more negative than the value for ethyl benzoate.

Other approximately isoentropic reaction series are the alkaline hydrolysis of substituted benzyl acetates and that of substituted phenyl acetates [8].

Table 12.2 Alkaline hydrolysis of aliphatic ethyl esters $RCOOC_2H_5$ in 56% by weight acetone–water[a]

R	$10^2 k$ *at 25°C*$_1$, *liters/mole-sec*	$\Delta\bar{S}^{\ddagger}$, *cal/deg*	$\Delta\bar{H}^{\ddagger}$, *kcal*
CH_3	4.65	−33.7	9.3
C_2H_5	2.20	−32.5	9.9
n-C_3H_7	0.881	−28.0	12.1
i-C_3H_7	0.55	−32.0	10.7
n-C_4H_9	0.192	−28.9	12.5
$(CH_3)_2CHCH_2$	0.218	−23.4	12.7
$(CH_3)_3C$	0.0223	−33.5	12.4
$(C_2H_5)_2CH$	0.0083	−31.2	13.7
n-C_6H_{13}	0.608	−28.9	11.8

[a] Data of Davies and Evans [7].

12.3 ISOENTHALPIC REACTION SERIES

When $\beta = 0$, Eqs. (2) and (3) reduce to

$$\delta_R \Delta \bar{H}^\circ = 0 \tag{9}$$

and

$$\delta_R \Delta \mu^\circ = -\delta_R T \Delta \bar{S}^\circ \tag{10}$$

Figure 12.2 plots $\Delta \bar{H}^\circ$ against $\Delta \mu^\circ$ for the ionization in water at 25°C of meta- and para-substituted phenols. The standard deviation of $\Delta \bar{H}^\circ$ from the mean is 0.30 kcal; the standard deviation from the least-squares line of slope 0.25 is 0.24. One has therefore little confidence that the trend is significant. Ortho-substituted phenols deviate somewhat more widely and in a random fashion.

The standard deviation from the mean of the $\Delta \bar{H}^\circ$ values for the ionization in water of meta- and para-substituted benzoic acids, excepting the methyl derivatives, is 0.11 kcal, and the deviations seem random. The value for the *m*-methyl substituent is, however, 1.1 kcal and that for the *p*-methyl substituent 1.0 kcal higher than the mean of the others [9]. Otherwise there seems to be no pattern whatsoever in the $\Delta \bar{H}^{\ddagger}$ and $\Delta S^{\ddagger}$ values for the ionization of carboxylic acids [3, p. 372].

12.4 THE ISOKINETIC TEMPERATURE

If Eq. (3) were exact and β were independent of temperature, $\Delta \mu^{\ddagger}$ would become zero for all reactants at the isokinetic temperature, $T = \beta$, and the rate would be independent of structure. Furthermore the order of the reactivities of a series of reactants would be reversed on opposite sides of this temperature. Because there are always random-seeming deviations from Eq. (3), the actual

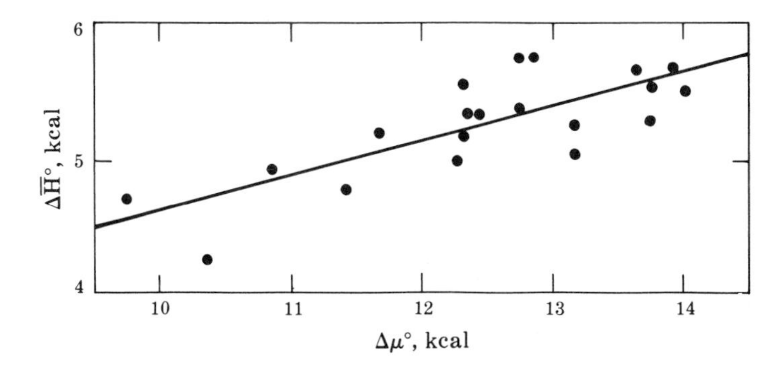

Fig. 12.2 Effect of meta and para substituents on $\Delta \bar{H}^\circ$ and $\Delta \mu^\circ$ for the ionization of phenol in water. Substituents range from p-NO_2 to p-OCH_3 and p-CH_3. (*Data of Bolton, Hall, and Reece* [20], *Chen and Laidler* [21], *Fernandez and Hepler* [22], *and Allen, Robinson, and Bower* [23].)

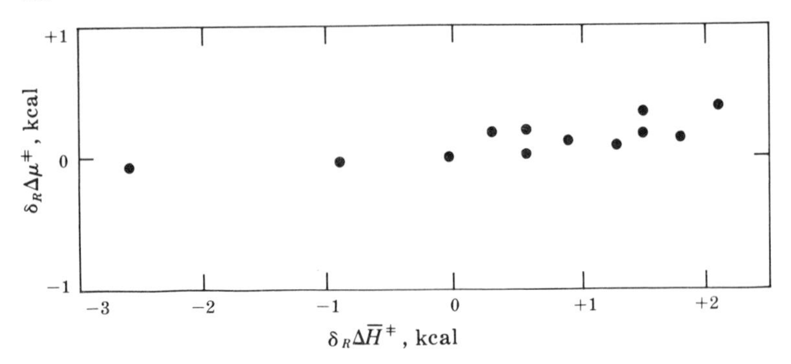

Fig. 12.3 Effect of meta and para substituents on $\Delta\mu^{\ddagger}$ and $\Delta\bar{H}^{\ddagger}$ for the rearrangement of benzoylazide. (*Data of Yukawa and Tsuno* [10].) Substituents in order of increasing $\Delta\bar{H}^{\ddagger}$: m-CH_3; p-t-C_4H_9; H; p-Br; p-Cl, m-Br and m-OCH_3; p-NO_2; p-CH_3; p-OCH_3 and p-OC_2H_5; p-OH; p-NO_2.

situation when observations are made at temperatures near β is likely to be one of a patternless scatter when $\Delta\mu^{\ddagger}$ is plotted against $\Delta\bar{H}^{\ddagger}$. Figure 12.3 shows such a plot based on the data of Yukawa and Tsuno [10] for the Curtius rearrangement

$$XC_6H_5CON_3 \rightarrow XC_6H_5NCO + N_2 \tag{I}$$

in toluene at temperatures in the neighborhood of 65°C. Given considerable optimism, one might discern a positive trend, but the total range of $\Delta\mu^{\ddagger}$ is only 3.5 times the standard deviation from the mean.

In the Dickinson-Eaborn study (Sec. 11.18) of the reaction of substituted benzophenones with hydroxylamine the total variation in $\Delta\mu^{\ddagger}$ is small and seems nearly random. As Fig. 12.4 shows, a plot of $\delta_R \Delta\bar{H}^{\ddagger}$ against σ makes a much better appearance than one of $\delta_R \Delta\mu^{\ddagger}$ against σ. This is, however, more apparent than real, for the standard deviation of the $\delta_R \Delta\bar{H}^{\ddagger}$ plot from the equation $\delta_R \Delta\bar{H}^{\ddagger} = 0.14 - 2.19\sigma$ is 0.12, while that from the plot $\delta_R \Delta\mu^{\ddagger} = 0.17 - 0.50\sigma$ is 0.16.

Since

$$\frac{d\delta_R \Delta\bar{H}^{\ddagger}}{dT} = \delta_R \Delta\bar{C}_p^{\ddagger} \tag{11}$$

and

$$\frac{d\delta_R \Delta\bar{S}^{\ddagger}}{dT} = \frac{\delta_R \Delta\bar{C}_p^{\ddagger}}{T} \tag{12}$$

where $\bar{C}_p$ is molal heat capacity, equation (1) implies that

$$\frac{d\beta}{dT} = \frac{\delta_R \Delta\bar{C}_p^{\ddagger}(1 - \beta/T)}{\delta_R \Delta\bar{S}^{\ddagger}} \tag{13}$$

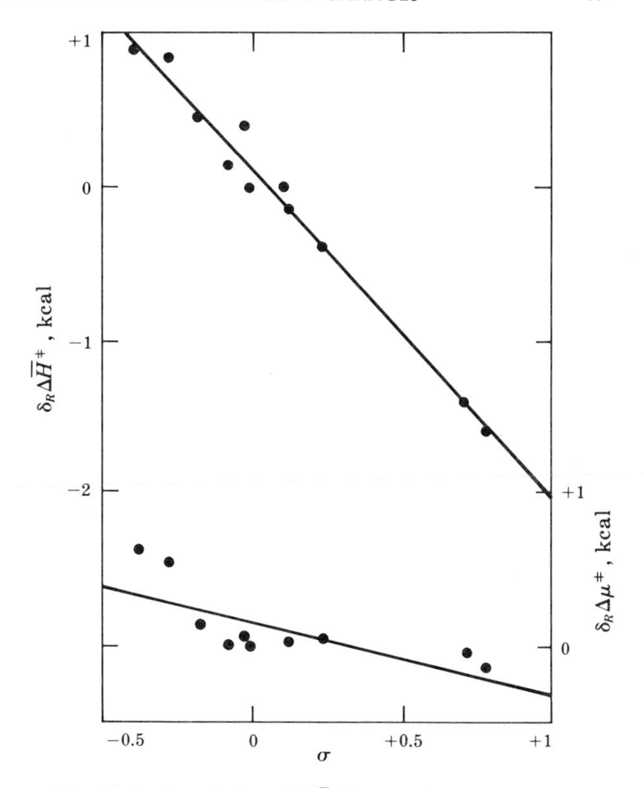

Fig. 12.4 Correlation of $\Delta \bar{H}^{\ddagger}$ (upper plot, scale on left) and $\Delta \mu^{\ddagger}$ (lower plot, scale on right) with σ for oximation of monosubstituted benzophenones. Substituents left to right: *p*-OH, *p*-OCH_3, *p*-CH_3, *m*-CH_3, *p*-C_6H_5, H, *m*-OCH_3, *m*-OH, *p*-Br, *m*-NO_2, *p*-NO_2. (*Data of Dickinson and Eaborn* [24].)

β can therefore be independent of temperature at all temperatures only if $\delta_R \Delta \bar{C}_p^{\ddagger} = 0$. There are reasons (Sec. 2.24) for doubting that this is in general the case.

12.5 THE VALIDITY OF THE ISOKINETIC RELATIONSHIP

An isokinetic relationship between calculated values of $\Delta \bar{H}^{\ddagger}$ and $\Delta \bar{S}^{\ddagger}$ can result from purely random experimental errors if the dependence of log k on structure is small (Sec. 2.23). As Exner [11] points out in a penetrating analysis, the operations involved in the estimation of $\Delta \bar{H}^{\ddagger}$ and $\Delta \bar{S}^{\ddagger}$ either consist in, or are equivalent to, the determination of k_1 values at temperature T_1 and of k_2 values at temperature T_2 together with the application of the relationships

$$\Delta \bar{H}^{\ddagger} = \frac{4.574 T_1 T_2}{T_2 - T_1} (\log k_2 - \log k_1) - \mathbf{R}T \tag{14}$$

and

$$\Delta\bar{S}^{\ddagger} = \frac{4.574(T_2 \log k_2 - T_1 \log k_1)}{T_2 - T_1} - 4.574 \log \frac{\mathbf{e}\mathbf{k}T}{\mathbf{h}} \tag{15}$$

T being a mean of T_1 and T_2. If $T_1 = 273$ and $T_2 = 298$, a positive error of 5 percent in k_2 leads in terms of these equations to a positive error of 300 cal in $\Delta\bar{H}^{\ddagger}$ and to one of 1.2 cal/deg in $\Delta\bar{S}^{\ddagger}$. Negative errors in k_2 lead to similar negative errors in $\Delta\bar{H}^{\ddagger}$ and $\Delta\bar{S}^{\ddagger}$. The slant lines attached to each point in Fig. 12.1 comprise the effect on the position of the point of a ± 5 percent uncertainty in k_2. Unless the errors in the Branch and Nixon specific rates are much larger than seems at all likely, one may have a high level of confidence that there is a physically real correlation of $\Delta\bar{H}^{\ddagger}$ with $\Delta\bar{S}^{\ddagger}$ for this reaction series with a slope in the neighborhood of 400. Furthermore there is a considerable probability that the larger deviations from the linear relationship represent physically real effects and not merely experimental uncertainty.

It follows from Eqs. (14) and (15) that

$$\delta_R \Delta\bar{H}^{\ddagger} = \frac{2.303\mathbf{R}T_1 T_2}{T_2 - T_1} \delta_R \log k_1(b - 1) \tag{16}$$

and

$$\delta_R \Delta\bar{S}^{\ddagger} = \frac{2.303\mathbf{R}T_2}{T_2 - T_1} \delta_R \log k_1 \left(b - \frac{T_1}{T_2}\right) \tag{17}$$

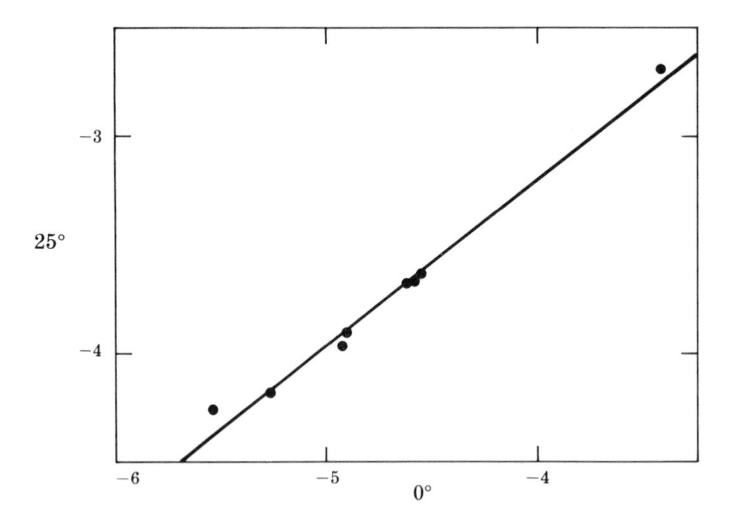

Fig. 12.5 Correlation of log k at 25°C with log k at 0° for solvolysis of para-substituted benzoyl chlorides. (*Data of Branch and Nixon* [4].) Order of substituents from OCH_3 at left to NO_2 at right.

and therefore that

$$\beta = T_2 \frac{1-b}{1-\tau b} \tag{18}$$

where $b = \delta_R \log k_2/\delta_R \log k_1$ is the slope of a plot of $\log k_2$ against $\log k_1$ and $\tau = T_2/T_1$. Figure 12.5 presents a plot of $\log k_{298}$ against $\log k_{273}$ for the benzoyl chloride solvolysis. The least-squares slope is 0.77, and by Eq. (18) β should be 430, a value which is in adequate agreement with the least-squares values of 411 from Fig. 12.4.

By differentiation of Eq. (18)

$$\frac{d\beta/\beta}{db/b} = \frac{b(\tau-1)}{(1-b)(1-\tau b)} \tag{19}$$

For $\tau = \frac{298}{273} = 1.092$ and $b = 0.77$, the values applicable to Figs. 12.1 and 12.4, the fractional uncertainty in β is 1.9 times that in b. For the same τ value the ratio of the uncertainties is 7.2 for $b = 0.85$, 48 for $b = 0.90$, and 48 for $b = 0.95$. Indeed the ratio is very large for all values of b between $1/\tau$ and 1, which are the only b values which lead to a negative value of β. There is nothing, in principle, which denies the possibility of a negative β, but it will be difficult ever to assign such a quantity any considerable level of confidence.

12.6 LIMITATIONS ON THE ISOKINETIC RELATIONSHIP

The example of the alkaline ester hydrolysis (Sec. 12.2), which is isoentropic for meta- and para-substituted benzoic esters but otherwise shows large entropy variations, suggests that any isokinetic relationship is likely to fail when the structural changes encroach closely on the reaction zone. Figure 12.6 presents a plot of $\log k_2$ against $\log k_1$, and Fig. 12.7 a plot of $\Delta\bar{H}^{\ddagger}$ against $\Delta\bar{S}^{\ddagger}$ for the formation of the semicarbazones of carbonyl compounds of a wide variety of structures. The least-squares line in Fig. 12.6 has a slope of 0.95, which even with the excellent correlation shown in this plot corresponds to an essentially indeterminate value of β. As in Fig. 12.1, the diagonal lines attached to each point in Fig. 12.7 indicate the effect on the position of the point of a ± 5 percent uncertainty in k. It is clear not only that there is no correlation of $\Delta\bar{H}^{\ddagger}$ and $\Delta\bar{S}^{\ddagger}$ but that the absence of correlation cannot be attributed to any reasonable estimate of experimental uncertainty. Similar results are obtained from data on the formation of oximes [13], on the formation of thiosemicarbazones [14], and on the formation of guanylhydrazones [15] of the same or nearly the same series of carbonyl compounds. Not only do the points in all these $\Delta\bar{H}^{\ddagger}$-$\Delta\bar{S}^{\ddagger}$ diagrams scatter widely, but there is no obvious relationship between the different scatter patterns.

It should be emphasized that the likelihood that these reactions go in at least two steps (Sec. 5.19) does not complicate the situation. The $\Delta\mu^{\ddagger}$

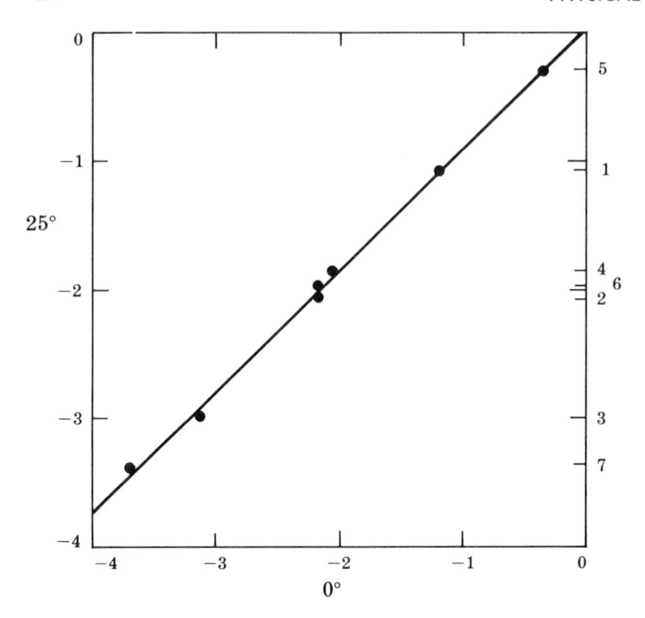

Fig. 12.6 Correlation of $\log k$ at 25°C with $\log k$ at 0° for semicarbazone formation. (*Data of Price and Hammett* [12].) Carbonyl compounds: 1 = acetone; 2 = diethyl ketone; 3 = pinacolone; 4 = cyclopentanone; 5 = cyclohexanone; 6 = furfural; 7 = acetophenone.

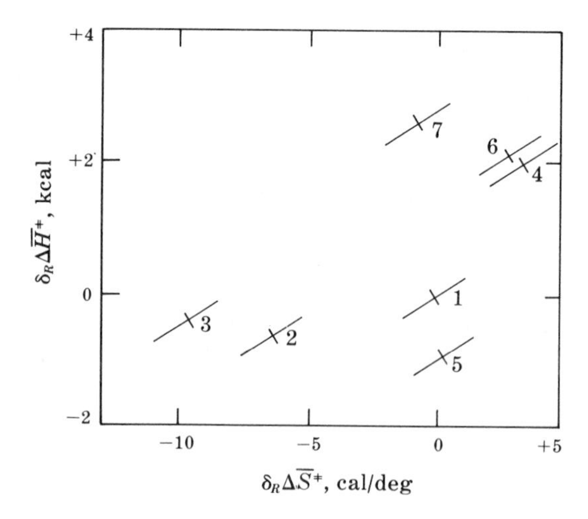

Fig. 12.7 Enthalpy and entropy effects in semicarbazone formation. (*Data of Price and Hammett* [12].) Numbering of carbonyl compounds is the same as in Fig. 12.6.

observed is the difference between the $\mu^{\ddagger}$ value of the transition state of the rate-determining step and the sum of the μ° values of carbonyl compound, nitrogen base, and acid catalyst. The observed $\Delta\bar{H}^{\ddagger}$ and $\Delta\bar{S}^{\ddagger}$ values are the corresponding enthalpy and entropy differences; none of the three quantities depends in any way on the properties of the intermediate.

12.7 THE WAYWARDNESS OF ENTHALPY AND ENTROPY EFFECTS

The representative points in a plot of log*k* for semicarbazone formation against log*k* for oxime formation (Sec. 11.5) undergo an interesting variety of translations, shown by the dotted lines in Fig. 12.8, when the temperature changes from 0 to 25°C. The slopes of these lines vary from 0.22 to 0.9 and the relative magnitudes from 1 to 6. There is a tendency for the magnitude to be less with the more reactive carbonyl compounds, but no such trend appears in the otherwise similar pattern that appears when specific rates for the formation of thiosemicarbazones are compared with those for guanylhydrazones.

In accordance with the random character of these translations, a plot (Fig. 12.9) of $\Delta\bar{H}^{\ddagger}$ for the semicarbazone formation against $\Delta\bar{H}^{\ddagger}$ for the oxime formation shows a random scatter. No better correlation appears when enthalpy effects on thiosemicarbazone formation and on guanylhydra-

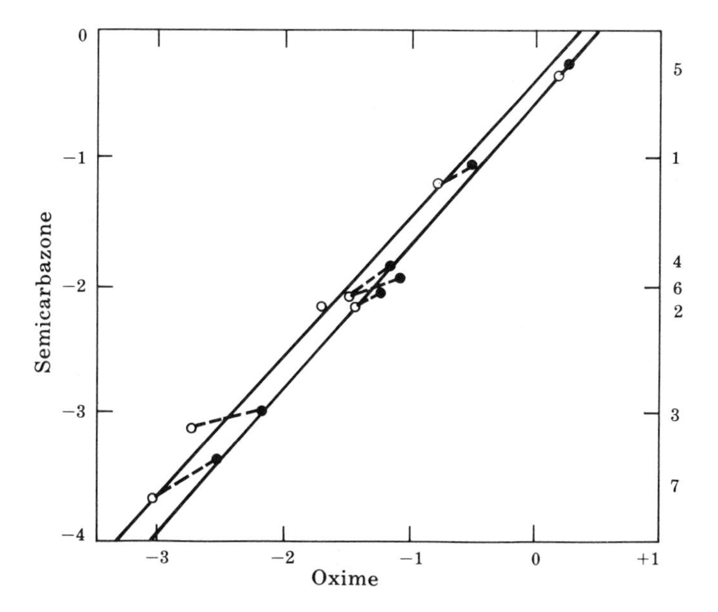

Fig. 12.8 Correlation of log *k* for semicarbazone formation with log *k* for oxime formation. ○ = 0°C; ● = 25°C. Numbers on right have the same significance as in Fig. 12.6.

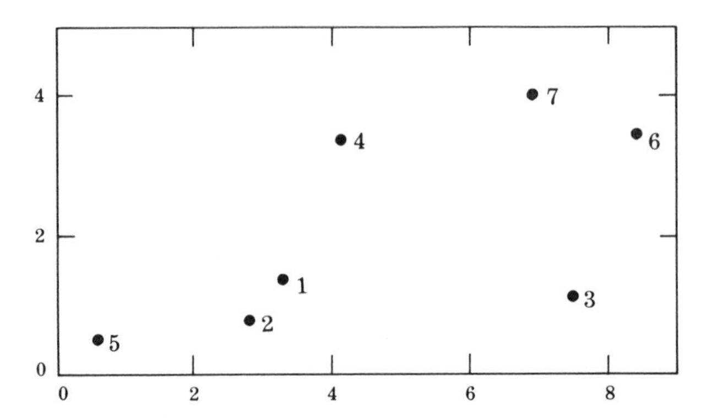

Fig. 12.9 Abscissa: $\Delta\bar{H}^{+}$ (in kilocalories) for oxime formation; ordinate: $\Delta\bar{H}^{+}$ for semicarbazone formation. Numbers indicate carbonyl compounds as in Fig. 12.6.

zone formation are compared with each other or with the effects on oxime or semicarbazone formation. Nor is there any correlation of entropy effects in the different reactions.

If there were an exact linear free-energy relationship between two reaction series and an exact isokinetic relationship applied to each series, there would be an exact linear relationship between the $\Delta\bar{H}^{+}$ values and between the $\Delta\bar{S}^{+}$ values of the two series. If, however, the deviation from the linear free-energy relationship and from the isokinetic relationships have the usual random character, a relatively poor correlation of $\Delta\bar{H}^{+}$ or $\Delta\bar{S}^{+}$ is to be expected.

12.8 STATISTICAL-MECHANICAL CONSIDERATIONS

The quantities $\delta_R\Delta\mu^\circ$, $\delta_R\Delta\bar{H}^\circ$, and $\delta_R\Delta\bar{S}^\circ$, any two of which determine the effect of a structural change represented by the operator δ_R on the equilibrium and the temperature coefficient of the equilibrium of a chemical reaction, are related to the fundamental molecular properties potential energy E_p, zero-point vibrational energy E_z, and partition function Q by the equations

$$\delta_R\Delta\mu^\circ = \delta_R\Delta E_p + \delta_R\Delta E_z - \mathbf{R}T\delta_R\Delta\ln Q \tag{20}$$

$$\delta_R\Delta\bar{H}^\circ = \delta_R\Delta E_p + \delta_R\Delta E_z + \mathbf{R}T^2\,\delta_R\Delta\frac{\partial\ln Q}{\partial T} \tag{21}$$

and

$$\delta_R\Delta\bar{S}^\circ = \mathbf{R}\delta_R\Delta\ln Q + \mathbf{R}T\delta_R\Delta\frac{\partial\ln Q}{\partial T} \tag{22}$$

Of the four quantities $\delta_R\Delta E_p$, $\delta_R\Delta E_z$, $\delta_R\Delta\ln Q$, and $\delta_R\Delta\,\partial\ln Q/\partial T$ only one, $\delta_R\Delta E_z$, can be estimated with any reliability either from experiment or from theory. If the four were independently variable, it would be extremely difficult to recognize any quantitative correlations in the field of structure and reactivity. Indeed it would have been nearly impossible to construct a systematic science of organic chemistry.

12.9 PROPOSITIONS

The observed phenomena in the field can, however, be accounted for in terms of the following propositions:

1. For changes in structure not close to the reaction zone the quantities $\delta_R \Delta E_p$, $\delta_R \Delta E_z$, and $\delta_R \Delta \ln Q$ are mutually proportional to a useful approximation, it being stipulated that one or more of them may be approximately zero.
2. The internal contributions both to $\delta_R \Delta \ln Q$ and to $\delta_R \Delta\, \partial \ln Q/\partial T$ are negligible for changes in structure not close to the reaction zone. By internal contributions is meant values which the quantities would have if reactants and products or reactants and transition state were present as constituents of a dilute gas. For no changes in structure do the internal contributions affect rate or equilibrium by more than an order of magnitude.
3. The external contribution to the temperature coefficient $\delta_R \Delta\, \partial \ln Q/\partial T$ is usually negligible unless the changes in structure are close to the reaction zone.
4. When neither $\delta_R \Delta \ln Q$ nor $\delta_R \Delta\, \partial \ln Q/\partial T$ is negligible, they are independently variable.
5. For two reaction series i and j the ratio $(\delta_R \Delta E_{p(j)})/(\delta_R \Delta E_{p(i)})$ is independent of structure to a useful approximation, certainly for structural changes not close to the reaction zone, and perhaps more generally.
6. When the reactions of series i and j are of very similar nature, the ratio $(\delta_R \Delta \ln Q_j)/(\delta_R \Delta E_{p(j)})$ is approximately equal to the ratio $(\delta_R \Delta \ln Q_i)/(\delta_R \Delta E_{p(i)})$ even when the structural changes are so close to the reaction zone that the ratio $(\delta_R \Delta \ln Q)/(\delta_R \Delta E_p)$ is variable.
7. For structural changes close to the reaction zone the ratio $(\delta_R \Delta\, \partial \ln Q_j/\partial T)/(\delta_R \Delta E_{p(j)})$ differs widely and randomly from the ratio $(\delta_R \Delta\, \partial \ln Q_i/\partial T)/(\delta_R \Delta E_{p(i)})$ even when reactions i and j are so similar that proposition 6 applies.

12.10 APPLICATIONS

By virtue of propositions 2 and 3 the Leffler coefficient β is given by

$$\beta = \frac{\delta_R \Delta (E_p + E_z)}{\mathrm{R}\delta_R \Delta \ln Q} \tag{23}$$

for structural changes not close to the reaction zone. By virtue of proposition 1 it is independent of structure for such changes, in agreement with a considerable amount of experimental evidence. For isentropic reactions $\delta_R \Delta \ln Q = 0$ and $\beta = \infty$. For isenthalpic reactions $\delta_R \Delta(E_p + E_z) = 0$ and $\beta = 0$. The isenthalpic situation arises no doubt from opposing internal and external contributions to $\delta_R \Delta E_p$ with perhaps further compensation from $\delta_R \Delta E_z$. When $\beta = T$,

$$\delta_R \Delta(E_p + E_z) \approx \mathbf{R}T\delta_R \Delta \ln Q \qquad \text{and} \qquad \delta_R \Delta\mu^\circ \approx 0$$

The slope ρ in correlations of the kind represented by the Hammett or Taft equations is given by

$$\rho = \frac{\delta_R \Delta E_{p(j)}}{\delta_R \Delta E_{p(i)}} \frac{1 + x_j - y_j}{1 + x_i - y_i} \tag{24}$$

where

$$x = \frac{\delta_R \Delta E_z}{\delta_R \Delta E_p} \tag{25}$$

and

$$y = \frac{\mathbf{R}T\delta_R \Delta \ln Q}{\delta_R \Delta E_p} \tag{26}$$

By virtue of proposition 5 the first factor in Eq. (24) is independent of structure, and by virtue of proposition 1 the second factor is independent of structure provided the structural changes are not close to the reaction zone. ρ is not independent of temperature even if reactions i and j are observed at the same temperature because the y's need not be the same function of temperature. It is even more dependent on temperature if the two reactions are not observed at the same temperature.

For correlations of the Hammett or Taft type

$$\frac{\delta_R \Delta \bar{H}_j^\circ}{\delta_R \Delta \bar{H}_i^\circ} = \frac{\delta_R \Delta(E_{p(j)} + E_{z(j)})}{\delta_R \Delta(E_{p(i)} + E_{z(i)})} \tag{27}$$

$\Delta\bar{H}^\circ$ or $\Delta\bar{H}^\ddagger$ are therefore better measures of $\Delta(E_p + E_z)$ than $\Delta\mu^\circ$ or $\Delta\mu^\ddagger$ are except when, as in the ionization of phenols or of meta- and para-substituted benzoic acids, the enthalpy quantities are small and irregular.

For correlations of the Gettler type it must be supposed that the y_j and the y_i of Eq. (24), although structure-dependent, have the same value for the two very similar reactions correlated. Consequently

$$\frac{\delta_R \Delta\mu_j^\ddagger}{\delta_R \Delta\mu_i} = \frac{\delta_R \Delta(E_{p(j)} + E_{z(j)})}{\delta_R \Delta(E_{p(i)} + E_{z(i)})} \tag{28}$$

But by virtue of proposition 7 the ratio

$$\frac{\delta_R \Delta \bar{H}_j^+}{\delta_R \Delta \bar{H}_i^+} = \frac{\delta_R \Delta(E_{p(j)} + E_{z(j)}) + \mathbf{R}T^2 \, \delta_R \Delta \, \partial \ln Q_j/\partial T}{\delta_R \Delta(E_{p(i)} + E_{z(i)}) + \mathbf{R}T^2 \, \delta_R \Delta \, \partial \ln Q_i/\partial T} \tag{29}$$

can be expected to be irregularly variable, in agreement with observation.

12.11 SUPPORTING CONSIDERATIONS AND CORROBORATING EVIDENCE

Proposition 2 seems necessary because of the unreasonableness of any correlation with ΔE_p of the internal contribution to $\Delta \ln Q$ whereas it is relatively easy to visualize a correlation of the external contribution. The validity of the proposition is strongly supported by the evidence (Sec. 3.13) that in the gas phase changes in structure not close to the reaction zone have very small effects on $\Delta S°$, even when they produce large effects on $\Delta\mu°$, and that even the substitution of a tertiary amine for ammonia leads to changes of only a few calories per degree in $\Delta S°$.

In terms of the electron-shift hypothesis the effect of a substituent on the ionization equilibrium of an acid operates through a push or pull exerted by the substituent on the electron density in the reaction zone which helps or hinders the addition of a proton to the anion. It is reasonable to suppose that the substituent exerts a parallel effect on the attachment of solvent molecules both to the acid and to the anion and that the change in intensity of solvation alters both ΔE_p and $\Delta \ln Q$. There is direct evidence for this kind of parallelism between the effects of solvation on ΔE_p and on $\Delta \ln Q$ from the work of Love, Cohen, and Taft [16]. Table 12.3 contains their $\delta_R \Delta\mu°$ and $\delta_R \Delta\bar{S}°$ values for the reaction

$$XCH_2NH_2B(CH_3)_3 + CH_3CH_2NH_2 \rightleftharpoons XCH_2NH_2 + CH_3CH_2NH_2B(CH_3)_3 \tag{II}$$

in the gas phase at 54°C and for the reaction

$$XCH_2NH_3^+ + CH_3CH_2NH_2 \rightleftharpoons XCH_2NH_2 + CH_3CH_2NH_3^+ \tag{III}$$

Table 12.3 Entropy effects in reactions in the gas phase and in solution[a]

	Reaction II		*Reaction III*	
Amine	$\delta_R \Delta\mu°$	$\delta_R \Delta\bar{S}°$	$\delta_R \Delta\mu°$	$\delta_R \Delta\bar{S}°$
$CH_3CH_2NH_2$	(0)	(0)	(0)	(0)
$FCH_2CH_2NH_2$	−1160	+0.1	−2510	−3.1
$F_2CHCH_2NH_2$	−2700	0.0	−4830	−3.4
$F_3CCH_2NH_2$	−3870	+0.1	−6850	−5.3

[a] Data of Love, Cohen, and Taft [16].

in aqueous solution at 25°C. The $\delta_R \Delta \bar{S}^\circ$ values are effectively zero in the gas-phase reaction; in solution they parallel the $\delta_R \Delta \mu^\circ$ values about as closely as can be expected.

The quantity $\delta_R \Delta E_z$ is small for reactions which do not involve a proton transfer. There is spectroscopic evidence that it is directly proportional to $\delta_R \Delta (E_p - \mathbf{R}T \ln Q)$ in the ionization of substituted phenols in water. Figure 12.10 plots the data of Goulden [17] on the frequency of the OH stretching vibration in carbon tetrachloride solution against the pK value in water of a series of meta- and para-substituted phenols. The standard deviation from the equation $\nu = 3{,}545 + 6.67\text{p}K$ is 1.9. There is the clear implication that the force constant of the vibration and the work of removal of a proton are functionally related.

It does not seem to have been shown that proposition 5 is a necessary consequence of quantum mechanics, but neither has it been shown that it is not. It is difficult to see how linear free-energy relationships could exist if it were not valid.

Many chemists, especially those who are not concerned with reactions in polar solvents, would like to forget the temperature coefficient $\delta_R \Delta\, \partial \ln Q / \partial T$. That it is a significant quantity for reactions in solution is demonstrated by the failure of enthalpy correlations for pairs of reactions involving large changes in structure to which the Gettler type of standard potential correlation does apply. To understand why it is significant one need only remember (Sec. 2.24) that involvement of reactant, reaction product, or transition state in a mobile equilibrium of solvation or of any other sort can easily lead to effects on $\Delta \bar{H}^\circ$ or $\Delta \bar{H}^\ddagger$ which are larger than the effects on $\Delta \mu^\circ$ or $\Delta \mu^\ddagger$ and which are sensitive to structure of reactant and to temperature.

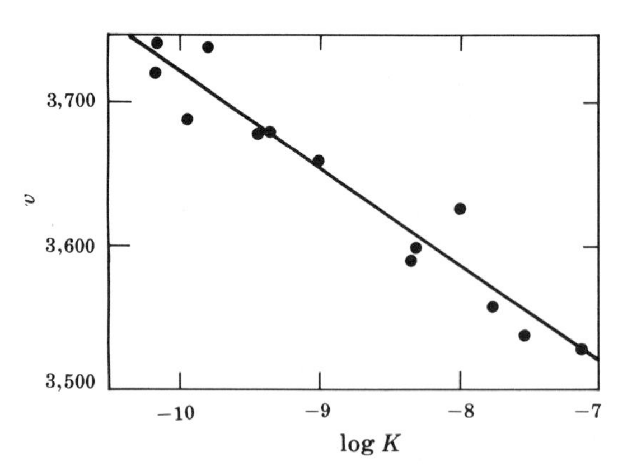

Fig. 12.10 Correlation of OH stretching frequency (*data of Goulden* [17]) and acidity constant of meta- and para-substituted phenols. Substituents range from p-OCH_3 and p-NH_2 to p-NO_2.

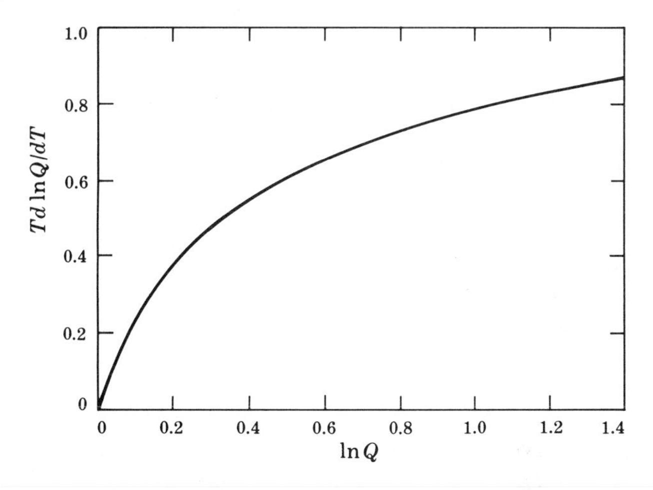

Fig. 12.11 Relation between $Td\ln Q/dt$ and $\ln Q$ for a harmonic oscillator.

Proposition 3, that the temperature coefficient is negligible for changes in structure not close to the reaction zone, is required by the existence of isoequilibrium and isokinetic relationships.

Proposition 4 is supported by the fact that for a single oscillator there is no correlation between the effect of a change in frequency on $\ln Q$ and the effect on $\partial \ln Q/\partial T$. This is shown to be the case for a harmonic oscillator by Fig. 12.11. If the proposition were not valid, the isokinetic or isoequilibrium relationship would apply to all reactions to which linear free-energy relationships apply.

12.12 A COMMENTARY ON OTHER APPROACHES

Hepler [18] has emphasized the importance of the distinction between internal and external contributions and has argued that the internal contribution to $\delta_R \Delta S^\circ$ is negligible. He proposes [19] that

$$\delta_R \Delta \bar{H}^\circ_{\text{ext}} - \beta \delta_R \Delta \bar{S}^\circ = \gamma \delta_R \Delta \bar{H}^\circ_{\text{int}} \tag{30}$$

in which β and γ are independent of structure. From this

$$\delta_R \Delta \bar{H}^\circ = (1+\gamma)\, \delta_R \Delta \bar{H}^\circ_{\text{int}} + \beta \delta_R \Delta \bar{S}^\circ \tag{31}$$

and

$$\frac{\delta_R \Delta \bar{H}^\circ}{\delta_R \Delta \bar{S}^\circ} = \beta + \frac{(1+\gamma)\, \delta_R \Delta \bar{H}^\circ_{\text{int}}}{\delta_R \Delta \bar{S}^\circ} \tag{32}$$

To account for the existence of isokinetic and isoequilibrium relationships it is necessary to add to his proposals the rule that the ratio $(\delta_R \Delta \bar{H}^\circ_{\rm int})/(\delta_R \Delta \bar{S}^\circ)$ is independent of structure for those changes to which the relationships apply.

Leffler and Grunwald [3] consider a failure of the isokinetic or isoequilibrium relationship to be evidence for the involvement of more than one mechanism by which a substituent interacts with the reaction zone. In these terms a $\delta_R \Delta \ln Q$ value which is neither zero nor proportional to $\delta_R \Delta E_p$ represents the superimposition of another interaction mechanism on the one which determines the value of $\delta_R \Delta E_p$. And a $\delta_R \Delta\, \partial \ln Q/\partial T$ value which is not zero represents still another interaction mechanism. One cannot, however, account directly for the failure of the isokinetic or isoequilibrium relationship to hold by a further subdivision of the quantity $\delta_R \Delta(E_p + E_z)$ into the effects of different interaction mechanisms. This quantity is independent of temperature, and, no matter how many times or in how many ways one slices it, it remains independent of temperature.

REFERENCES

1. Roginsky, S., and L. Rosenkewitsch: *Z. Physik. Chem.*, **B10:** 47 (1930); L. P. Hammett: *J. Chem. Phys.*, **4:** 613 (1936); R. A. Fairclough and C. N. Hinshelwood: *J. Chem. Soc.*, **1937:** 538, 1573.
2. Leffler, J. E.: *J. Org. Chem.*, **20:** 1202 (1955).
3. Leffler, J. E., and E. Grunwald: "Rates and Equilibria of Organic Reactions," John Wiley & Sons, Inc., New York, 1963.
4. Branch, G. E. K., and A. C. Nixon: *J. Am. Chem. Soc.*, **58:** 2499 (1936).
5. Tommila, E.: *Ann. Acad. Sci. Fennicae*, **A57**(13): 3 (1941).
6. Ingold, C. K., and W. S Nathan: *J Chem. Soc.*, **1936:** 222; D. P. Evans, J. J. Gordon, and H. B. Watson: *ibid.*, **1937:** 1430; H. A. Smith and H. S. Levenson: *J. Am. Chem. Soc.*, **61:** 1173 (1939).
7. Davies, G., and D. P. Evans: *J. Chem. Soc.*, **1940:** 339.
8. Tommila, E., and C. N. Hinshelwood: *J. Chem. Soc.*, **1938:** 1801.
9. Wilson, J. M., N. E. Gore, J. E. Sawbridge, and F. Cardenas-Cruz: *J. Chem. Soc.*, **B1967:** 852.
10. Yukawa, Y., and Y. Tsuno: *J. Am. Chem. Soc.*, **79:** 5530 (1957).
11. Exner, O.: *Collection Czech. Chem. Commun.*, **29:** 1094 (1964). See also J. Mandel and F. J. Linnig: *Anal. Chem.*, **29:** 743 (1957), and [3], p. 323.
12. Price, F. P., Jr., and L. P. Hammett: *J. Am. Chem. Soc.*, **63:** 2387 (1941).
13. Fitzpatrick, F. W., and J. D. Gettler: *J. Am. Chem. Soc.*, **78:** 530 (1956).
14. Fiarman, I. D., and J. D. Gettler: *J. Am. Chem. Soc.*, **84:** 961 (1962).
15. Brooks, D. W., and J. D. Gettler: *J. Org. Chem.*, **27:** 4469 (1962).
16. Love, P., R. B. Cohen, and R. W. Taft: *J. Am. Chem. Soc.*, **90:** 2455 (1968).
17. Goulden, J. D. S.: *Spectrochim. Acta*, **6:** 129 (1954).
18. Hepler, L. G.: *J. Am. Chem. Soc.*, **85:** 3089 (1963).
19. Larson, J. W., and L. G. Hepler: *J. Org. Chem.*, **33:** 3961 (1968).
20. Bolton, P. D., F. M. Hall, and I. H. Reece: *Spectrochim. Acta*, **22:** 1825 (1966); *J. Chem. Soc.*, **B1967:** 709.
21. Chen, D. T. Y., and K. J. Laidler: *Trans. Faraday Soc.*, **58:** 480 (1962).
22. Fernandez, L. P., and L. G. Hepler: *J. Am. Chem. Soc.*, **81:** 1783 (1959).
23. Allen, G. F., R. A. Robinson, and V. E. Bower: *J. Phys. Chem.*, **66:** 171 (1962).
24. Dickinson, J. D., and C. Eaborn: *J. Chem. Soc.*, **1959:** 3036.

Name Index

Subject Index